THE
THEORY OF SETS
AND
TRANSFINITE ARITHMETIC

SAUNDERS MATHEMATICS BOOKS

Consulting Editor
BERNARD R. GELBAUM, University of California

THE
THEORY OF SETS
AND
TRANSFINITE ARITHMETIC

ALEXANDER ABIAN

Associate Professor of Mathematics
The Ohio State University

W. B. SAUNDERS COMPANY
Philadelphia and London, 1965

The Theory of Sets and Transfinite Arithmetic

PREFACE

The present book is a self-contained exposition of the Theory of Sets and is intended to serve as a textbook for students who are majoring in mathematics. It can also serve as a textbook for anyone interested in the fundamental concepts of mathematics or anyone who has not had formal training in the Theory of Sets.

The importance of the Theory of Sets in all present-day mathematics is due to the fact that, as experience has shown, practically every mathematical concept can be defined conveniently in terms of set-theoretical concepts, and every mathematical sentence can conveniently be made into a set-theoretical sentence.

The basic set-theoretical concepts are just two in number; they are expressed by means of the basic set-theoretical vocabulary, consisting of:

$$set, \quad is \ an \ element \ of$$

Set-theoretical sentences are constructed by using this vocabulary together with the basic logical vocabulary, consisting of:

$$not, \quad or, \quad there \ exists$$

Thus, the study of the Theory of Sets is in part the study of a language whose basic vocabulary consists of:

$$set(s), \quad is \ an \ element \ of, \quad not, \quad or, \quad there \ exists$$

As one can see, the ideas involved in the above vocabulary are commonly understood, and are so primitive that to define them in terms of notions more primitive and more elemental seems inconceivable. Thus, in this book, the above vocabulary is taken as *undefined*; together with the auxiliary symbols introduced below, it serves to define various other set-theoretical concepts and to form set-theoretical sentences.

To render the communication of ideas concise and unambiguous, the undefined vocabulary is symbolized by the following *undefined formal symbols*:

$$x, \quad y, \quad z, \quad \ldots$$

each for a *set-variable*, and

$$\in, \quad \sim, \quad \vee, \quad \exists$$

for *is an element of*, *not*, *or* and *there exists*, respectively.

In the above the *comma*, which is used for separating symbols, is also taken as an undefined (auxiliary) formal symbol. Moreover, as a formal symbol, each of x, y, z, . . . is referred to as an *individual variable*.

In terms of the above symbols the sentence:

(i)   *There exists a set x such that x is an element of itself or x is not an element of itself*

is symbolized by the *formula*:

(ii) $(\exists x)((x \in x) \vee \sim(x \in x))$

where the parentheses (and) are used for grouping purposes and are also taken as undefined (auxiliary) formal symbols.

Similarly, the sentence:

(iii)   *There exists a set x such that there exists no set y that is an element of x*

is symbolized by the formula:

(iv) $(\exists x)(\sim(\exists y)(y \in x))$

An advantage of formulas (ii) and (iv) over the ordinary sentences (i) and (iii) is that they leave no room for ambiguity. A reader may be disturbed by the presence in (i) and (iii) of the words *such* and *that*, for example, and may ask for their definition. However, a similar question is irrelevant with respect to (ii) and (iv). This advantage is more pronounced when dealing with more complex sentences.

Thus, in mathematics, a sentence expressed symbolically (and called a *formula*) is preferable to a sentence written in ordinary language. Nevertheless, our familiarity with ordinary language has its psychological advantages. When an idea is expressed in terms of ordinary sentences it appears to be more accessible and more understandable than when it is expressed symbolically. For this reason in this book many sentences that are expressed symbolically (i.e., by formulas) are preceded or followed by their free translation into ordinary language.

The following is a complete list of the undefined set-theoretical formal symbols:

(v) x, y, z, . . . $\in$, $\sim$, $\vee$, $\exists$, (,)

These formal symbols are used to define various other logical and set-theoretical concepts, such as *and, implies, for every, equality, inclusion, relation, function, order, natural number, integer, rational number, real number, ordinal number, cardinal number*, and so forth.

The definitions of these are given by means of *set-theoretical formulas*. A set-theoretical formula in turn is a configuration formed of symbols appearing in (v), in strict accordance with the *formation rules of formulas*.

As suggested by list (v), in the entire Theory of Sets (and, hence, in practically all of mathematics) we confine ourselves to individual variables of one and only one type—namely, *set-variables*. Thus, we make no conceptual distinction between *an element of a set* and *a set*. Moreover, as (v) shows, in the entire Theory of Sets (and, hence, in practically all of mathematics) we confine ourselves to one and only one basic binary predicate—namely, $\in$.

Out of all this, the following question arises: what is the purpose of the Theory of Sets (or, in a sense, of mathematics)? Perhaps one answer is that essentially the purpose of the Theory of Sets is to infer set-theoretical formulas that are *valid* in the Theory of Sets (i.e., *theorems* of the Theory of Sets).

As to the question of what a valid set-theoretical formula is, we may answer that it is a set-theoretical formula that is accepted as valid initially (i.e., a set-theoretical *axiom*) or one that is produced by applying the formation rules of formulas to these axioms and whose validity is inferred by means of the *logical rules of inference*.

From the above, we see that a knowledge of the rudiments of *mathematical logic* is indispensable for the development of the Theory of Sets. For this reason we develop mathematical logic in Chapter I—but only in connection with and to the extent needed in the Theory of Sets.

In this book we develop the Theory of Sets based on the following six axioms of Zermelo-Fraenkel: *Extensionality*, *Replacement*, *Power-Set*, *Sum-Set. Infinity* and *Choice*. (This Theory of Sets is known as the *Zermelo-Fraenkel Theory of Sets*.) These six axioms are introduced in Chapter II, where also some of their immediate consequences are derived. In the same chapter, the axiom of *Regularity* is introduced also, although it is not used in our development of the Theory of Sets.

To give a concrete interpretation of set-theoretical concepts, the notion of a *set-theoretical model* is introduced in Chapter I. Beginning with simple examples of set-theoretical models (where none or only some of the Zermelo-Fraenkel axioms are satisfied), the reader is gradually familiarized with set-theoretical concepts and techniques. Owing to the fact that a model refers to a content (i.e., to a list of sets a, b, c, . . .), its treatment can be made rather concrete. Thus, a theory (and in particular the Theory of Sets) becomes much more meaningful if its study is preceded by or runs parallel to that of a model. In addition, the technical skill that is easily acquired while studying set-theoretical models is directly used in the development of the Theory of Sets. Indeed, a model differs from a theory mainly in that it refers to a content; in many other aspects its formal development resembles that of a theory. Another advantage of the introduction of set-theoretical models is that the rudiments of mathematical logic can be dealt with concretely. Thus, it is in connection with models that various rules of tagging formulas **T** (true) or **F** (false) are introduced and extended to the case of formulas involving predicates and quantifiers. (Incidentally, the rules of tagging formulas **T** or **F** are the basic motivation of formal mathematical logic.)

In this book the Theory of Sets is developed parallel to its intended interpretation. For example, formula (ii) (which is valid in the Theory of Sets regardless of its axioms) is interpreted in the usual way as asserting the existence of a set in the Theory of Sets. Similarly, formula (iv) (which is valid in the Theory of Sets owing to the axioms) is interpreted as asserting the existence (in the Theory of Sets) of a set that has no element. Thus, as soon as the validity of formula (iv) is inferred in the Theory of Sets, the *individual constant* $\varnothing$ is introduced as the *unique* (up to equality) *empty set* belonging to the (illusory) content of the Theory of Sets. Similarly, other individual constants such as 1, 2, . . . , ω, $\aleph$, and so forth, are introduced in the Theory of Sets as soon as the validity of certain formulas is inferred in the Theory of Sets.

Strictly speaking, for the development of the Theory of Sets there is no need for the introduction of individual constants. Likewise, for the development of the Theory of Sets there is no need to assume that it refers to a content. Nevertheless, for pedagogical reasons and for convenience and practicality we develop the Theory of Sets as though it were a model whose content includes the (up to equality) sets $\varnothing$, 1, 2, . . . , ω, $\aleph$, among other individual constants.

These generalities are treated in the first two chapters of this book. It is recommended that these chapters be studied carefully.

In the remaining chapters, the Theory of Sets is developed more or less along classical lines and in predominantly ordinary language. Topics such as *relations* in general, and *order*, *equipollence* and *similarity* in particular, are studied in detail. The last two chapters are devoted to the basic study of *ordinal* and *cardinal* numbers and their arithmetic (*Transfinite Arithmetic*).

Each section of the book contains many illustrative examples. Each new concept is introduced only after some preliminary motivation. At the end of each section there is a list of exercises. Examples and exercises will help the reader to grasp better the ideas involved.

At the end of each chapter a summary is given to recapitulate the essential ideas introduced.

Let us emphasize at this point that the Theory of Sets (and, hence, practically all of mathematics) is a language arising from the basic vocabulary given in (v) and having a comparatively limited number of grammatical rules—i.e., formation rules of formulas (sentences) and rules of inference (reasoning). However, in contrast to an ordinary language, the grammatical rules of mathematical language must be observed with utmost precision. Perhaps this circumstance is one of the reasons for the common complaint that the study of mathematics is difficult.

It is granted that the proper application of the rules of inference requires skill. However, this can be achieved by training and must not deter the student from pursuing his mathematical studies.

It is the author's deepest conviction that a person who speaks a language coherently should have no basic difficulty in mastering any branch of mathematics, and, in particular, its foundation—the Theory of Sets. Moreover, the sooner a student becomes acquainted with the Theory of Sets, the easier it will be for him to learn other phases of mathematics.

There are many explanatory and expository passages in this book; therefore, despite its size, its content can be covered in one quarter or one semester or two quarters, depending on the mathematical maturity of the student.

The author wishes to express his gratitude to Professor Paul Bernays for his invaluable help and advice during the preparation of the manuscript, and to

Mr. Samuel LaMacchia for many important remarks and helpful suggestions. Special thanks are due to Professor Bernard R. Gelbaum for his contribution toward the improvement of the manuscript, to Professor Isaac A. Barnett for his continued interest in the work of the author and to Dr. Jules Borenstein for many stimulating discussions.

This book initiates the W. B. Saunders Company's publications in mathematics under the general management of Mr. Walter E. Zablocki and editorship of Professor Bernard E. Gelbaum. I hope that the book will uphold the high standards of publications of the W. B. Saunders Company.

It is with pleasure that I express my gratitude to members of the staff of the W. B. Saunders Company for their excellent editorial work and efficient and expert cooperation.

It is unlikely that the book is free of errors or misprints. The author will be indebted to any of his readers who apprise him of oversights.

ALEXANDER ABIAN*

Columbus, Ohio

* Formerly, Smbat Abian.

CONTENTS

Chapter IV

ORDER AND ZORN'S LEMMA

Chapter V

EQUIVALENCE CLASSES
THE REAL NUMBERS

Chapter VI

EQUIPOLLENCE OF SETS

Chapter VII

SIMILARITY

Chapter VIII

ORDINAL NUMBERS AND THEIR ARITHMETIC

Chapter IX

CARDINAL NUMBERS AND THEIR ARITHMETIC

Chapter I

INTRODUCTION

1. SETS AND THE ELEMENTHOOD PREDICATE

In everyday life and especially in mathematics there is hardly any item or entity not related in some way to the notion of *set*.

For example, we speak of a set of encyclopedias, a set of weights, a set of twins, and so forth.

In plane geometry we constantly use the notion of a set of points of a plane. Likewise, in arithmetic we refer to the set of the multiples of a natural number. Again, in algebra we speak of the set of the roots of a polynomial, and so forth.

The Theory of Sets that is presented in this book develops to a higher degree of abstraction our intuitive notions concerning relations between sets. This theory has a twofold importance in mathematics. It constitutes an independent and fertile mathematical discipline on its own merits. Also, as experience has shown, the Theory of Sets serves as a sound foundation for almost all mathematical disciplines in the sense that almost all branches of mathematics can be developed most conveniently within the Theory of Sets.

The presentation and development of any theory, and in particular the Theory of Sets, is similar in many respects to the presentation and development of a foreign language.

In general, for communication *about* a foreign language some other language or method of conveying information is used. This other means of communication must be familiar to the person who presents the foreign language and to the person to whom the foreign language is presented.

In our case the foreign language involved is the *Zermelo-Fraenkel Theory of Sets*, which we will continue to call *the Theory of Sets*. The language used to communicate about the Theory of Sets is the ordinary English language.

In technical terminology the foreign language whose presentation is under consideration is called the *object language* and the language used to communicate about the object language is called the *metalanguage*. In our case the object language is the Theory of Sets and the metalanguage is the ordinary English language.

Clearly, the development of an object language has communication *within* that language as an objective. In this chapter we shall develop necessary machinery toward achieving this objective in the Theory of Sets.

Just as a specific foreign language is usually one of many foreign languages with a common origin, the Theory of Sets is one among what we might call *theories of sets* which are based on a common *set-theoretical language*.

Before developing the Theory of Sets we introduce some general set-theoretical notions that can be used in developing formally very simple examples of theories of sets.

As a first step in this direction, we introduce the formal notion of an *interpretation of a theory of sets*.

In technical terminology an interpretation of a theory of sets is called a *set-theoretical model*. We shall refer to the latter simply as a *model*.

At an elementary level the formal definition and development of a model run as follows. We introduce a *vocabulary* consisting of: certain symbols which are the *objects* of the model, one and only one *basic set-theoretical predicate symbol* and certain symbols for *punctuation* and for *connectives*. Then we introduce certain *rules for forming sentences*. Furthermore, we choose certain sentences (*postulates* of the model) describing certain initially prescribed relationships among the objects. Finally, based on postulates and according to certain rules of logic we make *inferences*.

In technical terminology, we refer to the vocabulary as *set-theoretical formal symbols*, or simply *formal symbols*. The objects of a model are called *individual constants* or *sets*. The one and only one basic set-theoretical predicate symbol is called the *elementhood predicate symbol*. The sentences are called *set-theoretical formulas*, or simply *formulas*. The rules for forming sentences are called *formation rules of formulas*. The postulates of a model are called its *axioms*. The rules for making inferences are called *formal rules of inference*, or simply *rules of inference*. Also, we say that the sets (objects) of a model constitute the *content* of that model.

The basic constituents of any model are essentially the same—namely, the ones just given. Of course, different lists of sets or different lists of axioms may give rise to essentially different models.

To a great extent the formal definition and development of a theory of sets (and in particular the Theory of Sets) resemble the definition and development of a model. The basic constituents and the corresponding technical terminology of a theory of sets are very much the same as those of a model. However, there is a major difference. *A theory of sets need not possess a list of objects.* In other words, a theory of sets (and in particular the Theory of Sets) is developed without necessarily referring to a list of sets or to a content. For this reason, a theory of sets has a more general and more abstract aspect than a model. And precisely for this reason it is advisable to precede the study of the formal development of a theory of sets (and in particular that of the Theory of Sets) with that of a model. We adopt this course in this book. Naturally, much of the technical skill acquired while studying models will be used in the study of the Theory of Sets.

The intimate relation between a model and a theory of sets will be especially apparent after the introduction of *individual variables* (set-variables) and *quantifiers*. In many cases it will be possible to formulate a model which is an interpretation of a given theory of sets.

Let us mention here that set-theoretical formal symbols are merely symbols devoid of any meaning in the usual sense. Thus, they are introduced without any meaningful definitions; for this reason, they are called *undefined.*

To clarify the above, perhaps it is worthwhile to observe that the notion of *set* is conceptualized by our intellect at such an early stage of our contact with the physical world that to define it in terms of notions more primitive and more elemental seems inconceivable. Almost every attempt to define the intuitive meaning of the word *set* results in replacing it with a synonym such as *collection, aggregate, family* or *class*. This is one of the reasons for abandoning the attempt to define sets and for taking them as undefined formal symbols of models.

For the time being, any one of the lower-case letters (from the beginning of the alphabet), with or without subscripts, such as

(1) $a, b, c, \ldots, a_1, b_1, c_1, \ldots, a_2, b_2, c_2, \ldots$

will constitute a set or an object of a model:

Let us emphasize that in the models that we shall encounter we need not and shall not make use of any category of individual constants (or objects) other than sets.

Thus, (1) gives some of the set-theoretical formal symbols, each being a *set* or an *individual constant* or an *object* of a model.

Inherent in the intuitive notion of set is the concept of *elementhood* or *membership* or *belonging*—i.e., the relation that exists between the objects forming a set and the set itself. For example, inherent in the notion of a set of encyclopedias is the concept that each volume of that set of encyclopedias is an element or a member of the whole set.

Let us also mention that nothing prevents us from considering an element of a set as being itself a set. In the above example, a volume, which is an element of a set of encyclopedias, is itself a set, namely, a set of pages. Consequently, there is no reason to make a conceptual distinction—even intuitively—between sets and elements of sets; we shall regard elements of sets as being themselves sets. This is compatible with our previous remark that in models we shall use no category of individual constants (or objects) other than sets.

The elementhood relation mentioned above, or the expression *is an element of*, is also such an elemental concept that again there is no suitable alternative but to take this expression as an undefined predicate called the *elementhood predicate*.

As a set-theoretical formal symbol the elementhood predicate is symbolized as

$$\in$$

Since $\in$ refers to a relation between two sets, it is customary to call $\in$ a *dyadic* or a *binary* or a *two-place set-theoretical predicate symbol*.

In the models that we shall encounter and in the entire Theory of Sets we need not and shall not make use of any basic predicate other than $\in$. All other set-theoretical predicates will be formed essentially in terms of $\in$.

Intuitively, in a model the role of the sets a, b, c, ... corresponds to that of proper nouns in ordinary language, and the role of the predicate $\in$ to that of a basic predicate in ordinary language.

Thus, with respect to a list of sets and subject to certain conditions, a model is a language that describes which sets are elements of which sets and which sets are not elements of which sets. Formally, this description is partially carried out by means of statements which are called *set-theoretical prime formulas*, defined as follows:

Definition 1. *Each configuration such as*

$$\in(a,a), \quad \in(a,b), \quad \in(a,c), \quad \ldots$$

where a, b, c, ... are sets is a set-theoretical prime formula.

Intuitively, $\in(a,b)$ corresponds to the declarative sentence: *the set a is an element of the set b.* As usual, a declarative sentence of our ordinary language is called a *statement*. Therefore, it is appropriate to refer to $\in(a,b)$ as a statement—or, more precisely, as a *set-theoretical statement*. In the sequel we shall encounter many other kinds of set-theoretical statements, of which a set-theoretical statement such as $\in(a,b)$ is the simplest form. This is the reason for calling a statement such as $\in(a,b)$ a set-theoretical prime formula.

In the configuration $\in(a,b)$ the *left parenthesis* (and the *right parenthesis*) and the *comma* , are also set-theoretical formal symbols which are customarily called *logical formal symbols*. These three symbols constitute the *punctuation marks* of the set-theoretical language.

The reason (and) and , (the comma) are called logical formal symbols is that usually the set-theoretical language is developed as an extension of another formal language called *formal logic* or *formal predicate calculus*, some of whose formal symbols are (and) and , (the comma). Therefore, it is to be expected that some of the set-theoretical formal symbols (as a matter of fact, all except $\in$ and the sets a, b, c, ...) will coincide with the logical ones and will be called *logical formal symbols*.

In its turn, formal logic is a theory that, motivated by the rules of our ordinary reasoning and inferences, formulates the rules of inference of a formal language—in particular those used in models and in the Theory of Sets. Thus, a knowledge of the rudiments of formal logic (especially in connection with the rules of inference mentioned above) is indispensable for the development of models and theories of sets and in particular of the Theory of Sets. In our case, we shall not develop the formal logic separately. Instead, we shall develop it simultaneously with the development of models, to the extent needed in the Theory of Sets and not quite formally.

We close this section by mentioning that it is customary to write $\in(a,b)$ also in the form:

$$(a \in b)$$

and, when no confusion is likely to arise, in the form:

$$a \in b$$

Also, any of the configurations:

$$\in(a,b) \quad \text{or} \quad (a \in b) \quad \text{or} \quad a \in b$$

is ordinarily read: *a is an element of b*, or *a is a member of b*, or *a belongs to b*, or *b contains a as an element* or *b has a as an element*.

EXERCISES

1. Verbalize the following set-theoretical prime formulas:

$$\in(a,b), \quad \in(c,b), \quad \in(b,a), \quad \in(b,c), \quad \in(a,a), \quad \in(c,a),$$
$$(b \in c), \quad (d \in b), \quad (b \in b), \quad (c \in d), \quad (d \in d), \quad (e \in a),$$
$$e \in a, \quad a \in e, \quad b \in e, \quad c \in e, \quad e \in c, \quad d \in g, \quad d \in c$$

2. Symbolize in three different ways each of the following set-theoretical statements:

a is an element of *b*	*b* is an element of *c*
c is an element of *e*	*e* is an element of *e*
d is a member of *a*	*a* is a member of *d*
c is a member of *c*	*c* is a member of *d*
a belongs to *e*	*b* belongs to *b*
c belongs to *a*	*a* belongs to *c*
a contains *b* as an element	*e* contains *e* as an element
b contains *b* as an element	*c* contains *a* as an element
e has *b* as an element	*d* has *b* as an element
e has *c* as an element	*c* has *d* as an element

2. CONSISTENCY. TRUTH TABLES OF MODELS

Let us consider the sets *a* and *b* and let us observe that there are altogether the following four set-theoretical prime formulas involving the sets *a* and *b*:

(2) $\qquad\qquad a \in a, \qquad b \in a, \qquad a \in b, \qquad b \in b$

The question arises, what can we do or what can we say about the statements listed in (2)? Intuitively, whenever within a context we are confronted with a statement of our ordinary language, our natural reaction is to label it *true* or *false* and *not both*. The process and conventions of labeling the statements of our ordinary language *true* or *false* constitute the essence of our ordinary reasoning and inferences. Here again, let us observe that the notions of *true* and *false* are conceptualized by our intellect at such an early stage of our contact with the physical world that they seem inborn, so to speak, and do not lend themselves to being defined in terms of concepts more primitive and more elemental than those of *true* and *false*. Consequently, we take *true* and *false* as metalinguistic undefined terms. We symbolize them respectively by **T** and **F**, i.e.,

$$\textbf{T} \quad \text{for} \quad \textit{true}$$

and

$$\textbf{F} \quad \text{for} \quad \textit{false}$$

It is customary to call each symbol **T** or **F** a *logical value*.

Intuitively, a sentence of our ordinary language is called a *declarative sentence* or a *statement*, if, while confronted with it, our natural reaction is to ask: *is it true or is it false*? In terms of the labels **T** (true) and **F** (false), we may say that a sentence of our ordinary language is called a statement if it lends itself to being tagged **T** or **F**.

Clearly, every statement of our ordinary language is a sentence. However, the converse is questionable.

Before continuing with our discussion, let us state once and for all that:

⊬ (3)   *Every statement written in this book is true unless the entire statement is inserted in single quotation marks, in which case it is not necessarily false.*

In our use of ordinary language, our natural tendency is to form statements so that within every context a statement is true or false and not both—i.e., to form statements that are not *self-contradictory* in any context. Another way of saying this is that we have an innate tendency to require that our ordinary language be *consistent*. The reason for this is that consistency gives us a feeling of security—an instinct which motivates many of our actions.

Obviously, if every statement of our ordinary language were both true and false (i.e., self-contradictory), then our ordinary language would be unreliable and useless as a means of communication.

Experience has shown that for practical purposes our ordinary language is quite reliable, regardless of the fact that it contains such statements as '*I am lying*' which are not true or false and not both. Such statements, which cannot be true or false and not both, are also called *paradoxical statements* or *paradoxes*. In the above, single quotation marks are used in accordance with (3).

The presence of paradoxes in our ordinary language is mainly due to the fact that, in general, the sentences of our ordinary language are not formed according to some accurate rules; also, labeling of statements *true* or *false* is not performed according to some strict laws that would prevent the occurrence of paradoxes.

In terms of *true* and *false*, our above-mentioned natural reaction and our innate tendency for the requirement of consistency is expressed as follows:

Within every context,

(4)   *Every statement is true or false*

and

(5)   *No statement is both true and false.*

Let us mention immediately that (4) and (5) are special cases of the intuitive interpretation of two of the laws of formal logic called respectively the *law of the excluded middle* and the *law of the excluded contradiction*.

In connection with (4) and (5), let us observe that (4) does not imply that within every context the truth or falsehood of every statement must actually be determined or even determinable, or as customarily expressed, *decidable*. For instance, someone may say:

> '*The label of the face of the coin that touched the palm of his hand for the first time in his life was heads.*'

Obviously the above is a statement. Moreover it is true or false and not both. In other words, it satisfies conditions (4) and (5). However, its truth or falsehood may be *undecidable* (undeterminable). In the above, single quotation marks are used in accordance with (3).

In view of the above let us emphasize that although (4) states that within every context every statement is true or false, (4) *does not imply that within every context the truth or falsehood of every statement must actually be determined or even decidable (determinable)*.

The laws of the excluded middle and the excluded contradiction, or their interpretation as given by (4) and (5), constitute the most essential laws on which we shall base all our reasoning and motivation in developing models and theories. If within a context a statement does not satisfy rule (5), we refer to that statement as being *self-contradictory* and we refer to the context as being *inconsistent*. Otherwise, a context is called *consistent*. We shall explain later why we reject any inconsistent context.

Just as in our ordinary language some sentences are called statements, in our set-theoretical language some formulas are called *statement-formulas*. Intuitively, in the set-theoretical language we may refer to a formula as being a statement-formula if it lends itself to being tagged **T** (for true) or **F** (for false).

Some examples of set-theoretical statement-formulas are given by the set-theoretical prime formulas: $a \in a$, $a \in b$, $c \in e$, $e \in e$, and so forth.

We shall be most concerned that within every context of our set-theoretical language rules (4) and (5) are obeyed, or at least that there is no evidence to the contrary. To this end, as shown in this chapter, the formulas of the set-theoretical language will be formed according to certain strict rules, and the tagging of its statement-formulas **T** or **F** will be performed according to certain strict laws, so that at least there will be no occurrence of evident paradoxes.

To emphasize the importance of rules (4) and (5), we mention here that (from an intuitive point of view), *with respect to a list of sets, any device whatsoever that indicates that some of the sets are or are not elements of themselves or of other of the sets, gives rise to a model (whose content consists of these sets). A model is called consistent if there is no evidence that any of its sets is both an element and not an element of itself or of another of its sets; otherwise, it is called inconsistent.*

Thus, in what follows, in view of (4) and (5) we shall accept the following: *In every model*,

(6) *Every statement-formula is tagged* **T** *or* **F**,

and in every consistent model,

(7) *No statement-formula is tagged both* **T** *and* **F**,

with the understanding that (6) *does not imply that in every model the tag* **T** *or* **F** *of every statement-formula must actually be determined or even determinable (decidable).*

Since (as explained later) we reject any *inconsistent model,* hereafter we shall refer to a *consistent model* simply as a *model.* (However, in the few cases when we consider the question of consistency or inconsistency we do by abuse of language speak of a consistent or an inconsistent model.)

Continuing with the statement-formulas given by (2) and motivated by (6) and (7), let us at will tag some of them **T** or **F** and none of them both **T** and **F**. Let us record the result of our tagging in a table as shown below:

(8)

$a \in a$	**T**
$b \in a$	**F**
$a \in b$	**T**

According to (8), the statement-formulas $a \in a$ and $a \in b$ are tagged **T** (i.e., are true) and the statement-formula $b \in a$ is tagged **F** (i.e., is false). Therefore, it is natural to say that within the context under consideration, the set a is an element of the set a and the set a is an element of the set b, whereas the set b is not an element of the set a. Let us observe also that in (8) condition (7) is satisfied—i.e., in (8) no statement-formula is tagged both **T** and **F**. Thus, we see that within the context under consideration and with respect to the sets a and b, (8) describes *without any inconsistency* which sets are elements of which sets and which sets are not elements of which sets. Consequently, with respect to the content consisting of the sets a and b, there exists a model whose axioms (i.e., conditions imposed on $\in$) are:

(i) The set a is an element of the set a.

(ii) The set b is not an element of the set a.

(iii) The set a is an element of the set b.

According to (8) and as indicated in (i), in the model under consideration the set a is an element of itself. This phenomenon may seem somewhat unintuitive; however, it is harmless.

Let us observe that (8) virtually describes the entire model under consideration. To emphasize this, we may call (8) a *truth table,* or simply a *table of the model* under consideration.

In reference to the model whose table is given by (8), we may make the following statements:

(iv) Its content consists of the sets a and b.

(v) In it the set a is its own element.

(vi) In it every set has at least one element.

As expected, in all of the above considerations and especially in setting up (8), we were guided by the two logical laws (6) and (7). It may seem, however, that in (8) condition (6) is not satisfied. According to (6), in every model every statement-formula is tagged **T** or **F**, and although $b \in b$ is a statement-formula pertaining to the model under consideration, $b \in b$ does not appear with a tag in (8). To clarify the apparent discrepancy, it is enough to point out that (8) pertains to the case of a model in which the truth or falsehood of one of its statement-formulas (in this case, $b \in b$) is undecidable.

We may further clarify the above point by replacing (8) with the following table:

$a \in a$	**T**
$b \in a$	**F**
$a \in b$	**T**
$b \in b$	**T** or **F** *and not both*

where we see at once that rules (6) and (7) are observed explicitly. However, in the above table, the last line gives absolutely no information as to whether or not b is an element of b. Hence, the presence of the fourth line in the above table is useless, and this is the reason why it was omitted from (8). Regardless of this omission, we shall still say that in (8) rules (6) and (7) are obeyed.

Let us again consider the sets a and b and the statement-formulas given by (2). Again, motivated by (6) and (7), let us form the following table:

(9)

$b \in a$	**T**
$a \in b$	**F**
$b \in b$	**F**

We see again that with respect to the sets a and b (9) describes, *without any inconsistency*, which set is an element of which set and which set is not an element of which set. Consequently, with respect to the content consisting of the sets a and b there exists a model whose axioms are:

(vii) The set b is an element of the set a.

(viii) The set a is not an element of the set b.

(ix) The set b is not an element of the set b.

According to (9) and as indicated by (viii) and (ix), in the model under consideration, the set b has no element. This phenomenon also may seem unintuitive; however, it also is harmless. If in a model it is known that a set has no element, then it is customary to call that set an *empty set* of the model. If, however, in a model it is known that a set has at least one element, then that set is called a *nonempty* set of the model. Thus, in the model whose table is given by (9), the set b is an empty set, whereas the set a is a nonempty set.

In connection with the model whose table is given by (9), we may make the following statements:

(x) Its content consists of the sets a and b.

(xi) In it the set b is not its own element.

(xii) In it not every set has at least one element.

Comparing statements (iv), (v) and (vi) to statements (x), (xi) and (xii), we see that (8) and (9) describe essentially two different models. For instance, the former has no empty sets, whereas in the latter b is an empty set. This explains our remark, mentioned in Section 1, that it is possible to develop various kinds of specific models by imposing various axioms which must be satisfied by the predicate symbol $\in$. Thus, in the model whose table is given by (8), the axioms imposed on $\in$ are given by (i), (ii) and (iii). On the other hand, in the model whose table is given by (9), the axioms imposed on $\in$ are given by (vii), (viii) and (ix).

In reference to the content consisting of the sets a and b, the following is a table of another model:

$a \in a$	**F**

In the above table, rules (6) and (7) are obeyed. However, in it the truth or falsehood of each of the statement-formulas $b \in a$, $a \in b$ and $b \in b$ is undecidable (undeterminable).

To emphasize the role of the predicate symbol $\in$, we may write (8) and (9) as follows:

$\in$			$\in$	
a,a	**T**		b,a	**T**
b,a	**F**		a,b	**F**
a,b	**T**		b,b	**F**

In general, let us call an $\in$-*truth table* a table which records taggings **T** or **F** of set-theoretical prime formulas. Thus, each of the above tables is an $\in$-truth table; so are the following two tables:

	$\in$				$\in$	
	a,a	**T**			a,a	**T**
(10)	b,a	**F**		(11)	b,a	**T**
	a,b	**T**			a,b	**T**
	b,a	**F**			b,a	**F**
	a,a	**T**			a,a	**T**
	b,b	**T**			b,b	**F**

Analyzing $\in$-truth tables (8), (9), (10) and (11), we see that in (8), (9) and (10), conditions (6) and (7) are satisfied. Neither in (8) nor in (9) nor in (10) is a statement-formula tagged both **T** and **F**, although in (10) each of the statement-formulas $\in(a,a)$ and $\in(b,a)$ appears twice. However, both appearances of $\in(a,a)$ are tagged **T** and those of $\in(b,a)$ are tagged **F**. This is not the case in $\in$-truth table (11). In (11), the statement-formula $\in(b,a)$ appears twice, once tagged **T** and the other time **F**. Thus, in (11) condition (7) is not satisfied.

To emphasize the fact that in an $\in$-truth table, condition (7) is satisfied (i.e., no statement-formula is tagged both **T** and **F**), we call such a table a *consistent*

∈-truth table or a *set-theoretical truth table*. Otherwise, an ∈-truth table is called *inconsistent*.

Accordingly ∈-truth tables (8), (9) and (10) are consistent, and hence each is a set-theoretical truth table. On the other hand, (11) is an inconsistent ∈-truth table, and hence is not a set-theoretical truth table. Clearly, every consistent ∈-truth table is a table of a model.

We close this section by observing that unless specific restrictions are imposed (by virtue of axioms) on ∈, it is possible to develop (consistent) models which are quite remote from our intuition.

For instance, let us consider the model whose content consists of the sets a, b and c and whose table is as follows:

$a \in a$	T		$a \in b$	T		$a \in c$	T
$b \in a$	F		$b \in b$	F		$b \in c$	T
$c \in a$	T		$c \in b$	T		$c \in c$	T

where, for the sake of convenience, the entire table is broken into three parts, one for each of the sets a, b and c.

We see that in the model whose table is given above:

(xiii) There is a set that is an element of itself.

(xiv) There is no empty set since every set has at least one element.

(xv) There is a *set of all sets*—namely, the set c, since each of the sets a, b and c is an element of c.

(xvi) The set a and the set b have the same elements, namely, a and c. However, a and b do not have the same set-theoretical properties. Specifically, a is an element of a whereas b is not an element of a, and a is an element of b whereas b is not an element of b.

Clearly, the above table describes a consistent model, even though situations (xiii), (xiv), (xv) and (xvi) are quite unintuitive.

In the Theory of Sets developed in this book the counterpart of situations (xiii), (xiv) and (xvi) will not occur, because, as we shall see, the axioms of the Theory of Sets (introduced in Chapter II) will prevent their occurrence.

Another example of a model which is remote from our intuition is the one whose content consists of the sets a, b and c and whose table is as follows:

$a \in a$	F		$a \in b$	F		$a \in c$	F
$b \in a$	F		$b \in b$	F		$b \in c$	T
$c \in a$	F		$c \in b$	F		$c \in c$	T

We see that in the model under consideration, each of the sets a and b is an empty set; however, one of them is an element of the set c whereas the other is not an element of c. Again, owing to the axioms of the Theory of Sets, the counterpart of such a situation will not occur in the Theory of Sets.

Again, consider the model whose content consists of the sets *a* and *b* and whose table is as follows:

$a \in a$	**T**		$a \in b$	**T**
$b \in a$	**T**		$b \in b$	**T**

We see that in the model under consideration, each of the sets *a* and *b* is a *set of all sets*. This is because every set of the content is an element of *a* as well as of *b*.

Without giving further examples, let us mention again that unless specific restrictions are imposed, a model may or may not have one or several sets that are elements of themselves; similarly, it may or may not have one or several *sets of all sets*; again, it may or may not have one or several *empty sets*. As mentioned above, the axioms of the Theory of Sets will prevent the occurrence of the counterpart of the above-mentioned unintuitive situations.

EXERCISES

1. Determine which of the following tables are consistent ∈-truth tables and hence set-theoretical truth tables.

∈			∈			∈	
a,a	**T**		*a,a*	**T**		*a,a*	**F**
b,a	**F**		*b,a*	**T**		*b,a*	**F**
a,a	**T**		*a,a*	**F**		*a,b*	**F**
b,b	**T**		*b,b*	**F**		*b,a*	**F**

2. Determine which of the following tables are consistent ∈-truth tables and hence set-theoretical truth tables.

∈			∈			∈	
a,a	**T**		*a,a*	**T**		*b,a*	**F**
b,a	**F**		*a,a*	**T**		*b,a*	**T**
a,a	**F**		*a,b*	**F**		*b,b*	**T**
b,a	**F**		*b,a*	**F**		*b,a*	**F**

3. Write down three consistent and two inconsistent ∈-truth tables involving the sets *a*, *b* and *c*.

4. Write down two set-theoretical truth tables involving only the set *a*.

5. Complete the following tables to form consistent ∈-truth tables:

∈			∈			∈	
a,a	**T**		*a,a*	**T**		*a,a*	**T**
a,a			*a,b*			*a,b*	
a,a			*a,a*			*b,a*	**F**
a,a			*a,b*	**F**		*b,b*	

6. Complete the following tables to form inconsistent ∈-truth tables:

∈	
a,a	T
a,b	F
a,a	T
a,b	
b,a	
c,a	F
a,c	

∈	
a,a	T
a,a	
a,a	T
b,a	F
a,b	F
b,b	F
a,b	

∈	
a,a	F
b,a	
c,a	T
c,a	
a,c	
c,a	T
b,b	

7. With respect to the content consisting of the sets *a*, *b* and *c*, consider three models whose tables are given respectively by:

∈	
a,a	T
b,a	F
c,a	F
a,b	F
b,b	F
c,b	F
a,c	F

∈	
a,a	F
a,b	F
b,b	T
c,b	T
a,c	F
b,c	F
c,c	F

∈	
a,a	F
a,b	F
b,b	T
c,b	T
a,c	F
b,c	F
c,c	T

In each of the models determine the empty sets (if any), the sets (if any) having only one element and the sets (if any) having only two elements.

8. With respect to the content consisting of the sets *a*, *b* and *c*, consider three models whose tables are given respectively by:

∈	
a,a	T
b,a	T
c,a	T
a,b	F
b,b	T
c,b	T
a,c	T
b,c	T
c,c	T

∈	
a,a	F
b,a	T
c,a	F
a,b	T
b,b	T
c,b	F
a,c	F
b,c	T
c,c	T

∈	
a,a	F
b,a	T
c,a	T
a,b	F
b,b	F
c,b	F
a,c	F
b,c	T
c,c	T

In each of the models determine the sets (if any) having only three elements; also, those sets having only one, two or three elements in common.

9. With respect to the content consisting of the sets *a*, *b* and *c*, consider three models whose tables are given respectively by:

$\in$	
a,a	**T**
b,a	**T**
a,b	**F**
b,b	**T**
c,b	**T**
b,c	**T**
c,c	**T**

$\in$	
b,a	**T**
c,a	**F**
a,b	**T**
c,b	**F**
a,c	**F**
b,c	**T**
c,c	**T**

$\in$	
b,a	**T**
c,a	**T**
a,b	**F**
b,b	**F**
c,b	**F**
a,c	**F**
b,c	**T**

In each of the models determine the empty sets (if any), the sets having at least one element, and the sets having at least two elements.

3. SOME EXAMPLES OF MODELS

In this section we shall discuss some general questions concerning models.

With respect to the content consisting of the sets *a* and *b*, let us consider the following table:

(12)

$\in$	
a,a	**T**
b,a	**F**
a,b	**T**
b,b	**F**

Clearly, (12) is a consistent $\in$-truth table and hence is a set-theoretical truth table. Therefore, (12) is a table of a model. In contrast to the models whose tables are given by (8) and (9), in the model whose content consists of the sets *a*, *b* and whose table is given by (12), the truth or falsehood of every one of its prime formulas is determined. In other words, in the model whose table is given by (12), given any set from its content, we can determine whether or not it is an element of itself; also, given any two sets from the content, we can determine whether or not one is an element of the other.

We call a model *prime-complete* if the truth or falsehood of every one of its prime formulas is determined (or decidable); otherwise, we call a model *prime-incomplete*. Thus, the models whose tables are given by (8) and (9) are *prime-incomplete*; whereas, the model whose table is given by (12) *is prime-complete*. Most of the interesting models are prime-incomplete.

In Section 2, we gave some examples of models by giving their tables in the form of consistent $\in$-truth tables, after which we made some statements pertaining to these models.

The question arises, are all models set up by giving their tables? The answer is in the negative. For instance, in cases where the content is very extensive or unlimited, or where the axioms imposed on ∈ involve a large number of sets of the content, the writing of tables may be impractical or even impossible. This is the situation in most of the interesting models.

In such cases the usual informal procedure for setting up and developing a model is as follows. First, we introduce the content of the supposed (consistent) model by some familiar means. Then, we express the axioms of the supposed model in ordinary English and accept them as being true. Furthermore, we form new sentences using the axioms. Finally, we apply our ordinary rules of reasoning (inference) to determine which of these sentences are true and which are false. If, as a result of the above process, a sentence is found to be true, then we call this process a *proof* of that sentence and we call the latter a *theorem* or a *provable* or a *valid* sentence of the supposed model. If on the other hand, as a result of the above process, a sentence is found to be false, then we call this process a *disproof* of that sentence and we call the sentence a *nonsatisfiable* or a *disprovable* sentence of the supposed model. In this connection, if a sentence is found to be neither provable nor disprovable, then we call it an *undecidable* sentence of the supposed model.

Naturally, if there is no evidence that a sentence is both true and false (i.e., self-contradictory) in the supposed model, then we may say that with respect to the given content there exists a model satisfying the given axioms. In other words, to accept the existence of a model we must be assured that there is no evidence that a sentence is both provable and disprovable in that model. This is another way of stating the requirement that a model must be *consistent*.

The above informal way of setting up and developing a model has not proved to be quite satisfactory. The absence of strict rules for forming sentences of our ordinary language and the absence of strict rules of inference (i.e., rules for evaluating the truth or falsehood of sentences) in our ordinary reasoning may yield (as has happened in the past) situations in which the existence of self-contradictory sentences is concealed for a long time. Moreover, because of these shortcomings of our ordinary language, the evaluation of the truth or falsehood of some sentences may depend largely on the personal interpretation of the investigator and thereby may be debatable.

The above-mentioned shortcomings are reduced partially by setting up and developing models in a strictly *formal* way. This involves the use of the set-theoretical formal vocabulary, the formation rules of set-theoretical formulas and the formal rules of inference (in setting up and developing models).

In view of the definite advantages of the formal development of models, we shall introduce in the sequel the formal machinery mentioned above. This machinery is also necessary for the formal development of any theory of sets and in particular the Theory of Sets. However, in the actual development of the Theory of Sets, we shall use ordinary English and the formal language intermittently. In this way, the text will be more readable and the mathematical rigor will not be compromised too much.

Below we give informally an example of a model for which it is impossible to write a truth table. The theorems are proved informally and the proofs are based on our assumed knowledge of some of the arithmetical properties of the positive natural numbers.

(i) The content consists of an unlimited number of sets $a_1, a_2, a_3, \ldots$

The axioms are:

(ii) a_1 is an empty set.

(iii) a_m is *not* an element of a_n *or* a_n is not an element of a_m *for every* two sets a_m and a_n.

(iv) a_m is an element of a_n or m is not less than n, for every m and n.

In the above, m and n are any two positive natural numbers.

Leaving aside the question of the impossibility of writing a truth table satisfying (i), (ii), (iii) and (iv), let us observe that it is even impossible to write an $\in$-truth table which will assert that a_1 is an empty set. This is because in such a table we have to list $a_1 \in a_1$, $a_2 \in a_1$, $a_3 \in a_1, \ldots$ and tag each of them **F**. Obviously, it is impossible to accomplish this task. Thus, we are confronted with a situation in which it is impossible to write a table for a supposed model whose content is given by (i) and axioms by (ii), (iii) and (iv). However, since with respect to the content under consideration the system of axioms (ii), (iii) and (iv) does not reveal any evidence of inconsistency, we may try to develop informally a model by making inferences based on (i), (ii), (iii) and (iv). For instance, we shall prove several theorems.

In the model whose content is given by (i) and whose axioms are given by (ii), (iii) and (iv) we have:

Theorem 1. *Every set except a_1 is nonempty.*

PROOF. Let n be a positive natural number greater than 1. Since it is not the case that 1 is not less than n, using (iv) we derive $a_1 \in a_n$. Thus, a_n is nonempty. On the other hand, since except for a_1 every set of the content has a subscript greater than 1, we conclude that every set except a_1 is nonempty.

Theorem 2. *No set is an element of itself.*

PROOF. Clearly, a_m is an element of a_m or a_m is not an element of a_m. If a_m is an element of a_m, then using (iii) we derive a_m is not an element of a_m. However, this cannot be the case, since it introduces a self-contradictory statement in the model under consideration. Therefore, no set of the content is an element of itself.

Theorem 3. *If a_m is an element of a_n, then m is less than n.*

PROOF. If a_m is an element of a_n, then using (iii) we derive a_n is not an element of a_m. But using (iv) we also derive n is not less than m. Consequently, m is less than or equal to n. However, in view of Theorem 2, obviously m cannot be equal to n. Hence, m is less than n, as desired.

The above is a typical example of an informal development of a model with a given content and a given system of axioms.

Let us observe that at this stage of our discussion, not only are we unable to give formal proofs of Theorems 1, 2 and 3, but we cannot even express formally axioms (ii), (iii) and (iv). The reason for this is that we have not yet introduced the formal counterparts of such key words as: *not, or* and *for every* which are used in (ii), (iii) and (iv). These words are almost indispensable for any kind of communication. They are used most frequently in the Theory of Sets. We will introduce them formally in the following sections.

The consistency of the above model is an open question. However, with respect to the content given by (i), and as a consequence of axioms (ii), (iii) and (iv), so long as there is no evidence that a sentence is both true (provable in the model) and false (disprovable in the model), we shall not reject the model under consideration on the ground of inconsistency.

Next, we give an example of a model that is demonstrably consistent.

(v) The content consists of the sets *a*, *b* and *c*.

The axioms are:

(vi) Every set is an element of itself.

(vii) Every set has at least two elements.

There can be no question of the existence of a consistent model whose content is given by (v) and whose axioms are given by (vi) and (vii). In each of the tables below, conditions (v), (vi) and (vii) are satisfied. Consequently, the existence of a model satisfying conditions (v), (vi) and (vii) is guaranteed.

	$\in$			$\in$			$\in$	
	a,a	T		a,a	T		a,a	T
	b,a	T		b,a	T		b,a	T
(13)	b,b	T	(14)	c,a	F	(15)	c,a	T
	c,b	T		a,b	T		a,b	T
	a,c	T		b,b	T		b,b	T
	c,c	T		c,b	T		c,b	F
				a,c	F		a,c	T
				b,c	T		b,c	T
				c,c	T		c,c	T

Although in each of the above tables conditions (v), (vi) and (vii) are satisfied, they describe three essentially different models: (13) is prime-incomplete, and (14) and (15) are prime-complete. In (14) there is only one set having three elements. In (15) there are two sets having three elements.

Clearly, any statement proved on the basis of conditions (v), (vi) and (vii) must be a theorem of each of the models whose tables are given by (13), (14) and (15). One such theorem is the following.

Theorem 4. *Every two of the sets a, b and c have an element in common.*

PROOF. In view of (vi) we have $a \in a$, $b \in b$ and $c \in c$. Since by (vii) every set has at least two elements, without loss of generality we may take the set *b* as the second element of *a*. In this case the sets *a* and *b* have an element in common. Now, if the second element of *c* is *b*, then the proof of Theorem 4 is obvious. On the other hand, if the second element of c is a, then no matter which of the sets a or c is the second element of the set b, the conclusion of Theorem 4 is again valid.

An axiom of a model is said to be *independent of the remaining axioms of the model* if there is a model (with the content of the model under consideration) in which the axiom under consideration is not satisfied while the remaining axioms are valid; otherwise, the axiom is called *dependent on the remaining axioms* of the model. If each of the axioms of a model is independent of the remaining ones, then the axioms are said to be *mutually independent in the model*.

The tables below show that axioms (vi) and (vii) are mutually independent in any model whose content is given by (v) and whose axioms are given by (vi) and (vii).

(16)	$\in$		(17)	$\in$	
	a,a	T		a,a	F
	b,a	F		b,a	T
	c,a	F		c,a	T
	b,b	T		a,b	T
	c,c	T		b,b	F
				c,b	T
				a,c	T
				b,c	T
				c,c	F

Clearly, in (16), axiom (vi) is valid, whereas axiom (vii) is not satisfied. In (17), axiom (vii) is valid, whereas axiom (vi) is not satisfied.

Below we give two more examples of models introduced by axioms expressed in ordinary English. The first model is given by:

(viii) The content consists of the sets a and b.

The only axiom is:

(ix) Every set is an empty set.

The existence of a model satisfying conditions (viii) and (ix) is secured by the table:

(18)	$\in$	
	a,a	F
	b,a	F
	a,b	F
	b,b	F

The model under consideration is prime-complete.

The next model is given by:

(x) The content consists of the sets a and b.

The only axiom is:

(xi) Every set has two elements.

The existence of a model satisfying conditions (x) and (xi) is secured by the table:

(19)

$\in$	
a,a	**T**
b,a	**T**
a,b	**T**
b,b	**T**

The model under consideration is prime-complete. Moreover, it has no empty sets. Furthermore, every two sets of it have the same elements.

Let us observe that with respect to a content consisting of a single set a there exist only two distinct (consistent) models. Their tables are given below:

(20)

$\in$	
a,a	**T**

(21)

$\in$	
a,a	**F**

Next, let us give an example where there exists no (consistent) model satisfying a given system of conditions.

Consider the following example.

(xii) The content consists of the single set a.

The axioms are:

(xiii) No set is empty.

(xiv) No set is its own element.

As (20) and (21) show there exists no (consistent) model whose content consists of the single set a and whose axioms are given by (xiii) and (xiv).

The table of any model satisfying conditions (xii), (xiii) and (xiv) must be of the form

$\in$	
a,a	**T**
a,a	**F**

Clearly the above is an inconsistent $\in$-truth table which gives rise to an inconsistent model (that as usual we reject).

Let us observe that in order to show that in a model whose content consists of the sets a, b and c, the only elements of a are b and c, we must have:

$$a \in a \text{ tagged } \textbf{F}$$
$$b \in a \text{ tagged } \textbf{T}$$
$$c \in a \text{ tagged } \textbf{T}$$

However, for visual purposes, it is customary to represent this set a as a pair of braces within which b and c are inserted and separated by a comma. In short, the set a whose only elements are b and c is customarily represented as:

(22) $\{b,c\}$

Let us emphasize that formally $\{b,c\}$ is not a set since $\{b,c\}$ is not a letter. However, the representation of the above-mentioned set a as $\{b,c\}$ is quite suggestive and helpful. This kind of representation of sets is standard; we shall use it frequently with the understanding that, say, in a model whose content consists of the sets a, b, c, d, the configuration $\{b,c,d\}$ stands for the set a if it is the case that $b \in a$, $c \in a$ and $d \in a$ are tagged **T** and $a \in a$ is tagged **F**.

Similarly, if in a model the only element of the set a is the set b, then the set a is represented by:

$$\{b\}$$

and if the only element of the set c is the set a, then the set c is represented by:

$$\{\{b\}\} = \{a\}$$

Likewise, if in a model the only elements of the set a are the sets b, c, d, e and h, then the set a is represented by:

$$\{b,c,d,e,h\}$$

Using configurations such as (22), we may write the following true set-theoretical prime formulas:

$$a \in \{a,b,c\}, \qquad b \in \{a,b,c\}, \qquad c \in \{a,b,c\}$$

The following set-theoretical prime formulas are also true:

$$a \in \{a, \{a\}, \{a,b\}, \{\{b\}\}\}$$
$$\{a\} \in \{a, \{a\}, \{a,b\}, \{b\}\}$$
$$\{a,b\} \in \{a, \{a\}, \{a,b\}, \{\{b\}\}\}$$
$$\{\{b\}\} \in \{a, \{a\}, \{a,b\}, \{\{b\}\}\}$$

In connection with notation (22), let us mention that in a model two differently lettered sets—say, a and b—may have precisely the same elements—say, m, n and p. In this case, according to (22), either of the sets a and b is represented as:

$$\{m,n,p\}$$

Consequently, the distinction between a and b is no longer maintained. As we shall see later, in the Theory of Sets (by virtue of a special axiom) any two sets having precisely the same elements will be considered indistinguishable. However, at present, to maintain the distinction between the above-mentioned sets a and b, and in the meantime to use notation (22), we may adopt the following notation:

$$\{m,n,p\}_a \qquad \text{and} \qquad \{m,n,p\}_b$$

For instance, in the model whose table is given by (18), if notation (22) is used, then the empty sets a and b must be represented as:

$$\{\ \}_a \qquad \text{and} \qquad \{\ \}_b$$

Likewise, in the model whose table is given by (19), if notation (22) is used, then the sets a and b must be represented as:

$$\{a,b\}_a \qquad \text{and} \qquad \{a,b\}_b$$

When no misunderstanding is likely to arise, subscripts in the above configurations may be dropped.

In many cases, a very useful device for setting up or describing a prime-complete model is the following.

Given a prime-complete model, we may describe it by writing (whenever possible) a list of all the sets of its content; under each set—say, a—of its content we write $m \in a$ if $m \in a$ is true; we do not write $m \in a$ if $m \in a$ is false. Clearly, this description is unambiguous when applied to the case of prime-complete models.

For instance, the prime-complete model whose table is given by (14) is described as follows:

(23)

a	b	c
$a \in a$	$a \in b$	$b \in c$
$b \in a$	$b \in b$	$c \in c$
	$c \in b$	

Similarly, the prime-complete model whose table is given by (17) is described as follows:

(24)

a	b	c
$b \in a$	$a \in b$	$a \in c$
$c \in a$	$c \in b$	$b \in c$

Inspecting (23) we assert that the only elements of a are a and b, the only elements of b are a, b and c and the only elements of c are b and c. Thus, according to notation (22), in the above prime-complete model the sets a, b and c are represented respectively as:

$$\{a,b\}, \qquad \{a,b,c\}, \qquad \{b,c\}$$

Similarly, inspecting (24) in the prime-complete model under consideration, we may represent the sets a, b and c respectively as:

$$\{b,c\}, \qquad \{a,c\}, \qquad \{a,b\}$$

Conversely, every table written in the form of (23) or (24) gives rise to a prime-complete model.

Consider, for instance, the following table:

(25)

a	b	c	d
$b \in a$		$a \in c$	$c \in d$
$c \in a$		$b \in c$	$d \in d$
$d \in a$			

This table gives rise to a prime-complete model whose content consists of the sets a, b, c, d, and in which b is an empty set and the sets a, c and d are non-empty. Here again, according to notation (22), the sets a, b, c and d of the prime-complete model described by (25) are represented respectively as:

$$\{b,c,d\}, \qquad \{\ \}, \qquad \{a,b\}, \qquad \{c,d\}$$

Naturally, we may also call (23), (24) and (25) tables of models.

We close this section by pointing out that the idea of a table can be extended to the case of a model whose content is unlimited. However, in such cases, we can actually write down only a *partial table* (i.e., a consistent partial $\in$-truth table). Nevertheless, in many instances even a partial table is a helpful device for accepting the existence of a model.

For instance, let us try to determine whether or not there exists a model satisfying the following conditions.

(xv) The content consists of an unlimited number of sets $a_1, a_2, a_3, \ldots$

The axioms are:

(xvi) Every set has only one element.

(xvii) No set is its own element.

(xviii) Corresponding to every set, there exists a set of which the former is an element.

As a partial table of a model whose content consists of the sets a_1, a_2, $a_3, \ldots$ and that satisfies the above axioms, we propose the following partial $\in$-truth table:

	$\in$
a_1, a_2	**T**
a_2, a_3	**T**
a_3, a_4	**T**
a_4, a_5	**T**
. . . . .	. .
. . . . .	. .

(26)

There is no reason to suspect that (26) is an inconsistent $\in$-truth table. We feel quite sure that no matter how long tabulations in (26) are continued [according to the obvious pattern suggested by conditions (xv) to (xviii)], no prime formula which is tagged both **T** and **F** will occur. Hence we accept (26) as a partial table of a model and we say that there exists a model satisfying conditions (xv) to (xviii).

EXERCISES

1. Represent the following in a manner similar to that given by (22).
   (i) The set whose only element is c.
   (ii) The set whose only elements are m, n, 5, p and 6.
   (iii) The set whose only element is $\{m\}$.
   (iv) The set whose only elements are a, $\{a\}$, $\{\{a\}\}$, $\{\{\{a\}\}\}$.

2. Using only three pairs of braces and the letter b, represent a set having only two elements.

3. Using only four pairs of braces and the letter b, represent a set having only three elements.

4. Using four pairs of braces and the letter b, represent a set having only two elements.

5. In a manner similar to that given by (22), represent a set having only four elements and such that, of each of the two elements of that set, one is an element of the other.

6. Determine whether or not there exists a model satisfying the following conditions. Use the method of $\in$-truth tables.
   (i) Its content consists of the sets a, b, c and d.
   (ii) In it there are only two empty sets.
   (iii) In it every nonempty set has only one element.
   (iv) In it no set is its own element.

7. Determine whether or not there exists a model satisfying the following conditions. Use the method of $\in$-truth tables.
   (i) Its content consists of the sets a, b and c.
   (ii) In it every set is its own element.

8. Determine whether or not there exists a model satisfying the following conditions. Use the method of $\in$-truth tables.
   (i) Its content consists of the sets a_1, a_2, a_3, ...
   (ii) In it every set has only two elements.
   (iii) In it no two sets having different subscripts have the same elements.

9. Determine whether or not there exists a model satisfying the following conditions. Use the method of $\in$-truth tables.
   (i) Its content consists of the sets a_1, a_2, a_3, ...
   (ii) In it every set has only one element.
   (iii) In it every two sets have the same elements.

10. Determine whether or not there exists a model satisfying the following conditions. Use the method of $\in$-truth tables.
   (i) Its content consists of the sets a, b and c.
   (ii) In it there exist only two empty sets.
   (iii) In it there exists only one nonempty set whose elements are the empty sets.

11. Make four statements about the prime-complete model whose table is given by:

a	b	c	d	e
$a \in a$		$b \in c$		$b \in e$
$b \in a$				$d \in e$

12. Construct the truth table for the prime-complete model described by (25).

4. NEGATION AND DISJUNCTION

In the previous section, the need for setting up and developing models in a formal way was pointed out. We mentioned there that the formal development requires set-theoretical formal machinery. This machinery is also used for setting up and developing formally any theory of sets and in particular the Theory of Sets.

In our pursuit of the necessary machinery for the formal development of a model we introduce in this section two new formal symbols which will enable us to form set-theoretical statement-formulas other than prime formulas. We also introduce the corresponding formal rules of inference, i.e., the rules of tagging the newly obtained statement formulas **T** or **F** in terms of the tags (**T** or **F**) of the prime formulas which occur in them.

Now, if in a model $a \in b$ is tagged **F**, we assert: *it is false that a is an element of b*. Intuitively, this amounts to the assertion: *a is not an element of b*. Clearly, in connection with any model, it is most desirable to be able to express formally a sentence such as: *a* is *not* an element of *b*. For this purpose, we introduce the formal symbol:

$$\sim$$

which is read: *not*. Moreover, we accept as set-theoretical formulas configurations such as: $\sim(a \in b)$, $\sim(c \in m)$, ... which are read respectively: *a* is *not* an element of *b* (or it is *not* the case that *a* is an element of *b*), *c* is *not* an element of *m*, ...

Let us mention here that $\sim$ like (and) and , (the comma) is a logical formal symbol. It is called the *negation sign*.

As indicated above, with the introduction of $\sim$ we have also introduced a new type of set-theoretical formula. Let us recall that the only set-theoretical formulas at our disposal prior to the introduction of $\sim$ were set-theoretical prime formulas such as: $a \in b$, $c \in m$, ... Now, after the introduction of $\sim$ configurations such as $\sim(a \in b)$, $\sim(c \in m)$, ... are also accepted as set-theoretical formulas.

Remark 1. Since in this book we are concerned with set-theoretical language, no misunderstanding will arise if (as we have done occasionally) we sometimes omit the word *set-theoretical* in referring to a *prime formula*, a *statement-formula* and a *formula*.

Motivated by the above, let us introduce for the time being the following *formation rules of formulas*.

(27)　　　　　　*Every set-theoretical prime formula is a formula.*

(28)　　*If each of P, Q, R, ... stands for a formula, then each of $\sim(P)$, $\sim(Q)$, $\sim(R)$, ... also stands for a formula.*

In the above, *P, Q, R, ...* are not set-theoretical formal symbols. They are *metalinguistic variables* standing for arbitrary set-theoretical formulas. For this reason, each of them is called a *formula scheme*.

In what follows, capital letters such as P, Q, R, ... except for **T** and **F**, represent formula schemes.

According to (27) and (28), the following configurations are examples of set-theoretical formulas, or simply formulas:

$$a \in b, \quad \sim(a \in b), \quad \sim(\sim(a \in b)), \quad \sim(\sim(\sim(a \in b)))$$

Given a formula such as $\sim(a \in b)$, we may ask: is $\sim(a \in b)$ true or false? Consequently, formulas such as $\sim(a \in b)$, $\sim(c \in m)$, ... are statement-formulas. As such, they lend themselves to being tagged **T** or **F**. Moreover, according to (6) and (7), in a model a statement-formula such as $\sim(a \in b)$ is tagged **T** or **F** and not both.

Intuitively it is clear that if in a model $a \in b$ is true, then $\sim(a \in b)$ is false; and if $a \in b$ is false, then $\sim(a \in b)$ is true. Accordingly, we introduce the following rules for tagging (**T** or **F**) a formula of the form $\sim(P)$ in terms of the tagging (**T** or **F**) of the formula for which P stands. This is done by means of the following table:

(29)

P	$\sim(P)$
T	**F**
F	**T**

where P stands for any formula, i.e., is a formula scheme.

It is customary to call $\sim(P)$ the *negation* of P and to read it: *not P*. When no confusion is likely to arise, $\sim(P)$ is written as $\sim P$. Also, (29) is called the *truth table corresponding to the negation sign*. According to truth table (29), if P stands for a true formula, then the formula for which $\sim(P)$ stands is false; and if P stands for a false formula, then the formula for which $\sim(P)$ stands is a true formula.

Thus, we have:

(30)

P	$\sim P$	$\sim(\sim P)$
T	**F**	**T**
F	**T**	**F**

It is also customary to introduce the following abbreviations:

$$(a \notin b) \quad \text{for} \quad \sim(a \in b)$$

and when no confusion is likely to arise we write:

$$a \notin b \quad \text{for} \quad \sim(a \in b), \quad \text{and} \quad \sim\sim P \quad \text{for} \quad \sim(\sim(P)).$$

Thus, in view of (29), the set-theoretical truth table:

(31)

$a \in a$	**T**
$b \in a$	**F**
$a \in b$	**F**
$b \in b$	**T**

can be rewritten as:

(32)

$a \in a$	**T**
$b \notin a$	**T**
$a \notin b$	**T**
$b \in b$	**T**

Let us observe that, prior to the introduction of the negation sign, we were unable to express formally the axioms of the model whose table is given by (31). However, now, in view of (32) and (3), the axioms of the above-mentioned model can be expressed formally as:

(i) $(a \in a)$

(ii) $\sim(b \in a)$

(iii) $\sim(a \in b)$

(iv) $b \in b$

So far, we have introduced only a portion of the necessary machinery for the formal development of a model. Nevertheless, using the formal symbols that have been introduced so far, we give below a precise description of the general outline of the formal development of a model. The model we consider is the one whose axioms are given by (i) to (iv) in the above.

 I. *Formal symbols*

    Set-theoretical:

        Individual constants (sets) a,b

        Predicate symbol (elementhood) $\in$

    Logical:

        (,) $\sim$

 II. *Formation rules of formulas*

    Every set-theoretical prime formula is a formula.

    If P stands for a formula, then $\sim(P)$ also stands for a formula.

III. *Axioms*

    Logical axiom scheme:

        If P stands for a *valid* formula, then the formula for which $\sim(\sim(P))$ stands is also *valid*.

    Set-theoretical axioms:

        $\sim\sim(a \in a)$, $\sim(b \in a)$, $\sim(a \in b)$, $(b \in b)$

IV. *Rules of inference*

    Every set-theoretical axiom is a *valid* formula.

    If a formula of the form $\sim(\sim(P))$ is *valid*, then the formula for which P stands is also *valid*.

One of the dominant features of the formal development of a model is that the theorems are derived as valid formulas starting with set-theoretical axioms (for instance, as given in III, above) and proceeding via formation rules of formulas (see II, above) and the rules of inference (see IV, above). Thus, the tags **T** and **F** do not enter into the formal development. Consequently, the notion of a *true formula* (i.e., a formula that is tagged **T**) is replaced by the notion of a *valid formula*.

Now, starting with the axioms and proceeding strictly according to the above rules, we will derive formulas which are valid in the above model. The process of derivation of a valid formula is called a proof of the formula. Thus,

$$\sim \sim (a \in a), \quad \sim\sim\sim\sim(a \in a), \quad \sim\sim\sim\sim\sim(b \in a), \quad \sim\sim\sim\sim\sim\sim(a \in b)$$

are examples of valid formulas in the above model.

The proof that, say, $(a \in a)$ is a valid formula in the above model runs as follows. Since $\sim\sim(a \in a)$ is an axiom, by Rule IV we conclude that $(a \in a)$ is valid. Again, to prove that, say, $\sim\sim\sim\sim\sim(b \in a)$ is a valid formula we proceed as follows. Since $\sim(b \in a)$ is an axiom, by repeated application of the logical axiom scheme mentioned in III, we conclude that $\sim\sim\sim\sim\sim(b \in a)$ is a valid formula.

As expected, a valid formula in a model is also called a *provable* or a *derivable* formula or a *theorem* of that model. As one can see, in the formal setup the proof of a theorem is undebatable and independent of the personal interpretation of the investigator. A formula whose negation is valid in a model is called a *nonsatisfiable* or a *disprovable* formula of that model. Clearly, the negation of a formula that is not provable in a model need not be provable. If a formula of a model is such that neither it nor its negation is provable in the model, then the formula is called *undecidable* in the model; otherwise, it is called *decidable* in the model. As expected, a model is called *consistent* if it is not the case that a formula and its negation are both provable in the model; otherwise, it is called *inconsistent*. An axiom of a model is called *independent* of the remaining axioms of the model if it is not provable in the model obtained (from the model under consideration) by omitting the axiom; otherwise the axiom is called *dependent* on the remaining axioms of the model. The axioms of a model are called *mutually independent* if each is independent of the remaining axioms of the model. Motivated by the notion of prime-completeness, a model is called *complete* if the adjunction to its axioms of a formula that is not a theorem of the model yields an inconsistent model; otherwise, the model is called *incomplete*. Finally, if there is a procedure for ascertaining whether or not each formula of the model is decidable in the model, then the model is called a *decidable* model; otherwise, it is called *undecidable*. Clearly, an undecidable model must have an undecidable formula. However, a decidable model may also have an undecidable formula.

The model given in the above example is consistent and its axioms are mutually independent. Moreover, the model is complete and decidable. If we omit one of its axioms, we obtain a model which is consistent, incomplete and decidable, and in which the omitted axiom is an undecidable formula.

The formal development of any model is based on the outline given by I, II, III and IV with some amplification, as will be introduced in the sequel.

As mentioned earlier, in the above outline of the formal development of a model there was no explicit mention made of the tags **T** or **F**. Nevertheless, the essence of all the above-mentioned machinery is based on (6), (7), (27), (28) and (29).

Next, let us consider the prime-complete model whose table is as follows:

	a	b	c
(33)	$a \in a$	$a \in b$	$a \in c$
	$b \in a$	$c \in b$	$b \in c$
			$c \in c$

In the above, we see at once that if a set belongs to *a or b*, then it also belongs to *c*. Clearly, in connection with any model it is most desirable to be able to express formally sentences such as: *a* is an element of *b or c*. For this purpose, we introduce the formal symbol:

$$\vee$$

which is read *or* and we accept as formulas such configurations as: $(a \in b) \vee (a \in c)$; $(a \notin m) \vee (c \notin b)$; ..., that are read respectively: *a* is an element of *b or a* is an element of *c*; *a* is not an element of *m or c* is not an element of *b*; ....

Let us mention here that $\vee$ like $\sim$ is also a logical formal symbol. It is called the *disjunction* sign.

As indicated above, the introduction of $\vee$ also introduces a new type of formula. Thus, in addition to (27) and (28) we introduce the following formation rule for formulas:

(34)   *If P and Q stand for formulas, then (P) $\vee$ (Q) also stands for a formula.*

Accordingly, the following configurations are examples of formulas:

$$(\sim(a \in b)) \vee (m \notin b) \qquad \text{and} \qquad (b \notin c) \vee (\sim(a \in m))$$

Given a formula such as $(a \in b) \vee (c \in m)$, we may ask: is $(a \in b) \vee (c \in m)$ true or false? Consequently, formulas such as $(a \in b) \vee (c \in m)$ are statement-formulas. Let us observe that in our ordinary discourse if one of two statements is known to be true, then the statement obtained by connecting these two with the connective *or* is also accepted as being true. On the other hand, if each of two statements is known to be false, then the statement obtained by connecting these two with the connective *or* is also accepted as being false.

Motivated by the above, we introduce the rules of tagging a formula of the form $(P) \vee (Q)$ in terms of the tags (**T** or **F**) of *P* and *Q*. This is done by means of the following table:

	P	Q	(P) $\vee$ (Q)
(35)	**T**	**T**	**T**
	T	**F**	**T**
	F	**T**	**T**
	F	**F**	**F**

where *P* and *Q* stand for any two formulas, i.e., are two formula schemes.

It is customary to call $(P) \vee (Q)$ the *disjunction* of *P* and *Q* and to read it:

P or Q. When no confusion is likely to arise, $(P) \vee (Q)$ is written as $P \vee Q$. Also, (35) is called the *truth table corresponding to the disjunction sign*.

Truth table (35) shows that if both of any two statement-formulas are false, then 'their disjunction is also false and vice versa. Otherwise, the disjunction is true. Thus, intuitively, $\vee$ is used as the *inclusive or*, i.e., *and/or*.

Now, in view of (29) and (35), in the model whose table is given by (33) we have the following true statement-formulas:

$$\sim(c \in a), \qquad \sim(b \in b), \qquad (a \in a) \vee (a \in b),$$
$$(b \in a) \vee (c \in a), \qquad (b \in b) \vee (c \in c),$$

and the following false statement-formulas:

$$(c \in a) \vee (b \in b), \qquad (a \notin c) \vee (a \notin a), \qquad (b \notin a) \vee (b \notin c).$$

Now, let *P* be any formula. Then, in view of (29) and (35) we have:

(36)

P	$\sim P$	$P \vee \sim P$
T	**F**	**T**
F	**T**	**T**

The above truth table shows that if *P* stands for any formula of a model, then the formula for which $P \vee \sim P$ stands is always true in that model. Clearly, this is very useful information, since according to it a *formula of the form $P \vee \sim P$ is always tagged* **T** (i.e., is always true) *in every model* to which it may pertain.

A formula that assumes **T** for every assignment of logical values (**T** or **F**) to the prime formulas that occur in it, is called a *tautology*. Hence, a tautology is a formula which is valid in every model to which it may pertain. For this reason, a tautology is also called a *universally valid formula*.

Thus, in view of (36) the formula $(a \in b) \vee (a \notin b)$ is a tautology. So is $(m \notin n) \vee (m \in n)$. Consequently, both are valid in every model to which they may pertain.

On the other hand, if *P* stands for any formula, then in view of (29) and (35) we have:

(37)

P	$\sim P$	$\sim(P \vee \sim P)$
T	**F**	**F**
F	**T**	**F**

which shows that *in every model a formula of the form $\sim(P \vee \sim P)$ is always tagged* **F** (i.e., is always false).

A formula that assumes **F** for every assignment of logical values to the prime formulas that occur in it, is called a *contradiction*. Hence, a contradiction is a formula which is nonsatisfiable in every model to which it may pertain. For this reason, a contradiction is also called a *nonsatisfiable formula*.

Thus, in view of (37) the formula $\sim((a \in b) \vee (a \notin b))$ is a contradiction; so is $\sim((h \notin a) \vee (h \in a))$. In this connection, a formula is called *satisfiable* if it is valid in a model.

Obviously, the negation of a tautology is a contradiction and the negation of a contradiction is a tautology.

Finally, a formula that is neither a tautology nor a contradiction is called *undecidable*. Clearly, an undecidable formula may be decidable in a model.

Let us emphasize that capital letters such as P, Q, ... are not formulas. They are formula schemes. Similarly, configurations such as P, $P \vee Q$, $P \vee \sim Q$, ... are not formulas. They are formula schemes, since each represents an arbitrary formula or the *form* of a formula. For instance, the formulas:

$$(a \in b) \vee (m \in c) \qquad \text{and} \qquad (\sim(m \in n)) \vee (a \in b)$$

are formulas of the form $P \vee Q$.

In view of (36) and (37), we may say that $P \vee \sim P$ is a *tautology scheme* and $\sim(P \vee \sim P)$ is a *contradiction scheme*. It is easily seen that $(\sim P) \vee P$ is also a tautology scheme, whereas $\sim((\sim P) \vee P)$ is a contradiction scheme. In short, *a formula scheme is a tautology scheme if every formula of that form is a tautology.* Also, *a formula scheme is a contradiction scheme if every formula of that form is a contradiction.* In this connection, a formula scheme is called *satisfiable* if a formula of that form is satisfiable. Obviously, the negation of a tautology scheme is a contradiction scheme and the negation of a contradiction scheme is a tautology scheme. Finally, a formula scheme that is neither a tautology scheme nor a contradiction scheme is called an *undecidable formula scheme*. For instance, $P \vee Q$ is an undecidable formula scheme. Similarly, as the following truth table shows, $(P \vee Q) \vee (\sim(P \vee \sim Q))$ is an undecidable formula scheme.

P	Q	$(P \vee Q) \vee (\sim(P \vee \sim Q))$
T	T	T
T	F	T
F	T	T
F	F	F

By the method of truth tables such as the one given above we can easily verify that each of the following formula schemes is a tautology scheme:

$$P \vee \sim(P \vee P)$$
$$(P \vee Q) \vee \sim P$$
(38) $\qquad (P \vee Q) \vee \sim(Q \vee P)$
$$((P \vee Q) \vee \sim(P \vee R)) \vee \sim(Q \vee \sim R)$$

Thus, every formula that is of the form of any one of the above formula schemes is a valid formula in every model to which it may pertain.

Also, from (35) it follows that:

(39)   *If P and $Q \vee \sim P$ stand for valid formulas in a model, then the formula for which Q stands is also valid in that model.*

Inference rule (39) is usually called *modus ponens* or the rule of *detachment*.

With the additional formal symbol ∨ and formation rule (34), the outline given by I, II, III and IV of the formal development of any model (page 26) is now modified as follows. The symbol ∨ is added to the symbols in I. Rule (34) is added to the rules in II. The logical axiom scheme given in III is replaced by the axiom schemes given by (38). The second rule of inference given in IV is replaced by rule (39). Naturally, the list of individual constants and set-theoretical axioms depends on the particular model which is under consideration.

Thus, if

(40) $a \in b$ and $c \notin b$

are the axioms of a model, then by (38)

$$((a \in b) \vee (c \notin b)) \vee \sim(a \in b)$$

is a valid formula of that model. Hence, by (39),

$$(a \in b) \vee (c \notin b)$$

is a theorem of that model.

Again, by (38),

$$((c \notin b) \vee (a \in b)) \vee \sim((a \in b) \vee (c \notin b))$$

is a valid formula in the model under consideration. Since $(a \in b) \vee (c \notin b)$ is also a theorem, in view of the above and (39) it follows that:

$$(c \notin b) \vee (a \in b)$$

is yet another theorem of that model.

The above are examples of the formal derivation of theorems in a model whose axioms are given by (40).

Let us observe that in the above proofs axiom schemes (38) and inference rule (39) played an important role. Although it can be shown that (prior to the introduction of the individual variables and quantifiers) any addition of axiom schemes to (38) or to (39) would be redundant, for practical purposes a greater list of axiom schemes would facilitate the formal process of deriving theorems.

Let us observe again that neither in the modified version of the outline given by I, II, III and IV nor in the proofs of the above two theorems was there any explicit mention made of the tags **T** or **F**. Nevertheless, here also the essence of all the formal machinery is based on (6), (7), (27), (28), (29), (34) and (35). It has also been shown that if the validity of a formula is obtained via tagging procedures as given by (6), (7), (29) and (35), then the validity of the same formula can be obtained by means of the modified outline of I, II, III and IV, and vice versa. Thus, essentially it does not matter which one of the above two methods is used to establish the validity of a formula in a model. Both are formal and neither depends on the personal interpretation of the investigator.

Using tagging techniques as given by (29) and (35), we may prove the **three** following theorems of a model whose axioms are given by (40):

$$(a \in b), \qquad (a \notin b) \vee (c \notin b), \qquad (a \in b) \vee \sim(a \in b)$$

To prove that, say, $(a \notin b) \vee (c \notin b)$ is a theorem of a model whose axioms are given by (40), it is enough to observe the following. Since $(c \notin b)$ is an axiom, it is tagged **T**. Consequently, by (35) the formula $(a \notin b) \vee (c \notin b)$ is also tagged **T** and thus is a theorem of the model under consideration. Clearly, the preceding proof is independent of the personal interpretation of the investigator.

To point out the importance of tautology schemes in inferring theorems of a model, let us consider a model whose axioms are given by (40) and use three of the tautology schemes given by (38), one at a time. As a result, we obtain the following theorems in the model under consideration:

$$(a \in b) \vee \sim((a \in b) \vee (a \in b))$$
$$((a \in b) \vee (c \notin b)) \vee \sim((c \notin b) \vee (a \in b))$$
$$(((a \in b) \vee (c \notin b)) \vee \sim((a \in b) \vee (a \in b))) \vee \sim((c \notin b) \vee \sim(a \in b))$$

EXERCISES

1. Referring to the model whose table is given by (14), determine which of the following formulas are theorems:

$$(a \in c) \vee (b \in c)$$
$$(a \notin c) \vee (c \notin b)$$
$$(b \notin c) \vee (c \in a)$$
$$(\sim(b \in c)) \vee (c \notin a)$$
$$((b \in a) \vee (c \notin c)) \vee (c \notin b)$$
$$((c \notin a) \vee (c \in c)) \vee ((a \in b) \vee (c \notin b))$$

2. Determine which of the following formulas are tautologies and which are contradictions.

$$(a \in \{a\}) \vee (b \in \{a, b\})$$
$$(b \in \{a\}) \vee (c \notin \{a\})$$
$$(\{a\} \in \{\{a\}\}) \vee (b \notin b)$$
$$(c \in \{a, c\}) \vee \sim(a \notin a)$$
$$(a \notin \{a, b\}) \vee (b \notin \{b\})$$

3. Determine which of the following formulas are tautologies, which are contradictions and which are neither.

$$(a \in a) \vee (a \notin a)$$
$$(\sim(b \notin b)) \vee (b \in b)$$
$$(\sim(a \in b)) \vee (c \notin d)$$
$$(\sim(c \in a)) \vee (c \in a)$$
$$\sim((c \in b) \vee (c \notin b))$$
$$\sim((m \notin h) \vee \sim(a \in b))$$

4. Prove that $P \lor Q$ is neither a tautology nor a contradiction scheme. Show that the same applies to $(\sim P) \lor Q$.

5. Prove that $(\sim P) \lor P$ is a tautology scheme and $\sim((\sim P) \lor P)$ is a contradiction scheme.

6. Prove that the following are tautology schemes:

$$P \lor \sim(P \lor P)$$
$$P \lor (Q \lor \sim P)$$
$$(P \lor Q) \lor \sim(P \lor Q)$$

7. Form a truth table for each of the following formula schemes:

$$((\sim P) \lor Q) \lor \sim R$$
$$(Q \lor R) \lor (P \lor Q)$$

8. Prove that every one of the following formulas is a theorem in the model whose table is given by (16):

$$(c \in c) \lor \sim(a \in a)$$
$$(c \in a) \lor (b \notin a)$$
$$(c \notin a) \lor (b \in a)$$
$$(a \in a) \lor (b \in b)$$

9. Prove that every one of the following formulas is a nonsatisfiable formula in the model whose table is given by (17):

$$(a \in a) \lor (c \in c)$$
$$(b \notin a) \lor (a \notin b)$$
$$((c \in c) \lor (c \notin b)) \lor ((b \notin c) \lor (b \in b))$$
$$\sim((b \in a) \lor (c \in b)) \lor ((a \notin b) \lor (c \notin a))$$

5. CONJUNCTION AND IMPLICATION

Considering again the theory of sets whose model is given by (33), we see that the set a that belongs to a *and* to b also belongs to c. Clearly, in any model it is desirable to be able to express formally statements such as: a is an element of b *and* c. However, let us observe that intuitively to assert that a is an element of b *and* c, amounts to asserting that it is *not* the case that a is *not* an element of b *or not* an element of c. This shows that it is possible to use the connectives *not* and *or* so as to render the use of the connective *and* unnecessary. Motivated by the above, we introduce the logical symbol:

$$\land$$

which is read *and*, merely to abbreviate the formula scheme $\sim((\sim P) \lor \sim Q)$. More precisely, we write:

(41) $(P) \land (Q)$ for $\sim((\sim P) \lor \sim Q)$

Accordingly, in view of (29), (35) and (41) we have:

(42)

P	Q	$(P) \wedge (Q)$
T	T	T
T	F	F
F	T	F
F	F	F

where, naturally, P and Q stand for any two formulas. The symbol $\wedge$ is called the *conjunction sign*. Moreover, $(P) \wedge (Q)$ is called the *conjunction* of P and Q and is read: *P and Q*. When no confusion is likely to arise, $(P) \wedge (Q)$ is written as $P \wedge Q$. Also, truth table (42) is called the *truth table corresponding to the conjunction sign*.

According to (42), if both of any two statement-formulas are true, then their conjunction is true and vice versa. Otherwise, the conjunction is false.

Thus, in view of (42) the following formula is true:

$$(a \in \{a\}) \wedge (b \in \{b\})$$

whereas

$$(a \notin \{a\}) \wedge (b \in \{b\})$$

is false.

In view of (29) and (42) we have:

P	$\sim P$	$P \wedge \sim P$
T	F	F
F	T	F

which shows that $P \wedge \sim P$ is a contradiction scheme. Consequently, $\sim(P \wedge \sim P)$ is a tautology scheme.

Again, let us consider the model whose table is given by (33). We see that if a set belongs to a or to b, then it belongs to c. Clearly, in any model it is most desirable to express formally statements such as: *if a is an element of b, then a is an element of c*. However, let us observe that, intuitively, to assert that: *if a is an element of b, then a is an element of c*, amounts to asserting that: *a is not an element of b or a is an element of c*. This shows that it is possible to use the connectives *not* and *or* so as to render the use of the connective *if, then* unnecessary. Motivated by the above, we introduce the logical symbol:

$$\rightarrow$$

merely to abbreviate the formula scheme $(\sim P) \vee Q$. More precisely, we write:

(43) $(P) \rightarrow (Q)$ for $(\sim P) \vee Q$

Accordingly, in view of (29), (35) and (43) we have:

(44)

P	Q	$(P) \to (Q)$
T	T	T
T	F	F
F	T	T
F	F	T

where, naturally, P and Q stand for any two formulas. The symbol $\to$ is called the *implication sign*. Moreover, $(P) \to (Q)$ is called an *implication scheme* and is read: *if P then Q*, or *P implies Q*. When no confusion is likely to arise, $(P) \to (Q)$ is written as $P \to Q$. Also, truth table (44) is called the *truth table corresponding to the implication sign*.

In the implication scheme $P \to Q$, it is customary to call P the *antecedent* or *hypothesis* or *assumption* of the implication scheme $P \to Q$, and Q the *consequent* or *conclusion* of $P \to Q$.

According to (44), if the hypothesis of an implication is true and its conclusion is false, then the implication is false and vice versa. Otherwise, an implication is true.

The distinction between the *truth of an implication* and the *truth of its conclusion* should be emphasized. As (44) shows, an implication may be true while its conclusion is false. Also, in many cases we are more interested in the truth of an implication than in the truth of its conclusion. We shall return shortly to a more detailed discussion of an implication.

If an implication is true, then its hypothesis is called a *sufficient condition* for its conclusion and the latter is called a *necessary condition* for the hypothesis.

Thus, in the true implication:

$$(a \in b) \to ((a \in b) \lor (a \in c))$$

the statement-formula $(a \in b)$ is a sufficient condition for $((a \in b) \lor (a \in c))$ and the latter is a necessary condition for $(a \in b)$.

In view of (44) every false formula is a sufficient condition for every formula and every formula is a necessary condition for every false formula.

As an application of truth tables (42) and (44), let us show that the formula scheme $(P \land (P \to Q)) \to Q$ is a tautology scheme:

P	Q	$P \to Q$	$P \land (P \to Q)$	$(P \land (P \to Q)) \to Q$
T	T	T	T	T
T	F	F	F	T
F	T	T	F	T
F	F	T	F	T

Since the last column of the above table is invariably **T**,

$$(P \land (P \to Q)) \to Q$$

is a tautology scheme.

The formal laws of tagging an implication **T** or **F** [i.e., the tagging rules given by truth table (44)] are of fundamental importance in proving theorems.

Clearly, any supposed theorem, say Q, is first of all a formula which may be of the form of a negation, a disjunction, an implication or any suitable combination of them. In general, the proof of the validity of a formula Q of a model reduces to forming formulas (starting with the axioms or some of the already-known theorems of that model and proceeding according to the formation rules of formulas), so that Q appears as the conclusion of a true implication —say, $P \to Q$, whose hypothesis is also true. In this case, according to (44), we infer the truth of Q and hence the proof of the validity of formula Q. This method of proof is called the method of *direct proof*. It is based on the fact that, as the above truth table shows, the formula scheme:

$$(P \wedge (P \to Q)) \to Q$$

is a tautology scheme. As we already know [see (39)], this scheme is called *modus ponens*. To emphasize the machinery involved in the method of direct proof, we register it as follows:

(45)
$$\frac{P, P \to Q}{Q}$$

which must be read: *from the truth of P and the truth of P $\to$ Q, we infer the truth of Q.*

Another efficient way of proving the validity of a formula, say Q, is the method of *indirect proof*. It is based on the fact that, as can be easily seen, the formula scheme:

$$((\sim Q) \to Q) \to Q$$

is a tautology scheme. Here again, Q appears as the conclusion of a true implication. Hence, to infer the truth of Q, is it enough [in view of (44)] to ascertain that $(\sim Q) \to Q$ is true. In practice, this amounts to proving that $\sim Q$ implies Q. In other words, to prove the validity of Q it is enough to assume the validity of the negation $\sim Q$ of Q and from this assumption to derive Q. This will guarantee the truth of Q. The method of indirect proof is registered as follows:

(46)
$$\frac{(\sim Q) \to Q}{Q}$$

which must be read: *from the truth of $(\sim Q) \to Q$, we infer the truth of Q.*

A second version of the method of indirect proof is based on the fact that, as can be easily seen, the formula scheme:

$$((\sim Q) \to \mathbf{F}) \to Q$$

is a tautology scheme. In the above, **F** stands for any false formula. Thus, according to the above, to prove the validity of Q it is enough to assume the validity of the negation $\sim Q$ of Q and from this assumption to derive any falsehood. This will guarantee the truth of Q. The second version of the method of indirect proof is registered as follows:

(47)
$$\frac{(\sim Q) \to \mathbf{F}}{Q}$$

which must be read: *from the truth of* $(\sim Q) \to \mathbf{F}$, *we infer the truth of Q.*

Either version of the method of indirect proof is called the law of *reductio ad absurdum*.

In many instances, a supposed theorem itself is of the form of an implication—say, $H \to C$. In this case, the proof of the theorem can be inferred from the tautology scheme:
$$((H \to P) \wedge (P \to C)) \to (H \to C)$$

which is called the law of the *hypothetical syllogism*. Here also, $H \to C$ appears as the conclusion of a true implication. Hence its truth is guaranteed whenever $(H \to P) \wedge (P \to C)$ is known to be true. This method of proof is registered as follows:

(48)
$$\frac{(H \to P), (P \to C)}{H \to C}$$

which must be read: *from the truth of* $H \to P$ *and the truth of* $P \to C$, *we infer the truth of* $H \to C$.

Throughout the development of the Theory of Sets, we shall prove theorems informally. However, all the proofs will be based on the formal ones mentioned above. Clearly, the closer an informal proof approximates a formal one, the more convincing and undebatable it becomes.

Let us emphasize that according to (44) whenever the hypothesis of an implication is known to be false, the entire implication is true. Thus, for instance, in the model whose table is given by (25), in view of the fact that b is an empty set, either of the following two statements is a theorem of that model:

$$(a \in b) \to (c \notin d), \qquad (c \in b) \to ((a \in c) \vee (b \in a))$$

According to (44), our formal rules of tagging an implication **T** or **F** are set up in such a way that an implication is true when its hypothesis is false. This may seem somewhat strange. However, a little thought shows that it is not really unintuitive and is in complete accordance with the rules of our ordinary reasoning, especially with those we use in our ordinary arithmetic. For instance, using the inference rules of our ordinary arithmetic, we may prove that the statement: *if* 1 *is equal to* 2 *then* 1.34 *is equal to* 5.789 is a theorem—i.e.,

(49)
$$(1 = 2) \to (1.34 = 5.789)$$

is a theorem in arithmetic. To see this, we simply observe that by virtue of our ordinary rules of inference in arithmetic, subtraction of 1 from both sides of $1 = 2$ yields $0 = 1$. Also, multiplication of both sides of $0 = 1$ by 1.34 yields $0 = 1.34$. Similarly, multiplication of both sides of $0 = 1$ by 5.789 yields $0 = 5.789$. Now, from $0 = 1.34$ and $0 = 5.789$, it follows that $1.34 = 5.789$, as desired. Thus, (49) is a theorem.

Incidentally, the above proof shows that the hypothesis $1 = 2$ implies that every real number is equal to 0 and hence every two real numbers are equal.

Thus from $1 = 2$, we may also infer [as expected, in view of (44)] that $3 = 3$, which is a true statement in arithmetic.

Naturally, once we accept (44) we do not require an elaborate proof of (49) as given above. We need only observe that implication (49) is true since its hypothesis is false.

We close this section by explaining why we reject any model if there is evidence that one of its formulas—say, S—is self-contradictory (i.e., is tagged both **T** and **F**). Indeed, let this be the case and let A be any formula of that model. Using the fact that S is false, we infer that

$$S \to A$$

is true. But then, in the above true implication, using the fact that S is true, we infer that A is true. Recalling that A is an arbitrary formula of the model, we conclude that if in a model there is a formula which is both true and false, then every formula A of that model is true and also false (since $\sim A$ is again an arbitrary formula of that model). Clearly, this highly objectionable situation renders the model under consideration absolutely trivial and useless.

EXERCISES

1. Determine which of the following formulas are theorems and which are nonsatisfiable in the model whose table is given by (33).

$$(a \in a) \wedge (b \notin a)$$
$$(a \in b) \wedge (c \in b)$$
$$(a \notin c) \to (c \in c)$$
$$(b \notin c) \to (b \in a)$$
$$(a \in a) \vee (b \notin b)$$
$$(c \in a) \to (a \in b)$$
$$((a \in b) \vee \sim(b \in c)) \to ((c \in a) \wedge (b \notin a))$$
$$((c \notin b) \wedge (a \notin b)) \to ((a \in c) \to (c \notin b))$$

2. Determine which of the following formulas are tautologies, which are contradictions and which are neither.

$$((b \in \{a, b\}) \vee (c \notin \{c\})) \to (d \in \{a, d\})$$
$$(b \notin \{b\}) \to ((a \in b) \vee (c \notin d))$$
$$((a \in b) \vee (c \notin c)) \to (\{m\} \in \{\{m\}, n\})$$
$$((a \in \{a, b, c\}) \vee (c \in d)) \wedge ((a \in b) \vee (c \in \{c\}))$$

3. Which of the following formulas are tautologies, which are contradictions and which are neither?

$$((a \in b) \wedge (c \in a)) \to (a \in b)$$
$$(m \in a) \to ((m \in a) \vee (b \in c))$$
$$((a \in b) \wedge (c \in d)) \to ((a \in b) \vee (c \in d))$$
$$\sim(((a \in b) \wedge (c \in d)) \to ((c \in d) \wedge (a \in b)))$$

4. Prove that the following are tautology schemes:

$$((\sim Q) \wedge (P \to Q)) \to \sim P$$
$$((\sim P) \wedge (P \vee Q)) \to Q$$
$$P \to (Q \to (P \wedge Q))$$

5. Which of the following are tautology schemes, which are contradiction schemes and which are neither?

$$\sim ((P \wedge Q) \to P)$$
$$P \to (P \vee Q)$$
$$(P \wedge Q) \to \sim (P \vee Q)$$
$$(P \to (Q \wedge \sim Q)) \to \sim P$$

6. BIIMPLICATION AND LOGICAL EQUIVALENCE

In the model whose table is given by (33), every element of a or b is an element of c and vice versa. In other words, *if* a set is an element of a or b, *then* it is an element of c, *and if* a set is an element of c, *then* it is an element of a or b. Clearly, in any model it is most desirable to be able to express formally statements such as: *if* a is an element of b, *then* a is an element of c, and *if* a is an element of c, *then* it is an element of b. However, let us observe that the above statement can be expressed formally by means of symbols already introduced in the following way:

$$((a \in b) \to (a \in c)) \wedge ((a \in c) \to (a \in b))$$

However, this is customarily expressed by the statement: a is an element of b *if and only if* a is an element of c.

Motivated by the above, we introduce the logical symbol:

$$\leftrightarrow$$

merely to abbreviate the formula scheme $(P \to Q) \wedge (Q \to P)$. More precisely, we write:

(50) $(P) \leftrightarrow (Q)$ for $(P \to Q) \wedge (Q \to P)$

Accordingly, in view of (42), (44) and (50), we have:

(51)

P	Q	$(P) \leftrightarrow (Q)$
T	T	T
T	F	F
F	T	F
F	F	T

where P and Q stand for any two set-theoretical formulas, i.e., are two formula schemes. The symbol $\leftrightarrow$ is called the *biimplication sign*. Moreover, $(P)\leftrightarrow(Q)$ is called a *biimplication* and is read: *P if and only if Q*. Furthermore, when no confusion is likely to arise, $(P)\leftrightarrow(Q)$ is written as $P\leftrightarrow Q$. Also, truth table (51) is called the *truth table corresponding to the biimplication sign*.

If a biimplication $P\leftrightarrow Q$ is true, then P is called a *necessary and sufficient condition* for Q and Q is called a necessary and sufficient condition for P. This is in accordance with the terminology introduced in the previous section.

Let us observe that, according to (51), a biimplication $P\leftrightarrow Q$ is true if P and Q are simultaneously true or if P and Q are simultaneously false and vice versa. Since there are only two logical values, **T** or **F**, it is reasonable to consider two formulas *logically indistinguishable* if it is the case that both are simultaneously true or both are simultaneously false.

In view of the above considerations and truth table (51), we see at once that P and Q are logically indistinguishable if $P\leftrightarrow Q$ is true and vice versa. To emphasize the logical equivalence of P and Q, we introduce the symbol:

$$\equiv$$

which is used interchangeably with $\leftrightarrow$. In other words,

(52)

P	Q	$(P) \equiv (Q)$
T	T	T
T	F	F
F	T	F
F	F	T

which is the same as the truth table given by (51). The symbol $\equiv$ is called the *logical equivalence* or simply the *equivalence* sign. Moreover, $(P) \equiv (Q)$ is called an *equivalence* and is read *P is equivalent to Q*. Furthermore, when no confusion is likely to arise, $(P) \equiv (Q)$ is written as $P \equiv Q$. Also, truth table (52) is called the *truth table corresponding to the equivalence sign*.

Let us emphasize again that $\leftrightarrow$ and $\equiv$ have the same role and that the latter —say, in $P \equiv Q$—is merely used to emphasize the logical indistinguishability between P and Q when $P \equiv Q$ is a tautology scheme. Thus, for instance, any two tautology schemes are logically equivalent and hence indistinguishable. The same is true for any two contradiction schemes. Consequently,

$$(P \lor \sim P) \equiv (Q \lor \sim Q)$$

is a tautology scheme. Similarly,

$$(P \land \sim P) \equiv (Q \land \sim Q)$$

is also a tautology scheme.

Also, let us mention that to establish the truth of a biimplication $P\leftrightarrow Q$, one has to establish the truth of $P \to Q$ and that of $Q \to P$.

Below, we give some useful tautology schemes which are very helpful in determining the truth or falsehood of various formulas.

However, first let us mention some conventions with respect to the use of parentheses. There is general agreement in giving equal priority to $\equiv$ and $\leftrightarrow$; then to $\rightarrow$; then to $\vee$ and $\wedge$ equally; and, finally, to $\sim$.

Thus,

$$\sim P \vee Q \rightarrow R \wedge S \equiv \sim P \leftrightarrow R$$

is an abbreviation for

$$((((\sim P) \vee Q) \rightarrow (R \wedge S))) \equiv ((\sim P) \leftrightarrow R)$$

With the above agreement on the use of parentheses, we give below the following tautology schemes:

$P \rightarrow q \equiv \sim P \vee q$

$P \equiv P$	reflexivity of $\equiv$ *same*
$(P \equiv Q) \leftrightarrow (Q \equiv P)$	symmetry of $\equiv$
$((P \equiv Q) \wedge (Q \equiv R)) \rightarrow (P \equiv R)$	transitivity of $\equiv$
$\sim\sim P \equiv P$	law of double negation
$P \vee P \equiv P$	idempotence of $\vee$
$P \wedge P \equiv P$	idempotence of $\wedge$
$(P \vee Q) \vee R \equiv P \vee (Q \vee R)$	associativity of $\vee$
$(P \wedge Q) \wedge R \equiv P \wedge (Q \wedge R)$	associativity of $\wedge$
$P \vee Q \equiv Q \vee P$	commutativity of $\vee$
$P \wedge Q \equiv Q \wedge P$	commutativity of $\wedge$
$(P \wedge Q) \vee R \equiv (P \vee Q) \wedge (Q \vee R)$	distributivity of $\vee$ with respect to $\wedge$
$(P \vee Q) \wedge R \equiv (P \wedge R) \vee (Q \wedge R)$	distributivity of $\wedge$ with respect to $\vee$
$\sim(P \vee Q) \equiv \sim P \wedge \sim Q$ $\sim(P \wedge Q) \equiv \sim P \vee \sim Q$	DeMorgan laws
$P \rightarrow Q \equiv \sim Q \rightarrow \sim P$	law of contraposition
$P \rightarrow (Q \rightarrow R) \equiv Q \rightarrow (P \rightarrow R)$ $(P \wedge Q) \rightarrow R \equiv Q \rightarrow (P \rightarrow R)$	laws of commutation
$P \vee \sim P$	law of excluded middle
$\sim(P \wedge \sim P)$	law of excluded contradiction

The tautology schemes given above are used most frequently in proving theorems. Below we give some of their immediate consequences.

In view of the law of contraposition, i.e.,

$$(53) \qquad\qquad (P \rightarrow Q) \equiv (\sim Q \rightarrow \sim P)$$

to prove the implication $P \rightarrow Q$, it is enough to prove $\sim Q \rightarrow \sim P$ and vice versa. In many cases, it is more convenient to prove $\sim Q \rightarrow \sim P$ than $P \rightarrow Q$.

Also, the tautology schemes listed above can be used to derive other tautology schemes without resorting to the more elaborate proofs by truth tables. For instance, to prove that $(P \wedge (P \to Q)) \to Q$ is a tautology scheme, we may proceed as follows. Since $\sim H \vee H$ is a tautology scheme, $H \to H$ is also a tautology scheme. Therefore, $(P \to Q) \to (P \to Q)$ is a tautology scheme. But then by the law of commutation $(P \wedge (P \to Q)) \to Q$ is a tautology scheme, as desired.

In view of the associativity of $\vee$, it is unambiguous to write $P \vee Q \vee R \vee \ldots \vee S$ without any parentheses, since any two different ways of inserting parentheses will yield logically equivalent formula schemes. The same is true for $P \wedge Q \wedge R \wedge \ldots \wedge S$. Also, in view of the commutativity of $\vee$, any change in the order of $P, Q, R, \ldots, S$ in $P \vee Q \vee R \vee \ldots \vee S$ will yield logically equivalent formula schemes. The same is true for $P \wedge Q \wedge R \wedge \ldots \wedge S$. Thus, in every pertinent model it is the case that:

$$(a \in b) \vee (c \notin b) \vee (b \in c) \equiv (b \in c) \vee (a \in b) \vee (c \notin b)$$

and

$$(a \in m) \wedge (m \notin n) \wedge (n \in a) \equiv (n \in a) \wedge (a \in m) \wedge (m \notin n)$$

In view of the above considerations and truth tables (35) and (42), we may conclude that *a disjunction of a limited number of statement-formulas is true if and only if at least one of them is true, and it is false if and only if every one of them is false.* However, *a conjunction of a limited number of statement-formulas is true if and only if every one of them is true and it is false if and only if at least one of them is false.*

Let us observe that there are altogether 2^{2^n} mutually nonequivalent formula schemes involving n $(n = 1, 2, 3, \ldots)$ formula schemes $P, Q, \ldots, S$. For $n \geq 2$, there is an algorithm for writing them in the so-called *disjunctive normal form* which consists of considering all possible disjunctions of n-termed conjunctions each involving every one of $P, Q, \ldots, S$ or its negation, plus a contradiction scheme—say, $P \wedge \sim P$.

For $n = 1$, the four mutually nonequivalent formula schemes are: P, $\sim P$, $P \vee \sim P$, $P \wedge \sim P$.

EXERCISES

1. Using the list of tautology schemes given in the text, prove that each of the following formula schemes is a tautology scheme:

$$P \vee (P \wedge Q) \equiv P$$
$$P \wedge (P \vee Q) \equiv P$$
$$(P \to Q) \vee (Q \to P)$$
$$(P \to Q) \vee (R \to P)$$
$$P \to (Q \vee R) \equiv (P \to Q) \vee (P \to R)$$
$$(P \to (Q \to R)) \to ((P \to Q) \to (P \to R)) \quad \textit{biconditional}$$

2. Verify that the following statement-formulas are valid in every model to which they may pertain:

$$(a \notin b) \rightarrow ((m \in n) \rightarrow (a \in b)) \quad \text{not} \checkmark$$
$$((a \in b) \rightarrow (m \in n)) \rightarrow (((a \in b) \rightarrow (m \notin n)) \rightarrow (a \notin b))$$
$$((a \in b) \rightarrow (m \in n)) \wedge ((a \notin b) \rightarrow (m \in n)) \equiv (m \in n)$$
$$((a \in b) \wedge (m \notin n)) \rightarrow (c \in e) \equiv (a \in b) \rightarrow ((m \in n) \vee (c \in e))$$
$$((a \in b) \rightarrow (m \in n)) \leftrightarrow ((m \notin n) \rightarrow (a \notin b))$$

3. Using tautology schemes, write each of the following statement-formulas in an equivalent disjunctive normal form:

$$(a \in b) \rightarrow ((m \in n) \wedge (a \notin b))$$
$$(a \notin a) \wedge ((b \in c) \vee (a \notin c))$$
$$((c \in e) \vee (a \notin b)) \rightarrow ((a \in a) \wedge (b \notin c))$$

4. Define a *conjunctive normal form* for a formula scheme involving n ($n = 2, 3, 4, \ldots$) formula schemes $P, Q, R, \ldots, S$ by replacing, in the definition of a disjunctive normal form, the words *disjunctive, disjunction* and *conjunction* respectively with *conjunctive, conjunction* and *disjunction*. Write each of the following statement-formulas in an equivalent conjunctive normal form:

$$(a \in a) \rightarrow (b \notin c)$$
$$((c \notin b) \vee (a \in b)) \wedge (a \notin a)$$
$$((a \in b) \rightarrow (c \notin b)) \vee (a \in e)$$
$$((a \in b) \wedge (b \in a)) \vee (c \notin d)$$

5. Determine which of the following statement-formulas are true and which are false:

$$(a \notin \{a, b\}) \wedge (a \in \{a, b\}) \rightarrow (m \in b)$$
$$((a \in b) \vee (c \in d)) \rightarrow (\{a\} \in \{\{a\}, \{b, c\}\})$$
$$(a \in \{a, b\}) \rightarrow ((m \in a) \wedge (m \notin a) \wedge (c \in e)) \quad \vdash$$
$$(a \in b) \vee (m \in n) \vee (c \in e) \vee (\{b\} \in \{a, \{b\}, c\}) \quad \top$$
$$(c \in d) \wedge (e \in a) \wedge (a \notin \{\{b\}, a, c, e\}) \wedge (b \in a) \quad \vdash$$

6. Using the double negation, the DeMorgan laws and (43), write formula schemes equivalent to the ones given below so that $\wedge$ and $\rightarrow$ do not appear in the final result:

$$(\sim P \rightarrow Q) \wedge R$$
$$(R \wedge Q) \rightarrow (P \wedge \sim Q)$$
$$(Q \wedge R \wedge P) \vee (\sim Q \wedge P)$$
$$(R \rightarrow Q) \wedge (Q \rightarrow R)$$

7. Write formula schemes equivalent to the ones given below without using $\rightarrow, \leftrightarrow$ and $\equiv$.

$$P \vee (P \wedge Q) \equiv P$$
$$(\sim Q \rightarrow P) \leftrightarrow (Q \vee P)$$
$$Q \leftrightarrow (P \rightarrow \sim Q)$$
$$(\sim Q \vee P) \equiv (R \rightarrow S)$$

7. INDIVIDUAL VARIABLES AND PREDICATES

Let us consider the prime-complete model whose content consists of the sets a, b, c, d and whose table is given by:

(54)

a	b	c	d
$a \in a$		$a \in c$	$a \in d$
$b \in a$		$b \in c$	$b \in d$
		$d \in c$	$c \in d$
			$d \in d$

As we can see from the above table, not every set of the content belongs to a. Intuitively, *belonging to a* is a *property* or a *predicate* which may or may not be satisfied by a set. Clearly, in view of (54), we may say that in the model under consideration, the property *belonging to a* is *satisfied* by the sets a and b and is *not satisfied* either by c or by d. This is because in (54) the statement-formulas $a \in a$ and $b \in a$ are present (i.e., are tagged **T**), whereas $c \in a$ and $d \in a$ are absent (i.e., are tagged **F**).

Let us observe that the formal symbols introduced so far are still inadequate to express formally a set-theoretical property such as the one given above. To overcome this inadequacy, we introduce a new category of formal symbols called set-theoretical individual variables, or simply *individual variables*, or *set-variables*. Unless otherwise specified, any one of the lower-case letters (from the latter part of the alphabet), with or without subscripts, such as:

(55) $x, y, z, \ldots, x_1, y_1, z_1, \ldots, x_2, y_2, z_2, \ldots$

will constitute an individual variable.

Intuitively, the role of an individual variable in the set-theoretical language corresponds roughly to the role of a pronoun in ordinary language. Thus, just as a pronoun stands for a proper noun without specifying it further, an individual variable stands for an arbitrary set.

As in the previous sections, here also the introduction of a new category of formal symbols will necessitate the introduction of a new formation rule for set-theoretical formulas. As we shall see shortly, configurations such as $\in(x,a)$, $\in(y,b), \ldots, \in(a,x), \in(c,z), \ldots, \in(x,y), \in(y,z), \ldots$ which are also written as $(x \in a), (y \in b), \ldots, (a \in x), (c \in z), \ldots, (x \in y), (y \in z), \ldots$ will be accepted as set-theoretical formulas.

In particular, we shall interpret a formula such as:

(56) $\in(x,a)$ or $(x \in a)$ or $x \in a$

as expressing the above-mentioned property or predicate: *belonging to a.*
Similarly, we shall interpret a formula such as:

(57) $\in(a,y)$ or $(a \in y)$ or $a \in y$

as expressing the property or predicate: *a belonging to,* and a formula such as:

(58) $\in(x,x)$ or $(x \in x)$ or $x \in x$

as expressing the property or predicate: *belonging to itself.*

In Section 1, we mentioned that in the entire Theory of Sets, we need not
and shall not make use of any basic predicate symbol other than $\in$. In this
connection, let us observe that the property *is an element of,* or simply *belonging,*
which is the basic predicate in the entire Theory of Sets, can be most appropriately expressed by any one of the formulas:

(59) $\in(x,y)$ or $(x \in y)$ or $x \in y$

or by the formulas $\in(y,z), \in(x,z), \ldots, (y \in z), (x \in z), \ldots.$

We may consider formulas given by (56), (57) and (58) as special cases of
those given by (59). For instance, $\in(x,a)$ is a special case of $\in(x,y)$ where the
set a is *assigned* to the individual variable y. Similarly, $\in(a,y)$ is a special case
of $\in(x,y)$ where a is assigned to x. Likewise, $\in(x,x)$ is a special case of $\in(x,y)$
where y is *substituted* by x. Therefore, with a suitable definition of a configuration involving individual variables as a set-theoretical formula, we may
take care of all the above-mentioned special cases. To this end, we first introduce
the notion of a *term* as follows:

(60)   *Every set is a term and every individual variable is a term.*

We shall represent terms by the symbols:

$$t_1, t_2, t_3, \ldots$$

which are *metalinguistic variables.*

Now, in addition to (28) and (34), we introduce the following formation rule
for formulas:

(61)   *If t_1 and t_2 are terms, then $\in(t_1,t_2)$ is a formula.*

As usual, $\in(t_1,t_2)$ is also written as $(t_1 \in t_2)$ or, when no confusion is likely to
arise, as $t_1 \in t_2$.

Let us observe immediately that formation rule (61) implies that configurations such as $a \in b, c \in d, \ldots$ are formulas. In other words, even if a configuration such as $a \in b$ were not defined independently as being a formula, it
would become one by virtue of formation rule (61).

Also, let us observe that in view of (61), configurations such as $(a \in x)$,
$(y \in b), (x \in y), (x \in x), \ldots$ are formulas. Moreover, by virtue of (28), (34)
and (61), configurations such as:

$$\sim(x \in a), \qquad (x \in a) \vee (y \in b), \qquad (a \in x) \wedge (x \notin c),$$
$$((x \in y) \rightarrow (a \in z)) \vee \sim((a \notin b) \rightarrow (z \in y))$$

are also formulas.

In view of the above, the formula schemes $P, Q, R, \ldots$, which previously stood for arbitrary formulas not involving individual variables $x, y, z, \ldots$, now will stand for arbitrary formulas that may involve individual variables. Thus, P may stand for any of the formulas $\sim(x \in a)$, $(y \in x)$, $(x \in a) \vee (y \in b)$, $\ldots$. In other words, a formula scheme now will represent arbitrary formulas that may involve individual variables. Thus, $P \rightarrow Q$ may stand for any of the formulas: $(x \in a) \rightarrow (y \in z)$ or $((x \notin b) \vee (y \notin x)) \rightarrow ((a \in z) \wedge (y \in c))$, $\ldots$.

We have introduced individual variables and formation rule (61) in order to express formally items that intuitively we call properties or predicates. Thus, in view of (61), (28) and (34), we are now able to express formally a great variety of properties or predicates that are pertinent to models. For instance, $\sim(x \in a)$ expresses the property *not belonging to a*. Similarly, $(x \in a) \vee (x \in b)$ expresses the property *belonging to a or to b*.

In contrast to a formula such as $(a \in b)$, a formula such as $(x \in b)$ is not a statement-formula. Intuitively, it does not make sense to inquire: is $(x \in b)$ true or false? However, we see immediately that if in $(x \in b)$ we assign to x a set—say, a—then $(x \in b)$ acquires the form $(a \in b)$ and consequently becomes a statement-formula. This can be done with respect to any predicate. For instance, the predicate:

$$((x \in c) \vee (a \in y)) \rightarrow (y \notin z)$$

although a formula, is not a statement-formula. However, upon assigning to x, y and z, say, the sets a, b and c respectively, the above predicate becomes:

$$((a \in c) \vee (a \in b)) \rightarrow (b \notin c)$$

which is a statement-formula.

Motivated by the above, we may extend the notion of truth tables to the case of predicates occurring in models.

Consider the prime-complete model whose content consists of the sets a, b, c and whose table is:

(62)

a	b	c
$a \in a$		$a \in c$
$c \in a$		$b \in c$
		$c \in c$

Next, consider the two predicates:

$$(x \in y) \rightarrow (y \notin a) \qquad \text{and} \qquad (x \in y) \rightarrow (y \in a)$$

There is an obvious way of constructing truth tables for these predicates in the model whose table is given by (62). On page 47, we give a combined truth table, whose construction is self-explanatory.

From this truth table, we see that in the model whose table is given by (62), the predicate $(x \in y) \rightarrow (y \notin a)$ does not take on the value **T** for every assignment of the sets a, b and c to the variables x and y. However, the predicate $(x \in y) \rightarrow (y \in a)$ takes on the value **T** for every assignment of the sets a, b and c to the variables x and y.

x	y	$x \in y$	$y \in a$	$(x \in y) \to (y \notin a)$	$(x \in y) \to (y \in a)$
a	a	T	T	F	T
b	a	F	T	T	T
c	a	T	T	F	T
a	b	F	F	T	T
b	b	F	F	T	T
c	b	F	F	T	T
a	c	T	T	F	T
b	c	T	T	F	T
c	c	T	T	F	T

The definitions of validity, nonsatisfiability and undecidability of a formula in a model that were given previously for the statement-formulas, can now be extended to the case of formulas in general. Thus, a formula which may involve individual variables $x, y, z, \ldots$, is called *valid in a model* (or is a theorem of that model), if for *every* assignment of sets selected from the *content of that model*, to the variables $x, y, z, \ldots$, the formula assumes the value **T**. Similarly, a formula which may involve individual variables $x, y, z, \ldots$ is called *nonsatisfiable in a model* if, for *every* assignment of sets, selected from the content of that model to the variables $x, y, z, \ldots$, the formula assumes the value **F**. In this connection, a formula is called *satisfiable in a model* if, at least *for one* of the above-mentioned assignments, the formula assumes the value **T**. Finally, a formula (which may involve individual variables $x, y, z, \ldots$) is called *undecidable in a model* if it is neither valid nor nonsatisfiable in that model.

For instance, the formula:

(63) $$(x \in y) \to (y \in a)$$

is valid in the model whose table is given by (62). However, the negation of the above formula, i.e.,

$$(x \in y) \land (y \notin a)$$

is nonsatisfiable in the same model. On the other hand, the formula:

$$(x \in y) \to (y \notin a)$$

is satisfiable but undecidable in the model whose table is given by (62). Obviously, a formula may be valid in a model and not valid in another one. For instance, (63) is a theorem of the model whose table is given by (62). However, it is not a theorem of the model whose table is given by (54), although it is satisfiable in the latter.

As expected, we shall call a formula (which may now involve individual variables) *universally valid* or a *tautology* if it is a valid formula in every model to which it may pertain. Also, we shall call a formula (which may now involve individual variables) *nonsatisfiable* or a *contradiction*, if it is nonsatisfiable in every model to which it may pertain.

Thus, the formulas:

$$(x \in y) \vee (x \notin y) \qquad \text{and} \qquad (z \in y) \to (z \in y)$$

are universally valid. On the other hand, the formulas:

$$(x \in a) \wedge (x \notin a)$$

and

$$\sim(((x \in y) \wedge (y \notin z)) \to (x \in y))$$

are nonsatisfiable. In this connection, a formula is called *satisfiable* if it is satisfiable in some model. For instance, the formula:

$$(x \in y) \vee (z \in a)$$

is satisfiable since it is satisfiable, say, in the model whose table is given by (62). Finally, a formula (which now may involve individual variables) is called *undecidable* if it is neither universally valid nor nonsatisfiable. For instance, the formula:

$$(x \in y) \vee (y \in x)$$

is undecidable. However, it is satisfiable in the model whose table is given by (62). Clearly, the same formula may be valid in another model.

Obviously, the negation of a satisfiable formula may again be satisfiable. However, the negation of an undecidable formula is always undecidable.

Motivated by the above, as expected, a formula scheme (which may now stand for formulas involving individual variables) shall be called a *universally valid* or *tautology scheme* if every formula of that form is universally valid or is a tautology. Moreover, a formula scheme shall be called a *nonsatisfiable* or *contradiction scheme* if every formula of that form is nonsatisfiable or is a contradiction. In this connection, a formula scheme shall be called *satisfiable* if a formula of that form is satisfiable. Finally, a formula scheme (which now may stand for formulas involving individual variables) shall be called *undecidable* if it is neither a universally valid nor a contradiction scheme.

With the introduction of individual variables, rule II of the modified outline of the formal development of any model, which was given by I, II, III and IV in Section 5, must now be further modified to include (61). Otherwise, I, II, III and IV apply in the modified form mentioned in Section 5.

Let us observe that formulas:

$$(x \in y) \to (y \in a)$$

and

$$(z \in y) \to (x \in c)$$

are theorems of the model whose table is given by (62). We may employ these theorems, to derive (and quite formally) other theorems of the model under consideration without resorting to (62) or to rule IV.

This may be done by starting with the above two theorems and then applying formation rules (61), (28), (34) and truth tables (29), (35), (42), (44), (51), (52) and using any tautology scheme.

Thus, for example, each of the following formulas is a theorem of the model whose table is given by (62):

$$((x \in y) \rightarrow (y \in a)) \leftrightarrow ((z \in y) \rightarrow (x \in c))$$
$$((x \in y) \rightarrow (x \in c)) \lor ((x \in y) \rightarrow (y \in a))$$
$$(x \notin y) \lor (y \in a) \lor (z \notin y) \lor (x \in c)$$

EXERCISES

1. Determine which of the following formulas (predicates) are satisfiable and which are valid in the model whose table is given by (54).

$$(x \in a) \lor (y \in x), \qquad (y \notin x) \rightarrow (a \in a)$$
$$(x \in b) \rightarrow (y \in x), \qquad ((x \in a) \lor (y \in b)) \rightarrow (x \in d)$$
$$\sim(x \in c) \land (y \in b), \qquad (x \in y) \land (y \notin b) \land (z \in b)$$

2. Determine which of the following formulas (predicates) are universally valid.

$$(x \in y) \rightarrow ((y \in a) \rightarrow ((x \in y) \land (y \in b)))$$
$$(z \in x) \rightarrow ((z \in x) \lor (x \in y) \lor (y \in z)) \top$$
$$((x \in a) \lor (x \in b)) \rightarrow (x \in c)$$
$$((y \in x) \land (x \in a)) \lor (x \in c)$$
$$((x \in y) \land (y \in z)) \rightarrow ((x \in y) \lor (y \in z)) \top$$
$$((x \in a) \land ((x \in a) \rightarrow (y \in b))) \rightarrow (y \in b)$$

3. Give two examples of predicates involving x and y that are satisfiable but not valid in the model whose table is given by (62).

4. Give two examples of predicates involving x and y that are not universally valid but that are valid in the model whose table is given by (62).

5. Give a table of a model in which the predicate

$$((x \in y) \lor (y \in x)) \rightarrow (x \notin y)$$

is satisfiable but not valid.

6. Give a table of a model in which the predicate

$$(x \in x) \rightarrow (x \in y)$$

is valid.

7. Give a table of a model in which the formula scheme

$$(P \land Q) \rightarrow \sim Q$$

is satisfiable.

8. Give an example of a formula such that it and its negation are satisfiable in the model whose table is given by (62).

9. Give an example of a valid formula in the model whose table is given by (54) such that the negation of that formula is not a contradiction. *outside the model*

10. Give an example of a formula which is nonsatisfiable in the model whose table is given by (62) such that the negation of that formula is not a tautology.

8. QUANTIFIERS

Let us again consider the model whose content consists of the sets a, b, c and whose table is given by (62). Let us also consider the predicate $x \in a$, i.e., a formula that expresses the property *belonging to a*. Clearly, as (62) shows, $x \in a$ is not satisfied by every set of the model under consideration. To assert the fact that for some of the sets a, b and c the formula $x \in a$ is satisfied in the model under consideration, we have to ascertain that $x \in a$ takes on the value **T** for at least one of the assignments of the sets a, b and c to the variable x. However, this amounts to ascertaining that the disjunction of the formulas obtained by replacing x in $x \in a$ by a, b and c in turn is a valid formula (in the model). Indeed, as mentioned in Section 6, the disjunction:

(64) $$(a \in a) \lor (b \in a) \lor (c \in a)$$

is valid if and only if at least one of $(a \in a)$, $(b \in a)$ and $(c \in a)$ is valid, i.e., if and only if $x \in a$ is satisfied by at least one of the sets a, b and c.

Clearly, in a model it is desirable to be able to express formally the fact that a property—say, $x \in a$—is satisfied by some of the sets of that model. For this purpose, we introduce the formal symbol:

$$\exists$$

which is read: *for some* or *for at least one* or *there exists at least one*. Moreover, we accept as set-theoretical formulas configurations such as: $(\exists x)(x \in a)$; $(\exists y)(y \notin b)$; .... These are read respectively: for some x, x is an element of a; for some y, y is not an element of b; ....

Let us mention here that $\exists$, like $\lor$, is a logical formal symbol. It is called the *existential quantifier*.

As indicated above, the introduction of $\exists$ also introduces a new type of formula. Thus, in addition to (61), (28) and (34), we introduce the following formation rule for formulas:

(65)   *If P stands for a formula and X stands for an individual variable, then $(\exists X)(P)$ stands for a formula.*

In (65), as usual, P is a metalinguistic variable which is a formula scheme. Similarly, X is a *metalinguistic variable* (an individual variable scheme) which may stand for any of the individual variables $x, y, z, \ldots$. When no confusion is likely to arise, $(\exists X)(P)$ is written as $(\exists X)P$.

The following configurations are examples of formulas involving $\exists$:

$$(\exists x)(a \in b), \quad (\exists y)(x \in y), \quad (\exists z)((z \in x) \lor (y \in z)) \land (z \in a),$$
$$(\exists x)(\exists y)((x \in a) \land (y \notin x) \rightarrow (y \notin x))$$

Naturally, the question arises, how are the validity, the nonsatisfiability and the undecidability of a formula that involves $\exists$ established in a model? First, we shall answer this question in connection with models whose contents are limited.

Thus, let us consider a model whose content consists of the sets a, b and c. Motivated by (64), we have:

(66) $(\exists x)(x \in a) \equiv (a \in a) \vee (b \in a) \vee (c \in a)$

in every model whose content consists of the sets a, b and c. Thus, the question of whether $(\exists x)(x \in a)$ is valid, nonsatisfiable or undecidable is the same as the question of whether the right side of $\equiv$ in (66) is valid, nonsatisfiable or undecidable. But we already know how to answer the latter. For instance, as we have already seen, the right side of $\equiv$ in (66) is a valid formula in the model whose table is given by (62). Therefore, $(\exists x)(x \in a)$ is a theorem of that model.

Similarly, motivated by (64), we have:

(67) $(\exists x)(x \in y) \equiv (a \in y) \vee (b \in y) \vee (c \in y)$

in every model whose content consists of the sets a, b and c. Consequently, $(\exists x)(x \in y)$ is valid, nonsatisfiable or undecidable in a model according to whether the right side of $\equiv$ in (67) is valid, nonsatisfiable or undecidable in that model. However, the right side of $\equiv$ in (67) is a formula involving the variable y and not $\exists$. Therefore, its validity, nonsatisfiability or undecidability can be determined by the methods already known to us. Thus, in view of (67), in the model whose table is given by (62), we have:

y	$a \in y$	$b \in y$	$c \in y$	$(\exists x)(x \in y)$
a	T	F	T	T
b	F	F	F	F
c	T	T	T	T

Therefore, $(\exists x)(x \in y)$ is not a theorem of that model (since the last column in the above table is not invariably **T**). Indeed, $(\exists x)(x \in y)$ is undecidable in that model. However, we can easily verify that:

$$(y \in y) \rightarrow (\exists x)(x \in y)$$

is a theorem in the model whose table is given by (62). Likewise, the following formulas are also theorems of that model:

$$(\exists x)(a \in b) \equiv (a \in b)$$
$$(\exists x)((\exists x)(x \in y)) \equiv (\exists x)(x \in y)$$

Again, motivated by (64), we have:

$$(\exists y)((\exists x)(x \in y)) \equiv (\exists y)((a \in y) \vee (b \in y) \vee (c \in y))$$
$$\equiv (a \in a) \vee (b \in a) \vee (c \in a) \vee$$
$$(a \in b) \vee (b \in b) \vee (c \in b) \vee$$
$$(a \in c) \vee (b \in c) \vee (c \in c)$$

in every model whose content consists of the sets a, b and c. In view of the above, we infer that $(\exists y)((\exists x)(x \in y))$, which may also be written as $(\exists y)(\exists x)(x \in y)$, is a theorem of the model whose table is given by (62).

In a formula of the form:

$$(\exists x)P \qquad \text{or} \qquad (\exists y)P \qquad \text{or} \qquad (\exists z)P, \qquad \ldots$$

the formula for which P stands is called the *scope* of the quantifier $\exists$.

Thus, the scope of the first $\exists$ in

$$(\exists x)((\exists y)(x \in y) \to (a \in x))$$

is the formula $(\exists y)(x \in y) \to (a \in x)$. The scope of the second $\exists$ in the above is the formula $(x \in y)$.

In a formula of the form $(\exists x)P$, the variable x is called *attached* to the quantifier $\exists$.

In a formula an attached occurrence of a variable to a $\exists$, or an occurrence of a variable in the scope of the $\exists$ to which it is attached, is called a *bound* occurrence of that variable in that formula. Otherwise, an occurrence of a variable in a formula is called a *free* occurrence.

Thus, in the formula:

$$(\exists x)(a \in b) \lor (x \in y) \lor (\exists x)(x \in y)$$

the first, the third and the fourth occurrences of x are *bound* and the second occurrence of x is free.

A variable is called *bound in a formula* if it has at least one bound occurrence in that formula, and it is called *free in a formula* if it has at least one free occurrence in that formula. Thus, in the above formula the variable x is both free and bound.

To express the fact that the variable x occurs (free or bound) in a formula P, we shall write

$$P(x)$$

Clearly, in $P(x)$, other variables may also occur (free or bound). To specify that in $P(x)$ the variable y also occurs, we shall write

$$P(x,y)$$

Thus, $P(x)$ may stand for either of the two formulas:

$$(\exists x)(a \in b) \qquad \text{or} \qquad (\exists x)(\exists y)(x \in y) \lor (a \in x) \lor (z \in y)$$

To express the fact that the variable x is the only free variable in a formula P, we shall write:

$$P(x)$$

Similarly, to express the fact that the variables x and y are the only free variables in a formula P, we shall write:

$$P(x,y)$$

and so forth.

Thus, $P(x)$ may stand for either of the formulas:

$$(\exists x)(x \in a) \vee (a \in x) \quad \text{or} \quad (\exists y)(x \in y) \rightarrow (\exists x)(x \in x)$$

Similarly, $P(x,y)$ may stand for

$$((\exists x)(x \in a) \rightarrow (\exists y)(x \in y)) \rightarrow (a \in y)$$

For obvious reasons, it is customary to call a formula of the form $P(x)$ *a predicate of one variable*, and a formula of the form $P(x,y)$ *a predicate of two variables, and so forth.*

Next, let us consider some of the questions that arise in connection with the *substitution* of an individual variable for another individual variable (of course at every occurrence of the latter) or the *substitution* of a formula for another formula (of course at every occurrence of the latter) in a given formula.

Consider the prime-complete model whose content consists of the sets a, b, and whose table is given by:

(68)
$$
\begin{array}{cc}
a & b \\
b \in a & a \in b
\end{array}
$$

In the above model we have:

(69)

x	y	$x \in y$	$x \notin y$	$x \notin x$	$(\exists x)(x \in y)$	$x \in a$
a	a	F	T	T	T	F
b	a	T	F	T	T	T
a	b	T	F	T	T	F
b	b	F	T	T	T	T

Thus, in the model whose table is given by (68), the formula $x \notin y$ is undecidable; however, upon substituting in it x for y, the resulting formula $x \notin x$, as (69) shows, is a theorem of that model.

Again, let us consider the formula:

$$(\exists x)(x \in y)$$

Motivated by (67), in the model whose table is given by (68), we have:

$$(\exists x)(x \in y) \equiv (a \in y) \vee (b \in y)$$

which, as (69) shows, is a theorem of that model. Now, let us substitute in $(\exists x)(x \in y)$ the variable x for y. As a result, we obtain $(\exists x)(x \in x)$. However, in the model whose table is given by (68), we have:

$$(\exists x)(x \in x) \equiv (a \in a) \vee (b \in b)$$

which is nonsatisfiable in that model. Thus, according to the above, although $(\exists x)(x \in y)$ is a theorem in the model whose table is given by (68), upon substituting in it x for y the resulting formula $(\exists x)(x \in x)$ is nonsatisfiable in the same model. The reason for this is the fact that in $(\exists x)(x \in y)$ the variable y is in the scope of $\exists$ to which x is attached.

Similarly, it is easy to verify that

$$(\exists x)(x \in y) \vee \sim((\exists z)(z \in y))$$

is a universally valid formula; however, upon substituting in it y for x, the resulting formula:

$$(\exists y)(y \in y) \vee \sim((\exists z)(z \in y))$$

ceases to be universally valid. The reason for this is the fact that in the original formula y is in the scope of $\exists$ to which x is attached.

Again, it is easy to verify that the formula:

$$(\exists x)(\exists y)(x \in y) \vee \sim((\exists x)(\exists z)(x \in z))$$

is universally valid; however, upon substituting in it x for y, the resulting formula:

$$(\exists x)(x \in x) \vee \sim((\exists x)(\exists z)(x \in z))$$

ceases to be universally valid.

Now, let us consider the universally valid formula:

$$(\exists x)((a \in b) \wedge (x \in a)) \rightarrow ((a \in b) \wedge (\exists x)(x \in a))$$

Let us substitute in the above the formula $(x \in a)$ for $(a \in b)$. As a result we obtain:

$$(\exists x)((x \in a) \wedge (x \in a)) \rightarrow ((x \in a) \wedge (\exists x)(x \in a))$$

which, as the last column of (69) shows, is not a valid formula in the model whose table is given by (68).

On the other hand, let us observe that the formula $(\exists x)(x \in y)$ remains valid in the model whose table is given by (68) if in it we substitute z for x or u for y. Clearly, the resulting formulas $(\exists z)(z \in y)$ and $(\exists x)(x \in u)$ are valid in the model whose table is given by (68). Similarly, if in the universally valid formula

$$(\exists x)(\exists y)(x \in y) \vee \sim((\exists x)(\exists z)(x \in z))$$

we substitute u for y, the resulting formula:

$$(\exists x)(\exists u)(x \in u) \vee \sim((\exists x)(\exists z)(x \in z))$$

remains universally valid. Again, if in the universally valid formula:

$$(\exists x)((a \in b) \wedge (x \in a)) \rightarrow ((a \in b) \wedge (\exists x)(x \in a))$$

we substitute the formula $(y \in z)$ for $(a \in b)$, the resulting formula:

$$(\exists x)((y \in z) \wedge (x \in a)) \rightarrow ((y \in z) \wedge (\exists x)(x \in a))$$

remains universally valid.

The above examples show that the validity of a formula may be destroyed if in it the substitution of variables for variables or formulas for formulas is performed without any restrictions. Clearly, in order that a valid formula remain valid after substitutions of variables or formulas are performed in it, the substitutions must be carried out according to certain rules, called *rules of substitution.* We shall not give these rules, and thus we caution the reader to exercise great care while performing substitutions in a formula.

Let us note that in view of (66) the introduction of ∃ would be redundant if we were interested solely in models with limited content. However, prior to the introduction of ∃, we had no way in general of expressing formally the fact that for some x a formula $P(x)$ is satisfied in a model with an unlimited content. The reason for this is that no formula can have an unlimited number of disjunctions.

Now, let us consider the question of inferring in general the validity or the nonsatisfiability of a formula involving ∃ in a model which may now have an unlimited content.

Clearly, we would like $(\exists x)P(x)$ to be valid in a model if and only if $P(x)$ is satisfiable in that model. Moreover, we would like $(\exists x)P(x)$ to be non-satisfiable in a model if and only if $P(x)$ is nonsatisfiable in that model. But then, clearly, it would be required that

(70) $$\sim P(Y) \vee (\exists X)P(X)$$

and

(71) $$(\exists X)(\sim P(X)) \vee P(Y)$$

be universally valid formula schemes *where X and Y stand for individual variables and $P(Y)$ is the result of substituting Y for each occurrence of X in $P(X)$.*

Likewise, it would also be required that:

$(\forall x)(\sim P(x)) \vee Q$

(72) *If $\sim P(X) \vee Q$ stands for a valid formula in a model, then $(\exists X)P(X) \vee Q$ also stands for a valid formula in that model.*

and

(73) *If $\sim Q \vee P(X)$ stands for a valid formula in a model, then*

$$\sim Q \vee \sim(\exists X)(\sim P(X))$$

also stands for a valid formula in that model.

where X stands for an individual variable and Q stands for a formula in which X has no free occurrence.

Considering again the model whose content consists of the sets a, b, c and whose table is given by (62), we see that *for every* set of the content the predicate $x \in c$ is satisfied. Clearly, in every model it is desirable to be able to express formally such statements as: the property, say, $x \in c$ is satisfied by *every* set of the content. However, intuitively, to assert that *for every* set of a content it is the case that $x \in c$ is satisfied, amounts to asserting that it is *not* the case that *for some* sets of that content, $x \in c$ is *not* satisfied. This shows that it is possible to use the connective *not* and the quantifier ∃ so as to render the use of the words *for every* unnecessary. Motivated by the above, we introduce the logical symbol:

∀

which is read *for every*, merely to abbreviate the formula scheme $\sim(\exists X)(\sim P)$. More precisely, we write:

(74) $(\forall X)(P)$ for $\sim(\exists X)(\sim P)$

In the above, as usual, X is a metalinguistic variable which stands for an individual variable such as $x, y, z, \ldots$. Similarly, P is a metalinguistic variable which stands for a formula.

The symbol $\forall$ is called the *universal quantifier*. When no confusion is likely to arise, $(\forall X)(P)$ is written as $(\forall X)P$.

The notions of the *scope* of $\forall$, *a variable attached to* $\forall$, a *bound* or a *free* *occurrence of a variable*, and so forth, are introduced with $\forall$ in a manner similar to that used in connection with $\exists$.

In view of (74) and (66), in a model whose content consists of the sets a, b and c, we have:

$$(\forall x)(x \in a) \equiv (a \in a) \wedge (b \in a) \wedge (c \in a)$$

Similarly, in a model whose content consists of the two sets a and b, we have:

(75) $(\exists y)(\forall x)(x \in y) \equiv (\exists x)((a \in y) \wedge (b \in y))$
$$\equiv ((a \in a) \wedge (b \in a)) \vee ((a \in b) \wedge (b \in b))$$

whereas,

(76) $(\forall x)(\exists y)(x \in y) \equiv (\forall x)((x \in a) \vee (x \in b))$
$$\equiv ((a \in a) \vee (a \in b)) \wedge ((b \in a) \vee (b \in b))$$

Thus, we see that (75) and (76) need not be equivalent. However,

$$(\exists y)(\forall x)(x \in y) \rightarrow (\forall x)(\exists y)(x \in y)$$

is a tautology.

Now, let $P(x, y)$ stand for any formula (or predicate) in which x and y are the only free variables; then in any model whose content consists of the two sets a and b, we have:

$$(\exists x)P(x,y) \equiv P(a,y) \vee P(b,y)$$
$$(\forall y)P(x,y) \equiv P(x,a) \wedge P(x,b)$$
$$(\exists y)(\exists x)P(x,y) \equiv (\exists y)(P(a,y) \vee P(b,y))$$
$$\equiv P(a,a) \vee P(b,a) \vee P(a,b) \vee P(b,b)$$
$$(\forall y)(\forall x)P(x,y) \equiv (\forall y)(P(a,y) \wedge P(b,y))$$
$$\equiv P(a,a) \wedge P(b,a) \wedge P(a,b) \wedge P(b,b)$$
$$(\forall y)(\exists x)P(x,y) \equiv (\forall y)(P(a,y) \vee P(b,y))$$
$$\equiv (P(a,a) \vee P(b,a)) \wedge (P(a,b) \vee P(b,b))$$
$$(\exists y)(\forall x)(Px,y) \equiv (\exists y)(P(a,y) \wedge P(b,y))$$
$$\equiv (P(a,a) \wedge P(b,a)) \vee (P(a,b) \wedge P(b,b))$$

where $P(a,y)$ stands for any formula of the form $P(x,y)$ in which every free occurrence of x is replaced by a. Similarly, $P(a,b)$ stands for any formula of the form $P(x,y)$ in which every free occurrence of x is replaced by a and that of y by b.

The above equivalences will help the reader to gain insight into formulas involving quantifiers.

It is clear from the above that whereas $P(x,y)$ stands for a formula in which x and y are the only free variables, $(\exists x)P(x,y)$ or $(\forall y)P(x,y)$ stand for formulas in which y or x respectively are the only free variables. Moreover, $(\exists x)(\forall y)P(x,y)$ or $(\exists y)(\forall x)P(x,y)$ stand for formulas having no free variables; they are in essence statements. Thus, we may extend the notion of a statement-formula and say, in general, that a *statement-formula* (or simply, a statement) is a formula having no free variables.

As expected, quantifiers are used rather frequently in models. For example, in a model the statement: *the sets a and b have common elements* is symbolized as:

$$(\exists x)((x \in a) \wedge (x \in b))$$

Similarly, the statement:

every element of a is an element of b

is symbolized as:

$$(\forall x)((x \in a) \rightarrow (x \in b))$$

Likewise, the statement:

for every set having at least one element, there exists a set whose elements are the elements and only the elements of that set

is symbolized as:

$$(\forall x)((\exists y)(y \in x) \rightarrow (\exists z)(\forall t)((t \in z) \leftrightarrow (\exists u)((t \in u) \wedge (u \in x))))$$

Let us observe that in view of (43), the law of double negation and (74), universally valid formula schemes (70) and (71) can now be written as:

(77) $$P(Y) \rightarrow (\exists X)P(X)$$

and

(78) $$(\forall X)P(X) \rightarrow P(Y)$$

where *X and Y stand for individual variables and $P(Y)$ is the result of substituting Y for each occurrence of X in $P(X)$.*

Likewise, in view of (43), (74) and the notation introduced in (45), we may write (72) and (73) as follows:

(79) $$\frac{P(X) \rightarrow Q}{(\exists X)P(X) \rightarrow Q}$$

and

(80) $$\frac{Q \rightarrow P(X)}{Q \rightarrow (\forall X)P(X)}$$

where *X stands for an individual variable and Q stands for a formula in which X has no free occurrence.*

Clearly, (79) and (80) may be used as rules of inference. They are called respectively the rule of *specification* and the rule of *generalization*.

The following is a very useful list of tautology schemes, each of which can be derived from (38), (77), (78), (45), (79) and (80), or inferred via the tagging (**T** or **F**) procedure as extended to the case of formulas in general.

(81)

$$(\forall x)P(x) \rightarrow (\exists x)P(x)$$

$$(\forall y)((\forall x)P(x) \rightarrow P(y))$$

$$(\forall y)(P(y) \rightarrow (\exists x)P(x))$$

$$(\exists x)((\exists y)P(y) \rightarrow P(x))$$

$$(\exists x)(P(x) \vee Q(x)) \equiv (\exists x)P(x) \vee (\exists x)Q(x)$$

$$(\forall x)(P(x) \wedge Q(x)) \equiv (\forall x)P(x) \wedge (\forall x)Q(x)$$

$$* \quad (\exists x)(P(x) \wedge Q(x)) \rightarrow (\exists x)P(x) \wedge (\exists x)Q(x)$$

$$* \quad (\forall x)P(x) \vee (\forall x)Q(x) \rightarrow (\forall x)(P(x) \vee Q(x))$$

$$(\exists y)(\forall x)P(x,y) \rightarrow (\forall x)(\exists y)P(x,y)$$

$$(\forall x)(\forall y)P(x,y) \rightarrow (\exists y)(\forall x)P(x,y)$$

$$(\forall x)P(x,x) \rightarrow (\forall y)(\exists x)P(x,y)$$

$$(\forall x)P(x,x) \rightarrow (\forall x)(\exists y)P(x,y)$$

$$(\exists x)P(x,x) \rightarrow (\exists x)(\exists y)P(x,y)$$

The introduction of $\exists$ completes the list of the formal symbols of the set-theoretical language. Moreover, (77) and (78) complete the list of logical axiom schemes, and (79) and (80) complete the list of rules of inference for the formal derivation of theorems in models. Accordingly, the modified outline of the formal development of a model which was given by I, II, III and IV in Section 5, must be modified once more. In the next section, we shall give a summary of the final version of the above-mentioned outline in connection with the formal development of a theory of sets.

EXERCISES

1. Verbalize the following formulas and determine which of them are valid in the model whose content consists of the sets a, b and whose table is given by (31).

$$(\forall x)(\exists y)(x \in y \vee y \in x)$$

$$(\forall x)(\forall y)(\exists z)(x \in y \rightarrow y \in z)$$

$$(\exists x)(\forall y)(\exists z)(x \notin y \wedge y \notin z)$$

$$(\exists x)(x \in a) \rightarrow (\forall y)(\exists z)(y \in b \vee z \in y)$$

2. Symbolize the following statements and determine which of them are valid in the model whose content consists of the sets a, b and whose table is given by (12).

  (i) There exists a set such that every set is an element of that set.

  (ii) There exists a set such that no set is an element of that set.

  (iii) For every two sets, there exists a set that is an element of both.

  (iv) For every two sets, there exists a set of which they are elements.

3. Determine which of the following are tautology schemes:

$$(\exists x)(\forall y)P(x,y) \equiv \sim(\forall x)(\exists y)\sim P(x,y)$$
$$(\forall y)(\sim\exists x)P(x,y) \equiv \sim(\exists y)(\forall x)\sim P(x,y)$$
$$(\forall y)(\exists x)P(x,y) \to (\exists x)(\forall y)P(x,y) \quad no$$
$$(\forall x)(\exists y)P(x,y) \to (\exists y)(\forall x)P(x,y) \quad no$$
$$(\forall x)(\forall y)P(x,y) \to (\exists x)(\forall y)P(x,y)$$
$$(\exists x)P(x,x) \to (\forall x)(\exists y)P(x,y)$$
$$(\forall x)P(x,x) \to (\exists x)P(x,x)$$

4. Give an example of a model in which the following is a valid formula:

$$(\exists x)(\exists y)(x \in y) \to (\forall x)(\exists y)(x \in y)$$

5. Give an example of a model in which the following is a valid formula:

$$(\forall x)(\exists y)(x \notin y) \to (\exists y)(\forall x)(x \notin y)$$

6. For each of the following formulas, construct a truth table in the model whose content consists of the sets a, b and whose table is given by (31):

$$(\exists x)(x \in a) \to (\forall y)(x \in y)$$
$$(\forall x)(\forall y)((x \in y) \lor (y \in x))$$
$$(\exists x)(y \in x) \to ((y \in b) \lor (x \in a))$$
$$(y \in x) \to (\exists y)(\forall x)(x \notin y)$$

7. Verify that the following are tautology schemes:

$$(\exists x)(\exists y)P(x,y) \equiv (\exists y)(\exists x)P(x,y)$$
$$(\forall x)(\forall y)P(x,y) \equiv (\forall y)(\forall x)P(x,y)$$
$$(\forall x)(\forall y)P(x,y) \to (\forall x)P(x,x)$$
$$(\exists x)(\forall y)P(x,y) \to (\exists x)P(x,x)$$
$$(\exists y)(\forall x)P(x,y) \to (\exists x)(\exists y)P(x,y)$$

9. THE FORMAL DEVELOPMENT OF A THEORY OF SETS

In previous sections of this chapter, we introduced the necessary machinery for the formal development of a set-theoretical model (or simply a model). In Section 1, we mentioned that a major difference between a model and a theory of sets (or simply a theory) is that the latter need not refer to a content (i.e., to a list of sets). For this reason a theory has a general and abstract character, whereas a model is more concrete and contextual. Except for this difference, the formal development of a model and that of a theory have many features in common. In both the formal symbols are the same, except that a theory need not possess a list of individual constants (sets). In both the formation rules of formulas are the same, except that in a theory the prime formulas may be only of the type $x \in y$, $y \in z$, $x \in z$, ... where $x, y, z, ...$ are individual variables (set-variables). In both the logical axiom schemes and rules of inference are the same. The notion of a valid formula in a theory is similar to that of a valid formula in a model. Thus, a formula that is formed (employing logical axiom schemes or the axioms of the theory under consideration) according to the formation rules of formulas [see (83) below] and whose validity is inferred by the rules of inference [see (85) below] is called a *valid* or *derivable* or *provable* formula or a *theorem* of the theory under consideration. As expected, a formula whose negation is valid in a theory is called a *nonsatisfiable* or *disprovable* formula of that theory. A formula that is neither provable nor disprovable in a theory is called an *undecidable* formula of that theory.

Naturally, an aim in the development of any theory is to derive theorems of that theory.

With the formal machinery at hand, a theory of sets is characterized by its axioms.

Below we give an example of the formal development of a theory of sets whose axioms are:

(i) $(\forall x)(x \in x)$
(ii) $(\exists y)(\forall x)(y \in x)$
(iii) $(\forall x)(\forall y)((x \in y) \rightarrow (y \in x))$

The axioms are far from being those of the Theory of Sets with which we are primarily concerned in this book.

In the outline below, $\wedge$, $\rightarrow$ and $\forall$ are not listed among the logical formal symbols. However, they are used for convenience. These logical symbols were introduced respectively by (41), (43) and (74). Thus, for instance, the first four logical schemes below, written in terms of $\vee$ and $\rightarrow$, are equivalent to the axiom schemes given by (38).

Now, we give an outline of the formal setup of the theory of sets whose axioms are (i), (ii) and (iii). Also, we derive some of the theorems of the theory of sets under consideration.

(82)   *Formal symbols*
          Set-theoretical:
              Predicate symbol (elementhood) $\in$
          Logical:
              Individual variables   x, y, z, ...
              Connectives $\sim$ $\vee$
              Quantifier $\exists$
              Auxiliary   (,)

(83)   *Formation rules of formulas*

    (61) $(X \in Y)$
         is a formula where X and Y stand for individual variables.
    (28) *If P stands for a formula, then ~(P) also stands for a formula.*
    (34) *If P and Q stand for formulas, then $(P) \vee (Q)$ also stands for a formula.*
    (65) *If P stands for a formula and X stands for an individual variable, then $(\exists X)(P)$ also stands for a formula.*

(84)   *Axioms*
    Logical axiom schemes:

$$(P \vee P) \to P$$

    (38) $P \to (P \vee Q)$

$$(P \vee Q) \to (Q \vee P)$$

$$(P \to Q) \to ((R \vee P) \to (R \vee Q))$$

    (77) $P(Y) \to (\exists X)P(X)$

    (78) $(\forall X)P(X) \to P(Y)$
        where P, Q and R stand for formulas, X and Y stand for individual variables, and $P(Y)$ is the result of substituting Y for each occurrence of X in $P(X)$.

    Set-theoretical axioms:
    (i) $(\forall x)(x \in x)$
    (ii) $(\exists y)(\forall x)(y \in x)$
    (iii) $(\forall x)(\forall y)((x \in y) \to (y \in x))$

(85)   *Rules of inference*
    Every logical axiom scheme stands for a valid formula. Every set-theoretical axiom is a valid formula.

    (45) $\dfrac{P, P \to Q}{Q}$

    (79) $\dfrac{P(X) \to Q}{(\exists X)P(X) \to Q}$ (80) $\dfrac{Q \to P(X)}{Q \to (\forall X)P(X)}$

    where in (45) P and Q stand for formulas, and in (79) and (80) X stands for an individual variable, and Q stands for a formula in which X has no free occurrence.

(86)   *Rules of substitution* (see the remarks on page 53).

  Now, using $(x \in x)$ instead of $P(X)$ in (78), we obtain the valid formula:

$$(\forall x)(x \in x) \to (y \in y)$$

However, in view of axiom (i) and (45), we infer that $(y \in y)$ is also a theorem. Moreover, in view of (77) and (45), we again infer that

$$(\exists x)(x \in x)$$

is a theorem (naturally, of the theory of sets under consideration).

Again, from (38), (i) and (ii), we infer that the following are theorems:

$$(\forall x)(x \in x) \to (\exists y)(\forall x)(y \in x)$$
$$(\exists y)(\forall x)(y \in x) \to (\exists y)(\forall x)(y \in x)$$

It has been shown that if the validity of a formula of the predicate calculus is inferred via tagging procedures [as given by (29), (35) and their extension to the case of formulas involving individual variables and quantifiers], then the validity of the same formula can be inferred by means of the formal machinery described by (82), (83), (84), (85) and (86). Therefore, in deriving theorems of a theory of sets we may use any of the tautology schemes given in Sections 5, 6 and 8. For instance, in view of axiom (iii), (45) and the tenth tautology scheme given in (81), we infer that:

$$(\exists y)(\forall x)((x \in y) \to (y \in x))$$

is a theorem.

Similarly, from (ii), (45) and the ninth tautology scheme given in (81), we infer that:

$$(\forall x)(\exists y)(y \in x)$$

is also a theorem (of the theory of sets under consideration).

Clearly, we may continue along these lines and derive many other theorems of the theory of sets under consideration.

As expected, a theory is called *consistent* if it is not the case that a formula and its negation are both provable in the theory; otherwise, it is called *inconsistent*. In this connection the axioms of a theory are said to form a *consistent system of axioms* if the corresponding theory is consistent; otherwise, they are said to form an *inconsistent system of axioms*. An axiom of a theory is called *independent* of the remaining axioms of the theory if it is not provable (a theorem) in the theory obtained (from the theory under consideration) by omitting the axiom; otherwise, the axiom is called *dependent* on the remaining axioms of the theory. The axioms of a theory are called *mutually independent* if each is independent of the remaining axioms of the theory. A theory is called *complete* if the adjunction to its axioms of a formula that is not a theorem of the theory, yields an inconsistent theory; otherwise, it is called *incomplete*. If a formula of a theory is such that neither it nor its negation is provable in the theory, then that formula is called *undecidable* in the theory; otherwise, it is called *decidable* in the theory. Finally, a theory is called *decidable* if there is a procedure for ascertaining whether or not each formula of the theory is decidable; otherwise, it is called *undecidable*.

Now that we have introduced models and theories, we say that a model is a *model of a theory* if every axiom of the latter is a theorem of the former.

Let us observe that the theory of sets described above is consistent. Either of (86) or (87) is a table of a model of the theory of sets whose axioms are given by (i), (ii) and (iii).

∈			∈	
a,a	T		a,a	T
b,a	T		b,a	T
c,a	T		c,a	T
a,b	T		a,b	T
b,b	T		b,b	T
c,b	F		c,b	T
a,c	T		a,c	T
b,c	F		b,c	T
c,c	T		c,c	T

(86) on the left, (87) on the right.

However, the theory of sets described above is not complete. Indeed, $(\forall x)(\forall y)(x \in y)$ is a formula which, as (86) shows, is not a theorem of the theory of sets described above; nevertheless, its adjunction to axioms (i), (ii) and (iii), as (87) shows, does not yield an inconsistent theory.

EXERCISES

1. Prove that the following formulas are theorems of the theory of sets whose axioms are given by (i), (ii) and (iii) in Section 9.

$$(\forall x)(\exists y)((y \notin y) \rightarrow (x \in y))$$
$$(\forall z)((y \in z) \rightarrow (z \in y))$$
$$\sim(\exists x)(\exists y)((x \in y) \wedge (y \notin x))$$

2. Derive four theorems of the theory of sets whose axioms are:

$$(\exists x)(\forall y)(y \notin x) \quad \text{and} \quad (\exists x)(\forall y)(y \in x).$$

Give a table of a model of the above theory of sets whose content consists of the sets a, b and c.

3. Derive four theorems of the theory of sets whose axioms are:

$$(\exists x)(\exists y)((x \in y) \vee (y \in x)) \quad \text{and} \quad (\forall x)(\exists y)(x \in y).$$

Give a table of a model of the above theory of sets whose content consists of the sets a, b, c and d.

10. SUMMARY

In this chapter we introduced the vocabulary (*formal symbols*), the formation rules of sentences (*formulas*) and the laws of reasoning (*logical axiom schemes*

and rules of inference) of the set-theoretical language. These items were introduced gradually and in connection with the formal development of a set-
theoretical model. The formal notion of a model (see Section 4) is almost
indispensable for the study of the formal development of a theory of sets (see
Section 9) and in particular the Theory of Sets.

The types of formal symbols (vocabulary) of the set-theoretical language
are few in number. The symbols are: $x, y, z, \ldots, \sim, \vee, \exists, (, \ )$ together with
$a, b, c, \ldots$, which are used in connection with models. The formulas (sentences) of the set-theoretical language are merely suitable configurations made
up of the above symbols according to certain rules (*formation rules of formulas*).
The laws of reasoning are based on our natural tendency to label a statement
true (**T**) or *false* (**F**) and not both. These laws are given in the form of logical
axiom schemes and rules of inference.

In the formal development of a theory of sets (as well as of a model), the
notion of truth or falsehood of formulas is replaced respectively by *validity*
(provability, derivability) and *nonsatisfiability* (disprovability). However, the
techniques of tagging formulas **T** or **F** according to truth tables (29) and (35)
and the extension of these techniques to the case of formulas involving individual variables and quantifiers constitute the essence of formal inference.

The formal development of a theory of sets has many advantages. Since
there is a very limited formal vocabulary, communication is unambiguous.
Moreover, since the proofs of theorems are obtained formally, they become
undebatable in the sense that they do not depend on the personal interpretation
of the investigator.

Chapter II

AXIOMS OF
THE THEORY OF SETS

1. GENERALITIES. EXISTENCE IN THE
THEORY OF SETS

In this and subsequent chapters we shall develop the Zermelo-Fraenkel Theory of Sets, which we continue to call the Theory of Sets. The basic formal vocabulary used in the Theory of Sets is that introduced in Chapter I in connection with the set-theoretical language. Thus, except for the set-variables $x, y, z, \ldots$ no other category of individual variables will enter into the Theory of Sets. Similarly, except for the binary predicate $\in$ (*is an element of*), no other basic predicate will enter into the Theory of Sets. Consequently, formulas such as $x = y$ (*x is equal to y*) and $x \subset y$ (*x is a subset of y*), which are also called *predicates*, will be defined in terms of $\in$ and various logical symbols such as (,), $\sim$, $\vee$, $\wedge$, $\rightarrow$, $\exists$, $\forall$ and set-variables $x, y, z, \ldots$.

To prevent any misunderstanding, ambiguity or arbitrary interpretation, the essential definitions as well as the axioms of the Theory of Sets will be introduced symbolically via formulas and in strict accordance with the formation rules of formulas [see (83), page 61]. However, to render the text more accessible, most of the symbolic expressions will be translated into ordinary English.

Were we interested solely in deriving formally some of the theorems of the Theory of Sets we could easily do so. First, we would replace axioms (i), (ii) and (iii) in (84), page 61, by the six axioms (introduced in this chapter) of the Theory of Sets. Then, we would derive some theorems in the manner used in connection with the theory of sets with axioms (i), (ii) and (iii) given in (84) above.

However, our main interest in this book is the application of the Theory of Sets to the basic notions of mathematics. We are interested in formulating within the Theory of Sets fundamental notions such as *relation, function, natural number, integer, rational number, real number, ordinal number* and *cardinal number*. We are also interested in developing within the Theory of Sets the arithmetic of the natural numbers, integers and real numbers, as well as the arithmetic of the ordinal and cardinal numbers (*Transfinite Arithmetic*).

65

In this way the Theory of Sets will serve as a foundation for almost all mathe-matical disciplines. As a matter of fact this foundation has proved to be a rather sound one.

To pursue these objectives in a meaningful and useful way there is practically no alternative but to develop the Theory of Sets parallel with its *intended interpretation*. Thus, in spite of the fact that *a theory need not refer to any content*, for reasons of expediency we have practically no alternative but to introduce in the process of developing the Theory of Sets symbols such as $\varnothing, 1, 2, \ldots, \omega, \aleph, \ldots$ and to refer to each as a *set* (or an object or individual constant) of the Theory of Sets. Thus, in some respects, we shall treat the Theory of Sets as though it were an illusory model where symbols such as $\varnothing, 1, 2, \ldots, \omega, \aleph, \ldots$ constitute a part of its content.

It may seem rather paradoxical that although neither the notion of an individual constant (set) nor the actual symbols $\varnothing, 1, 2, \ldots, \omega, \aleph, \ldots$ are required for the development of the Theory of Sets, these symbols are used in a very fundamental way in the Theory of Sets. We will clarify this seemingly paradoxical situation in what follows.

Consider the formula

(i) $(\exists x)((x \in x) \lor (x \notin x))$

which is a tautology and therefore valid in every theory of sets and in particular in the Theory of Sets. In the intended interpretation of the Theory of Sets, formula (i) is interpreted as asserting the existence of some *sets* in the Theory of Sets. To see this it is enough to observe that (i) is usually read: *there exists x such that* .... Similarly, as we shall see, owing to the axioms of the Theory of Sets many formulas of the form

(ii) $(\exists x)P(x)$

are valid in the Theory of Sets. Again we interpret a formula such as that given by (ii) as asserting the existence in the Theory of Sets of a set satisfying condition $P(x)$.

The above justifies our treating the Theory of Sets as though it referred to an illusory content.

Next, we explain why in the Theory of Sets we actually introduce symbols such as $\varnothing, 1, 2, \ldots, \omega, \aleph, \ldots$ and treat them as individual constants (objects or sets) of the Theory of Sets.

As we shall see in Section 4 of this chapter, owing to the axioms of the Theory of Sets, the formula

(iii) $(\exists x)(\forall y)(y \notin x)$

is derivable in the Theory of Sets. We interpret (iii) as asserting the existence of an *empty set* in the Theory of Sets. To see this it is enough to observe that (iii) is usually read: *there exists an x such that no y is an element of x.*

It will be apparent from the development of the Theory of Sets that formula (iii) has many extremely important and frequently used consequences. Clearly, each such consequence is a formula which usually involves formula (iii). An example is given by:

(iv) $\qquad (\exists u)(\forall v)((v \in u) \leftrightarrow (\forall z)((z \in v) \leftrightarrow (\exists x)(\forall y)((y \notin x) \wedge (z \in x))))$

which is a derivable formula in the Theory of Sets.

Formulas such as (iv) can be shortened in a natural way by the introduction of some customary abbreviations.

For instance, (iii) is abbreviated as:

(v) $\qquad\qquad\qquad\qquad (\forall y)(y \notin \varnothing)$

in which case (iv) becomes

(vi) $\qquad (\exists u)(\forall v)((v \in u) \leftrightarrow (\forall z)((z \in v) \leftrightarrow (z \in \varnothing)))$

Again, formula (vi) is further abbreviated as:

(vii) $\qquad\qquad (\forall v)((v \in 1) \leftrightarrow (\forall z)((z \in v) \leftrightarrow (z \in \varnothing)))$

Let us observe that in the above abbreviations we still do not employ $\varnothing$ or 1 as individual constants of the Theory of Sets. As a matter of fact we could continue to use $\varnothing$ or 1 exclusively in connection with abbreviations of formulas without any further interpretation. However, it is practically impossible to carry on meaningful discussions in the further development of the Theory of Sets and Transfinite Arithmetic unless we consider symbols $\varnothing, 1, 2, \ldots, \omega,$ $\aleph, \ldots$ as objects or sets (or individual constants) which are introduced in the Theory of Sets by appropriate definitions such as (v) and (vii). This is especially justified in connection with $\varnothing, 1, 2, \ldots, \omega, \aleph, \ldots$ since, as we shall see, their definition also implies their uniqueness (up to equality). Thus, in contrast to our procedure in connection with models, we introduce symbols $\varnothing, 1, 2, \ldots, \omega,$ $\aleph, \ldots$ in the Theory of Sets not as required formal symbols, but as auxiliary and *defined* symbols. Nevertheless, we shall treat symbols $\varnothing, 1, 2, \ldots, \omega,$ $\aleph, \ldots$ as *sets* (i.e., objects or individual constants) of the Theory of Sets.

Moreover, just as in the case of models, we shall allow configurations such as $\varnothing \in 1$, $1 \in 2$, $5 \in 8$, and so forth, to be considered as prime formulas of the Theory of Sets. Also, as in the case of models, *we will not need and we will not make use of any category of objects other than sets* in the entire Theory of Sets (and hence in mathematics). Thus (in the Theory of Sets), *relations, functions, one-to-one correspondences, natural numbers, integers, rational numbers, real numbers, ordinal numbers, cardinal numbers*, and so forth, will be introduced and defined as special sets satisfying special conditions. Naturally, we shall continue to refer to the individual variables $x, y, z, \ldots$ of the Theory of Sets as *set-variables* and we shall frequently use expressions such as: *a set x is an element of a set y* (instead of: x is an element of y). Moreover, we shall speak of *the empty set $\varnothing$, the set* 1, *the set* 2, *the set of all natural numbers ω*, and so on.

Furthermore, prior to the introduction of the axioms of the Theory of Sets we shall use symbols such as $a, b, c, \ldots$ as sets of the Theory of Sets belonging to its illusory content. Thus, for instance, whenever in the Theory of Sets we are confronted with a statement such as *there exists a set x whose elements are sets b and c, and there exists a set u whose elements are sets x, b and m*, then we may take this statement as implying that a table such as the following appears as a part of the illusory table which describes the Theory of Sets (i.e., when the latter is treated as though it were an illusory model):

$$
\begin{array}{cc}
a & e \qquad \cdots \\
b \in a & a \in e \\
c \in a & b \in e \\
& m \in e
\end{array}
$$

Now, if in the Theory of Sets an axiom or a theorem asserts that *for every two sets there exists a set whose elements are the elements of either of these two sets*, then we may assume that in the above illusory table we must find listed a set, say k, whose elements are a, b, c and m, i.e.,

$$
\begin{array}{ccc}
a & e & k \qquad \cdots \\
b \in a & a \in e & a \in k \\
c \in a & b \in e & b \in k \\
& m \in e & c \in k \\
& & m \in k
\end{array}
$$

The above considerations show how we may interpret more concretely the notion of *existence* in the Theory of Sets. In short, if an axiom or a theorem of the Theory of Sets asserts that *if certain sets (with such and such sets as their elements) exist, then a certain set (with such and such sets as its elements) also exists*, we shall interpret this as: *if certain sets (with the elements of each set written under the corresponding set) are listed in the above illusory table, then a certain set (with its elements written under it) must also be listed in the same illusory table.*

With the exception of the axiom of Infinity, all other axioms and most of the theorems of the Theory of Sets assert the existence (interpreted in the above sense) of certain sets when the existence (interpreted in the above sense) of certain other sets is presupposed.

For many reasons it is not feasible for us to set up a model of the Theory of Sets. Because of this and because of other considerations concerning axiomatic theories in general, the *consistency* of the Theory of Sets is not known. However, up to the present time, there is no evidence that the Theory of Sets (developed as based on the axioms given in this chapter) may turn out to be inconsistent. On the other hand, the *incompleteness* and the *undecidability* (see page 62) of the Theory of Sets have been established.

In what follows, we shall prove theorems by using the techniques that are most convenient. Sometimes the proofs will be formal, sometimes informal. We shall use any suitable logical axiom scheme introduced in Chapter I, and on many occasions we shall resort to the method of indirect proof. Naturally, in order that there be no evidence of inconsistency, there must be no evidence that a certain set is both an element and not an element of itself or of another set.

EXERCISES

1. Motivated by the conditions given below, add some sets to the following list and under each set added write its elements:

a	b	c	d	e	f
$a \in a$	$a \in b$	$b \in c$	$a \in d$	$c \in e$	
	$c \in b$	$c \in c$	$b \in d$		
		$m \in c$	$c \in d$		
			$m \in d$		

 (i) For every two sets, there exists a set whose elements are just the elements of either of those two sets.
 (ii) For every two sets, there exists a set whose elements are just the common elements of those two sets.

2. Motivated by the conditions given below, add some sets to the following list and under each set added write its elements:

a	b	c	$\cdots$
$m \in a$	$c \in b$	$b \in c$	
$n \in a$	$m \in b$	$c \in c$	
$p \in a$	$n \in b$	$m \in c$	

 (i) For every two sets, there exists a set whose elements are just the sets that are elements of either of those two sets but not of both.
 (ii) For every set, there exists a set whose only element is that set.

3. Motivated by the conditions given below, add some sets to the following list and under each set added write its elements:

a	b	c	d	e	inf	inf
$a \in a$	$a \in b$	$b \in c$	$a \in d$	$b \in e$		
$b \in a$	$n \in b$	$m \in c$	$b \in d$	$c \in e$		
$m \in a$		$n \in c$				

 (i) For every set, there exists a set whose elements are just the sets that are elements of one but not of the other of these two sets.
 (ii) For every two sets, there exists a set whose elements are just these two sets.
 (iii) For every three sets, there exists a set whose elements are just these three sets.

2. EQUALITY OF SETS. AXIOM OF EXTENSIONALITY

Let us consider two models, each with the content consisting of the sets a, b and c and having, respectively, the tables shown on page 70.

	$\in$				$\in$	
	a,a	**F**			a,a	**T**
	b,a	**T**			b,a	**T**
	c,a	**T**			c,a	**F**
(1)	a,b	**T**	(2)		a,b	**T**
	b,b	**T**			b,b	**T**
	c,b	**T**			c,b	**T**
	a,c	**T**			a,c	**T**
	b,c	**T**			b,c	**T**
	c,c	**T**			c,c	**T**

From (1) we infer:

(3)   *The sets b and c have the same elements—i.e., if a set is an element of b, then that set is also an element of c and vice versa.*

(4)   *The sets b and c belong to the same sets—i.e., if b is an element of a set, then c is also an element of that set and vice versa.*

Now, since the only basic predicate of the set-theoretical language is the predicate

$$x \in y$$

it follows that in the model whose table is given by (1), whatever statement is made about the set b can also be made about the set c. The reason for this is the fact that, as was fully explained in Chapter I, every set-theoretical statement is a formula whose basic components are of the form $x \in y$. Consequently, in view of (3) and (4), in the model whose table is given by (1), whatever formula is satisfied by the set b must also be satisfied by the set c and vice versa.

For example, in the model whose table is given by (1), the formula $(x \in a) \lor (x \in b) \lor (c \in x)$ is satisfied by b. Hence, in view of (3) and (4), the same formula is satisfied by c.

In view of the above considerations we see that in the model whose table is given by (1) the sets b and c are *set-theoretically indistinguishable*. They have the same set-theoretical properties—i.e., every formula satisfied by b is also satisfied by c and vice versa.

Thus, if in a model two sets—say, b and c—fulfill conditions (3) and (4), then they are set-theoretically indistinguishable in that model. Naturally, it is appropriate to call each of these two sets *equal* to the other in the model under consideration.

However, let us observe that condition (3) does not imply condition (4), nor does (4) imply (3). This can be readily seen from (2). In (2) condition (3) is satisfied by the sets b and c since they have the same elements; nevertheless, $b \in a$ and $c \notin a$; i.e., condition (4) is not satisfied by b and c. Again in (2) condition (4) is satisfied by the two sets a and b since they belong to the same sets; nevertheless, $c \in b$ and $c \notin a$—i.e., condition (3), is not satisfied by a and b.

As explained above, in any model complete set-theoretical indistinguishability between two sets—say, b and c—is achieved when conditions (3) and

(4) are satisfied. On the other hand, as explained above also, conditions (3) and (4) are logically independent. Consequently, in general if in a theory of sets one of (3) or (4) is taken as motivation for the definition of *equality* between sets, the other must be assured by an axiom of that theory of sets. For the Theory of Sets we shall take (3) as motivation for the definition of equality and we shall take (4) as motivation for an axiom called the *axiom of Extensionality*. Thus, we introduce:

Definition 1.   *We say that a set x is equal to a set y if x and y have the same elements.*

Formally,

$$(5) \qquad (x = y) \equiv (\forall z)((z \in x) \leftrightarrow (z \in y))$$

The right side of $\equiv$ in (5) is a predicate of two variables x and y. Hence, $x = y$ is also a predicate of two variables x and y and as such it could be written more appropriately as:

$$= (x,y)$$

The symbol $=$ is called *the predicate symbol of equality* and is read: *is equal to*. Moreover, $x = y$ is read: *x is equal to y*.

Let us observe that $=$ is a new predicate symbol. However, as expected and as (5) shows, $x = y$ is defined in terms of the set-theoretical basic predicate symbol $\in$ and other logical symbols.

Since, as explained above, the definition of equality of two sets does not guarantee their set-theoretical indistinguishability, we introduce:

The Axiom of Extensionality.   *Equal sets are elements of the same sets.*

Formally,

$$(6) \qquad (\forall x)(\forall y)((x = y) \to (\forall z)((x \in z) \to (y \in z)))$$

Thus, in the model whose table is given by (1), the axiom of Extensionality is satisfied. However, in the model whose table is given by (2), the axiom of Extensionality is not satisfied. Since the axiom of Extensionality is one of the axioms of the Theory of Sets, (2) cannot serve as a table or a partial table of a model of the Theory of Sets.

Based on Definition 1, we can easily prove that:

(i) Every set is equal to itself.

(ii) If a set x is equal to a set y, then y is equal to x.

(iii) If a set x is equal to a set y and y is equal to a set z, then x is equal to z.

Formally,

$$(7) \qquad (\forall x)(x = x) \qquad\qquad\qquad\qquad \text{(reflexivity of } =)$$

$$(8) \qquad (\forall x)(\forall y)((x = y) \to (y = x)) \qquad\qquad \text{(symmetry of } =)$$

$$(9) \qquad (\forall x)(\forall y)(\forall z)(((x = y) \land (y = z)) \to (x = z)) \quad \text{(transitivity of } =)$$

In view of Definition 1 and the axiom of Extensionality,

$$(10) \qquad (\forall x)(\forall y)((x = y) \to (P(x) \to P(y)))$$

where $P(x)$ stands for any formula (or predicate) in which x has an occurrence and $P(y)$ is the result of substituting y for each occurrence of x in $P(x)$. Naturally, (10) is a theorem scheme showing that equal sets are set-theoretically indistinguishable.

Remark 1.   Hereafter, unless we specify otherwise, we shall assume that in every model and in the Theory of Sets *equality* $(=)$ is defined by Definition 1 and that the axiom of Extensionality is valid.

Lemma 1.   *Two sets u and v are equal if and only if for every element x of u there exists an element y of v such that $x = y$ and for every element y of v there exists an element x of u such that $x = y$.*

PROOF.   The necessity follows from Definition 1. To prove the sufficiency assume $x \in u$. Then, since $y \in v$ and $x = y$, by the axiom of Extensionality $x \in v$. Similarly, if $y \in v$, then since $x \in u$ and $x = y$ we have $y \in u$. Thus, $u = v$, as desired.

Remark 2.   In view of the notation introduced on page 19, a set whose elements are a, b, c, . . . now can be represented as:

(11) $\{a, b, c, \ldots\}$

Although $\{a, b, c, \ldots\}$ represents *any* set whose elements are a, b, c, . . . this representation is fully justified and unambiguous. Indeed, by virtue of the axiom of Extensionality any two sets represented by (11) are set-theoretically indistinguishable. Moreover, we say that there exists (in a model or in the Theory of Sets, as the case may be) *one and only one* or a *unique* set whose elements are a, b, c, ... This is the sense in which we shall use expressions such as "*there exists one and only one set*" or "*there exists a unique set*" without explicitly mentioning that the uniqueness involved is *up to equality*.

Remark 3.   In view of Lemma 1, a representation such as (11) can be modified by allowing the omission of one of every two equal sets appearing inside the braces. Furthermore, a representation such as (11) can be modified by including as many copies as we wish of any set that is equal to a set already appearing inside the braces.

Thus, if $a = d$, then:

$$\{a,b,c,d\} = \{a,b,c\}$$

Furthermore, if $d = b$, then:

$$\{a,b,c\} = \{a,a,b,b,c,b,d,c\}$$

Let us note also that neither the order nor the repetition of elements in (11) is relevant.

Remark 4.   If in a model (or in the Theory of Sets) all the elements of a set s are equal to a set—say, a—then according to Remark 3, the set s can be represented by $\{a\}$ and

$$s = \{a\}$$

In this case we say "*s has one and only one element a*" or "*s is a set whose one and only element is a*" or "*s has a unique element a*" and so forth. This is the sense in which we shall use expressions such as "*a set has one and only one element*" or "*a set has a unique element*" and so forth, without explicitly mentioning that the uniqueness involved is *up to equality*.

In this connection we say that a set has *at most one element* if every two elements of it are equal. Moreover, we say that a set *s* has *two and only two distinct* elements *a* and *b* if $a \in s$, $b \in s$ and $a \neq b$ and every element of *s* is equal to *a* or to *b*.

In general, we say that there exists a set *x* with one and only one element if

$$(\exists x)(\exists y)((y \in x) \wedge (\forall z)((z \in x) \rightarrow (z = y)))$$

Moreover, we say that there exists a set *x* with *at most* one element if

$$(\exists x)(\forall y)(\forall z)((y \in x) \wedge (z \in x) \rightarrow (z = y))$$

Also, we say that there exists a set *x* with two and only two distinct elements if

$$(\exists x)(\exists y)(\exists z)((y \neq z) \wedge (y \in x) \wedge (z \in x) \wedge (\forall u)((u \in x) \rightarrow (u = y) \vee (u = z)))$$

In view of the double negation law, we may write (5) equivalently as:

(12) $$(x = y) \equiv \sim(\exists z)(((z \in x) \wedge (z \notin y)) \vee ((z \notin x) \wedge (z \in y)))$$

In other words, *two sets are equal if and only if we cannot exhibit a set that is an element of one and is not an element of the other.*

The above is a very useful form of the definition of equality between sets.

If two sets fail to be equal, then we say that they are *different, distinct, unequal* or simply *not equal*. If two sets *a* and *b* are unequal, then

$$\sim(a = b)$$

is a true statement. Accordingly, in view of Definition 1, we have:

$$\sim(x = y) \equiv \sim(\forall z)((z \in x) \leftrightarrow (z \in y))$$
$$\equiv (\exists z)(((z \in x) \wedge (z \notin y)) \vee ((z \notin x) \wedge (z \in y)))$$

Thus, *two sets are unequal if and only if there exists a set that is an element of one and is not an element of the other.*

The predicate symbol $\neq$ is used to express the fact that two sets are not equal, i.e.,

$$\sim(x = y) \equiv (x \neq y)$$

Clearly, if *a*, *b* and *c* are distinct sets, then

$$\{a,b\} \neq \{a,b,c\}$$

In the above we required that the sets, *a*, *b* and *c* be distinct; otherwise, the inequality may not hold.

Given a set *a*, we cannot immediately assert that

$$a \neq \{a\}$$

It may happen that a is a set whose only element is a. In this case, $a \in a$ and

$$a = \{a\}$$

As (1) and (2) show, there is no logical or set-theoretical necessity to prevent a set from being its own element. Some authors expressly forbid the existence of sets that are members of themselves. This is done, for instance, by introducing the so called *axiom of Regularity*. However, this restriction is not essential for the Theory of Sets.

Now, let us consider the two sets

$$m = \{a,b\} \qquad \text{and} \qquad n = \{a,b,c\}$$

Comparing m with n, we observe that every element of m is an element of n. It is natural to call m a *subset* of n. Thus, we introduce:

Definition 2.   *We say that a set x is a subset of a set y if every element of x is also an element of y.*

Formally,

(13) $$(x \subset y) \equiv (\forall z)((z \in x) \rightarrow (z \in y))$$

The right side of $\equiv$ in (13) is a predicate of two variables x and y. Hence, $x \subset y$ is also a predicate of two variables x and y, and as such could be written more appropriately as:

$$\subset (x,y)$$

The symbol $\subset$ is called the predicate symbol of *inclusion* and $x \subset y$ is read: *x is included in y* or *x is a subset of y*. Furthermore, $y \supset x$ is read: *y includes x*.

Here also, let us observe that $\subset$ is a new predicate symbol. However, as expected, and as (13) shows, $x \subset y$ is defined in terms of the set-theoretical basic predicate symbol $\in$ and other logical symbols.

Clearly,

$$\{a\} \subset \{a\}, \qquad \{a\} \subset \{a,b\}, \qquad \{a\} \subset \{a,\{a\}\}$$

From (13), in view of the double negation law, we have:

(14) $$(x \subset y) \equiv \sim(\exists z)((z \in x) \wedge (z \notin y))$$

In other words, *a set x is a subset of a set y if and only if we cannot exhibit a set that is an element of x and is not an element of y.*

We shall prove some theorems about $\subset$.

Theorem 1.   *Every set is a subset of itself*, i.e.,

$$(\forall x)(x \subset x)$$

PROOF.   Since we cannot exhibit a set that is an element of x and is not an element of x, it follows from (14) that $x \subset x$, for every set x.

The formal proof of Theorem 1 runs as follows:

Since

$$(\forall x)(\forall z)((z \in x) \rightarrow (z \in x))$$

is a tautology, it follows from (13) that $(\forall x)(x \subset x)$, as desired.

Since, according to Theorem 1, every set is its own subset, it is customary to call $\subset$ a *reflexive* binary predicate symbol.

Theorem 2.   *Two sets are equal if and only if each is a subset of the other*, i.e.,

$$(\forall x)(\forall y)((x \subset y) \wedge (y \subset x) \leftrightarrow (x = y))$$

PROOF.   From $x \subset y$, it follows that every element of x is an element of y, and from $y \subset x$, it follows that every element of y is an element of x. Hence, in view of (5) we conclude that $x = y$. Conversely, from $x = y$, in view of Theorem 1 it follows that $x \subset y$ and $y \subset x$.

Since by Theorem 2, for every two sets x and y, $x \subset y$ and $y \subset x$ imply $x = y$, it is customary to call $\subset$ an *antisymmetric* binary predicate symbol.

Theorem 2 shows that *the proof of equality of two sets consists of two parts*, one for each inclusion. In other words, to prove that x is equal to y we have to show that every element of x is an element of y (i.e., $x \subset y$), and also that every element of y is an element of x (i.e., $y \subset x$).

Theorem 3.   *A subset of a subset of a set is a subset of that set*, i.e.,

$$(\forall x)(\forall y)(\forall z)(((x \subset y) \wedge (y \subset z)) \rightarrow (x \subset z))$$

PROOF.   From the hypothesis $x \subset y$ and $y \subset z$, we have to conclude that $x \subset z$, i.e., we have to conclude that every element t of x is an element of z. However, since $x \subset y$, if $t \in x$ then $t \in y$. But then from $y \subset z$ and $t \in y$, it follows that $t \in z$.

Since by Theorem 3 for every three sets x, y and z, $x \subset y$ and $y \subset z$ imply $x \subset z$, it is customary to call $\subset$ a *transitive* binary predicate symbol.

Theorems 1, 2 and 3 assert respectively that $\subset$ is a reflexive, antisymmetric and transitive binary predicate symbol.

Definition 3.   *We say that a subset of a set is a proper subset of that set if it is not equal to that set*, i.e.,

$$x \text{ is a proper subset of } y \text{ if } x \subset y \text{ and } x \neq y$$

Thus, if a, b and c are distinct sets, then $\{a,b\}$ is a proper subset of $\{a,b,c\}$, whereas $\{a,b,c\}$ is not a proper subset of $\{a,b,c\}$.

Sometimes, $\subsetneq$ is used to indicate that x is a proper subset of y. Thus, for the above example, we may write:

$$\{a,b\} \subsetneq \{a,b,c\}$$

In this section, we have introduced the binary predicates $x = y$, $x \subset y$, $x \neq y$ and $x \subsetneq y$. Clearly, we may introduce many more binary predicates, such as:

$$p(x,y) \equiv xpy \equiv (x \in y) \rightarrow (x = y)$$
$$q(x,y) \equiv xqy \equiv (x \subset y) \vee (x \in y)$$
$$r(x,y) \equiv xry \equiv (x \in a) \rightarrow (y \notin x)$$

Motivated by (7), (8) and (9), we say that in a theory of sets a binary predicate

$P(x,y)$ is *reflexive*, if $(\forall x)P(x,x)$

$P(x,y)$ is *symmetric*, if $(\forall x)(\forall y)(P(x,y) \rightarrow P(y,x))$

$P(x,y)$ is *transitive*, if $(\forall x)(\forall y)(\forall z)((P(x,y) \wedge P(y,z)) \rightarrow P(x,z))$

And in a theory of sets in which $=$ is defined,

$P(x,y)$ is *antisymmetric* if $(\forall x)(\forall y)((P(x,y) \wedge P(y,x)) \rightarrow (x = y))$

As we shall see later, owing to the axioms of the Theory of Sets, $\in$ is neither a reflexive nor a symmetric nor a transitive nor an antisymmetric predicate symbol. However, $=$ and $\subset$ are reflexive and transitive predicate symbols. Moreover, $=$ is both symmetric and antisymmetric, whereas $\subset$ is antisymmetric but not symmetric.

EXERCISES

1. Give a formal proof for each of Theorems 2 and 3.

2. Prove that the set $\{a\}$ is equal to the set $\{a,a,a,a,a\}$.

3. Consider the content consisting of the sets a, b, c and the $\in$-truth table given by (1). In reference to (1), determine whether or not $\in$ is a reflexive, symmetric and transitive binary predicate.

4. Give an example of a set two elements of which are also subsets of that set.

5. Assume that no set is an element of itself. Give an example of a set having four elements, three of which are also subsets of that set.

6. Consider the natural numbers 1, 2, 3, ... as sets and let

$$x \in y \quad \text{read:} \quad x \text{ is even and divides } y.$$

Define $x = y$ according to Definition 1. Would $=$ satisfy the axiom of Extensionality? Prove your answer.

7. Consider the natural numbers 1, 2, 3, ... as sets and let

$$x \in y \quad \text{read:} \quad x \text{ is a prime number that divides } y.$$

Define $x = y$ according to Definition 1. Would $=$ satisfy the axiom of Extensionality? Prove your answer.

8. Let a, b, c and d be four distinct sets. How many distinct subsets. each having two elements, does the set $\{a,b,c,d\}$ have?

9. Construct a table of a model whose content consists of the sets a, b and c such that $\subset$ (as defined by Definition 2) becomes a symmetric binary predicate in that model.

10. Consider the model whose table is given by (1) and the binary predicate:

$$p(x,y) \equiv (x \in y) \vee (x \in a)$$

Is $p(x,y)$ a reflexive, symmetric or transitive predicate in that model? If $=$ is defined according to Definition 1, is $p(x,y)$ an antisymmetric predicate in that model? Prove your answer.

11. Consider the model whose table is given by (2). Which of the following predicates are reflexive, which are symmetric and which are transitive in that model?

$$q(x,y) \equiv (x \subset y) \vee (x \notin y)$$
$$r(x,y) \equiv (x \subset y) \rightarrow (x \in y)$$

12. Consider the natural numbers 0, 1, 2, 3, . . . as constituting the content of a model. Let

$$x \in y \quad \text{read:} \quad x \text{ is less than } y.$$

Define $x = y$ according to Definition 1. Would $=$ satisfy the axiom of Extensionality? Prove your answer. Also, in the model under consideration, determine which of the following statements are true and which are false:

$$
\begin{array}{llll}
4 \in 8, & 3 \in 7, & 2 \in 1, & 3 \subset 5 \\
0 \in 3, & 0 \subset 3, & 4 \in 0, & 5 \subset 0 \\
3 \in 1, & 1 \in 3, & 2 \in 9, & 2 \subset 9
\end{array}
$$

3. BINARY PREDICATES $F(x,y)$, FUNCTIONAL IN x

According to the notation introduced on page 52, $P(x,y)$, $Q(x,y)$, $R(x,y)$, . . . stand for formulas whose only free variables are x and y. As we know, a formula for which $P(x,y)$ stands is a *binary* or *dyadic* or *two-place predicate*. Clearly, to begin with, a binary predicate is a formula formed according to the formation rules of formulas, as discussed in Chapter I.

Now, let $p(x,y)$ be a binary predicate. If in a model $p(a,m)$ is true, then (in that model) we call the set m a *mate* of the set a with respect to $p(x,y)$.

Let us give an example. Consider the model whose content consists of the sets a, b, c and d and whose table is given by:

	$\in$		$\in$		$\in$		$\in$
a,a	F	a,b	F	a,c	T	a,d	F
b,a	T	b,b	F	b,c	F	b,d	T
c,a	F	c,b	F	c,c	T	c,d	F
d,a	F	d,b	F	d,c	F	d,d	F

(15)

where, for convenience, we have broken the truth table into four parts.

In view of Definition 1, in the model whose table is given by (15), the sets a and d are equal, i.e., $a = d$, whereas a, b and c are three distinct sets. Incidentally, we observe that in (15) the axiom of Extensionality is not valid.

Next, consider the binary predicate:

(16) $$f(x,y) \equiv ((a \in x) \rightarrow (x \in c)) \wedge (x \in y)$$

From (15) we see that

$$f(a,y) \equiv ((a \in a) \rightarrow (a \in c)) \wedge (a \in y)$$

is true (i.e., tagged **T**), if and only if y is replaced by c. Thus, we may conclude that, with respect to $f(x,y)$, the set a has *one and only one* (i.e., *unique*) *mate*, namely, c.

Again, from (15) we see that

$$f(b,y) \equiv ((a \in b) \rightarrow (b \in c)) \wedge (b \in y)$$

is true (i.e., tagged **T**), if and only if y is replaced by a or d. However, since $a = d$, we may conclude that with respect to $f(x,y)$ the set b has one and only one (i.e., unique) mate, say, a.

Similarly, from (15) we see that

$$f(c,y) \equiv ((a \in c) \rightarrow (c \in c)) \wedge (c \in y)$$

is true if and only if y is replaced by c. Thus, with respect to $f(x,y)$, the set c has one and only one (i.e., unique) mate, namely, c.

On the other hand, from (15) we see that

$$f(d,y) \equiv ((a \in d) \rightarrow (d \in c)) \wedge (d \in y)$$

is false when y is replaced by a or b or c or d. Thus, with respect to $f(x,y)$, the set d has *no* mate.

In short, in the model whose table is given by (15), the binary predicate $f(x,y)$ given by (16) assigns to every set x of the content *at most one* set y for which $f(x,y)$ is true. Thus,

to	a,	$f(x,y)$ assigns	c
to	b,	$f(x,y)$ assigns	a and d, with $a = d$
to	c,	$f(x,y)$ assigns	c
to	d,	$f(x,y)$ assigns	no mate

Even though the same set c is the mate of both of the sets a and c, *every set of the content has at most one mate with respect to $f(x,y)$*.

If in a model a binary predicate $p(x,y)$ is such that, for every set x of the content, *there exists at most one* set y such that $p(x,y)$ is satisfied (true) in that model, then $p(x,y)$ is called a *binary predicate, functional in x in that model.*

Thus, the predicate

$$f(x,y) \equiv ((a \in x) \rightarrow (x \in c)) \wedge (x \in y)$$

is a binary predicate, functional in x, in the model whose table is given by (15).

However, the binary predicate

$$r(x,y) \equiv (x \in y) \vee (y \in x)$$

is not functional in x in that model. This can readily be seen from (15), which shows that

$$r(a,b) \quad \text{and} \quad r(a,c)$$

are both true. Consequently, the set a has two distinct mates a and b with respect to $r(x,y)$. Therefore, $r(x,y)$ is not a binary predicate, functional in x, in the model whose table is given by (15).

If a binary predicate $p(x,y)$ is functional in x in a model, then the unique mate y of x is customarily denoted by $p(x)$, i.e.,

$$y = p(x)$$

For instance, since $f(x,y)$ given by (16) is functional in x in the model whose table is given by (15),

$$c = f(a), \qquad d = a = f(b), \qquad c = f(c)$$

are true statements in that model.

Motivated by the above, <u>let us call a binary predicate $F(x,y)$ *functional in x if it is functional in x in every model in which $=$ is defined by Definition 1.*</u>

In view of these considerations, we introduce:

Definition 4. *We say that a binary predicate $F(x,y)$ is functional in x if*

(17) $$(\forall x)(\forall y)(\forall z)((F(x,y) \wedge F(x,z)) \to (y = z))$$

Clearly, we interpret (17) as stating that <u>x has at most one mate y such that $F(x,y)$ is true in every model.</u>

A very significant binary predicate scheme $F(x,y)$ which is functional in x is given by:

(18) $$F(x,y) \equiv ((x = y) \wedge P(y))$$

where $P(y)$ stands for any predicate in which y is the only free variable—i.e., $P(y)$ stands for a predicate of one variable or a *one-place* predicate or a *unary* or *monadic* predicate.

The fact that $F(x,y)$ given by (18) is a predicate scheme functional in x follows from the symmetry and transitivity of $=$.

Other examples of binary predicates $F(x,y)$ functional in x are given by:

$$g(x,y) \equiv (x = y) \quad \text{and} \quad h(x,y) \equiv (x = \{y\})$$

Clearly,

$$(\forall x)(\forall y)(\forall z)((x = y) \wedge (x = z) \to (y = z))$$

Also,

$$(\forall x)(\forall y)(\forall z)((x = \{y\}) \wedge (x = \{z\}) \to (y = z))$$

However, neither of the predicates:

$$x \in y \quad \text{or} \quad y \in x$$

is functional in x, since a set may be an element of many distinct sets and many distinct sets may be elements of a set.

Similarly, neither of the predicates

$$x \subset y \quad \text{or} \quad y \subset x$$

is functional in x, since a set may be a subset of many distinct sets and many distinct sets may be subsets of a set.

EXERCISES

1. Determine which of the following predicates are functional in x:

$$p(x,y) \equiv \{y\} = \{x\}$$
$$q(x,y) \equiv \{y,\{y\}\} = \{x,\{x\}\}$$
$$r(x,y) \equiv (x \in y) \to (y \in x)$$
$$s(x,y) \equiv \{x,\{y\}\} = \{y,\{x\}\}$$
$$u(x,y) \equiv (x = y) \wedge (y \in y)$$
$$v(x,y) \equiv (x = \{y\}) \wedge (y \in x)$$

2. Assume in a model

$$m = \{a,b,c\} \quad \text{and} \quad n = \{a,b,p\}$$

where a, b, c and p are distinct sets. Determine which of the following binary predicates are functional in x in that model:

$$p(x,y) \equiv ((x \in m) \vee (y \in n)) \to (x = y)$$
$$q(x,y) \equiv (y = x) \wedge (x \in m) \wedge (x \in n)$$
$$r(x,y) \equiv (x \in m) \to (y \in n)$$
$$s(x,y) \equiv ((x \in m) \wedge (y \in n)) \to (x = y)$$

3. Assume in a model

$$m = \{a,b\} \quad \text{and} \quad n = \{a,b,c\}$$

where a, b and c are distinct sets. Determine which of the following predicates are functional in x in that model:

$$p(x,y) \equiv (x \subset m) \wedge (y \subset n)$$
$$q(x,y) \equiv (x \in m) \wedge (y \subset m) \wedge (x \in y)$$
$$r(x,y) \equiv (x \in m) \to ((y \in m) \wedge (x = y))$$

4. Consider the natural numbers 0, 1, 2, 3, . . . as sets, and let:

$$x \in y \quad \text{read:} \quad x \text{ is less than } y.$$

Determine which of the following predicates are functional in x in the model under consideration:

$$p(x,y) \equiv (x \in 4) \wedge (x \in y) \wedge (y \in 2)$$
$$q(x,y) \equiv (y \in x) \wedge (x \in 2)$$
$$r(x,y) \equiv (x \in y) \leftrightarrow (y \in x)$$

4. THE AXIOM OF REPLACEMENT

Consider the model whose content consists of the sets a, b and c and whose table is given by:

(19)

$\in$			$\in$			$\in$	
a,a	**F**		a,b	**F**		a,c	**T**
b,a	**T**		b,b	**F**		b,c	**T**
c,a	**F**		c,b	**T**		c,c	**F**

Let us consider the binary predicate:

$$h(x,y) \equiv x = \{y\}$$

which is functional in x. Clearly,

$$h(a) = b \qquad \text{and} \qquad h(b) = c$$

and c has no mate.

As (19) shows, in the model with this table there exists a set—namely, c—whose only elements are a and b; however, in the same model there does not exist a set whose only elements are b and c. This means that in the model whose table is given by (19), corresponding to some binary predicate $F(x,y)$, functional in x [for instance, $h(x,y)$, above], and some set s (for instance, the set c), *there does not exist* the set of the mates of all the elements of s with respect to $F(x,y)$.

For a satisfactory development of the Theory of Sets, the existence of the set of the mates, with respect to any binary predicate $F(x,y)$, functional in x, of all the elements of a set, is found to be necessary. Since in the model whose table is given by (19) this requirement is not fulfilled (even though in that model the axiom of Extensionality is valid), we introduce the following as an axiom scheme of the Theory of Sets.

The Axiom Scheme of Replacement. *For every set s and every binary predicate* $F(x,y)$, *functional in x, there exists the set whose elements are the mates and only the mates of all the elements of s with respect to* $F(x,y)$.
Formally,

(20) $\quad (\forall s)((\forall x)(\forall y)(\forall z)(((x \in s) \wedge F(x,y) \wedge F(x,z)) \to (y = z))$
$\to (\exists t)(\forall y)((y \in t) \leftrightarrow (\exists x)((x \in s) \wedge F(x,y))))$

Obviously, the first part of (20) merely states that $F(x,y)$ is functional in x. The second part asserts the existence of a set t that is the set of the mates of all the elements of s with respect to $F(x,y)$. The uniqueness of t follows from (5).

Because of the arbitrariness of $F(x,y)$, except for its being functional in x, (20) is a formula scheme embodying many formulas each corresponding to a particular choice of $F(x,y)$. This is the reason for calling (20) an axiom scheme.

However, for the sake of simplicity, it is customary to call (20) *the axiom of Replacement.*

Accordingly, (19) cannot serve as a table of a model of the Theory of Sets, since in it the axiom of Replacement is not valid.

Let us observe that by means of the axiom of Replacement, we can assert the existence of a great variety of sets in the Theory of Sets, when the existence of some other sets is presupposed.

For instance, if in the Theory of Sets the following two sets exist:

$$s = \{a,b,c\} \quad \text{and} \quad r = \{\{a,m\}, \{b,n\}, \{c,n\}\}$$

then the set

$$t = \{m,n\}$$

must also exist. To see this, it is enough to consider the predicate:

$$(x \in s) \wedge (\{x,y\} \in r)$$

Clearly, the above predicate is functional in x and the mates of a, b and c are respectively m, n and n. Hence, by the axiom of Replacement, the set t whose elements are the mates and only the mates of all the elements of $\{a,b,c\}$ must exist. But obviously, $t = \{m,n\}$.

Again, let us assume that in the Theory of Sets the set

$$s = \{a,b,c\}$$

where a, b and c are distinct sets, exists. Then, the set

$$t = \{b,c\}$$

must also exist. To see this, it is enough to consider the predicate:

$$(x = y) \wedge (y \neq a)$$

Clearly, the above predicate is functional in x and the mates of b and c are respectively b and c, whereas a has no mates. Consequently, in view of the axiom of Replacement, the set t whose elements are the mates and only the mates of all the elements of $\{a,b,c\}$ must exist. But obviously, in this case $t = \{b,c\}$.

The reason for requiring that $F(x,y)$ in (20) be functional in x is that otherwise, as will be shown shortly, (20) will lead to a paradox (Russell's paradox).

When the existence of a set t is asserted by the axiom of Replacement via a binary predicate $F(x,y)$, functional in x, and the existence of a set s, then it is customary to represent t as follows:

(21) $$t = \{y \mid (\exists x)((x \in s) \wedge F(x,y))\}$$

which is read: *t is the set of all sets y such that $F(x,y)$ is satisfied for some $x \in s$.*

Now, we shall give one of the most important consequences of the axiom of Replacement. This consequence is usually called the theorem of Separation. As mentioned earlier, the predicate scheme:

(18) $$F(x,y) \equiv ((x = y) \wedge P(y))$$

where $P(y)$ stands for any predicate of one variable, is a predicate scheme, functional in x. Replacing $F(x,y)$ given by (18) in (20), by virtue of modus ponens [given by (45), page 36], we find that

$$(\forall s)(\exists t)(\forall y)((y \in t) \leftrightarrow (\exists x)((x \in s) \wedge (x = y) \wedge P(y)))$$

is a valid formula in the Theory of Sets. However, it is easily seen that the above is equivalent to:

$$(\forall s)(\exists t)(\forall y)((y \in t) \leftrightarrow ((y \in s) \wedge P(y)))$$

which states that *in the Theory of Sets if a set s exists, then the set t of all those elements of s that satisfy a monadic predicate P(y) also exists.* Clearly, t is a subset of s. Thus, we have:

The Theorem of Separation. *For every set s and every monadic predicate P(x), the set of all those elements of s that satisfy P(x) exists.*

Formally,

(22) $\qquad (\forall s)(\exists t)(\forall x)((x \in t) \leftrightarrow ((x \in s) \wedge P(x)))$

Naturally, in the above $P(x)$ is a formula whose only free variable is x, and $P(x)$ is formed by means of the set-theoretical vocabulary (see page 60) and in accordance with the formation rules of formulas.

Here also because of the arbitrariness of $P(x)$, (22) is a formula scheme embodying many formulas, each corresponding to a particular choice of $P(x)$. Thus, although (22) is a theorem scheme, for the sake of simplicity it is called a theorem.

Let us observe that the theorem scheme of Separation asserts the existence of certain subsets of a set. For this reason, the theorem scheme of Separation is also called the *theorem scheme of Subsets,* or simply the *theorem of Subsets.*

It is important to note that the theorem of Separation *does not assert* the existence of the set of all those sets that satisfy a predicate $P(x)$. It only asserts the existence of the set of all those sets that satisfy the predicate $P(x)$ and *that are elements of a set.*

When the existence of a subset t of a set s is derived by means of the theorem of Separation via a monadic predicate $P(x)$, then it is customary to write:

(23) $\qquad t = \{x \mid (x \in s) \wedge P(x)\}$

which is read: *t is the set of all those elements x of s that satisfy P(x).*

Motivated by (21) and (23), in general, a configuration of the form:

(24) $\qquad \{x \mid \ldots\}$

is read: *the set of all* (sets) *x's that satisfy such and such a condition* [written in place of the dots in (24)]. Clearly, the dots in (24) cannot be filled in arbitrarily; the axiom of Replacement and in particular the theorem of Separation give instructions to this effect.

Next, we make an important observation pertaining to the Theory of Sets. We mentioned above that presupposing the existence of certain sets, the axiom of Replacement and the theorem of Separation assert the existence of additional sets in the Theory of Sets. Now, we give a significant application of the theorem of Separation (which is of course a consequence of the axiom of Replacement) which asserts the existence of an *empty set* in the Theory of Sets. To see this it is enough to replace $P(x)$ in (22) by $x \neq x$. As a result we obtain

$$(25) \qquad (\forall s)(\exists t)(\forall x)((x \in t) \leftrightarrow ((x \in s) \wedge (x \neq x)))$$

However,

$$(\forall s)(\forall x)((x \in s) \wedge (x \neq x))$$

is nonsatisfiable and therefore,

$$(26) \qquad (\exists t)(\forall x)(x \notin t)$$

is a derivable formula (i.e., a theorem) in the Theory of Sets. But then, as fully explained in Section 1 of this chapter, we interpret formula (26) as asserting the existence of an *empty set* (i.e., a set having no elements) in the Theory of Sets.

The theorem below justifies our introducing the symbol

$$\varnothing$$

as *the empty set* of the Theory of Sets.

Theorem 4. *There exists a unique empty set, and the empty set is a subset of every set.*

PROOF. As mentioned above, the existence of an empty set in the Theory of Sets is asserted by formula (26). To prove the uniqueness, let us assume that there exist two empty sets $\varnothing$ and e. Since both $\varnothing$ and e are empty, we cannot exhibit a set that is an element of one and not an element of the other. Therefore, in view of Definition 1, we conclude that $\varnothing = e$. Thus, in the Theory of Sets there exists a *unique* (of course, up to equality) empty set, namely,

$$\varnothing$$

which is often denoted by 0 and is also called the *null* set. Next, let s be any set. Since we cannot exhibit a set that is an element of $\varnothing$ and not an element of s, in view of Definition 2 we conclude that $\varnothing$ is a subset of every set. Moreover, if s is not the empty set $\varnothing$, then $\varnothing$ is a proper subset of s.

In view of Theorems 1 and 4, we have:

$$\varnothing \subset s, \quad \textit{for every set } s$$

As another application of the theorem of Separation, let us show that, from the existence of the set $\{a,b,c\}$, where a, b and c are distinct sets, we may derive the existence of its subsets—say, $\{a\}$ and $\{a,b\}$. To this end, it is enough to consider the following predicates, respectively:

$$(x \neq b) \wedge (x \neq c) \qquad \text{and} \qquad (x \neq c)$$

Now, using notation (23), we obtain:

$$\{a\} = \{x \mid (x \in \{a,b,c\}) \wedge (x \neq b) \wedge (x \neq c)\}$$

and

$$\{a,b\} = \{x \mid (x \in \{a,b,c\}) \wedge (x \neq c)\}$$

EXERCISES

1. Consider the set $\{a,b,c\}$, where a, b and c are distinct sets. How many distinct subsets does $\{a,b,c\}$ have? Prove the existence of each subset you indicate by using the theorem of Separation.

2. Give a formal proof to the effect that the empty set is a subset of every set.

3. How many distinct subsets does $\varnothing$ (the empty set) have?

4. Give two examples of predicates other than the ones given in the text, which, in view of the theorem of Separation, will yield the empty set.

5. Can you prove the existence (in the Theory of Sets) of the set $\{\varnothing\}$ using only the axioms of Extensionality and Substitution? Give reasons.

6. Assuming the existence of a set s, give two examples of binary predicates $F(x,y)$ such that, in view of the axiom of Replacement, each will yield the existence of the empty set.

5. THE AXIOM OF POWER-SET

Read & study — defn of ordered pair, standard

Although the axioms of Extensionality and Replacement (and in particular, the theorem of Separation) yield the existence of subsets of a set s, they do not assert the existence of the set of all the subsets of the set s.

For instance, consider a model whose content consists of $\varnothing$ (the empty set). Clearly, the axioms of Extensionality and Replacement are valid in this model. Also, it is obvious that in this model any set whose existence is asserted via the axiom of Replacement will necessarily be empty. Consequently, in the model under consideration, the existence of the set $\{\varnothing\}$ of all the subsets of $\varnothing$ cannot be asserted, regardless of the validity of the axioms of Extensionality and Replacement. For a satisfactory development of the Theory of Sets, the existence of the set of all the subsets of a set is found to be necessary. Thus, motivated by the above discussion, we introduce the following as an axiom of the Theory of Sets.

The Axiom of Power-Set. *For every set s, the set whose elements are all the subsets and only the subsets of s exists.*

Formally,

$$(\forall s)(\exists t)(\forall x)((x \in t) \leftrightarrow (x \subset s))$$

The set whose elements are all the subsets and only the subsets of a set s is called the *set of all the subsets of s* or the *power-set of s*. The uniqueness of the power-set of s follows from its definition and (5). The power-set of s is usually denoted by:

$$\mathscr{P}(s)$$

Thus,

$$\mathscr{P}(s) = \{x \mid x \subset s\}$$

The axiom of Power-Set is an effective device for asserting the existence of more and more sets in the Theory of Sets.

For example, in view of the axiom of Power-Set, from the existence of $\varnothing$ (the empty set), we assert the existence of $\{\varnothing\}$, since

$$\mathscr{P}(\varnothing) = \{\varnothing\}$$

Similarly, in view of the axiom of Power-Set, from the existence of $\{\varnothing\}$ we assert the existence of $\{\varnothing,\{\varnothing\}\}$, since

$$\mathscr{P}(\{\varnothing\}) = \{\varnothing,\{\varnothing\}\}$$

Likewise, the set

$$\mathscr{P}(\{\varnothing,\{\varnothing\}\}) = \{\varnothing,\{\varnothing\},\{\{\varnothing\}\},\{\varnothing,\{\varnothing\}\}\}$$

exists in the Theory of Sets.

It is easy to show that the above three sets are distinct. Thus, in view of the axioms of Extensionality, Replacement and Power-Set, it is possible to assert that the following three (and many more) distinct sets

$$\varnothing, \quad \{\varnothing\}, \quad \{\varnothing,\{\varnothing\},\{\{\varnothing\}\},\{\varnothing,\{\varnothing\}\}\}$$

exist in the Theory of Sets.

We shall prove later that a set cannot equal its power-set. However, we show now that if a set s has n distinct elements ($n = 0, 1, 2, \ldots$), than its power-set $\mathscr{P}(s)$ has more than n distinct elements and hence,

$$s \neq \mathscr{P}(s)$$

Remark 5. In what follows, prior to the formal introduction of the natural numbers, integers, rationals and reals, any reference to them and to their usual arithmetic is made informally. Likewise, until the formal introduction of these items, theorems involving them are proved informally. These theorems are not necessary for the formal development of the Theory of Sets and are given only by way of illustration.

Theorem 5. *If a set s has n distinct elements ($n = 0, 1, 2, \ldots$), then the power-set $\mathscr{P}(s)$ has 2^n distinct elements.*

PROOF. Obviously, the number m of elements of an arbitrary subset of s is such that $0 \leq m \leq n$. On the other hand, the set s has $\binom{n}{m}$ subsets each containing m distinct elements,

where

$$\binom{n}{m} = \frac{n!}{m!\,(n-m)!}$$

(the number of different combinations of n objects taken m at a time). Therefore, the number of elements of $\mathscr{P}(s)$ is

$$\binom{n}{0} + \binom{n}{1} + \cdots + \binom{n}{n} = (1+1)^n = 2^n$$

where

$$\binom{n}{0} = \binom{n}{n} = 1$$

That the 2^n subsets of $\mathscr{P}(s)$ are distinct follows immediately from our assumption that s has n distinct elements.

Let us observe that, in the above, m and n stand for natural numbers 0, 1, 2, ...

For instance, the set $\{a,b,c\}$, where a, b and c are distinct, has the $2^3 = 8$ distinct subsets:

$$\varnothing, \quad \{a\}, \quad \{b\}, \quad \{c\}, \quad \{a,b\}, \quad \{a,c\}, \quad \{b,c\}, \quad \{a,b,c\}$$

The following alternate proof of Theorem 5 is also of interest.

A subset of the set s that has n ($n = 0, 1, 2, \ldots$) distinct elements is a set such that some of the n elements of s belong to that set and some do not. Hence, corresponding to a subset of s, each element of s has two choices, either of belonging or of not belonging to that subset. Since s has n elements, it follows that altogether there are 2^n distinct subsets of s.

Let us observe that with the help of the axiom of Power-Set and the theorem of Separation one can prove (in the Theory of Sets) the existence of a set with any number, n ($n = 0, 1, 2, \ldots$) of elements.

For instance, let us prove the existence of a set with three elements.

By repeated application of the axiom of Power-Set, the existence of the set

$$a = \mathscr{P}(\mathscr{P}(\mathscr{P}(\varnothing))) = \{\varnothing, \{\varnothing\}, \{\{\varnothing\}\}, \{\varnothing, \{\varnothing\}\}\}$$

having four distinct elements is established, from which by the theorem of Separation we derive a set with three distinct elements, as follows:

$$\{x \mid (x \in a) \wedge (x \neq \{\varnothing, \{\varnothing\}\})\}$$

Hence, the set

$$\{\varnothing, \{\varnothing\}, \{\{\varnothing\}\}\}$$

containing three distinct elements, exists in the Theory of Sets.

Motivated by the above, we prove:

Theorem 6. *For every n, with $n = 0, 1, 2, \ldots$, a set that has precisely n distinct elements exists.*

PROOF. If $n = 0$, then the null set $\varnothing$ is a set which has 0 elements.

Now, let n be any nonzero natural number, i.e., $n = 1, 2, 3, \ldots$. Consider the set p obtained as the result of the n-fold formation of power-sets beginning with $\varnothing$, i.e.,

$$p = \mathscr{P}(\cdots \mathscr{P}(\mathscr{P}(\varnothing)) \cdots)$$

Clearly, by virtue of the axiom of Power-Set, the set p exists. Also, it is obvious that p possesses the following n distinct elements.

$$\varnothing, \quad \{\varnothing\}, \quad \{\{\varnothing\}\}, \quad \ldots, \quad \{\cdots\{\varnothing\}\cdots\}$$

Now, consider the following set:

$$q = \{x \mid (x \in p) \wedge ((x = \varnothing) \vee (x = \{\varnothing\}) \vee \cdots \vee (x = \{\cdots\{\varnothing\}\cdots\}))\}$$

which exists by virtue of the theorem of Separation and the existence of p. Clearly, the set q has precisely n distinct elements, since

$$q = \{\varnothing, \{\varnothing\}, \{\{\varnothing\}\}, \ldots, \{\cdots\{\varnothing\}\cdots\}\}$$

Next, we prove:

Theorem 7. *For every n sets $a_1, a_2, \ldots, a_n$, with $n = 1, 2, 3, \ldots$, the set $\{a_1, a_2, \ldots, a_n\}$ exists.*

PROOF. By Theorem 6, for any $n = 1, 2, 3, \ldots$ there exists the set q given by:

$$q = \{\varnothing, \{\varnothing\}, \{\{\varnothing\}\}, \ldots, \{\cdots\{\varnothing\}\cdots\}\}$$

which has precisely n distinct elements.

Now, consider the predicate

$$f(x,y) \equiv ((x = \varnothing) \wedge (y = a_1)) \vee ((x = \{\varnothing\}) \wedge (y = a_2))$$
$$\vee \cdots$$
$$\vee ((x = \{\cdots\{\varnothing\}\cdots\}) \wedge (y = a_n))$$

which is functional in x.

In view of the axiom of Replacement, the set

$$t = \{y \mid ((\exists x)(x \in q) \wedge f(x,y))\}$$

exists. But obviously,

$$t = \{a_1, a_2, \ldots, a_n\}$$

Hence, from the existence of $a_1, a_2, \ldots, a_n$, we derived the existence of the set $\{a_1, a_2, \ldots, a_n\}$, as desired.

Below we mention two obvious corollaries of Theorem 7.

Corollary 1. *For every set s, the set $\{s\}$ whose one and only element is s exists.*

The set $\{s\}$ is usually called the *unit-set of s* or *the singleton of s*.

Therefore, the existence of a set s ensures the existence of its singleton $\{s\}$. The axioms of the Theory of Sets so far introduced do not prevent the equality of a set and its singleton $\{s\}$. However,

$$\varnothing \neq \{\varnothing\}$$

since the empty set has no element, whereas $\{\varnothing\}$ has one element.

Corollary 2. *For every two sets u and v, the set $\{u,v\}$ exists.*

This corollary is usually called the *theorem of Pairing*. The set $\{u,v\}$ is called the *unordered pair* formed by u and v, since, as we know,

$$\{u,v\} = \{v,u\}$$

Thus, $\{u,v\}$ remains equal to itself, regardless of the order in which u and v are written inside the braces.

Clearly, the axioms of the Theory of Sets so far introduced do not prevent the possibility that

$$u = \{u,v\} \qquad \text{or} \qquad v = \{u,v\}$$

Theorem 8. *For every two sets u and v, the set $\{\{u\}, \{u,v\}\}$ exists.*

PROOF. By Corollary 1, if the set u exists, then $\{u\}$ exists. By Corollary 2, if u and v exist, then $\{u,v\}$ exists. But then, in view of Corollary 2, $\{\{u\}, \{u,v\}\}$ exists.

Theorem 9. *For every four sets u, v, x and y,*

$$\{\{u\}, \{u,v\}\} = \{\{x\}, \{x,y\}\}$$

if and only if $u = x$ and $v = y$.

PROOF. Clearly, if $u = x$ and $v = y$, then

(i) $$\{\{u\},\{u,v\}\} = \{\{x\},\{x,y\}\}$$

Now, if (i) holds and $u = v$, then the left side of (i) reduces to $\{\{u\}\}$ implying that $x = y$ on the right side of (i). Thus, in this case (i) reduces to $\{\{u\}\} = \{\{x\}\}$ and therefore, $u = x$. However, from $u = v$ and $x = y$, it then follows that $u = x = v = y$. Consequently, in this case we have $u = x$ and $v = y$, as desired.

Next, if (i) holds and $u \neq v$, then $\{u\} \neq \{u,v\}$, and therefore (i) implies $\{u\} = \{x\}$ and $\{u,v\} = \{x,y\}$, which in turn imply $u = x$ and $v = y$, as desired.

From Theorem 9, it follows that:

(27) $$\text{if} \quad u \neq v, \quad \text{then} \quad \{\{u\},\{u,v\}\} \neq \{\{v\},\{u,v\}\}$$

Customarily, $\{\{u\},\{u,v\}\}$ is denoted by (u,v) or $\langle u,v \rangle$ and is called *the ordered pair* formed by u and v, i.e.,

(28) $$(u,v) = \langle u,v \rangle = \{\{u\},\{u,v\}\}$$

Accordingly, the set used twice in $\{\{u\},\{u,v\}\}$ is written as the first entry in (u,v).

In view of (27),

(29) $$(u,v) \neq (v,u) \qquad \text{for} \qquad u \neq v$$

Thus, as (29) shows, when $u \neq v$, the order in which u and v are written in (u,v) or $\langle u,v \rangle$ is material. This is the reason for calling $\{\{u\},\{u,v\}\}$ *the ordered pair* formed by u and v. In (u,v) or $\langle u,v \rangle$, the set u is called the *first* set or the *first coordinate* and the set v is called the *second* set or the *second coordinate* of (u,v) or of $\langle u,v \rangle$.

Obviously, if $u = v$ then $\{\{u\},\{u,v\}\}$ reduces to $\{\{u\},\{u,u\}\} = \{\{u\}\}$ and is a set having only one element. Thus,

$$(u,u) = \{\{u\}\} \qquad \text{for every} \quad u$$

We close this section by explaining the reason for requiring that $F(x,y)$ in the axiom of Replacement be functional in x.

Russell's Paradox. According to the axiom of Replacement, corresponding to every set s and every predicate $F(x,y)$, functional in x, there exists the set of the mates and only the mates of all the elements of s, denoted by:

(30) $$\{y \mid ((\exists x)(x \in s) \wedge F(x,y))\}$$

Now, let us see what will happen if in (30) the requirement that $F(x,y)$ be functional in x is removed. Consider the predicate

$$x \subset y$$

We have proved that in the Theory of Sets the distinct sets $\varnothing$, $\{\varnothing\}$ and $\{\{\varnothing\}\}$ exist and that $\varnothing$ is a subset of every set (see Theorem 4). Thus, for $x = \varnothing$ the predicate $x \subset y$ is satisfied by assigning to y each of the three distinct sets $\varnothing$, $\{\varnothing\}$ and $\{\{\varnothing\}\}$. Consequently, $x \subset y$ is not functional in x.

Replacing s by $\varnothing$ and $F(x,y)$ by $x \subset y$ in (30) we obtain:

$$u = \{y \mid ((\exists x)(x \in \{\varnothing\}) \wedge (x \subset y))\}$$

Now, since by Theorem 4 the empty set is a subset of every set, the above asserts the existence of a set u that is *the set of all sets*, i.e.,

$$(\forall y)(y \in u)$$

However, by virtue of the theorem of Separation, from the existence of u, we derive the existence of the set n of all those sets that are not elements of themselves. This can be done by considering the predicate $y \notin y$ and by writing:

$$n = \{y \mid (y \in u) \wedge (y \notin y)\}$$

Consequently,

$$(y \in n) \leftrightarrow (y \notin y) \qquad \text{for every } y$$

Substituting n for y in the above, we derive

$$(n \in n) \leftrightarrow (n \notin n)$$

which is a contradiction. This shows that if in the axiom of Replacement, the requirement that $F(x,y)$ be functional in x is dropped, then the Theory of Sets becomes inconsistent.

Hence, the restriction that in the axiom of Replacement $F(x,y)$ be functional in x, is essential and cannot be removed.

Let us mention here that in view of the above neither *the set of all sets* nor *the set of all sets that are not elements of themselves* exist in the Theory of Sets.

EXERCISES

1. Prove that for every two sets x and y:

$$(x \in y) \leftrightarrow (\{x\} \subset y)$$
$$(x \subset y) \leftrightarrow (\mathscr{P}(x) \subset \mathscr{P}(y))$$
$$(x = y) \leftrightarrow (\mathscr{P}(x) = \mathscr{P}(y))$$
$$(\mathscr{P}(x) \in \mathscr{P}(y)) \rightarrow (x \in y)$$

2. Prove that the following sets exist (in the Theory of Sets) and that they are distinct.

$$\{\{\varnothing\}\}, \quad \{\{\{\varnothing\}\}\}, \quad \{\{\{\{\varnothing\}\}\}\}, \quad \{\{\{\{\{\varnothing\}\}\}\}\},$$
$$\{\varnothing,\{\varnothing\}\}, \quad \{\varnothing,\{\varnothing\},\{\varnothing,\{\varnothing\}\}\}, \quad \{\varnothing,\{\varnothing\},\{\varnothing,\{\varnothing\}\},\{\varnothing,\{\varnothing\},\{\varnothing,\{\varnothing\}\}\}\}$$

3. Give an example of a set in the Theory of Sets having four distinct elements such that each element of that set is also a subset of that set.

4. Let m and n be two distinct natural numbers (i.e., $m, n = 0, 1, 2, \ldots$) and let s be a set that has a limited number of elements and such that it has as many distinct subsets, each having m elements, as it has distinct subsets, each having n elements. Determine the number of the elements of s.

5. If $b = \{\{\{\varnothing\}\}\}$ and $c = \{\varnothing,\{\varnothing\}\}$, which of the following formulas are true and which are false?

$$b \in c, \qquad b \notin \mathscr{P}(c), \qquad b \in \mathscr{P}(\mathscr{P}(c))$$

6. Let $b = \{x \mid (x \in a) \wedge (x \notin x)\}$. Prove that $a \notin b$.

7. Prove that if

$$\{x, \{x,y\}\} = \{u, \{u,v\}\}$$

then it is not necessarily true that $x = u$ and $y = v$. On the basis of this, explain why $\{x, \{x,y\}\}$ is not used to define an ordered pair of x and y and why $\{\{x\}, \{x,y\}\}$ is used instead.

8. Assuming the existence of the two sets u and v, prove the existence of the sets:

$$\{u,\varnothing\}, \qquad \{v,\{\varnothing\}\}, \qquad \{\{u,\varnothing\},\{v,\{\varnothing\}\}\}$$

and show that

$$\{\{x,\varnothing\}, \{y,\{\varnothing\}\}\} = \{\{u,\varnothing\}, \{v,\{\varnothing\}\}\}$$

if and only if $x = u$ and $y = v$.

9. Assuming the existence of the sets a, b and c, prove the existence of the set $\{\{a\}, \{a,b\}, \{a,b,c\}\}$.

6. THE AXIOM OF SUM-SET

Let us assume that in a model the axioms of Extensionality, Replacement and Power-Set are valid. Moreover, let us assume that in that model, s is a set having a limited number of elements, say, a_1, a_2 and a_3, i.e.,

$$s = \{a_1, a_2, a_3\}$$

Let us also assume that each element of s in turn has a limited number of elements, say,

$$a_1 = \{a,b,c\}, \qquad a_2 = \{m,n\}, \qquad a_3 = \{p,q\}$$

Since in the model under consideration Theorem 7 is valid, we may conclude that the set:

$$t = \{a,b,c,m,n,p,q\}$$

exists in that model. We observe that the set t is the set of all the elements of all the elements of s. However, if s had an unlimited number of elements and if each one of the elements of s in turn had an unlimited number of elements, then, as one can easily show, the existence of t could not have been derived based on the axioms so far introduced. This means that if in a model the axioms of Extensionality, Replacement and Power-Set are valid, we still cannot in general assert the existence of the set of all the elements of all the elements of a set of that model.

For satisfactory development of the Theory of Sets, the existence of the set of all the elements of all the elements of a given set is found to be necessary. Hence, we introduce the following as an axiom of the Theory of Sets.

The Axiom of Sum-Set. *For every set s the set of the elements and only the elements of all the elements of s exists.*

Formally,

$$(\forall s)(\exists t)(\forall x)((x \in t) \leftrightarrow (\exists z)((z \in s) \wedge (x \in z)))$$

The set of all the elements of all the elements of a set s is called the *sum-set* of s, or the *union* of the elements of s. Its uniqueness follows from (5). Moreover, the sum-set of s is usually denoted by:

$$\cup s$$

Thus, according to notation (23), we have:

(31) $$\cup s = \{x \mid (\exists z)((z \in s) \wedge (x \in z))\}$$

For instance, if

$$a = \{m,n\}, \qquad b = \{p,q,r\}, \qquad c = \{e,d\}$$

then

$$\cup\{a,b,c\} = \{m,n,p,q,r,e,d\}$$

Clearly, for every set s, it is the case that

$$s = \{z \mid z \in s\}$$

Hence, in view of (31), we have:

$$\cup s = \cup\{z \mid z \in s\}$$

Motivated by the above, we introduce the notation

$$\bigcup_{z \in s} z$$

to represent $\cup s$. Clearly,

(32)
$$\cup s = \bigcup_{z \in s} z = \bigcup_{x \in s} x = \bigcup_{y \in s} y$$

Theorem 10. *The sum-set of the empty set and the sum-set of the unit-set of a set s are equal respectively to the empty set and to s;* i.e.,

$$\cup \varnothing = \varnothing \qquad \text{and} \qquad \cup \{s\} = s$$

PROOF. Assume the contrary, i.e.,

$$\cup \varnothing = \{a, \ldots\} \neq \varnothing$$

Then $\varnothing$ must have at least one element whose element is a, contradicting the fact that $\varnothing$ has no elements. Thus, $\cup \varnothing = \varnothing$.

To prove that $\cup \{s\} = s$, let us observe that for this case, (31) reduces to:

$$\cup \{s\} = \{x \mid x \in s\} = s$$

Thus, the theorem is proved.

Let us note that in general $\cup s \neq s$. For example,

$$\cup \{\varnothing, \{\varnothing\}\} = \{\varnothing\} \neq \{\varnothing, \{\varnothing\}\}$$

However, as an exception, $\cup \varnothing = \varnothing$.

Also, in view of Theorem 10 and notation (32),

(33)
$$\bigcup_{x \in \varnothing} x = \bigcup_{x \in \{\varnothing\}} x = \varnothing$$

Theorem 11. *For every set s the set t of the unit-sets of all the elements of s exists and the sum-set of t is equal to s.*

PROOF. The application of the axiom of Replacement to the set s with the the binary predicate

$$y = \{x\}$$

functional in x, yields the desired set t. Hence, t exists. To prove that

$$s = \cup t$$

let us observe that if $x \in s$, then by hypothesis $\{x\} \in t$, and consequently x is an element of an element of t, and therefore $x \in \cup t$. On the other hand, if $x \in \cup t$, this means that x is an element of an element of t. However, by hypothesis, every element of t is a set containing one and only one element of s. Therefore, $x \in s$. Thus, Theorem 11 is proved.

According to Theorem 11, we have, for instance:

$$\{a,b,c\} = \cup \{\{a\}, \{b\}, \{c\}\}$$

Let us also note that Theorem 11 can be equivalently stated as: *every set is the sum-set of the set of all its one-element subsets.*

Next, we prove:

(34) $$\cup(\cup\{a, b, c, \ldots\}) = \cup\{\cup a, \cup b, \cup c, \ldots\}$$

To prove (34) we shall show that if x is an element of the left side of (34), then it is an element of the right side of (34) and vice versa. Now, if

$$x \in \cup(\cup\{a, b, c, \ldots\})$$

then x is an element of an element of $\cup\{a, b, c, \ldots\}$. But an element of $\cup\{a, b, c, \ldots\}$ is an element of a, or b, or c, ... Consequently, $x \in \cup a$, or $x \in \cup b$, or $x \in \cup c$, ... But this means precisely that $x \in \cup\{\cup a, \cup b, \cup c, \ldots\}$. The converse is established by reversing the steps in the above proof.

In view of notation (32), we may rewrite (34), as:

(35) $$\bigcup_{\substack{x \in \cup t \\ t \in \{a,b,c,\ldots\}}} x \quad = \quad \bigcup_{h \in \{\cup a, \cup b, \cup c, \ldots\}} h$$

Now, let us assume that the two sets a and b exist in the Theory of Sets. By Corollary 2, the set $\{a,b\}$ also exists; in view of the axiom of Sum-Set, the set

$$\cup\{a,b\}$$

exists; and, accordingly, in view of (31) we have:

$$\cup\{a,b\} = \{x \mid (x \in a) \vee (x \in b)\}$$

Thus, corresponding to every two sets u and v, the set t whose elements are the elements and only the elements of u or v exists. This set t is called the *union* of u and v and is denoted by $u \cup v$. Hence,

(36) $$u \cup v = \cup\{u,v\} = \{x \mid (x \in u) \vee (x \in v)\}$$

For example, if $a = \{m,n\}$ and $b = \{p,q,r\}$, then

$$a \cup b = \{m,n\} \cup \{p,q,r\} = \{m,n,p,q,r\}$$

Similarly,

$$\{\varnothing, \{\varnothing\}\} \cup \{\{\varnothing\}\} = \{\varnothing, \{\varnothing\}\}$$

Each of the symbols $\cup$ and $\cup$ appearing in, say, $\cup s$ and $u \cup v$ respectively, is called a *union operator*. In the first case, $\cup$ operates on the elements of s by uniting the elements of the elements of s into the set $\cup s$. In the second case, $\cup$ operates on u and v by uniting their elements into the set $u \cup v$.

As is easily seen from (36), the union operator $\cup$ in the Theory of Sets is the counterpart of the logical operator $\vee$. As such, $\cup$ is an associative, commutative and idempotent operator; i.e., for every x, y and z,

(37) $(x \cup y) \cup z = x \cup (y \cup z)$ (associativity of $\cup$)

(38) $x \cup y = y \cup x$ (commutativity of $\cup$)

(39) $x \cup x = x$ (idempotence of $\cup$)

Moreover,

(40) $$x \cup \varnothing = x$$

The proof of (37) follows immediately from (36) and the associativity of ∨. However, to indicate the connection between (37) and (34), we shall prove (37) as follows:

$$(x \cup y) \cup z = \cup\{x,y\} \cup (\cup\{z\}) = \cup\{\cup\{x,y\},\cup\{z\}\}$$

Hence, by (34),

$$(x \cup y) \cup z = \cup(\cup\{\{x,y\},\{z\}\}) = \cup\{x,y,z\}$$

On the other hand,

$$x \cup (y \cup z) = x \cup(\cup\{y,z\}) = \cup\{\cup\{x\}, \cup\{y,z\}\}$$

Hence, by (34),

$$x \cup (y \cup z) = \cup(\cup\{\{x\}, \{y,z\}\}) = \cup\{x,y,z\}$$

Therefore, indeed,

$$(x \cup y) \cup z = x \cup (y \cup z)$$

In view of the above, (34) is called the *generalized associative law of* ∨. In view of the associativity of ∨, if the sets $a_1, a_2, \ldots, a_n$ exist, then

$$a_1 \cup a_2 \cup \cdots \cup a_n$$

is a well defined set which, in view of the axiom of Sum-Set, exists. Clearly,

$$a_1 \cup a_2 \cup \cdots \cup a_n = \cup\{a_1, a_2, \ldots, a_n\}$$

To prove (38), all we have to do is observe that in view of (36) we have:

$$x \cup y = \cup\{x,y\} = \cup\{y,x\} = y \cup x$$

The proofs of (39) and (40) run as follows:

$$x \cup x = \cup\{x,x\} = \cup\{x\} = x$$
$$x \cup \varnothing = \cup\{x,\varnothing\} = \cup\{x\} = x$$

In view of the associativity and commutativity of ∨, we have:

$$a_1 \cup a_2 \cup a_3 = a_2 \cup a_1 \cup a_3 = a_3 \cup a_2 \cup a_1 = \cup\{a_1,a_2,a_3\}$$

It is worth observing that by means of the axioms introduced so far, we still cannot assert the existence of a set whose elements are the elements and only the elements of an unlimited number of sets $a_1, a_2, a_3, \ldots$. In other words, the axioms introduced so far do not justify an expression such as:

(41) $$a_1 \cup a_2 \cup a_3 \cup \cdots$$

However, if there exists a set b, such that

$$b = \{a_1, a_2, a_3, \ldots\}$$

then we may agree to let (41) stand for $\cup b$, i.e.,

$$\cup\{a_1, a_2, a_3, \ldots\} = a_1 \cup a_2 \cup a_3 \cup \cdots$$

For visual purposes, it is customary to represent (whenever possible) each

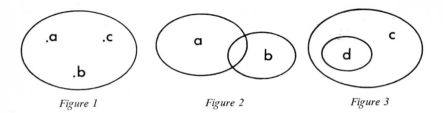

Figure 1   Figure 2   Figure 3

element of a set by a point on the sheet of paper. Thus, the elements of a set, say, $\{a,b,c\}$, with three distinct elements a, b and c, are represented in Figure 1 by the points a, b and c, and the entire set $\{a,b,c\}$ is represented as a contour encircling the three points a, b and c. When a set is represented only by a contour, it is understood that every point of the portion of the paper on the contour or inside it represents an element of the set under consideration.

Thus, in Figure 2 the sets a and b are represented respectively by the ovals a and b. Similarly, in Figure 3 the sets c and d are represented by the ovals c and d.

Let us mention that this graphical representation of sets is merely to help visualize intuitively various operations on sets and relations between sets; it is not theoretically rigorous.

In Figure 2 the union $a \cup b$ is represented by the portion of the plane covered by the oval a or the oval b. Also, as Figure 2 shows, neither of the sets a and b is a subset of the other. However, as Figure 3 shows, d is a proper subset of c. Also, from Figure 3, we see that $d \cup c = c$, which is an intuitive verification of the following true statement in the Theory of Sets:

(42) $(x \subset y) \leftrightarrow (x \cup y = y)$ for every x and y

Graphically, the empty set is the portion of the paper occupied by no points. Thus, we see that (40) is also easily verified by means of the graphical representation.

Likewise, (37), (38) and (39) can be easily verified when sets are represented graphically.

EXERCISES

1. Derive (39), (40) and (42) formally.

2. Prove that $x \subset \cup\{x, y, z, \ldots\}$.

3. Prove that if $x \subset y$, then $\cup x \subset \cup y$.

4. Prove that every set having at least two elements is equal to the sum-set of all its two-element subsets.

5. Prove that $x = \cup \mathscr{P}(x)$, for every x.

6. Prove that the sum-set of an ordered pair of two sets is equal to the unordered pair of these two sets.

7. Prove that if $\cup\{x,y\} = y$ and $\cup\{z,y\} = y$ then

$$\cup\{\cup\{x,z\},y\} = y$$

8. Prove that if $\cup\{x,y\} = y$ and $\cup\{u,v\} = v$, then

$$\cup\{\cup\{x,u\}, \cup\{y,v\}\} = \cup\{y,v\}$$

9. Prove that for every x, y and z,

$$\cup(x \cup y \cup z) = (\cup x) \cup (\cup y) \cup (\cup z)$$

10. Prove that for every x and y,

$$\mathscr{P}(x) \cup \mathscr{P}(y) \subset \mathscr{P}(x \cup y)$$

11. Prove that for every y and z,

$$(\forall x)((x \in y) \to (x \subset z)) \to (\cup y \subset z),$$
$$\cup(\cup(y,z)) = y \cup z$$

7. INTERSECTION OF SETS

Let us assume that in the Theory of Sets (in which the axioms of Extensionality, Replacement, Power-Set and Sum-Set have been introduced so far) there exists a set b such that

$$b = \{a_1,a_2,a_3\}$$

with

$$a_1 = \{m,n,p\}, \qquad a_2 = \{m,n,q\}, \qquad a_3 = \{m,n,p,q\}$$

where m, n, p and q are distinct sets. Then by virtue of our axioms, the set

$$\cup b = \{m,n,p,q\}$$

exists. Consequently, in view of the theorem of Separation, the set

$$\{m,n\} = \{x \mid (x \in \cup b) \wedge (x \in a_1) \wedge (x \in a_2) \wedge (x \in a_3)\}$$

also exists. Let us observe that $\{m,n\}$ is the set of all the common elements of all the elements of b. It is customary to call $\{m,n\}$ the *intersection-set* or the *meet-set* of the set b and to denote it by $\cap b$. Thus,

$$\cap b = \cap\{a_1,a_2,a_3\} = \{m,n\}$$

The existence of the *intersection-set* t of any set s is also a consequence of our axioms. According to our axioms, we have:

$$(\forall s)(\exists t)(\forall x)((x \in t) \leftrightarrow ((x \in \cup s) \wedge (\forall z)((z \in s) \to (x \in z))))$$

Motivated by the above, we introduce:

Definition 5. *For every set s, the subset of $\cup s$ consisting of all the common elements of all the elements of s is called the intersection-set of s and is denoted by:*

$$\cap s$$

Thus, in view of notation (23), we have:

(43) $\cap s = \{x \mid (x \in \cup s) \wedge (\forall z)((z \in s) \rightarrow (x \in z))\}$

Accordingly, if

$$c = \{a,b\}, \qquad a = \{m,n\}, \qquad b = \{e,m\}$$

where m, n and e are distinct sets, then

$$\cap c = \cap\{a,b\} = \{m\}$$

since m is the only common element of the sets a and b.

Again, if

$$h = \{c,d\}, \qquad c = \{p,q\}, \qquad d = \{e,h\}$$

where p, q, c and h are distinct sets, then

$$\cap h = \cap\{c,d\} = \varnothing$$

since the sets c and d have no common elements.

Since for every set s,

$$s = \{z \mid z \in s\}$$

we have, in view of (43),

$$\cap s = \cap\{z \mid z \in s\}$$

Motivated by the above, we introduce the notation:

$$\underset{z \in s}{\cap} z \; = \cap s$$

to represent $\cap s$. Clearly,

(44) $\cap s = \underset{z \in s}{\cap} z = \underset{x \in s}{\cap} x = \underset{y \in s}{\cap} y$

Comparing (31) with (43), we see at once that

(45) $\cap s \subset \cup s \qquad$ for every s

Theorem 12. *The intersection-set of the empty set and the intersection-set of the unit-set of a set s are equal respectively to the empty set and to s, i.e.,*

$$\cap \varnothing = \varnothing \qquad and \qquad \cap\{s\} = s$$

PROOF.   By (45), we have $\cap \varnothing \subset \cup \varnothing$ and since by Theorem 10, $\cup \varnothing = \varnothing$, we see that $\cap \varnothing \subset \varnothing$. Consequently, $\cap \varnothing = \varnothing$, as desired. On the other hand, in view of (31), we have:

$$\cap\{s\} = \{x \mid x \in s\} = s$$

Thus, the theorem is proved.

Let us observe that in general $\cap s \neq s$. For example,

$$\cap\{\varnothing,\{\varnothing\}\} = \varnothing \neq \{\varnothing,\{\varnothing\}\}$$

However, as an exception, $\cap \varnothing = \varnothing$.

In view of Theorem 12 and notation (44), we have:

(46) $\underset{x \in \varnothing}{\cap} x = \underset{x \in \{\varnothing\}}{\cap} x = \varnothing$

Now, let us assume that the sets u and v exist in the Theory of Sets. Then, as explained above, the set

$$\cap\{a,b\} = \{x \mid (x \in a) \wedge (x \in b)\}$$

exists. Thus, for every two sets u and v, the set t whose elements are the common elements and only the common elements of u and v exists. This set t is called the *intersection* of u and v and is denoted by $u \cap v$. Hence,

(47) $$u \cap v = \cap\{u,v\} = \{x \mid (x \in u) \wedge (x \in v)\}$$

For example, if $a = \{m,n\}$ and $b = \{m,q\}$, where m, n and q are distinct sets, then

$$a \cap b = \{m,n\} \cap \{m,q\} = \{m\}$$

Each of the symbols $\cap$ and $\cap$, appearing in, say, $\cap s$ and $u \cap v$ respectively, is called an *intersection operator*. In the first case, $\cap$ operates on the elements of s producing the set $\cap s$ of the common elements of the elements of the elements of s. In the second case, $\cap$ operates on u and v producing the set $u \cap v$ of the common elements of u and v.

As suggested by (47), the intersection operator $\cap$ in the Theory of Sets is the counterpart of the logical operator $\wedge$. As such, $\cap$ is an associative, commutative and idempotent operator; that is, for every x, y and z,

(48) $$(x \cap y) \cap z = x \cap (y \cap z) \qquad \text{(associativity of } \cap\text{)}$$

(49) $$x \cap y = y \cap x \qquad \text{(commutativity of } \cap\text{)}$$

(50) $$x \cap x = x \qquad \text{(idempotence of } \cap\text{)}$$

Moreover,

(51) $$x \cap \varnothing = \varnothing$$

The proofs of the above equalities follow immediately from (47) and are left to the reader.

In view of the associativity of $\cap$, if the sets $a_1, a_2, \ldots, a_n$ exist, then

$$a_1 \cap a_2 \cap \cdots \cap a_n$$

is a well defined set which, in view of our axioms, exists. Clearly,

$$a_1 \cap a_2 \cap \cdots \cap a_n = \cap\{a_1, a_2, \ldots, a_n\}$$

From the associativity and commutativity of $\cap$, we have:

$$a_1 \cap a_2 \cap a_3 = a_2 \cap a_1 \cap a_3 = a_3 \cap a_2 \cap a_1 = \cap\{a_1,a_2,a_3\}$$

Here also the generalized associativity law for $\cap$ holds, i.e.,

seems strange

$$\cap(\cup\{a, b, c, \ldots\}) = \cap\{\cap a, \cap b, \cap c, \ldots\}$$

provided $\varnothing \notin \{a, b, c, \ldots\}$. In view of notation (44), the above equality can be written as:

(52) $$\bigcap_{\substack{x \in \cup t \\ t \in \{a,b,c,\ldots\}}} x = \bigcap_{h \in \{\cap a, \cap b, \cap c,\ldots\}} h \qquad \text{with} \quad \varnothing \notin \{a, b, c, \ldots\}$$

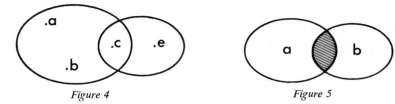

Figure 4   Figure 5

Graphically, the fact that

$$\{a,b,c\} \cap \{c,e\} = \{c\}$$

where a, b, c and e are distinct sets, is represented as in Figure 4.

Also, in Figure 5 and Figure 6 the shaded areas represent respectively $a \cap b$ and $d \cap c$. From Figure 6, we see that $d \cap c = d$, which is an intuitive verification of the following true statement in the Theory of Sets:

(53) $(x \subset y) \leftrightarrow (x \cap y = x)$ for every x and y

It is worth observing that with only the axioms introduced so far, we still cannot assert the existence of a set whose elements are the common elements

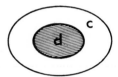

Figure 6

and only the common elements of an unlimited number of sets $a_1, a_2, a_3, \ldots$. In other words, the axioms introduced so far do not justify an expression such as:

(54) $a_1 \cap a_2 \cap a_3 \cap \cdots$

However, if there exists a set b such that

$$b = \{a_1, a_2, a_3, \ldots\}$$

then we may agree to let (54) stand for $\cap b$, i.e.,

$$\cap\{a_1, a_2, a_3, \ldots\} = a_1 \cap a_2 \cap a_3 \cap \cdots$$

EXERCISES

1. Prove (52) and (53) formally.

2. Prove that for every x and y, $(x \cap y) \subset x$, and, in general,

$$x \supset \cap\{x, y, z, \ldots\}$$

3. Prove that $(\varnothing \in x) \to (\cap x = \varnothing)$, for every x.

4. Prove that for every x and y,

$$\cap(\cap(x,y)) = x$$
$$(x \subset (x \cup y)) \to ((x \cap y) \subset x), \qquad \cap x \supset \cap(x \cup y)$$

5. Prove that for every x, y and z,

$$\cap(x \cup y \cup z) = (\cap x) \cap (\cap y) \cap (\cap z), \quad \text{with} \quad \varnothing \notin \{\cap x, \cap y, \cap z\}$$
$$\cap(x,y) = \{x\}$$
$$\mathscr{P}(x) \cap \mathscr{P}(y) = \mathscr{P}(x \cap y)$$
$$(x \in y) \to (\cap y \subset x)$$
$$((x \in y) \wedge (x \subset z)) \to (\cap y \subset z)$$

6. Prove that for every x and y,

$$\cup(\cap(x,y)) = x \qquad \text{and} \qquad \cap(\cup(x,y)) = x \cap y$$

8. THE AXIOM OF INFINITY. THE NATURAL NUMBERS

The axioms of Extensionality, Replacement, Power-Set and Sum-Set do not guarantee the existence of a set with an unlimited number of elements. This must not be confused with the fact that the same axioms secure the existence of an unlimited number of distinct sets, since it may still be the case that each set has only a limited number of elements. For example, as a consequence of our axioms, in the Theory of Sets the following unlimited number of distinct sets exist:

$$\varnothing, \quad \{\varnothing\}, \quad \{\{\varnothing\}\}, \quad \{\{\{\varnothing\}\}\}, \quad \{\{\{\{\varnothing\}\}\}\}, \ldots$$

However, each of them, except $\varnothing$, has precisely one element.

Similarly, as a consequence of our axioms, the following unlimited number of distinct sets exist:

(55)
$$\varnothing, \quad \{\varnothing\}, \quad \{\varnothing, \{\varnothing\}\}, \quad \{\varnothing, \{\varnothing\}, \{\varnothing, \{\varnothing\}\}\},$$
$$\{\varnothing, \{\varnothing\}, \{\varnothing, \{\varnothing\}\}, \{\varnothing, \{\varnothing\}, \{\varnothing, \{\varnothing\}\}\}\}, \ldots$$

They have respectively 0, 1, 2, 3, 4, ... distinct elements. Thus, again each set listed in (55) contains a limited number of elements.

We observe that every set given in (55) has the following property: if x is an element of the set, then with one exception $x \cup \{x\}$ is also an element of that set. Thus, we see that in

(56)
$$\{\varnothing, \{\varnothing\}, \{\varnothing, \{\varnothing\}\}\}$$

except for $x = \{\varnothing, \{\varnothing\}\}$, if x is an element of the set given by (56), then so is $x \cup \{x\}$.

For a satisfactory development of the Theory of Sets, the existence of a set having an unlimited number of elements is found to be necessary. Thus, motivated by our above-mentioned observation, we introduce the following as an axiom of the Theory of Sets.

The Axiom of Infinity.   *There exists a set W such that:*

(57) $\varnothing \in W$

and

(58)   *If* $x \in W$,   *then* $(x \cup \{x\}) \in W$

Formally,

$$(\exists W)((\varnothing \in W) \wedge (\forall x)((x \in W) \to ((x \cup \{x\}) \in W)))$$

Clearly, some of the elements of W are the following:

$$\varnothing$$
$$\varnothing \cup \{\varnothing\} = \{\varnothing\}$$
$$\{\varnothing\} \cup \{\{\varnothing\}\} = \{\varnothing,\{\varnothing\}\}$$
$$\{\varnothing,\{\varnothing\}\} \cup \{\{\varnothing,\{\varnothing\}\}\} = \{\varnothing,\{\varnothing\},\{\varnothing,\{\varnothing\}\}\}$$

Besides elements obtained in this manner from $\varnothing$, the set W may also contain another set, say, q, and hence also the set $\{q,\{q\}\}$, and so forth, as its elements.

Let us observe that in view of conditions (57) and (58), W has an unlimited number of elements, in the sense that one cannot finish counting the elements of W. This is why the axiom asserting the existence of W is called the axiom of Infinity.

We prove below that there exists a unique set ω satisfying conditions (57) and (58) and which is the *minimal* set satisfying these conditions. That is to say, if V is any set satisfying conditions (57) and (58), then

(59) $\omega \subset V$

For a set x, let us call $x \cup \{x\}$ *the immediate successor of* x and let us denote it by x^+.

Thus,

$$x^+ = x \cup \{x\} \text{ is } \textit{the immediate successor} \text{ of } x.$$

Now, we prove the following:

Theorem 13.   *There exists a unique set ω such that*

(60) $\varnothing \in \omega$

and

(61)   *If x is an element of ω, so is its immediate successor x^+*

(i.e., $x \cup \{x\}$).

Moreover, ω is a subset of any other set satisfying conditions (60) *and* (61).

PROOF.   Let W be a set which satisfies conditions (60) and (61) and which, by virtue of the axiom of Infinity, exists. Hence, W is a set such that $\varnothing \in W$, and whenever x belongs to W so does the immediate successor x^+. Consider the power-set $\mathscr{P}(W)$, and let H be the set of all those subsets h of W each satisfying conditions (60) and (61). In other words, every element h of H is a set such that $\varnothing \in h$, and if $x \in h$ then $x^+ \in h$. Obviously, H is a subset of $\mathscr{P}(W)$ which exists by virtue of the theorem of Separation. Now, consider

$$\omega = \cap H = \bigcap_{h \in H} h$$

which exists by virtue of (43).

We now show that ω satisfies conditions (60) and (61). Since $\varnothing \in h$ for every $h \in H$, we see that $\varnothing \in \bigcap_{h \in H} h$. So indeed $\varnothing \in \omega$. Hence, ω satisfies condition (60). Furthermore, assume $x \in \omega$, i.e., $x \in h$ for every $h \in H$. Since each h satisfies condition (61) and since we assumed that $x \in h$ for every $h \in H$, we see that $x \cup \{x\} = x^+$ also belongs to every h. Consequently, x^+ belongs to their intersection $\bigcap_{h \in H} h = \omega$. Thus, $x^+ \in \omega$, and ω satisfies condition (61).

To prove the minimality of ω, i.e., to establish (59), let us observe that if V is any set satisfying conditions (60) and (61), then by a proof analogous to the one above we can easily show that

$$\omega \cap V$$

is also a set satisfying conditions (60) and (61).

However,

$$\omega \cap V \subset \omega \subset W$$

and thus, $\omega \cap V$ is one of the h's described above. Therefore,

$$\omega \subset \omega \cap V$$

which implies that

$$\omega \subset V$$

as desired.

To prove the uniqueness of ω, let v be another set having the properties of ω. Applying (59) to ω and v, we obtain respectively,

$$\omega \subset v \qquad \text{and} \qquad v \subset \omega$$

Consequently, $\omega = v$ and thus ω is unique.

Obviously, $\varnothing$, $\{\varnothing, \{\varnothing\}\}$, $\{\varnothing, \{\varnothing\}, \{\varnothing, \{\varnothing\}\}\}$, and so forth, are some of the elements of ω.

The set ω, which exists by virtue of Theorem 13, is called the *set of all natural numbers*, in the sense that the familiar number 0 (zero) is defined as the null set $\varnothing$, the familiar number 1 (one) as the set $\{\varnothing\}$, the number 2 (two) as the set $\{\varnothing, \{\varnothing\}\}$, and so on. (As we shall see later, ω is also the set of all *finite ordinal numbers* and also the set of all *finite cardinal numbers*.) Thus, we introduce:

Definition 6.   *An element of the set ω is called a natural number.*

Accordingly, we introduce the following familiar notation for the elements of ω:

(62)

$$0 = \varnothing$$
$$1 = \{\varnothing\} = \{0\}$$
$$2 = \{\varnothing,\{\varnothing\}\} = 1 \cup \{1\} = \{0,1\}$$
$$3 = \{\varnothing,\{\varnothing\},\{\varnothing,\{\varnothing\}\}\} = 2 \cup \{2\} = \{0,1,2\}\}$$
$$4 = 3 \cup \{3\} = \{0,1,2,3\}$$
$$5 = 4 \cup \{4\} = \{0,1,2,3,4\}$$
$$6 = 5 \cup \{5\} = \{0,1,2,3,4,5\}$$
$$\cdot \ \cdot \ \cdot$$

What is worth noting in (62) is that every *natural number is a set*. This emphasizes the fact that such a fundamental mathematical notion as that of a natural number can be introduced most conveniently as a set, thereby eliminating the necessity of introducing new undefined individual constants for the purpose of introducing natural numbers.

In terms of *immediate successors* (62) can be written as:

$$1 = 0^+ \qquad (1 \text{ is the immediate successor of } 0)$$
$$2 = 1^+ \qquad (2 \text{ is the immediate successor of } 1)$$
$$3 = 2^+ \qquad (3 \text{ is the immediate successor of } 2)$$
$$\cdot \cdot \cdot \qquad\qquad\qquad \cdot \cdot \cdot$$

The set ω of all natural numbers, which in view of Theorem 13 exists, is a set with an unlimited number of elements in the sense that one cannot finish counting its elements. By means of the axioms of Replacement, Power-Set and Infinity, we may infer the existence of more and more extensive sets.

For instance, from the set ω, in view of the axioms of Power-Set and Replacement, we derive the existence of the set

$$A = \{\omega, \mathscr{P}(\omega), \mathscr{P}(\mathscr{P}(\omega)), \ldots\}$$

from which, by the axiom of Sum-Set, we infer the existence of the set $\cup A$, a rather extensive set.

Now, assume that in the Theory of Sets the unlimited number of sets $a_1, a_2, a_3, \ldots$ exist. Then, in view of the axiom of Replacement, as given by (21), with

$$s = \omega \qquad \text{and} \qquad F(x,y) \equiv (y = x_y)$$

we infer the existence of the set

(63) $$\{a_1, a_2, a_3, \ldots\}$$

from which, by the axiom of Sum-Set, we infer the existence of the set

(64) $$\cup\{a_1, a_2, a_3, \ldots\}$$

Also, in view of the theorem of Separation, from (64) we infer the existence of the set

(65) $\cap \{a_1, a_2, a_3, \ldots\}$

Thus, we see that after the introduction of the axiom of Infinity, the questions raised in connection with (41) and (54) can be answered in the affirmative. Accordingly (by virtue of the axioms introduced so far), if an unlimited number of sets $a_1, a_2, a_3, \ldots$ exist in the Theory of Sets, then the sets given by (63), (64) and (65) also exist.

An immediate corollary of Theorem 13, is:

Corollary 3. *If a subset N of ω is such that $\varnothing \in N$ and $x^+ \in N$ whenever $x \in N$, then $N = \omega$.*

PROOF. Since N satisfies conditions (60) and (61) of Theorem 13, we see that $\omega \subset N$. On the other hand, by the hypothesis of the corollary, $N \subset \omega$. Therefore, $N = \omega$, as desired.

Corollary 3, whose proof is given above, is also known as the principle of Finite (or Mathematical) Induction. Thus, it is a theorem of our Theory of Sets. We restate it as:

beautiful

The Theorem of Finite Induction. *If a set N of natural numbers is such that $0 \in N$ and $n^+ \in N$ whenever $n \in N$, then N is equal to the set of all natural numbers, i.e., $N = \omega$.*

The theorem of Finite (or Mathematical) Induction is the main tool in proving properties of the natural numbers. For instance, if we are to prove that every natural number n (i.e., every element of the set ω) satisfies a predicate $P(x)$ (i.e., has the property P), then the course to follow is first to consider the set N of all those natural numbers that satisfy $P(x)$ and then to prove $\omega = N$. The latter can be established if we prove that 0 satisfies $P(x)$ and that whenever an arbitrary natural number n satisfies $P(x)$ so does its immediate successor n^+, where $n^+ = n \cup \{n\}$. Clearly, this means that $0 \in N$ and if $n \in N$ then $n^+ \in N$. Hence, by the theorem of Finite Induction, we conclude that $\omega = N$, implying the fact that every natural number satisfies $P(x)$, or has the property P.

Next, let us investigate some properties of the natural numbers (i.e., the elements of ω). Let us recall that *every natural number is a set*, and thus we can speak about the elements and the subsets of a natural number.

For example, in view of (62) we have:

$$2 = \{0,1\} \quad \text{and} \quad 3 = \{0,1,2\}$$

Clearly, $2 \in 3$ and since $\{0,1\} \subset \{0,1,2\}$, we see that $2 \subset 3$. Thus, the element 2 of 3 is also a subset of 3.

Motivated by the above, we prove:

Theorem 14. *Every element of a natural number is also a subset of that natural number.*

PROOF. Let N be the set of all those natural numbers each of which has the property stated in Theorem 14. This means that if $n \in \omega$ is such that

(66) $$(\forall x)(x \in n \to x \subset n)$$

then $n \in N$.

Clearly, $0 \in N$ because, since the hypothesis of (66) is false for $n = \varnothing$, the whole implication is true for $n = 0$.

Now, assume $n \in N$ and let us prove that $n \cup \{n\}$ is also an element of N. In other words, assuming (66) is true for n, we have to prove that

$$(\forall x)((x \in n \cup \{n\}) \to (x \subset n \cup \{n\}))$$

However, if $x \in (n \cup \{n\})$, then $x \in n$ or $x = n$. But if $x \in n$, then by (66) we have $x \subset n$ and obviously $x \subset n \cup \{n\}$. On the other hand, if $x = n$, then again $x \subset n \cup \{n\}$. Therefore, $n \cup \{n\}$ indeed satisfies (66). Consequently, the above-mentioned set N is such that $0 \in N$ and whenever $n \in N$, so is $n \cup \{n\}$. Thus, by the theorem of Finite Induction, $N = \omega$, and Theorem 14 is proved.

Corollary 4. *An element of an element of a natural number is an element of that natural number.*

PROOF. Let n be a natural number and let $x \in n$. By Theorem 14, $x \subset n$. Hence, if $y \in x$, then necessarily $y \in n$.

Theorem 15. *Every element of a natural number is also a natural number.*

PROOF. Let N be the set of all those natural numbers each of which has the property stated in Theorem 15. This means that if $n \in \omega$ is such that

(67) $$(\forall x)(x \in n \to x \in \omega)$$

then $n \in N$.

Clearly, $0 \in N$ because, since the hypothesis of (67) is false for $n = \varnothing$, the whole implication is true for $n = 0$.

Now, assume $n \in N$ and let us prove that $n \cup \{n\}$ is also an element of N. In other words, assuming (67) is true for n, we have to prove that

$$(\forall x)((x \in n \cup \{n\}) \to (x \in \omega))$$

However, if $x \in n \cup \{n\}$, then $x \in n$ or $x = n$. But if $x \in n$, then by (67) we have $x \in \omega$. On the other hand, if $x = n$, then since n is a natural number, again $x \in \omega$. Consequently, the above-mentioned set N is such that $0 \in N$ and whenever $n \in N$ so is $n \cup \{n\}$. Thus, by the theorem of Finite Induction, $N = \omega$ and Theorem 15 is proved.

Theorem 16. *No natural number is an element of itself.*

PROOF. Clearly, 0 is not an element of itself. Now, assume $n \notin n$ and let us prove that $(n \cup \{n\}) \notin (n \cup \{n\})$. If we suppose on the contrary that $(n \cup \{n\}) \in (n \cup \{n\})$, then $(n \cup \{n\}) \in n$ or $(n \cup \{n\}) \in \{n\}$. But in view of Theorem 14, $(n \cup \{n\}) \in n$ implies $n \cup \{n\} \subset n$, which in turn implies that

return to assumed condition of n

$n \in n$, contrary to the assumption that $n \notin n$. On the other hand, $(n \cup \{n\}) \in \{n\}$ implies $n \cup \{n\} = n$, which in turn implies again that $n \in n$, contrary to the assumption that $n \notin n$. Thus, our supposition is false and $n \notin n$ indeed implies $(n \cup \{n\}) \notin (n \cup \{n\})$. Hence, in view of the theorem of Finite Induction, Theorem 16 is proved.

Theorem 17.   *No natural number is a subset of any of its elements.*

PROOF.   Assume on the contrary that there exists a natural number n such that $x \in n$ and $n \subset x$. By Theorem 14, $x \in n$ implies $x \subset n$, and since $n \subset x$, we have $x = n$. However, since $x \in n$, the latter implies that $n \in n$, which contradicts Theorem 16. Hence, our assumption is false and the theorem is proved.

Theorem 18.   *If the immediate successors of two natural numbers are equal, then the two natural numbers are equal,* i.e.,

$$(n^+ = m^+) \to (n = m), \quad \text{for every two elements } n \text{ and } m \text{ of } \omega$$

PROOF.   Assume on the contrary that there exist two natural numbers n and m such that:

$$n \cup \{n\} = m \cup \{m\} \quad \text{and} \quad n \neq m$$

Now, since n is an element of the left side of the above equality, we must have:

$$n \in m \quad \text{or} \quad n = m$$

Similarly,

$$m \in n \quad \text{or} \quad m = n$$

However, $n \neq m$. Hence, $n \in m$ and $m \in n$. But this, in view of Theorem 14, implies

$$n \subset m \quad \text{and} \quad m \subset n$$

which contradicts $n \neq m$. Thus, our assumption is false and the theorem is proved.

Let us observe that the immediate successor of any natural number is different from 0 (i.e., from $\varnothing$). The reason for this is the fact that the immediate successor of a natural number contains that natural number as its element. Hence, no immediate successor of a natural number can be equal to the empty set, and thus,

$$n^+ \neq 0, \quad \text{for every element } n \text{ of } \omega$$

The natural number 0 (i.e., the empty set $\varnothing$) is called the *zero natural number* and every other natural number is called a *nonzero* natural number.

Let us call a natural number m an *immediate predecessor* of a natural number n, if

$$m^+ = m \cup \{m\} = n$$

Corollary 5.   *Every nonzero natural number has a unique immediate predecessor and 0 has no immediate predecessor.*

PROOF. As mentioned in the above, $n^+ \neq 0$, for every element n of ω. Hence, 0 has no immediate predecessor. To complete the proof of the corollary, in view of Theorem 18 it is enough to show that every nonzero natural number has an immediate predecessor. Let M be the set of all natural numbers each of which has an immediate predecessor and let $N = M \cup \{0\}$. Now, let $n \neq 0$ be an element of N. Then there exists a natural number m such that $m^+ = n$. But then $(m^+)^+ = n^+$, which implies that n^+ has an immediate predecessor m^+. Thus, $N \subset \omega$ is such that $0 \in N$ and whenever $n \in N$ so is n^+. Consequently, by the theorem of Finite Induction $N = \omega$, from which the proof of the corollary follows.

The unique immediate predecessor of a nonzero natural number n is denoted by n^- and is called *the immediate predecessor* of n. Clearly,

$$(n^-)^+ = n, \qquad \text{for every nonzero natural number } n$$

Thus, for every two nonzero natural numbers m and n, we have:

$$n^- = m^- \leftrightarrow n = m \leftrightarrow n^+ = m^+$$

Now, let us list some of the important properties of the natural numbers (or the elements of the set ω).

(i) $\qquad\qquad\qquad\qquad\qquad 0 \in \omega$

(ii) $\qquad\qquad\qquad$ *If $n \in \omega$, then $n^+ \in \omega$*

(iii) $\qquad\qquad$ $n^+ \neq 0$, *for every element n of ω*

(iv) *If $n^+ = m^+$ then $n = m$, for every two elements n and m of ω*

(v) *If $N \subset \omega$ is such that $0 \in N$ and whenever n is an element of N so is n^+, then $N = \omega$.*

The above five statements can serve as axioms defining natural numbers, in the sense that if one defines the set ω subject to the above five conditions, then ω will possess all the properties of the set of all natural numbers.

In mathematics the above five statements are called the Peano Axioms. It is shown that the entire theory of the rational, real and complex number systems can be developed from these five axioms. It is worth mentioning here that since the above-mentioned five statements are derivable in the Theory of Sets, the Theory of Sets furnishes adequate machinery for the development of one of the most basic disciplines in all of mathematics.

Let us proceed by proving additional theorems concerning natural numbers.

Lemma 2. *For any natural number n*

$$0 = n \qquad or \qquad 0 \in n$$

PROOF. Let $N(0)$ be the set of all those natural numbers satisfying the condition stated in the lemma. Clearly, $0 \in N(0)$ since $0 = 0$. Now, assume $n \in N(0)$, i.e., $n = 0$ or $0 \in n$. But then in either case $0 \in (n \cup \{n\})$. Hence, $0 \in N(0)$, and whenever $n \in N(0)$, we have $n^+ \in N(0)$. Consequently, $N(0) = \omega$ and Lemma 2 is proved.

Definition 7.   *If two natural numbers m and n are such that*

$$m = n \qquad or \qquad n \in m \qquad or \qquad m \in n$$

then m and n are said to be comparable.

In view of this definition, 0 is comparable to every natural number (Lemma 2).

Lemma 3.   *If a natural number n is comparable to every natural number, then so is its immediate successor n^+.*

PROOF.   To establish the lemma we shall prove that if n is comparable to every natural number, then the set $N(n^+)$ of all those natural numbers that are comparable to n^+ is ω.

First of all, by Lemma 2, we have $0 \in N(n^+)$.

Now, in addition to the hypothesis of Lemma 3, we shall show that if the natural number m is such that $m \in N(n^+)$, then $m^+ \in N(n^+)$. This means that if we assume:

(i) $m = n^+$, or (ii) $n^+ \in m$, or (iii) $m \in n^+$, then we have to prove that

(i′) $m^+ = n^+$, or (ii′) $n^+ \in m^+$, or (iii′) $m^+ \in n^+$.

However, if $m = n^+$, then since $m \in m^+$, we derive $n^+ \in m^+$. Hence, (i) implies (ii′).

Similarly, if $n^+ \in m$, then clearly $n^+ \in m^+$. Hence, (ii) implies (ii′).

Now, let $m \in n^+$, i.e., $m \in n \cup \{n\}$, which means $m = n$ or $m \in n$. If $m = n$, clearly, $m^+ = n^+$ and in this case (iii) implies (i′).

It remains to prove that $m \in n$ implies (i′) or (ii′) or (iii′).

Let us recall that in view of the hypothesis of Lemma 2, since n is comparable to every natural number,

$$n = m^+ \qquad or \qquad m^+ \in n \qquad or \qquad n \in m^+$$

Now, if $m \in n$, then $n \in m^+$ cannot be true, because $n \in m^+$ implies $n = m$ or $n \in m$, each of which is incompatible with $m \in n$. To see this, it is enough to observe that $n = m$ and $m \in n$ imply $n \in n$, which contradicts Theorem 16. Similarly, in view of Corollary 4, $n \in m$ and $m \in n$ imply $n \in n$, which again contradicts Theorem 16. Thus $m \in n$ implies $n = m^+$ or $m^+ \in n$, each of which implies $m^+ \in n^+$. Hence, $m \in n$ implies (iii′).

Consequently, (i) or (ii) or (iii) imply (i′) or (ii′) or (iii′), and in view of the fact that $0 \in N(n^+)$, we have $N(n^+) = \omega$.

In view of Lemmas 2 and 3, we see that the set N of all natural numbers, each comparable to every natural number, is equal to the set ω of all natural numbers. This is because by Lemma 2, $0 \in N$, and by Lemma 3 if $n \in N$, so is n^+, and therefore by the theorem of Finite Induction $N = \omega$.

In short, we have proved that if m and n are any two natural numbers, then

$$n = m \qquad or \qquad m \in n \qquad or \qquad n \in m$$

Now, it is easy to see that out of the above three cases, one and only one case can hold. Indeed, if $n = m$, then either of $m \in n$ or $n \in m$ would imply $n \in n$, which contradicts Theorem 16. Similarly, if $m \in n$, then in view of Corollary 4, $n \in m$ would imply $n \in n$, which again contradicts Theorem 16.

In view of the above considerations and Theorem 14, we have:

Theorem 19.   *If m and n are any two natural numbers, then one and only one of the three cases:*

$$n = m \qquad or \qquad m \in n \qquad or \qquad n \in m$$

must hold. Moreover, for every two natural numbers m and n,

$$m \subset n \qquad or \qquad n \subset m$$

Now, we shall prove:

Theorem 20.   *If S is a nonempty subset of a natural number n, then there exists a unique natural number m that is an element of S and such that m is an element of every element of S different from m.*

PROOF.   The uniqueness of m is established by observing that if m and m' are two distinct elements each satisfying the conclusion of the theorem, then on the one hand $m \in m'$, and on the other hand $m' \in m$, which, in view of Corollary 4, imply $m \in m$. However, this contradicts Theorem 16.

Next, let us prove that the set N of all those natural numbers n each of which satisfies the property stated in Theorem 20, is ω.

Clearly, $0 \in N$. Now, let us assume that $n \in N$, i.e., that n satisfies the property stated in Theorem 20, and let Q be a nonempty subset of $n^+ = n \cup \{n\}$. Clearly,

$$\text{(i)} \qquad Q \subset n \qquad or \qquad \text{(ii)} \qquad Q = S \cup \{n\}$$

where S is a nonempty subset of n,   or

$$\text{(iii)} \qquad\qquad\qquad Q = \{n\}$$

If (i) is the case, then in view of our assumption there exists an element m of Q such that m is an element of every element of Q different from m.

If (ii) is the case, then again there exists an element m of S such that m is an element of every element of S different from m. But since $m \in S$ and $S \subset n$, we see that $m \in n$. Therefore, m is an element of every element of Q different from m.

Finally, if (iii) is the case, then n itself is such that it is an element of every element of Q different from n (naturally, in this case, Q does not contain any element different from n).

Therefore, since $0 \in N$ and since whenever $n \in N$ so is n^+, we infer that $N = \omega$ and thus the theorem is proved.

Theorem 21.   *If S is a nonempty set of natural numbers, then there exists a unique natural number m that is an element of S such that m is an element of every element of S different from m.*

PROOF.   The uniqueness of m is established precisely as in the proof of Theorem 20.

Now, since S is nonempty, let h be an element of S. If there exists no element of S that is an element of h, then in view of Theorem 19, h is an element of any element of S different from h, and thus h can serve as the desired m mentioned in the theorem. However, if there exist some elements of S each of which is an element of h, let M be the set of all such elements. Since every element of M is also an element of h, we see that M is a nonempty subset of h, and therefore, by Theorem 20, there exists an element m of M such that m is an element of every element of M different from m. On the other hand, any element of S that is not an element of M is either h or a natural number n such that (in view of Theorem 19) $h \in n$. Now, since $m \in M$, clearly $m \in h$, and for the remaining elements of S, since $h \in n$, then by Corollary 4, $m \in n$. Therefore, m is indeed an element of S such that m is an element of every element of S different from m. Thus, Theorem 21 is proved.

In what follows, we shall frequently use natural numbers $0, 1, 2, 3, \ldots$, especially in connection with the examples. A natural number different from 0 is called a *positive natural number*.

EXERCISES

1. Prove that
$$\cup \omega = \omega$$

2. Prove that
$$\cup \{\varnothing, \{\varnothing\}\} = \cup \{0, 1\} = \cup 2 = 1$$
Similarly,
$$\cup 0 = 0, \qquad \cup 1 = 0, \qquad \cup 3 = 2, \qquad \cup 4 = 3$$

3. Prove that if n is a natural number, then
$$\cup n^+ = n$$

4. Prove that if n is a natural number, then n is different from n^+.

5. Prove that any positive natural number is an immediate successor of some natural number.

6. Prove that the set of all positive natural numbers exists.

7. Is a subset of a natural number a natural number? Justify your answer.

8. Are the union and the intersection of two natural numbers, natural numbers? Prove your answer.

9. Evaluate:
$$4 \cup 5, \qquad 3 \cup 2, \qquad 5 \cup 3 \cup 1, \qquad 3 \cap 2, \qquad 6 \cap 2,$$
$$(3 \cup 4) \cap 5, \qquad (0 \cap 5) \cup 3, \qquad (2 \cup 5) \cap (3 \cup 4)$$

10. Are the unit-set, power-set and intersection-set of a natural number, natural numbers? Prove your answer.

11. Which of the following statements are true and which are false?
$$2 \in 5, \qquad 3 \in 3, \qquad 5 \subset 5, \qquad 6 \subset 7, \qquad 9 \subset 3,$$
$$5 \in 7, \qquad 7 \in 5, \qquad 3 \subset 9, \qquad 9 \in 10, \qquad 4 \subset 2$$

12. If n and m are two natural numbers, is $n \cup \{m\}$ a natural number? Discuss your answer.

13. Evaluate the following:

$$\cup\{3,4,5\} \cap (\cup\{5,6,9\})$$
$$\cup\{2,5,6,8,9\}$$
$$\cup(\cup\{2,5,6,8,9\}) = \cup\cup\{2,5,6,8,9\}$$
$$\cup\cup\cup\{2,5,6,8,9\}$$
$$\{0,1,2\} \cup \{3,4,5\} \cup \{6\}$$
$$\{7,9\} \cup \{5,7,8,6,4\} \cup \{3,1,0,2\}$$

14. Prove that if m and n are two natural numbers, then

$$m \subset n \quad \text{or} \quad n \subset m$$

Also,

$$\text{if} \quad n \subset m, \quad \text{then} \quad n \in m \quad \text{or} \quad n = m$$

15. Prove that if m and n are two distinct natural numbers, then

$$m \subset n \quad \text{implies} \quad m \in n$$

16. Prove that if m and n are two natural numbers, then

$$n \in m \quad \text{implies} \quad n \cup m = m \quad \text{and} \quad n \cap m = n$$

17. Let an element k of a set S be called a last element of S if $x \in k$ or $x = k$, for every element x of S.

Prove that every positive natural number has a unique last element.

18. Prove that every nonempty subset of a natural number has a unique last element (see Problem 17).

19. Prove that if k is the last element of a natural number n, then $k^+ = n$ (see Problem 17).

20. Prove that if m and n are natural numbers such that $m \in n$, then $m^+ \in n^+$.

21. Prove that if m^+ is a natural number, then so is m. Also, if n is a natural number and if $m \in n$, then

$$m^+ \subset n$$

22. Find a suitable predicate $P(x,y)$ that will serve to infer the existence of the subset (with an unlimited number of distinct elements)

$$\{\varnothing, \{\varnothing\}, \{\{\varnothing\}\}, \{\{\{\varnothing\}\}\}, \ldots\}$$

of ω.

9. THE AXIOM OF CHOICE

Let us assume that there exists a set s given by:

(68) $$s = \{a,b,c\}$$

where

(69) $\qquad a = \{d,e\}, \qquad b = \{h,k\}, \qquad c = \{p,q,r\}$

such that $a \cap b = a \cap c = b \cap c = \varnothing$.

Clearly, our axioms guarantee the existence of a set t such as:

(70) $\qquad t = \{x \mid (x \in \cup s) \wedge ((x = d) \vee (x = k) \vee (x = r))\}$

i.e.,

$$t = \{d,k,r\}$$

We observe that the set t has one and only one element from each of the elements a, b, c of s, and no other elements.

Let us call a set t a *choice-set* or a *selection-set* of a set s if *for every element z of s the set t has one and only one element that belongs to z and no other elements.* Clearly, t is a subset of $\cup s$.

In view of (68) and (69), the set $\{d,k,r\}$ is a choice-set of the set s. Likewise, each of the sets

$$\{e,h,q\}, \qquad \{d,h,p\}, \qquad \{e,k,r\}$$

is a choice-set of the set s given by (68) and (69).

If the empty set $\varnothing$ is an element of a set s, then s *has no* choice-set or selection-set. On the other hand, if s is the empty set, then s has one and only one choice-set, namely, the empty set $\varnothing$.

Let us call two sets a and b *disjoint* if they have no common elements, i.e., if $a \cap b = \varnothing$. Also, let us call a set *disjointed* if its distinct elements are pairwise disjoint.

Using a method similar to that used in deriving the set t in (70), we may observe that *if s is a disjointed set having a limited number of elements, none of which is the empty set, then s has at least one selection-set (or choice-set).*

In other words, our axioms (introduced so far) guarantee the derivability of

(71) $\qquad (\exists t)(\forall z)((z \in s) \rightarrow (\exists w)(\forall x)(((x \in t) \wedge (x \in z)) \leftrightarrow (x = w)))$

where s is a *disjointed set having a limited number of elements such that* $\varnothing \notin s$. As one can see, formula (71) merely states that t is a choice-set of s since it has one and only one element from each one of the elements z of s and no other elements.

To explain why (71) is derivable in the Theory of Sets, with the axioms introduced so far and with the above restrictions imposed on the set s, let us consider the set

$$s = \{a_1, a_2, \ldots, a_n\}$$

where, for example:

$$a_1 = \{m,e\}, \quad a_2 = \{p,q\}, \quad \ldots, \quad a_n = \{h,k,u,v\}$$

are pairwise disjoint nonempty sets. As in (70), here also the axioms of Sum-Set and Replacement (or even the theorem of Separation) secure the existence of a choice-set t of the set s; for example:

(72) $\qquad t = \{x \mid (x \in \cup s) \wedge f(x)\}$

with:

(73) $$f(x) \equiv (x = e) \lor (x = p) \lor \cdots \lor (x = u)$$

The situation is quite different if the disjointed set s (with $\varnothing \notin s$) has an unlimited number of elements. In this case, the axioms introduced so far for the Theory of Sets do not in general secure the existence of a choice-set of s. To explain this point, let us consider the set w given by:

(74) $$w = \{A_1, A_2, A_3, \ldots\}$$

where, for example:

(75) $$A_1 = \{m,e\}, \quad A_2 = \{p,q\}, \quad A_3 = \{k,v,b\}, \quad \ldots$$

are pairwise disjoint nonempty sets. In this case, any attempt to write down a predicate $f(x)$ by means of which a choice-set of w may be formed [the way t, in (72), is formed by means of $f(x)$, given by (73)] will fail, in general. The reason for this is that w has an unlimited number of elements and that in general there is no way of writing a *single formula* that will indicate which element, from the pairwise disjoint nonempty sets $A_1, A_2, A_3, \ldots$, is chosen for the formation of a selection-set of w. Naturally, from a given set A_n, listed in (75), we can always choose an element by means of a suitable predicate $h(x)$. For instance, to choose the element p from the set A_2, we may use $h(x) \equiv (x = p)$. Nevertheless, the writing of a predicate $f(x)$, in the form:

$$f(x) \equiv (x = e) \lor (x = p) \lor \ldots$$

for the purpose of forming a choice-set for the set w, is not only impermissible, but is even impossible. However, in special cases, it is possible to write a predicate $f(x)$ that will choose one element from each one of the elements of a disjointed set A that has an unlimited number of elements and is such that $\varnothing \notin A$. For instance, if

(76) $$A = \{a_1, a_2, a_3, \ldots\}$$

and

(77) $$a_1 = \{c_1,e_1\}, \quad a_2 = \{c_2,e_2\}, \quad \ldots, \quad a_n = \{c_n,e_n\}, \quad \ldots$$

are pairwise disjoint nonempty sets, then

(78) $$f(x) = (\exists y)(x = c_y)$$

is a predicate that may be used to derive a selection-set t of the set A, i.e.,

$$t = \{x \mid (x \in \cup A) \land (\exists y)(x = c_y)\}$$

Obviously, $t = \{c_1, c_2, c_3, \ldots\}$ is a choice-set of the set A given by (76) and (77).

The reason we were successful, in this case, in obtaining a predicate $f(x)$ that yielded a selection-set t of A, is that there exists a property, expressible as a set-theoretical formula, that differentiates among the elements in each of the unlimited number of nonempty sets $a_1, a_2, a_3, \ldots$. This common differentiating property is given by the predicate $f(x)$, described in (78). Clearly, by means of $f(x)$, we formed that subset of $\cup A$ whose elements are of the form c_y for $y = 1, 2, 3, \ldots$. In general, however, a property (expressed as a set-theoretical formula) that can serve as a common differentiating property among the elements of each of the unlimited number of nonempty sets $A_1, A_2, \ldots$ may not exist. Thus, for example, if w is the set given by (74) and (75), there does not appear to be a set-theoretical formula that will yield a selection-set of w. We cannot consider a selection-set of w to be, for example, the set of all the first elements of the sets $A_1, A_2, \ldots$ since, as we know, there is no order relation among the elements of the sets $\{m,e\}, \{p,q\}, \{k,v,b\}, \ldots$. As a matter of fact, it has been established that in general the axioms of Extensionality, Replacement, Power-Set, Sum-Set and Infinity, do not assert the existence of a selection-set (or a choice-set) for a disjointed set s having an unlimited number of elements and such that $\varnothing \notin s$.

However, let us observe that, using the same axioms, we can derive the existence of the *set of all the selection-sets of a disjointed set*. This is shown by:

Theorem 22. *If s is a disjointed set, then the set S of all the selection-sets of s exists.*

PROOF. By the axiom of Sum-Set, the set $\cup s$ exists. Also, by virtue of the axiom of Power-Set, the set $\mathscr{P}(\cup s)$ exists. Now, using the theorem of Separation with

$$P(y) \equiv (\forall x)((x \in s) \rightarrow ((y \cap x) \text{ is a unit-set})),$$

we derive the set S given by:

$$S = \{y \mid y \in \mathscr{P}(\cup s) \wedge (\forall x)((x \in s) \rightarrow ((y \cap x) \text{ is a unit-set}))\}$$

which is the desired set S of all the selection-sets of s.

Let us observe that Theorem 22 does not secure the existence of a selection-set of a disjointed set s such that $\varnothing \notin s$, since the set S of all the selection-sets of s may be empty.

For a satisfactory development of the Theory of Sets, the existence of a selection-set of a disjointed set s with $\varnothing \notin s$, is found to be necessary. Thus, we introduce the following as an axiom of the Theory of Sets.

The Axiom of Choice. *For every disjointed set s not containing the empty set as one of its elements, there exists a selection-set t of s.*

Formally,

$$(\forall s)((\forall z)(\forall y)(((z \in s) \wedge (y \in s) \wedge (z \neq y)) \rightarrow$$
$$(\exists u)((u \in z) \wedge (\forall v)((v \notin z) \vee (v \notin y)))) \rightarrow$$
$$(\exists t)(\forall z)((z \in s) \rightarrow (\exists w)(\forall x)(((x \in t) \wedge (x \in z)) \leftrightarrow (x = w))))$$

The first line of the above formula contains the statement that the elements of s are distinct. The second line contains the statement that the elements of s are nonempty and are pairwise disjoint, i.e., $\varnothing \notin s$ and s is disjointed. The third line, as in the case of (71), asserts the existence of a selection-set t of s.

As mentioned previously, if a disjointed set s is such that $\varnothing \in s$, then s has no selection-set, and consequently the set of all the selection-sets of s is the empty set. Now, in view of the axiom of Choice, we may prove:

Theorem 23. *The set S of all the selection-sets of a disjointed set s is the empty set if and only if $\varnothing \in s$.*

p113

PROOF. As mentioned above, if $\varnothing \in s$, then s has no selection-set and hence $S = \varnothing$. Now, if $\varnothing \notin s$, then by the axiom of Choice, s has at least one selection-set, hence S is not empty. Thus, the theorem is proved.

Let us observe that neither in the axiom of Choice nor in Theorem 22 is it required that $s \neq \varnothing$. As a matter of fact, as previously noted, *when $s = \varnothing$, then $\varnothing$ is a selection-set of s*, and in this case *the set of all selection-sets of s is* $\{\varnothing\}$, which is not the empty set since it has one element.

The axiom of Choice, as well as Theorem 23, ensures the existence of a selection-set of a disjointed set s with $\varnothing \notin s$. In order to extend the notion of a selection-set of a set that is not necessarily disjointed, we shall first give another version of the axiom of Choice. This version is formulated in terms of a predicate $F(x,y)$, functional in x.

Consider,

(79) $$s = \{a,b\}$$

with

$$a = \{m,n\} \quad \text{and} \quad b = \{p,q,r\}$$

where m, n, p, q and r are distinct sets.

Naturally,

(80) $$h = \{m,p\}$$

is a selection-set of s. Also, it is obvious that the predicate:

(81) $$h(x,y) \equiv (x \in s) \wedge (y \in (x \cap h))$$

is functional in x; moreover,

$$h = \{y \mid (\exists x)h(x,y)\}$$

is precisely the same selection-set of s as that given by (80).

Conversely, every predicate $t(x,y)$, functional in x, such that to every $x \in s$ there corresponds a (unique) $y \in x$ for which $t(x,y)$ is true, determines the set

(82) $$t = \{y \mid (\exists x)((x \in s) \wedge t(x,y))\}$$

which is a selection-set of the set s given by (79).

We see at once that the above considerations are readily applicable to the case of any disjointed set s with $\varnothing \notin s$. Thus, if h is a selection-set of s, then *there exists* a predicate $h(x,y)$, as given by (81), functional in x, such that to every element x of s there corresponds an (unique) element y of x for which $h(x,y)$ is true. Conversely, if a predicate $t(x,y)$, functional in x, is such that to every element x of s there corresponds an (unique) element y of x for which

$t(x,y)$ is true, then there exists a set t, as given by (82), which is a selection-set of s.

Motivated by the above, we introduce the following version of the axiom of Choice.

The Principle of Choice. *For every disjointed set s not containing the empty set as one of its elements, there exists a predicate F(x,y), functional in x, such that for every element x of s there corresponds an (unique) element y of x satisfying F(x,y).*

In the above, $F(x,y)$ is called a *selection-function* or a *choice-function of s*.

The Principle of Choice is so worded that it can be most conveniently extended to the case where s is not necessarily disjointed. As a matter of fact, we shall prove that the Principle of Choice (and, consequently, the axiom of Choice) is equivalent to:

The General Principle of Choice. *For every set s not containing the empty set as one of its elements, there exists a predicate F(x,y), functional in x, such that to every element x of s there corresponds an (unique) element y of x satisfying F(x,y).*

In the above, $F(x,y)$ is also called a *selection-function* or a *choice-function of s*.
For example, if

(83) $$s = \{a,b,c\}$$

and

(84) $$a = \{m,n\}, \qquad b = \{m,q,n\}, \qquad c = \{n,p,q\}$$

then the predicate

$$g(x,y) \equiv ((x = a) \wedge (y = m)) \vee ((x = b) \wedge (y = n)) \vee ((x = c) \wedge (y = q))$$

is a selection-function of s given by (83) and (84). The selection-function $g(x,y)$ assigns to a its element m, to b its element n and to c its element q. Strictly speaking, the set

$$\{m,n,q\}$$

which is the set of the mates of the elements of s, is not a selection-set of s, since the intersection of $\{m,n,q\}$ with the elements of s are not singletons. Also, let us remark that since the set s, given by (83) and (84), is not a disjointed set to begin with, the notion of a selection-set of s is not applicable to s.

Before establishing the equivalence between the Principle of Choice (or the axiom of Choice) and the General Principle of Choice, we shall prove:

Theorem 24. *For every two* non empty *sets x and y the set of all ordered pairs (u,v) with u ∈ x and v ∈ y exists.*

PROOF. In view of Theorem 8, for every two sets u and v, the ordered pair

$$(u,v) = \{\{u\},\{u,v\}\}$$

exists. Clearly,   Cartesian product

$$(u,v) \in \mathscr{P}(\mathscr{P}(x \cup y))$$

Consequently, by virtue of the theorem of Separation, the set

$$\{z \mid (\exists u)(\exists v)((u \in x) \wedge (v \in y) \wedge (z = \overset{(u,v)}{(x,y)}))\}$$

which is a subset of $\mathscr{P}(\mathscr{P}(x \cup y))$, exists.

In view of the above, we introduce:

Definition 8. *The set of all ordered pairs (u,v) with $u \in x$ and $v \in y$ is called the Cartesian product of x and y (in this order) and is denoted by $x \times y$.*

Thus, if

$$x = \{a,b\} \quad \text{and} \quad y = \{m,n\}$$

then

$$x \times y = \{(a,m),(a,n),(b,m),(b,n)\}$$

In contrast with $\cup$ and $\cap$, the operator $\times$ is neither associative nor commutative; i.e., in general,

$$(a \times b) \times c \neq a \times (b \times c)$$
$$a \times b \neq b \times a$$

However,

$$(\forall x)(\forall y)((x \times y) = \varnothing \leftrightarrow ((x = \varnothing) \vee (y = \varnothing)))$$

✳ **Theorem 25.** *The General Principle of Choice is equivalent to the axiom of Choice.*

PROOF. The fact that the General Principle of Choice implies the axiom of Choice is obvious since the former trivially implies the Principle of Choice.

To prove that the axiom of Choice implies the General Principle of Choice, let s be a set with $\varnothing \notin s$. For every $x \in s$, let us consider the Cartesian product $x \times \{x\}$. Let S be the set of all Cartesian products $x \times \{x\}$ with $x \in s$. The set S exists by virtue of the axiom of Replacement. Thus,

$$S = \{z \mid (\exists x)((x \in s) \wedge (z = x \times \{x\}))\}$$

Clearly, S is a disjointed set and $\varnothing \notin S$; hence, by the axiom of Choice, S has a selection-set t. But then the predicate

$$t(x,y) \equiv (y,x) \in t$$

which is clearly functional in x, is a choice-function of the set s.

Thus, Theorem 25 is proved.

The following example illustrates the above proof.

Let

$$s = \{a,b\}$$

where

$$a = \{m,n\} \quad \text{and} \quad b = \{m,p\}$$

The set S of all Cartesian products $x \times \{x\}$ with $x \in s$ is given by

$$S = \{\{m,n\} \times \{a\},\{m,p\} \times \{b\}\}$$
$$= \{\{(m,a),(n,a)\},\{(m,b),(p,b)\}\}$$

Clearly, S is a disjointed set such that $\varnothing \notin S$. Let

$$t = \{(m,a),(p,b)\}$$

which is a selection-set of S. The predicate $t(x,y)$ is then given by

$$t(x,y) \equiv ((y,x) = (m,a)) \lor ((y,x) = (p,b))$$

which, in view of Theorem 9, implies

$$t(x,y) \equiv (x = a \land y = m) \lor (x = b \land y = p)$$

Obviously, $t(x,y)$ is a choice-function of s.

EXERCISES

1. Determine the set of all selection-sets of the empty set.

2. Determine the set of all selection-sets of $\{\varnothing\}$.

3. Determine the set of all selection-sets of $\{\{a,b\},\{m,n\}\}$, where a, b, m and n are distinct sets.

4. Determine all selection-functions of $\{\{a,b\}, \{a,b,c\}\}$.

5. Prove that the Cartesian product is neither an associative nor a commutative operator.

6. Prove that for every s and t

$$(s \times t = \varnothing) \leftrightarrow ((s = \varnothing) \lor (t = \varnothing))$$
$$((s \times t) = (t \times s)) \leftrightarrow ((s = \varnothing) \lor (t = \varnothing) \lor (s = t))$$

7. Prove that for every s, u and v

$$s \times (u \cup v) = (s \times u) \cup (s \times v)$$
$$(u \cup v) \times s = (u \times s) \cup (v \times s)$$
$$s \times (u \cap v) = (s \times u) \cap (s \times v)$$

8. Prove that for every s, t, u and v

$$(s \cap t) \times (u \cap v) = (s \times u) \cap (t \times v)$$
$$(s \subset t) \rightarrow ((u \times s) \subset (u \times t))$$
$$((s \subset t) \land (u \subset v)) \rightarrow ((s \times u) \subset (t \times v))$$

9. Prove that for every s and t

$$((s \times s) = (t \times t)) \rightarrow (s = t)$$

10. Prove that if s has m elements and t has n elements (m, n natural numbers), then $s \times t$ has mn elements,

11. Prove that the axiom of Choice is equivalent to: For every set s there exists a predicate $F(x,y)$, functional in x, such that if x is a nonempty subset of s, then $y \in x$.

10. THE AXIOM OF REGULARITY

The axioms of Extensionality, Replacement, Power-Set, Sum-Set, Infinity and Choice are sufficient for the purposes set forth in this book. However, these axioms do not prevent the existence (in the Theory of Sets) of sets which are elements of themselves (see pages 74 and 89), or the existence of two distinct sets each of which is an element of the other. For theoretical reasons, it is found to be advantageous to prevent the occurrence (in the Theory of Sets) of such unintuitive sets. As shown below, this is accomplished by adding the following axiom to the list of the six axioms above.

The Axiom of Regularity. *Every nonempty set x has an element y such that x and y have no element in common.*
Formally,

$$(\forall x)((\exists z)(z \in x) \rightarrow (\exists y)((y \in x) \wedge (\forall u)((u \in x) \rightarrow (u \notin y))))$$

In our development of the Theory of Sets, we shall not use the axiom of Regularity and we shall limit ourselves to giving the following two consequences of this axiom.

Theorem 26. *The axiom of Regularity implies that there exist no two sets such that each is an element of the other.*

PROOF. Assume the contrary, that there exist two sets s and v such that $s \in v$ and $v \in s$. In view of Corollary 2, page 88, the set $\{s,v\}$ exists. But then on the one hand, $s \in v$ and $s \in \{s,v\}$, and on the other hand, $v \in s$ and $v \in \{s,v\}$. Thus, each of the elements s and v of the nonempty set $\{s,v\}$ has an element in common with the set $\{s,v\}$. This contradicts the axiom of Regularity. Therefore, our assumption is false and the theorem is proved.
As an immediate consequence of Theorem 26, we obtain:

Corollary 6. *The axiom of Regularity implies that no set is an element of itself.*

EXERCISES

1. Prove that the axiom of Regularity implies that no limited number of sets $s_1, s_2, \ldots, s_n$ exist such that

$$s_1 \in s_2, \qquad s_2 \in s_3, \qquad \ldots, \qquad s_{n-1} \in s_n, \qquad s_n \in s_1$$

2. Prove that the axiom of Regularity implies that no sequence of sets $s_1, s_2, \ldots, s_n, \ldots$ exists such that

$$s_2 \in s_1, \qquad s_3 \in s_2, \qquad \ldots, \qquad s_{n+1} \in s_n, \qquad \ldots$$

3. Prove that the axiom of Regularity implies that no nonempty set s is a subset of the Cartesian product $s \times s$.

4. Prove that the axiom of Regularity implies that $\in(x,y)$ is neither a reflexive nor a symmetric nor a transitive binary predicate.

11. SUMMARY

In Chapter I, Section 9 a general outline of the formal development of a theory of sets was given by (82), (83), (84), (85) and (86). Following that outline for the development of the Theory of Sets, we introduced in this chapter the axioms of the Theory of Sets. In this book, the Theory of Sets is developed from the following six Zermelo-Fraenkel axioms: Extensionality, Replacement, Power-Set, Sum-Set, Infinity and Choice. For this reason, the Theory of Sets developed in this book is also called the Zermelo-Fraenkel Theory of Sets.

In view of the axiom of Extensionality the definition of equality between sets implies the complete indistinguishability of equal sets with respect to the basic set-theoretical predicate $\in$. The axiom of Replacement in particular asserts the existence of the empty set $\varnothing$ in the Theory of Sets. The axioms of Replacement, Power-Set, Sum-Set, Infinity and Choice assert the existence of more and more extensive sets.

Specifically, the axiom of Infinity asserts the existence of the set

$$\omega = \{\varnothing, \{\varnothing\}, \{\varnothing, \{\varnothing\}\}, \{\varnothing, \{\varnothing\}, \{\varnothing, \{\varnothing\}\}\}, \dots\}$$

called the set of all natural numbers. Thus, in the Theory of Sets one of the most fundamental concepts in all mathematics, namely, that of a natural number, is reduced to the concept of a set. Accordingly, we introduced the symbols 0, 1, 2, 3, . . . for natural numbers, e.g.,

$$0 = \varnothing, \qquad 1 = \{0\}, \qquad 2 = \{0,1\}, \qquad 3 = \{0,1,2\}, \dots$$

In many instances, sets are introduced by configurations such as:

$$\{y \mid (\exists x)(x \in s) \wedge F(x,y)\}$$

and

$$\{x \mid (x \in s) \wedge P(x)\}$$

It is imperative to bear in mind that in the above $F(x,y)$ stands for a binary predicate, functional in x, and as such it is a formula formed according to the formation rules of set-theoretical formulas explained in Chapter I. Similarly, in the above, $P(x)$ stands for a one-place predicate also formed according to the formation rules of set-theoretical formulas. Thus, both $F(x,y)$ and $P(x)$ stand for suitable configurations made up of symbols $x, y, z, \dots, \sim, \vee, \wedge, \rightarrow, \leftrightarrow, \exists, \forall, (,\ ), \in$ and symbols such as 0, 1, 2, 3, ...

In the present book, only the above-mentioned six axioms will be used. However, new definitions in terms of symbols $x, y, z, \dots, \sim, \vee, \exists, (,\ ), \in$ 0, 1, 2, . . . and according to the formation rules of formulas, will be introduced. Also, new theorems will be derived from the axioms according to the rules of inference.

The consistency of the Theory of Sets (based on the above-mentioned six axioms) is not known. However, so far there is no evidence of inconsistency, i.e., there is no evidence that as a consequence of these axioms, a certain set is and is not an element of itself or of another set. However, the incompleteness and undecidability of the Theory of Sets have been established. Moreover, under the assumption that the axioms of Extensionality, Replacement, Power-Set, Sum-Set, Infinity and Regularity form a consistent system of axioms, it has been established that the axiom of Choice is consistent with (K. Goedel) and independent of (P. J. Cohen) that system of axioms.

Chapter III

ALGEBRA OF SETS
RELATIONS AND FUNCTIONS

1. COMPLEMENTS

As indicated in the preceding chapter, the axioms of the Theory of Sets ensure the existence of the union $x \cup y$ and the intersection $x \cap y$ of every two sets x and y. Clearly, $x \cup y$ and $x \cap y$ are respectively the set of all those sets that are elements of x or y, and the set of all those sets that are simultaneously elements of x and y. In this section, we shall define the *difference* between two sets x and y (in that order), also called the *complement* of y with respect to x. The *existence* and the *uniqueness* of the complement of a set with respect to another set are ensured respectively by the theorem of Separation and the definition of equality between two sets.

Definition 1. *The complement of a set y with respect to a set x, denoted by $\mathsf{C}_x y$, or the difference between x and y, denoted by $x \frown y$, is the set of all those elements of x that are not elements of y.*
Symbolically,

$$\mathsf{C}_x y = x \frown y = \{z \mid (z \in x) \wedge (z \notin y)\}$$

Thus, if $a = \{e,c,d\}$ and $b = \{d,p,q\}$, where distinct letters are distinct sets, then

$$\mathsf{C}_a b = a \frown b = \{e,c,d\} \frown \{d,p,q\} = \{e,c\}$$

In Figure 7 the set $e \frown c$ is represented by the horizontally shaded area and the set $c \frown e$ by the vertically shaded area.

In Figure 8 the set $m \frown n$ is represented by the horizontally shaded area and the set $n \frown m$ by the vertically shaded area.

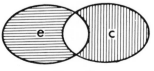

Figure 7

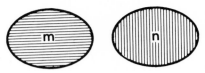

Figure 8

In the same way that $\cup$ and $\cap$ are respectively called the union and the intersection operators, we may call $\frown$ the *subtraction operator*.

In view of Definition 1, for every set x, we have:

$$x \frown \varnothing = x, \qquad \varnothing \frown x = \varnothing, \qquad x \frown x = \varnothing$$

The first two of the above equalities with $x \neq \varnothing$ show that *subtraction is not a commutative operation*. Similarly, in view of the above equalities, for every set x we have

$$(x \frown \varnothing) \frown x = \varnothing \qquad \text{and} \qquad x \frown (\varnothing \frown x) = x$$

which with $x \neq \varnothing$ show that *subtraction is not an associative operation*.

It is interesting to note that the notion of inclusion can be expressed in terms of *difference*, i.e.,

(1) $$(x \subset y) \leftrightarrow (x \frown y = \varnothing) \qquad \text{for every} \quad x \text{ and } y$$

Moreover, the intersection of any two sets can be expressed in terms of differences, i.e.,

(2) $$x \cap y = x \frown (x \frown y) \qquad \text{for every} \quad x \text{ and } y$$

A significant and useful theorem concerning complements is given by:

Theorem 1. *For every three sets x, y and z the following hold:*

(3) $$\mathbf{C}_z(x \cup y) = \mathbf{C}_z x \cap \mathbf{C}_z y$$

(4) $$\mathbf{C}_z(x \cap y) = \mathbf{C}_z x \cup \mathbf{C}_z y$$

PROOF.   To show (3), let us observe that if u is an element of $\mathbf{C}_z(x \cup y)$, i.e., if u belongs to z and not to x or y, then u belongs simultaneously to $\mathbf{C}_z x$ and $\mathbf{C}_z y$. Thus,

$$\mathbf{C}_z(x \cup y) \subset (\mathbf{C}_z x \cap \mathbf{C}_z y)$$

On the other hand, if u belongs simultaneously to $\mathbf{C}_z x$ and $\mathbf{C}_z y$, then u belongs to z and not to x or y. Thus,

$$(\mathbf{C}_z x \cap \mathbf{C}_z y) \subset \mathbf{C}_z(x \cup y)$$

In view of the above two inclusions, the truth of (3) is established. The proof of (4) is established in a similar way.

Formally, we prove (3) as follows:

$$u \in \mathbf{C}_z(x \cup y) \leftrightarrow (u \in z) \wedge (u \notin (x \cup y))$$
$$\leftrightarrow (u \in z) \wedge \sim((u \in x) \vee (u \in y))$$
$$\leftrightarrow (u \in z) \wedge (u \notin x) \wedge (u \notin y)$$
$$\leftrightarrow (u \in z) \wedge (u \notin x) \wedge (u \in z) \wedge (u \notin y)$$
$$\leftrightarrow (u \in \mathbf{C}_z x) \wedge (u \in \mathbf{C}_z y)$$
$$\leftrightarrow u \in (\mathbf{C}_z x \cap \mathbf{C}_z y)$$

Likewise, the formal proof of (4) is given as:

$$u \in C_z(x \cap y) \leftrightarrow (u \in z) \wedge (u \notin (x \cap y))$$
$$\leftrightarrow (u \in z) \wedge \sim((u \in x) \wedge (u \in y))$$
$$\leftrightarrow (u \in z) \wedge ((u \notin x) \vee (u \notin y))$$
$$\leftrightarrow ((u \in z) \wedge (u \notin x)) \vee ((u \in z) \wedge (u \notin y))$$
$$\leftrightarrow (u \in C_z x) \vee (u \in C_z y)$$
$$\leftrightarrow u \in (C_z x \cup C_z y)$$

Equalities (3) and (4) are called *DeMorgan laws*. Clearly, DeMorgan laws hold for the union and intersection of any limited number of sets. Thus, in particular, for every four sets x, y, z and s, we have:

$$C_s(x \cup y \cup z) = C_s x \cap C_s y \cap C_s z$$

and

$$C_s(x \cap y \cap z) = C_s x \cup C_s y \cup C_s z$$

EXERCISES

1. Prove the following equivalences for every three sets x, y and z:

$$((x \smallsetminus y) = x) \leftrightarrow ((y \smallsetminus x) = y)$$
$$(y = \emptyset) \leftrightarrow ((x \cup y) = (x \smallsetminus y))$$
$$((x \smallsetminus y) = (y \smallsetminus x)) \leftrightarrow (x = y)$$
$$(x \subset (y \cup z)) \leftrightarrow ((x \smallsetminus y) \subset z)$$
$$((y \smallsetminus x) \subset z) \leftrightarrow ((y \smallsetminus z) \subset x)$$

2. Prove the following equalities for every four sets x, y, z and s:

$$(x \smallsetminus y) \cup z = (x \smallsetminus (y \smallsetminus z)) \cup (z \smallsetminus x)$$
$$x \cup (y \smallsetminus z) = ((x \cup y) \smallsetminus z) \cup (x \cap z)$$
$$(x \smallsetminus y) \cup z = ((x \cup z) \smallsetminus y) \cup (y \cap z)$$
$$(x \smallsetminus y) \cap (z \smallsetminus s) = (x \cap z) \smallsetminus (y \cup s)$$
$$(x \smallsetminus y) \smallsetminus (z \smallsetminus s) = (x \smallsetminus (y \cup z)) \cup ((x \cap s) \smallsetminus y)$$
$$x \smallsetminus (y \smallsetminus (z \smallsetminus s)) = (x \smallsetminus y) \cup ((x \cap z) \smallsetminus s)$$
$$x \smallsetminus (x \smallsetminus (y \smallsetminus (y \smallsetminus z))) = x \cap y \cap z$$

3. For every four sets x, y, z and s, prove that

$$(x \smallsetminus s) \subset ((x \smallsetminus y) \cup (y \smallsetminus z) \cup (z \smallsetminus s))$$

4. Prove that subtraction is distributive with respect to union and also with respect to intersection, i.e.,

$$(x \cup y) \smallsetminus z = (x \smallsetminus z) \cup (y \smallsetminus z)$$

and

$$(x \cap y) \smallsetminus z = (x \smallsetminus z) \cap (y \smallsetminus z)$$

for every three sets x, y and z.

5. Prove the following equalities for every three sets x, y and z:

$$x \smallsmile (y \cup z) = (x \smallsmile y) \smallsmile z$$
$$(x \smallsmile y) \cap z = (x \cap z) \smallsmile (y \cap z) = (x \cap z) \smallsmile y$$
$$x \smallsmile (y \smallsmile z) = (x \smallsmile y) \cup (x \cap z)$$
$$x \smallsmile (y \cap z) = (x \smallsmile y) \cup (x \smallsmile z)$$

6. Determine a set a of six elements such that $e \in a$, $c \in a$ and such that the difference of any two sets that are elements of a is again an element of a.

7. Prove that the Cartesian product is distributive with respect to union and subtraction, i.e., for every three sets x, y and z, we have:

$$(x \cup y) \times z = (x \times z) \cup (y \times z)$$
$$z \times (x \cup y) = (z \times x) \cup (z \times y)$$

and

$$(x \smallsmile y) \times z = (x \times z) \smallsmile (y \times z)$$
$$z \times (x \smallsmile y) = (z \times x) \smallsmile (z \times y)$$

8. Prove formally (1) and (2).

9. Prove that the following equality holds for every four sets x, y, z and s:

$$(x \times y) \smallsmile (z \times s) = ((x \smallsmile z) \times y) \cup (x \times (y \smallsmile s))$$

2. PRINCIPLE OF DUALITY

In this section, we shall assume that *all sets considered are subsets of a fixed set V and all complements are with respect to the fixed set V.* To emphasize this, we shall denote $\complement_V x$ or $V \smallsmile x$, simply by x'. Thus,

$$\complement_V x = V \smallsmile x = x' \qquad \text{for every} \quad x$$

and we shall call x' the *dual* of x.

In terms of our new notation, the two DeMorgan laws (3) and (4) are expressed respectively as:

(5) $$(x \cup y)' = x' \cap y'$$

(6) $$(x \cap y)' = x' \cup y'$$

and are read respectively: *the dual of the union of any two sets is equal to the intersection of their duals*, and *the dual of the intersection of any two sets is equal to the union of their duals*.

Let us observe that in the context of our present discussion—i.e., where all the sets under consideration are subsets of V—for every three sets x, y and z, we have:

(7) $$((z \notin V) \lor ((z \in x) \rightarrow (z \in y))) \leftrightarrow ((z \in x) \rightarrow (z \in y))$$

To see this, it is enough to note that if $(z \notin V)$ is true, then $(z \in x)$ is false; consequently, $(z \in x) \rightarrow (z \in y)$ is true.

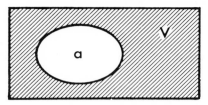

Figure 9

Also, since in the present context $x \subset V$ for every x, for every x and z we have:

(8) $$((z \in V) \wedge ((z \notin V) \vee (z \in x))) \leftrightarrow (z \in x)$$

To see this, it is enough to note that if $(z \in x)$ is true then $(z \in V)$ is also true.

Now, we prove that for every x and y,

(9) $$(x \subset y) \leftrightarrow (y' \subset x')$$

In view of (7), the formal proof of (9) runs as follows:

$$x \subset y \leftrightarrow (\forall z)((z \in x) \rightarrow (z \in y))$$
$$\leftrightarrow (\forall z)((z \notin V) \vee ((z \in x) \rightarrow (z \in y)))$$
$$\leftrightarrow (\forall z)(((z \notin V) \vee (z \in x)) \rightarrow ((z \notin V) \vee (z \in y))) \quad \textit{law of contraposition}$$
$$\leftrightarrow (\forall z)(((z \in V) \wedge (z \notin y)) \rightarrow ((z \in V) \wedge (z \notin x)))$$
$$\leftrightarrow y' \subset x'$$

Next, we prove that for every x,

(10) $$(x')' = x \qquad \text{(the law of double dual)}$$

In view of (8), the formal proof of (10) runs as follows:

$$z \in (x')' \leftrightarrow ((z \in V) \wedge (z \notin x'))$$
$$\leftrightarrow ((z \in V) \wedge \sim(z \in x'))$$
$$\leftrightarrow ((z \in V) \wedge \sim((z \in V) \wedge (z \notin x)))$$
$$\leftrightarrow ((z \in V) \wedge ((z \notin V) \vee (z \in x)))$$
$$\leftrightarrow z \in x$$

Graphically, if V represents the rectangular area in Figure 9, then the dual of a is represented by the shaded area.

In Figure 10 the set $(a \cap b)'$ is represented by the shaded area.

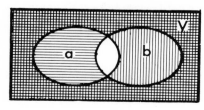

Figure 10

It is obvious from Figure 10 that $(a \cap b)' = a' \cup b'$, where a' is given by the vertically and b' by the horizontally shaded area.

Now we prove:

The Principle of Duality. *Two sets are equal if and only if their duals are equal,* i.e., *for every x and y,*

$$(x = y) \leftrightarrow (x' = y')$$

PROOF. By the definition of equality, we have

$$x = y \leftrightarrow (x \subset y) \wedge (y \subset x)$$

On the other hand, in view of (9),

$$x = y \leftrightarrow (y' \subset x') \wedge (x' \subset y')$$

and hence,

$$x = y \leftrightarrow x' = y'$$

Thus, the principle of Duality is proved.

Let us observe that the following are true equalities:

(11) $$\varnothing' = V$$

(12) $$V' = \varnothing$$

and for every x,

(13) $$x \cup x' = V$$

(14) $$x \cap x' = \varnothing$$

If x and y are not subsets of V, then in general (9) does not hold, i.e.,

$$(x \subset y) \leftrightarrow (\mathsf{C}_z y \subset \mathsf{C}_z x)$$

is not true for some sets x, y and z. On the other hand, (10), (11), (12), (13) and (14) in general acquire the following forms respectively:

$$\mathsf{C}_y(\mathsf{C}_y x) = x \cap y \qquad \text{for every} \quad x \text{ and } y$$
$$\mathsf{C}_y \varnothing = y \qquad \text{for every} \quad y$$
$$\mathsf{C}_y y = \varnothing \qquad \text{for every} \quad y$$
$$x \cup \mathsf{C}_y x = x \cup y \qquad \text{for every} \quad x \text{ and } y$$
$$x \cap \mathsf{C}_y x = \varnothing \qquad \text{for every} \quad x \text{ and } y$$

Now we prove that union is distributive with respect to intersection and that intersection is distributive with respect to union; i.e., for every x, y and z:

(15) $$(x \cap y) \cup z = (x \cup z) \cap (y \cup z)$$

and

(16) $$(x \cup y) \cap z = (x \cap z) \cup (y \cap z)$$

As the reader may expect, the proof of (15) is based on the distributivity of $\vee$ with respect to $\wedge$, proved on page 41. To prove (15), let us observe that for every u, x, y and z,

$$u \in ((x \cap y) \cup z) \leftrightarrow (u \in (x \cap y)) \vee (u \in z)$$
$$\leftrightarrow ((u \in x) \wedge (u \in y)) \vee (u \in z)$$
$$\leftrightarrow ((u \in x) \vee (u \in z)) \wedge ((u \in y) \vee (u \in z))$$
$$\leftrightarrow (u \in (x \cup z)) \wedge (u \in (y \cup z))$$
$$\leftrightarrow u \in ((x \cup z) \cap (y \cup z))$$

Now, to prove (16), let us take $x \cup y \cup z$ for the set V mentioned in the beginning of this section. According to (15) we have:

$$(x' \cap y') \cup z' = (x' \cup z') \cap (y' \cup z')$$

Applying the principle of Duality to the above equality, we find:

$$((x' \cap y') \cup z')' = ((x' \cup z') \cap (y' \cup z'))'$$

But then by (5) and (6), we obtain

$$(x' \cap y')' \cap (z')' = (x' \cup z')' \cup (y' \cup z')'$$

which in view of (5), (6) and (10), yields

$$(x \cup y) \cap z = (x \cap z) \cup (y \cap z)$$

for every x, y and z.

EXERCISES

1. Let $V = \{a,b,c,d,e,g\}$ where distinct letters are distinct sets. Determine

$$\{a,b\}', \qquad \{c,d,e\}', \qquad \{a,b,g\}'$$

and prove that for every subset x and y of V, we have:

$$((x \cap y' = \varnothing) \wedge (y \cap x' = \varnothing)) \rightarrow (x = y)$$

2. Prove that for every subset x, y and z of a fixed set V, the following equalities hold:

$$(x \cap (y \cup y'))' = x' \cup (y \cup y')' = x' \cup \varnothing = x'$$
$$x \cap z' = x \cap (y \cup y') \cap z'$$
$$x \cap (y \cup y') \cap z' = (x \cap y \cap z') \cup (x \cap y' \cap z')$$
$$x \smallsmile y = x \cap y'$$

3. Find the duals of the following sets in terms of the duals of A, B, C and D where the latter are subsets of V:

$$(A \cup B) \cap C$$
$$A \cup (B \cap C)$$
$$(A \smallsmile B) \cap C$$
$$(A \cup B \cup C) \cap (A \cup D)$$
$$(B \smallsmile C) \cup (C \smallsmile B)$$
$$((A \smallsmile B) \smallsmile C) \cup ((D \smallsmile B) \cap C)$$

4. Prove that for every x, y and z (subsets of V):

$$(x \cap y' = z \cap z') \leftrightarrow (x \cap y = x)$$
$$(x \cup y' = z \cup z') \leftrightarrow (x \cup y = x)$$
$$(x' \cup y')' \cup (x' \cup y)' = x$$
$$(x \cap y' = \varnothing) \wedge (x' \cap y = \varnothing) \rightarrow (x = y)$$

5. Prove that

$$x \subset y \leftrightarrow C_z y \subset C_z x \qquad \text{and} \qquad C_z(C_z x) = x$$

are not true for some x, y and z.

6. Prove equalities (10), (11), (12), (13) and (14).

3. SYMMETRIC DIFFERENCE

In this section we introduce the *symmetric difference* of two sets x and y. The existence and the uniqueness of the symmetric difference (sometimes also called *symmetric sum*) of any two sets are ensured respectively by the axiom of Sum-Set, the theorem of Separation and the definition of equality between two sets.

Definition 2.   *The symmetric difference of x and y, denoted by $x \oplus y$, is the set of all those sets that are elements of x or y and not of both.*

Symbolically,

$$x \oplus y = (x \cup y) \smallsetminus (x \cap y)$$

Thus, if $a = \{m,n,p,q\}$ and $b = \{p,q,r,s\}$, where distinct letters are distinct sets, then

$$a \oplus b = \{m,n,p,q\} \oplus \{p,q,r,s\} = \{m,n,r,s\}$$

In Figure 11, $e \oplus c$ is represented by the shaded area.

Clearly,

(17) $x \oplus y = (x \smallsetminus y) \cup (y \smallsetminus x)$ for every x and y

The above justifies calling $\oplus$ the *symmetric difference* operator. Obviously, $\oplus$ is an associative operator, i.e.,

(18) $(x \oplus y) \oplus z = x \oplus (y \oplus z)$ for every x, y and z

Moreover, $\oplus$ is a commutative and nilpotent operator, i.e.,

(19) $x \oplus y = y \oplus x$ for every x and y

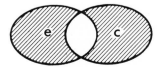

Figure 11

and

(20) $x \oplus x = \varnothing$ for every x

Furthermore, $\cap$ is distributive with respect to $\oplus$, i.e.,

(21) $(x \oplus y) \cap z = (x \cap z) \oplus (y \cap z)$,   for every x, y and z

Finally,

(22) $x \oplus \varnothing = x$ for every x

Perhaps one of the most significant features of $\oplus$ consists in the property described below, which is enjoyed neither by $\cup$ nor by $\cap$. Let us observe that for two sets a and b, it is not always the case that there exists a set x such that

(23) $a \cup x = b$

or

(24) $a \cap x = b$

It could happen that neither equation (23) nor equation (24) has a solution. However, it could also happen that either of the equations (23) or (24) has many solutions. For instance, if $a = \{m,n\}$ and $b = \{m\}$, where m and n are distinct sets, then (23) has no solution, whereas (24) has many solutions, such as

$$x = \{m\}, \qquad x = \{m,p\}, \qquad x = \{m,p,q,r,s\}, \ldots$$

where m, p, q, r and s are distinct sets. Again, if $a = \{m,n\}$ and $b = \{m,n,p,q\}$, where m, n, p and q are distinct sets, then (23) has many solutions, such as

$$x = \{p,q\}, \qquad x = \{p,q,m\}, \qquad x = \{p,q,m,n\}$$

whereas (24) has no solution.

The situation is quite different when we consider an equation of the form:

(25) $a \oplus x = b$

where a and b are two given sets. We show below that equation (25) always has a unique solution.

To prove that equation (25) has a unique solution, let us observe that (25) yields

$$a \oplus (a \oplus x) = a \oplus b$$

which in view of (18) implies

$$(a \oplus a) \oplus x = a \oplus b$$

Thus, in view of (20) and (22) we have

(26) $x = a \oplus b$

Hence, $a \oplus b$ is the unique solution of (25).

Let us observe that the existence and uniqueness of a solution of the equation $a \oplus x = b$ is in sharp contrast with the possible nonexistence or possible nonuniqueness of solutions of equations $a \cup x = b$ and $a \cap x = b$.

Clearly, in view of the commutativity of $\oplus$, an equation of the form

$$x \oplus a = b$$

also always has a unique solution given by (26).

We observe that $\cup$ and $\smile$ can be expressed in terms of $\oplus$ and $\cap$. Thus, for every x and y we have:

(27) $$(x \cup y) = (x \oplus y) \oplus (x \cap y)$$

and

(28) $$(x \smile y) = (x \oplus y) \cap x$$

Moreover, for every x, y and z, we have:

$$(x \oplus y) \cup z \supset (x \cup z) \oplus (y \cup z)$$
$$\checkmark (x \oplus y) \cup z \supset (x \cap z) \oplus (y \cap z)$$
$$\checkmark (x \cup y) \oplus z \subset (x \oplus z) \cup (y \oplus z)$$
$$(x \cup y) \oplus z \supset (x \oplus z) \cap (y \oplus z)$$
$$\checkmark (x \cap y) \oplus z \supset (x \oplus z) \cap (y \oplus z)$$
$$(x \cap y) \oplus z \subset (x \oplus z) \cup (y \oplus z)$$

Furthermore, for every x, y, z and u we have:

$$(x \cup y) \oplus (z \cup u) \subset (x \oplus z) \cup (y \oplus u)$$
$$(x \smile y) \oplus (z \smile u) \subset (x \oplus z) \cup (y \oplus u)$$
$$(x \cap y) \oplus (z \cap u) \subset (x \oplus z) \cup (y \oplus u)$$

EXERCISES

1. Prove (17) to (22), (27) and (28).

2. Prove that for every x, y and z,

$$(x \smile y) \subset (x \oplus y)$$
$$(x = y) \leftrightarrow (x \oplus y = \varnothing)$$
$$(x \oplus y = y \oplus z) \rightarrow (x = z)$$
$$(x \oplus y) \subset ((x \oplus z) \cup (y \oplus z))$$

3. Solve the following equations for x:

$$(x \oplus a) \oplus (x \oplus b) = x \oplus c$$
$$(x \oplus m) \oplus (x \oplus n) \oplus (x \oplus p) = \varnothing$$

4. Let

$$m = \{a,b,c\}, \qquad n = \{a,c,m\}, \qquad p = \{a,b,m\}$$

where a, b, c and m are distinct sets. Whenever possible, for each of the following equations determine a set x which satisfies the equation.

$$m \cup x = n$$
$$m \cap x = p$$
$$(m \cup n) \cap x = p \cup x$$
$$(m \cap n) \smallsmile x = p \cap x$$
$$(m \oplus x) \smallsmile n = p$$
$$(m \cap x) = n \cup x$$
$$(m \oplus n) = x \cap p$$
$$(m \oplus x) = p \cup x$$
$$(m \oplus p) \smallsmile x = m \oplus x$$

5. Prove that

$$(x \oplus y) \cup (y \oplus z) = (x \cup y \cup z) \smallsmile (x \cap y \cap z)$$
$$(x \oplus y) \cup (y \oplus z) \cup (z \oplus s) = (x \cup y \cup z \cup s) \smallsmile (x \cap y \cap z \cap s)$$

hold for every x, y, z and s.
Generalize the above.

6. Prove that for every x and y

$$(x \oplus y) \cap x \cap y = \varnothing$$

and solve the equation

$$((a \oplus x) \cap (a \cap x)) \oplus x = \varnothing$$

for x.

7. Referring to the definition of a natural number given by Definition 6, page 104, prove that if x and y are natural numbers, then in general $x \oplus y$ is not a natural number.

4. BOOLEAN RINGS

Obviously, not every set s is such that the intersection and the symmetric difference of every two elements of s are again elements of s. For instance, the set

$$3 = \{0,1,2\}$$

does not contain $1 \oplus 2$ as its element, since $1 \oplus 2 = \{1\}$ and $\{1\}$ is not an element of 3.

On the other hand, the set

$$2 = \{0,1\}$$

is such that the intersection and the symmetric difference of every two elements of 2 are again elements of 2.

In connection with the above, we introduce:

Definition 3. *A set s is called a Boolean ring if the intersection and the symmetric difference of every two elements of s are again elements of s.*

In other words, a set s is called a Boolean ring if

(29) $$(x \oplus y) \in s \quad \text{and} \quad (x \cap y) \in s$$

for every two elements x and y of s.

In view of (29), it is customary to say that a Boolean ring is *closed* under $\oplus$ and $\cap$.

Theorem 2. *Let s be a nonempty Boolean ring. Then*

(30) $$\varnothing \in s$$

(31) $$(x \cup y) \in s \quad \text{and} \quad (x \frown y) \in s$$

for every two elements x and y of s.

Moreover, if s has a limited number of elements, then s has a unique element u such that

(32) $$x \cap u = x \quad \text{for every element} \quad x \text{ of } s$$

PROOF. The truth of (30) follows from (29) and (20). The truth of (31) follows from (29), (27) and (28). Now, if s has a limited number of elements, then by (31), $\cup s \in s$. Let $\cup s = u$. Clearly, $x \cap u = x$, for every $x \in s$. Thus, (32) is true. The uniqueness of u follows from the fact that if $v \in s$ is such that $x \cap v = x$, for every $x \in s$, then $u = u \cap v = v$ and hence, $u = v$. Thus, Theorem 2 is proved.

If a Boolean ring s has an element u satisfying (32), then u is called *the unit* element of s. A Boolean ring with a unit is called a *Boolean algebra*.

Corollary 1. *For every set s, the power-set $\mathscr{P}(s)$ is a Boolean algebra.*

PROOF. $\mathscr{P}(s)$ is a Boolean ring, since it is closed under $\oplus$ and $\cap$. On the other hand, $\mathscr{P}(s)$ is a Boolean algebra, since $\cup \mathscr{P}(s) = s$ and $s \in \mathscr{P}(s)$.

EXERCISES

1. Give examples of Boolean rings having respectively one, two and four elements. Verify that each one is a Boolean algebra.

2. Prove that if a Boolean ring has a limited number of elements then it has 2^n elements for some natural number n. Moreover, for every natural number n there exists a Boolean ring with 2^n elements.

3. Prove that if a Boolean ring s has more than two elements, then for every nonempty element b of s there exists a nonempty element c of s such that $b \cap c = \varnothing$.

4. Consider the power-set $\mathscr{P}(\omega)$ of the set of all natural numbers ω. Let B be the set of all elements of $\mathscr{P}(\omega)$ having a limited number of elements. Prove that B is a Boolean ring and not a Boolean algebra.

5. RELATIONS

In accordance with our general aim of defining every mathematical object as a set, in this section we define relations as sets.

Definition 4. *A relation is a set whose elements are ordered pairs.*

For instance, $\{(a,b)\}$ and $\{(a,2), (3,3)\}$ are relations having respectively one and two elements. Clearly, the empty set $\varnothing$ is also a relation having no element.

In what follows, along with small letters such as a, b, c, . . . , capital letters such as A, B, C, . . . , with or without subscripts, will constitute sets. Similarly, along with small letters such as x, y, z, . . . , capital letters such as X, Y, Z, . . . , with or without subscripts, will constitute individual variables.

Now, let us consider the following relation:

$$R = \{(a,b), (a,n), (p,q), (s,q)\}$$

The set of all first coordinates of elements of R—i.e., the set $\{a,p,s\}$—is called the *domain* of R and is denoted by dom R. The set of all second coordinates of elements of R—i.e., the set $\{b,n,q\}$—is called the *range* of R and is denoted by rng R. Thus, for the relation R above, we have

$$\text{dom } R = \{a,p,s\} \quad \text{and} \quad \text{rng } R = \{b,n,q\}$$

In general for a relation

(33) $$R = \{(x,y) \mid \cdots\}$$

we define the domain of R as:

(34) $$\text{dom } R = \{x \mid (\exists y)((x,y) \in R)\}$$

and the range of R as:

(35) $$\text{rng } R = \{y \mid (\exists x)((x,y) \in R)\}$$

As mentioned on page 117, the Cartesian product $X \times Y$ of every two sets X and Y exists. In view of (33) every subset of a Cartesian product is a relation. In particular, in view of (34) and (35), we have:

$$R \subset (\text{dom } R) \times (\text{rng } R)$$

Let R be a relation that is a subset of a Cartesian product $X \times Y$. Then, it is customary to call the domain of R, the *projection of R on X* and to denote it by $\text{pr}_X R$. Also, it is customary to call the range of R, the *projection of R on Y* and to denote it by $\text{pr}_Y R$. Thus, if $R \subset X \times Y$, then

(36) $$\text{dom } R = \text{pr}_X R \quad \text{and} \quad \text{rng } R = \text{pr}_Y R$$

Let R be a relation. To express the fact that (x,y) is an element of R, we often write

$$xRy \quad \text{or} \quad R(x,y)$$

and we call *y* a *mate* of *x* with respect to the relation *R*. Accordingly, rng *R* is equal to the set of all mates of the elements of dom *R*. In general, an element of the domain of a relation may have many distinct mates with respect to that relation. Also, it may happen that several distinct elements of the domain of a relation have the same mate.

If an element of the domain of a relation *R* has several distinct mates, then *R* is called a *one-to-many* relation. If several distinct elements of the domain of *R* have the same mate, then *R* is called a *many-to-one* relation. Clearly, a relation may be both one-to-many and many-to-one. However, if a relation is neither one-to-many nor many-to-one, then it is called a *one-to-one* relation.

For instance, if *a*, *b*, *c*, *m*, *n* and *p* are distinct sets, then

$$\{(a,m), (a,n), (b,p), (c,p)\}$$

is both a one-to-many and many-to-one relation, whereas

$$\{(a,p), (b,m), (c,n)\}$$

is a one-to-one relation.

Let *R* be a relation that is a subset of a Cartesian product $X \times Y$, i.e.,

$$R \subset X \times Y$$

If dom $R = X$, then *R* is called a relation *from X into Y*. If rng $R = Y$, then *R* is called a relation *onto Y*. Finally, if dom $R = X$ and rng $R = Y$, then *R* is called a relation *from X onto Y*.

For example, if

$$A = \{a,b,c,d\} \quad \text{and} \quad B = \{m,n,p\}$$

where distinct letters are distinct sets, then

$$\{(a,m), (b,m), (c,n), (d,n)\}$$

is a relation from *A* into *B*. On the other hand,

$$\{(a,m), (a,n), (c,p)\}$$

is a relation onto *B*. Finally,

$$\{(a,m), (b,p), (c,n), (d,p)\}$$

is a relation from *A* onto *B*.

Sometimes, relations can be represented most conveniently by diagrams such as Figure 12, where the arrows emanate from the elements of the domain

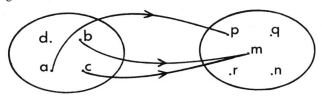

Figure 12

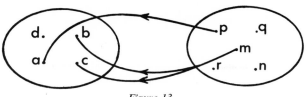

Figure 13

of the relation under consideration and terminate at their respective mates in the range of the relation. Thus, Figure 12 represents the relation

$$\{(a,p), (b,m), (c,m)\}$$

Let us observe that the directions of the arrows in a relation-diagram are of utmost importance. In general, the same relation-diagram will represent an entirely different relation when in it the directions of the arrows are reversed. Let us take, for example, Figure 13, which is similar to Figure 12 except for the directions of the arrows. Figure 13 represents the relation

$$\{(p,a), (m,b), (m,c)\}$$

which is quite different from the relation represented by Figure 12.

Relation-diagrams are quite often drawn in more systematic and conventional ways. For instance, instead of joining the elements of the domain of a relation to their mates with haphazard curves, we may choose vertical and horizontal paths for this purpose. This is shown in Figure 14, which represents the relation

$$R = \{(a,m), (b,m), (b,n), (c,p), (d,m)\}$$

with

$$A = \text{dom } R = \{a,b,c,d\} \qquad \text{and} \qquad B \neq \text{rng } R = \{m,n,p\}$$

In Figure 14, the collection of dots C, D, E, G, H is indispensable, since otherwise there will be ambiguity as to which elements of the domain are related to which elements of the range. For example, the fact that on the vertical line passing through c there is no other dot except E, shows that the only mate of c with respect to this relation is p.

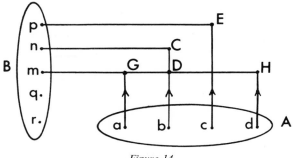

Figure 14

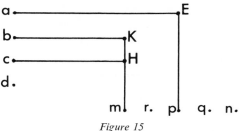

Figure 15

For the sake of definiteness, we shall call relation-diagrams such as the one given by Figure 14, *Cartesian* diagrams. In a Cartesian diagram the above-mentioned collection of dots, arising in connection with a relation R, is called the *graph* of R.

Now, if we agree that in a Cartesian diagram the set containing the domain of a relation is always represented horizontally, and the set containing the range of that relation is always represented vertically (as in Figure 15), then we may omit the arrows without creating any ambiguity. Accordingly, the relation represented by Figure 13 has the Cartesian diagram shown in Figure 15.

Let us observe that since relations are sets, we may apply various set-theoretical operations among relations. Accordingly, two relations Q and R will be called equal to each other, if as sets $Q = R$. Similarly, a relation Q will be called a subset of a relation R, if as sets $Q \subset R$. Likewise, we form the union, the intersection, the difference and the symmetric difference of two relations Q and R respectively by considering $Q \cup R$, $Q \cap R$, $Q \smallsmile R$ and $Q \oplus R$. Naturally, if Q and R are relations, then so are $Q \cup R$, $Q \cap R$, $Q \smallsmile R$ and $Q \oplus R$.

It can be easily proved that for every two relations Q and R, we have:

(37)
$$\begin{cases} \mathrm{dom}\,(Q \cup R) = (\mathrm{dom}\,Q) \cup (\mathrm{dom}\,R) \\ \mathrm{dom}\,(Q \cap R) \subset (\mathrm{dom}\,Q) \cap (\mathrm{dom}\,R) \\ \mathrm{dom}\,(Q \smallsmile R) \supset (\mathrm{dom}\,Q) \smallsmile (\mathrm{dom}\,R) \\ \mathrm{dom}\,(Q \oplus R) \supset (\mathrm{dom}\,Q) \oplus (\mathrm{dom}\,R) \end{cases}$$
$$\begin{aligned} \mathrm{rng}\,(Q \cup R) &= (\mathrm{rng}\,Q) \cup (\mathrm{rng}\,R) \\ \mathrm{rng}\,(Q \cap R) &\subset (\mathrm{rng}\,Q) \cap (\mathrm{rng}\,R) \\ \mathrm{rng}\,(Q \smallsmile R) &\supset (\mathrm{rng}\,Q) \smallsmile (\mathrm{rng}\,R) \\ \mathrm{rng}\,(Q \oplus R) &\supset (\mathrm{rng}\,Q) \oplus (\mathrm{rng}\,R) \end{aligned}$$

If the order of every element of a relation R is reversed, then the result is a relation which is called the *converse* of R, denoted by R_{-1}. For instance, if
$$R = \{(a,b),\, (c,c),\, (m,a)\}$$
then the converse of R is
$$R_{-1} = \{(b,a),\, (c,c),\, (a,m)\}$$

Thus, if $R = \{(x,y) \mid \cdots\}$ is any relation, its converse is the relation $R_{-1} = \{(y,x) \mid (x,y) \in R\}$. Clearly, the diagram of R_{-1} is that of R in which the directions of the arrows are reversed. For instance, Figures 12 and 13 show relations that are the converses of each other. Obviously,

(38) $$\text{dom } R = \text{rng } R_{-1} \quad \text{and} \quad \text{rng } R = \text{dom } R_{-1}$$

for every relation R. Moreover,

(39) $$(R_{-1})_{-1} = R \quad \text{for every relation } R$$

Also, it can be easily proved that for any two relations Q and R, we have:

(40)
$$(Q \cup R)_{-1} = Q_{-1} \cup R_{-1}$$
$$(Q \cap R)_{-1} = Q_{-1} \cap R_{-1}$$
$$(Q \smile R)_{-1} = Q_{-1} \smile R_{-1}$$
$$(Q \oplus R)_{-1} = Q_{-1} \oplus R_{-1}$$

Let R be a relation. We define the *restriction* of R to a set S, denoted by $R|_S$, as follows:

(41) $$R|_S = R \cap (S \times \text{rng } R)$$

Thus, if $R = \{(a,b), (c,m), (e,r), (e,h)\}$ and $S = \{a,c\}$, where distinct letters are distinct sets, then
$$R|_S = \{(a,b), (c,m)\}$$

Again, if $Q = \{(m,n), (d,m), (m,c)\}$ and $H = \varnothing$, then according to (41),
$$Q|_H = Q|_\varnothing = \varnothing$$

It can be easily proved that for every relation R and every two sets S and H, we have:

(42)
$$R|_{(S \cup H)} = R|_S \cup R|_H, \quad R|_{(S \cap H)} = R|_S \cap R|_H$$
$$R|_{(S \smile H)} = R|_S \smile R|_H, \quad R|_{(S \oplus H)} = R|_S \oplus R|_H$$

Let R be a relation. We define the *image of a set S under R*, denoted by $R^1(S)$, as follows:

(43) $$R^1(S) = \text{rng } R|_S$$

Thus, if $R = \{(a,m), (a,n), (b,a), (c,a), (e,h)\}$ and $S = \{a,b\}$, where distinct letters are distinct sets, then according to (43) we have:
$$R^1(S) = \{a,m,n\}$$

Remark 1. For the sake of simplicity, $R^1(S)$, given by (43), is usually denoted by $R(S)$.

It can easily be proved that for every relation R and every two sets S and H, we have:

(44)
$$(S \subset H) \to R^1(S) \subset R^1(H)$$
$$R^1(S \cup H) = R^1(S) \cup R^1(H)$$
$$R^1(S \cap H) \subset R^1(S) \cap R^1(H)$$
$$R^1(S \smile H) \supset R^1(S) \smile R^1(H)$$
$$R^1(S \oplus H) \supset R^1(S) \oplus R^1(H)$$

Let R be a relation. We define the *inverse image of a set S under R*, denoted by $R^{-1}(S)$, as follows:

(45) $$R^{-1}(S) = R^1_{-1}(S)$$

where R_{-1} is the converse of R. Thus, the inverse image of a set S under a relation R is equal to the image of S under the relation R_{-1}, the converse of R.

Thus, if $R = \{(a,b), (n,m), (a,c), (b,m), (e,h), (h,h), (p,m)\}$ and $S = \{m,h\}$, where distinct letters are distinct sets, then according to (45), we have:

$$R^{-1}(S) = \{n,b,p,e,h\}$$

Significant examples of relations are provided by functions, which are treated in the next section. Equally significant are the so-called relations defined in a set. We say that R is a *relation in a set S*, if R is a relation from S into S. For example, if $S = \{a,b,c\}$, then

$$R = \{(a,c), (a,b), (b,c), (c,a)\}$$

is a relation in S. To the category of relations defined in a set belong equivalence relations and various kinds of order relations defined in the sequel.

In closing this section, let us observe that every relation R gives rise to a binary predicate $P(x,y)$, where

$$P(x,y) \equiv (x,y) \in R$$

Also, every binary predicate $P(x,y)$ with $x \in A$ and $y \in B$ (where A and B are two given sets) gives rise to the relation R given by:

(46) $$R = \{(x,y) \mid ((x,y) \in A \times B) \wedge P(x,y)\}$$

Naturally, in the above, $P(x,y)$ is a set-theoretical formula formed according to the formation rules of formulas, as explained in Chapter I.

The existence of R in (46) is secured by our axioms. Below we give some examples of relations introduced according to (46).

$$R = \{(x,y) \mid ((x,y) \in \omega \times \omega) \wedge (y = x^+)\}$$

Clearly, in this case,

$$R = \{(0,1), (1,2), (2,3), (3,4), \ldots\}$$

Next, consider:

$$Q = \{(x,y) \mid ((x,y) \in \omega \times \omega) \wedge (x \in y)\}$$

Clearly, in this case,

$$Q = \{(0,1), (0,2), (0,3), \ldots, (1,2), (1,3), \ldots, (2,3), \ldots\}$$

Finally, consider:

$$P = \{(x,y) \mid ((x,y) \in 2 \times 3) \wedge (x = y)\}$$

Clearly, in this case,

$$P = \{(0,0), (1,1)\}$$

EXERCISES

1. Consider the relation

$$R = \{(a,b), (a,m), (c,b), (e,h)\}$$

which is a subset of $A \times B$, with

$$A = \{a,c,e,b\} \quad \text{and} \quad B = \{b,m,h,a\}$$

and where distinct letters are distinct sets.
Determine $\text{pr}_A R$ and $\text{pr}_B R$, as given by (36).

2. Consider the two sets A and B, given in the above problem. Give two examples of one-to-many relations from A into B. Also, give two examples of many-to-one relations from A into B. Finally, give two examples of one-to-one relations from A onto B.

3. Draw diagrams for the following relations:

$$\{(a,a), (b,b), (c,c), (e,e)\}$$
$$\{(a,m), (m,a), (b,n), (n,b)\}$$

4. Consider the following relations:

$$\{(3,1), (2,2), (5,1), (6,2), (3,4)\}$$
$$\{(0,0), (3,5), (2,1), (1,1), (5,0)\}$$
$$\{(3,7), (2,9), (1,0), (0,3), (7,5)\}$$

Write the converse of each of the above relations.
Find the restrictions of each of the above relations to the sets $\{1,5,2\}$, $\{3,4,0\}$ and $\{1,0,7\}$.
Find the images of S, H and K under each of the above relations, where:

$$S = \{1,3,5,2\}, \quad H = \{0,5,9,4\}, \quad K = \{3,2,9,0\}$$

Find the inverse images of A, B and C under each of the above relations, where:

$$A = \{3,4,5\}, \quad B = \{1,2,0\}, \quad C = \{2,3,5,4\}$$

5. Prove (37), (40), (42) and (44).

6. Prove that for every relation R,

$$R^1(\varnothing) = \varnothing \quad \text{and} \quad R^{-1}(\varnothing) = \varnothing$$

7. Prove that the following hold for every relation R and every two sets S and H.

$$S \subset H \rightarrow R^{-1}(S) \subset R^{-1}(H)$$
$$R^{-1}(S \cup H) = R^{-1}(S) \cup R^{-1}(H)$$
$$R^{-1}(S \cap H) \subset R^{-1}(S) \cap R^{-1}(H)$$
$$R^{-1}(S \smallsmile H) \supset R^{-1}(S) \smallsmile R^{-1}(H)$$
$$R^{-1}(S \oplus H) \supset R^{-1}(S) \oplus R^{-1}(H)$$

8. Let *A* and *B* be two sets with *m* and *n* elements respectively (*m* and *n* are natural numbers). How many distinct relations are there from *A* into *B*? How many of these relations are onto *B*?

9. Let *A* and *B* be two sets each having *m* elements (*m* is a natural number). How many distinct one-to-one relations are there from *A* onto *B*?

10. Let *A* and *B* be two sets with *m* and *n* elements respectively, where the natural number *n* is greater than the natural number *m*. How many distinct one-to-one relations are there from *A* into *B*?

6. FUNCTIONS   *Read carefully to p 151. Prove any 3 things left for reader*

In the definition of a relation *R*, we made no restrictions as to the number of the distinct mates of an element of the domain of *R*. For instance, in the case of the relation

$$R = \{(1,2), (1,6), (1,7), (2,6), (2,7), (3,4)\}$$

the element 1 has three distinct mates, namely 2, 6 and 7; the element 2 has two distinct mates, 6 and 7; and the element 3 has one mate, 4.

In many cases, the above one-to-manyness is not desirable. A one-to-many relation does not specify a unique mate for every element of its domain and thus entails an ambiguity. Naturally, relations without this ambiguity play an important role in mathematics. They are called *functions*.

Definition 5.   *A relation whose distinct elements have distinct first coordinates is called a function.*

In short, a function is a many-to-one or a one-to-one relation.
Symbolically, a relation
$$F = \{(x,y) \mid \cdots\}$$
is a function, if and only if

$$F = \{(x,y) \mid (\forall x)(\forall y)(\forall z)(((xFy) \wedge (xFz)) \rightarrow (y = z))\}$$

Diagrammatically, a relation is a function if from every element of its domain one and only one arrow emanates. Thus, Figure 16 represents the function

(47) $f = \{(a,m), (b,m), (c,p)\}$

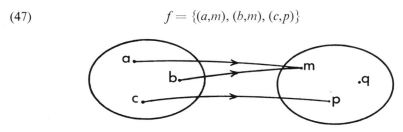

Figure 16

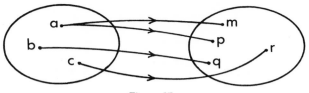

Figure 17

However, Figure 17 does not represent a function, since from *a* two arrows emanate.

On the other hand, Figure 18 represents a function, since from every element of its domain one and only one arrow emanates. The function represented in Figure 18 is

(48) $g = \{(a,m), (b,m), (c,m), (d,m)\}$

Notice that the second coordinate of every element of *g* is the same set *m*. A function whose every element has the same second coordinate is called a *constant function.* Thus, *g* in (48) is a constant function and Figure 18 represents a constant function. However, *f* in (47) is not a constant function and Figure 16 does not represent a constant function.

Let us observe that *in order that a Cartesian diagram of a relation f represent a function, it is necessary and sufficient that there exists one and only one dot on every vertical line passing through an element of the domain of f.*

Thus, Figure 19 is a Cartesian diagram of a function.

The function represented by Figure 19 is evidently:

$$\{(a,m), (b,n), (c,n), (d,n), (e,p)\}$$

Let us observe that every function *F* gives rise to a binary predicate *F(x,y)* with

$$F(x,y) \equiv (x,y) \in F$$

where *F(x,y)* is functional in *x*.

Conversely, in view of the axiom of Replacement, every binary predicate *F(x,y)*, functional in *x*, with the additional condition that $x \in D$ (where *D* is a given set), gives rise to the function

(49) $F = \{(x,y) \mid (x \in D) \wedge F(x,y)\}$

whose domain is *D* and whose range is given by:

$$\text{rng } F = \{y \mid (\exists x)((x \in D) \wedge F(x,y))\}$$

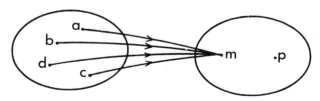

Figure 18

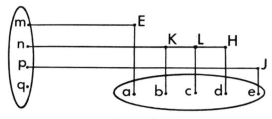

Figure 19

Thus, the function

$$F = \{(x,y) \mid (x \in 4) \wedge (y = \{x\})\}$$

is the set

$$F = \{(0,1), (1,\{1\}), (2,\{2\}), (3,\{3\})\}$$

A function that is a many-to-one relation is called a *many-to-one function.* Similarly, a function that is a one-to-one relation is called a *one-to-one function.*

A function that is a relation from B is naturally called a *function from A into B*; if it is a relation from A onto B, then it is called a *function from A onto B.*

For instance, Figure 18 represents a function from $\{a,b,c,d\}$ *into* $\{m,p\}$ that is not a one-to-one function.

Let $f(x,y)$ be a binary predicate, functional in x for every $x \in D$. To emphasize this, we write:

(50) $y = f(x)$ for every $x \in D$

Moreover, instead of representing the function defined by $f(x,y)$ according to (49), i.e., as

(51) $f = \{(x,y) \mid (x \in D) \wedge f(x,y)\}$

we represent it as:

$$f = \{(x,y) \mid (x \in D) \wedge (y = f(x))\}$$

The notation $y = f(x)$, or simply $f(x)$, is widely used, especially in reference to a function. Thus, instead of saying:

let f be a function given by (51)

it is customary to say:

for every $x \in D$, let $f(x)$ be a function

and when there is no ambiguity as far as the domain D is concerned, then it is said:

let $f(x)$ be a function

or

let $y = f(x)$ be a function of x

Actually, $f(x)$ is not a function, because to begin with it is not a set of ordered pairs. Naturally, what is meant by saying:

let $f(x)$ be a function

is precisely what is conveyed by (51).

In what follows, we shall constantly use expressions such as: *let* $y = f(x)$ *be a function*, or *the function* $f(x)$, with the understanding that the meaning of these expressions is conveyed by (51).

In a way, the notation $y = f(x)$ is not too unrelated to the idea of a function. After all, the essential idea involved in a function f is the formation of ordered pairs (x,y) such that for every $x \in D$, x and y satisfy a given binary predicate $f(x,y)$, functional in x. But the latter means that for every x in D there exists one and only one y such that $f(x,y)$ is true. Consequently, it is quite natural to write $y = f(x)$ where y denotes precisely the unique element that satisfies $f(x,y)$ for a given x in D.

In connection with the functional notation $y = f(x)$ for a function f, it is customary to refer to y as the *value* that f *takes on* or *assumes* at the *argument* x. Thus, if

(52) $f = \{(5,3), (b,c), (c,m), (2,3), (a,b)\}$

then, using the notation $y = f(x)$ for this function, we write

$$3 = f(5), \quad c = f(b), \quad m = f(c), \quad 3 = f(2), \quad b = f(a)$$

and we say that f takes on the value 3 at 5 (or when the argument is 5) and c at b, and so forth.

The notation $y = f(x)$ also suggests expressions such as f *maps* or *sends* or *transforms* x to y or x onto y; also, it is said that f *operates on x and yields y* or that f *makes y correspond to x*; and quite often y is called the *mate* or the *image* of x. For instance, in reference to the function given by (52), we say that 3 is the mate of 5, or c is the image of b, and so forth.

Motivated by the above, we use the words *map, mapping, transformation* and *correspondence* as synonyms for *function*. In particular, a *one-to-one onto function* is called a *one-to-one correspondence*.

To emphasize the fact that a function from a set D into a set S maps or sends or transforms the elements of D into the elements of S, the following notation is used quite frequently:

$$f : D \to S$$

Clearly, S need not be the range of f. However, it is always the case that

$$\operatorname{rng} f \subset S$$

The function $y = f(x)$ is called a function of one variable (or one argument) x. If the domain of a function is a subset of a Cartesian product, then the function is called a function of *two* variables.

For instance,

(53) $f = \{((a,b),m), ((c,5), t), ((3,2),4)\}$

is a function of two variables. Clearly, in (53), the elements of f are sets. For example,

$$((a,b),m) = \{\{(a,b)\}, \{(a,b), m\}\} = \{\{\{\{a\}, \{a,b\}\}\}, \{\{\{a\}, \{a,b\}\}, m\}\}$$

A notation such as $z = f(x,y)$, instead of $z = f((x,y))$, is more convenient and is used for functions of two variables x and y. For instance, in reference to (53) we write:

$$m = f(a,b), \qquad t = f(c,t), \qquad 4 = f(3,2)$$

Let us also mention that the set of all functions from D into S exists because this set is a subset of the power-set of the Cartesian product $D \times S$.

The set of all functions from D into S is denoted by:

(54) S^D

There are many ways of producing new functions from one or more given functions. For instance, since any subset of a function is again a function, a new function may be obtained simply by considering a proper subset of a given function. Thus, if

$$f = \{(a,5), (b,2), (3,7), (5,m)\}$$

is a given function, then

$$g = \{(b,2), (3,7)\}$$

is a new function where $g \subset f$.

Clearly, as a relation, g is a restriction of f. More precisely,

$$g = f|_{\{b,3\}}$$

In this connection, f is called *an extension of g.*

Now, let

$$f : A \rightarrow B \qquad \text{and} \qquad g : B \rightarrow C$$

From the functions f and g, we may produce a third function from A into C called the *composite* of g and f (in that order) and denoted by $g \cdot f$.

Before giving the formal definition of the composite $g \cdot f$, we illustrate the idea involved in it by an example.

Let

$$f = \{(a,5), (b,m), (c,h)\}$$

and

$$g = \{(5,t), (m,k), (h,2), (r,7)\}$$

where distinct letters are distinct sets.

Diagrammatically, this is shown in Figure 20.

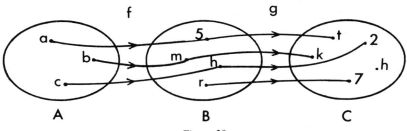

Figure 20

From Figure 20 we see that there is an arrow emanating from a and ending at t; similarly, an arrow from b to k; and a third one from c to 2. Clearly, these arrows describe the function

$$h = \{(a,t), (b,k), (c,2)\}$$

which is from A into C. We say h is formed by composing the two functions g and f and we denote it by $g \cdot f$.

The above diagram shows that:

$$h(a) = (g \cdot f)(a) = g(f(a)) = g(5) = t$$
$$h(b) = (g \cdot f)(b) = g(f(b)) = g(m) = k$$
$$h(c) = (g \cdot f)(c) = g(f(c)) = g(h) = 2$$

Now, we introduce the formal definition of the composite of the two functions g and f.

Definition 6. *Let $f : A \to B$ and $g : B \to C$; then the composite of g and f, denoted by $g \cdot f$, is the set:*

$$g \cdot f = \{(x,y) \mid (x \in A) \wedge (\exists z)(((x,z) \in f) \wedge ((z,y) \in g))\}$$

which is a function from A into C.

Using the notation analogous to that given by (50), we may write:

(55) $(g \cdot f)(x) = g(f(x))$ for every $x \in A$

Theorem 3. *Composition of functions is associative, i.e.,*

$$(h \cdot g) \cdot f = h \cdot (g \cdot f)$$

PROOF.   Let us first observe that if two functions p and q have the same domain D and if $p(x) = q(x)$ for every $x \in D$, then $p = q$.

Now, let D be the domain of the function f. By Definition 6, we see that the domain of $(h \cdot g) \cdot f$ is D and that of $h \cdot (g \cdot f)$ is equal to the domain of $(g \cdot f)$, which again is equal to D. Hence, $(h \cdot g) \cdot f$ and $h \cdot (g \cdot f)$ have the same domain D.

On the other hand, in view of (55),

$$((h \cdot g) \cdot f)(x) = (h \cdot g)(f(x)) = h(g(f(x)))   \text{ for every } x \in D$$

Similarly,

$$(h \cdot (g \cdot f))(x) = h((g \cdot f)(x)) = h(g(f(x)))   \text{ for every } x \in D$$

Thus,

$$((h \cdot g) \cdot f) = (h \cdot (g \cdot f))$$

as desired.

The reader should note that *not every two functions have a composite*.

From a given binary relation R, we may create two functions of two variables as shown below.

Let

$$R = \{(a,b), (a,c), (m,c), (t,c)\}$$

Then
$$f = \{((a,b),a), ((a,c),a), ((m,c),m), ((t,c),t)\}$$
and
$$g = \{((a,b),b), ((a,c),c), ((m,c),c), ((t,c),c)\}$$

are two functions of two variables.

Motivated by (36) on page 135, we may call f the *projection function from R onto the domain of R*, and g the *projection function from R onto the range of R*.

Generally, if R is a binary relation $\{(x,y) \mid \cdots\}$, then the projection function from R onto the domain of R (sometimes called the *first projection function*) is defined as:

$$\{((x,y),x) \mid (x,y) \in R\}$$

and the projection function from R onto the range of R (sometimes called the *second projection function*) is defined as:

$$\{((x,y),y) \mid (x,y) \in R\}$$

The projection functions are sometimes represented as:

$$f:(x,y) \rightarrow x$$
and
$$g:(x,y) \rightarrow y$$

There are three functions that occur frequently in mathematics. They are: the *identity mapping*, the *inclusion (injection* or *embedding) mapping* and the *characteristic function of a subset B of A*.

The identity mapping in a set A is a function f that maps the elements of a set onto themselves. Specifically, $f:A \rightarrow A$ is the identity mapping in A if $f(x) = x$ for every $x \in A$—i.e., $f = \{(x,x) \mid \cdots\}$, for every $x \in A$.

The inclusion mapping is a restriction of the identity mapping. Specifically, if $B \subset A$, then $g:B \rightarrow A$ is an inclusion (injection or embedding) mapping if $g(x) = x$ for every $x \in B$.

The characteristic function of a subset B of A is a function from A into 2 (where, we recall, 2 is the set $\{0,1\}$) which takes on the value 1 at every $x \in B$, and the value 0 at every $x \in (A \smallsmile B)$. The characteristic function of a subset B of A is denoted by $\text{Ch}_{B|A}$. More precisely, $\text{Ch}_{B|A}:A \rightarrow 2$ is the characteristic function of the subset B of A, if $\text{Ch}_{B|A}(x) = 1$, for every $x \in B$, and $\text{Ch}_{B|A}(x) = 0$, for every $x \in (A \smallsmile B)$.

Let us mention here that the converse of a function need not necessarily be a function. Thus, if $a \neq c$ and

$$f = \{(a,b), (c,b), (m,n), (q,p)\}$$

then as mentioned in Section 5, its converse is the set

$$f_{-1} = \{(b,a), (b,c), (n,m), (p,q)\}$$

which is not a function since b has two distinct mates a and c, a fact that is incompatible with the definition of a function.

EXERCISES

1. How many functions are there from the set $\{3,2,1\}$ into the set $\{0,1\}$? How many of them are onto functions?

2. Let f and g be two functions. Are $f \cap g, f \cup g, f \smile g$ and $f \oplus g$ necessarily functions? Justify your answers.

3. Give an example of a function whose converse is also a function.

4. Give an example of two functions f and g for which the composites $g \cdot f$ and $f \cdot g$ are defined and, moreover, $g \cdot f = f \cdot g$.

5. Prove that:
$$(f \cdot g)|_B = f \cdot (g|_B)$$

6. Prove that if f and g are both one-to-one functions then $g \cdot f$ (if it exists) is also a one-to-one function.

7. Prove that the set of all functions from the empty set $\varnothing$ into a set R has exactly one element. Also, prove that the set of all functions from a nonempty set D into the empty set is the empty set.

8. Give an example of a function f such that $f \cdot f_{-1}$ can be defined and such that:
$$f \cdot f_{-1} = f_{-1} \cdot f = \text{identity mapping}$$

9. Let $A = \{2,3,5,0,1\}$ and $B = \{1,2,0\}$. Construct the characteristic function of the subset B of A.

10. Prove that there are precisely eight distinct characteristic functions of the subsets of the set $\{a,b,c\}$ consisting of three distinct elements.

11. What is a necessary and sufficient condition that the intersection of two characteristic functions of two subsets S and Q of a set A be a characteristic function of a subset of A? $S = Q$

12. What is a necessary and sufficient condition that the union of two characteristic functions of two subsets S and Q of a set A be a characteristic function of a subset of A? $S = Q$

13. Let the binary predicate $y = f(x)$ be described as follows:

$f(x) = 6 - x$ for $x = 2$ and $x = 4$
$f(x) = $ prime divisors of x for $x = 4$ and $x = 9$
$f(x) = x^2$ for $x = 1$ and $x = 2$

Is $y = f(x)$ a function from $\{1,2,4,9\}$ into ω (the set of all natural numbers)?

14. Describe the ternary predicate involved in the function
$$\{((1,2),3),\ ((3,5),8),\ ((7,2),9),\ ((1,0),1)\}$$

15. Describe the ternary predicate involved in the function
$$\{((2,3),6),\ ((0,5),0),\ ((3,1),3),\ ((1,1),1)\}$$

7. IMAGES AND INVERSE IMAGES UNDER A FUNCTION

The *image of a set S* under a function f, denoted by

$$f^1(S)$$

is defined as the image of S under the relation f, given by (43) on page 139. Thus,

$$f^1(S) = \operatorname{rng} f|_S$$

where $f|_S$ is the restriction of f to S, given by (41) on page 139.

Clearly, if S is disjoint from the domain D of f, i.e., if $S \cap D = \varnothing$, then $f^1(S) = \varnothing$. Hence,

$$f^1(S) = f^1(S \cap D)$$

where D is the domain of f. Therefore, without loss of generality, in speaking about the images under f of various sets, we may confine the latter to being subsets of the domain of f.

Obviously, if f is a function from D into R, then f^1 is a function from the power-set $\mathscr{P}(D)$ of D into the power-set $\mathscr{P}(R)$ of R, i.e.,

$$\text{if } f : D \to R. \quad \text{then } f^1 : \mathscr{P}(D) \to \mathscr{P}(R)$$

where

$$f^1(S) = \{y \mid (\exists x)((x \in S) \wedge (y = f(x)))\}$$

for every $S \in \mathscr{P}(D)$.

In short, $f^1(S)$ *is the set of the mates, under f, of all the elements of S.*

For instance, if $f : D \to R$ is the function represented by Figure 21, then

$$f^1(\{a,b,c\}) = \{h,r\} \quad \text{and} \quad f^1(\{d,e\}) = \{p,q\}$$

Likewise,

$$f^1(\{m\}) = \{q\} \quad \text{and} \quad f^1(\varnothing) = \varnothing$$

Remark 2.   As mentioned in Remark 1 on page 139, for the sake of simplicity $f^1(S)$ is usually denoted by $f(S)$.

The implication, equality and inclusions given in (44) on page 139, which are valid for R^1, where R is a relation, are certainly valid for f^1, where f is a function. Moreover, as is easily seen, the implication and inclusions cannot be improved respectively to an equivalence and equalities.

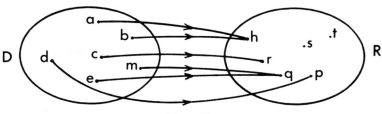

Figure 21

For instance, as Figure 21 shows,

$$f^1(\{m\}) \subset f^1(\{e\})$$

although $\{m\}$ is not a subset of $\{e\}$.

Also,

$$f^1(\{m\} \cap \{e\}) = \varnothing \neq f^1(\{m\}) \cap f^1(\{e\}) = \{q\}$$
$$f^1(\{m,e\} \smile \{e\}) = \{q\} \neq f^1(\{m,e\}) \smile f^1(\{e\}) = \varnothing$$
$$f^1(\{m\} \oplus \{e\}) = \{q\} \neq f^1(\{m\}) \oplus f^1(\{e\}) = \varnothing$$

Also, if $f : D \to R$, then

$$\operatorname{rng} f = f^1(D) \subset R$$

Moreover, if $f : D \to R$ and $g : R \to Q$, then

$$(g \cdot f)^1 = g^1 \cdot f^1$$

is a function from $\mathscr{P}(D)$ into $\mathscr{P}(Q)$.

The *inverse image* of a set S under a function f, denoted by

$$f^{-1}(S)$$

is defined as the inverse image of S under the relation f, given by (45) on page 140. Thus,

$$f^{-1}(S) = f^1_{-1}(S)$$

where f_{-1} is the relation that is the converse of the function f.

Here again, in speaking about the inverse images under $f : D \to R$, of various sets, we may confine these various sets to subsets of R.

Let us observe that if f is a function from D into R, then in general f_{-1} is not a function from R into D. However, f^1_{-1} is a function from $\mathscr{P}(R)$ into $\mathscr{P}(D)$, i.e.,

$$\text{if} \quad f : D \to R \qquad \text{then} \quad f^{-1} : \mathscr{P}(R) \to \mathscr{P}(D)$$

where

$$f^{-1}(S) = \{x \mid f(x) \in S\}$$

for every $S \in \mathscr{P}(R)$.

In short $f^{-1}(S)$ is *the set of all the elements of the domain of f that are mapped into the elements of S.*

For instance, as Figure 21 shows:

$$f^{-1}(\{h,t,s\}) = \{a,b\}, \qquad f^{-1}(\{p,q\}) = \{m,e,d\}$$
$$f^{-1}(\{t,s\}) = \varnothing, \qquad f^{-1}(\varnothing) = \varnothing$$

Now, let f be a function from D into R. Then, in contrast to the behavior of f^1, *for every two subsets S and H of R, the following hold:*

(56)

$$S \subset H \to f^{-1}(S) \subset f^{-1}(H)$$
$$f^{-1}(S \cup H) = f^{-1}(S) \cup f^{-1}(H)$$
$$f^{-1}(S \cap H) = f^{-1}(S) \cap f^{-1}(H)$$
$$f^{-1}(S \smile H) = f^{-1}(S) \smile f^{-1}(H)$$
$$f^{-1}(S \oplus H) = f^{-1}(S) \oplus f^{-1}(H)$$

go back and use what was already proved (37)

In view of (56), it is customary to say that f^{-1} preserves inclusion, union, intersection, difference and symmetric difference. On the other hand, as (44) shows, f^1 preserves inclusion and union only.

Moreover, $f : D \to R$ is an *onto* mapping if and only if

(57) $(S \subset H) \leftrightarrow f^{-1}(S) \subset f^{-1}(H)$

for every two subsets S and H of R.

The proofs of (56) and (57) are straightforward and are left to the reader.

It is clear that if $f : D \to R$, then

$$f^{-1}(R) = f^{-1}(\mathrm{rng}\, f) = f^{-1}(f^1(D)) = D$$

To apply the above we prove that

(58) $f^{-1}(\mathbf{C}_R S) = \mathbf{C}_D f^{-1}(S)$

for every subset S of R.

Indeed:

$$f^{-1}(\mathbf{C}_R S) = f^{-1}(R \smallsetminus S) = f^{-1}(R) \smallsetminus f^{-1}(S) = D \smallsetminus f^{-1}(S) = \mathbf{C}_D f^{-1}(S)$$

It is a matter of direct verification that if $f : D \to R$ and $g : R \to Q$, then

(59) $(g \cdot f)^{-1} = f^{-1} \cdot g^{-1}$

is a function from $\mathscr{P}(Q)$ into $\mathscr{P}(D)$.

Now, if $f : D \to R$, then, as we know, $f^1 : \mathscr{P}(D) \to \mathscr{P}(R)$ and $f^{-1} : \mathscr{P}(R) \to \mathscr{P}(D)$. Hence,

$$f^1 \cdot f^{-1} \qquad \text{and} \qquad f^{-1} \cdot f^1$$

are functions, the former from $\mathscr{P}(R)$ into $\mathscr{P}(D)$ and the latter from $\mathscr{P}(D)$ into $\mathscr{P}(R)$.

Moreover, it is easy to verify that if $f : D \to R$, then

(60) $(f^{-1} \cdot f^1)(X) = f^{-1}(f^1(X)) \supset X$ for every $X \subset D$

and

(61) $(f^1 \cdot f^{-1})(Y) = f^1(f^{-1}(Y)) \subset Y$ for every $Y \subset R$

Furthermore, f *maps D onto R if and only if*

(62) $(f^1 \cdot f^{-1})(Y) = f^1(f^{-1}(Y)) = Y$ for every $Y \subset R$

EXERCISES

1. Let f be the function indicated in Figure 21. Determine:

$$f^1(\{e,b,m\}), \qquad f^1(\{a,e,d\}), \qquad f^1(\{b,d,m\})$$
$$f^{-1}(\{t\}), \qquad f^{-1}(\{r,s\}), \qquad f^{-1}(\{h\})$$
$$f^1(\{a,b,e,m\}), \qquad f^{-1}(\{t,s\}), \qquad f^{-1}(\{r,n\})$$
$$f^{-1}(\{p,h,q\}), \qquad f^{-1}(\{s,p,r\}), \qquad f^{-1}(\{r,h,q\})$$

2. Let f be the function indicated in Figure 21. Find a subset A of D and an element $x \in D$ such that

$$x \notin A \qquad \text{and} \qquad f(x) \in f^1(A)$$

3. Let $D = \{a,b,c\}$ and $R = \{p,q,r\}$. Find a function f from D into R such that

$$f^1(X \smallsetminus Y) = f^1(X) \smallsetminus f^1(Y)$$

for every subset X and Y of D.

4. Let f be a function from D into R. Prove that a necessary and sufficient condition that the inverse image under f of a nonempty subset of R be a nonempty subset of D, is that f be a function from D *onto* R.

5. Prove (56), (57), (59), (60), (61) and (62).

6. Let f be a function from D into R. Prove that

$$f^{-1}(X) = f^{-1}(X \cup f^1(D))$$

where $X \subset R$.

7. Let f be a function from D into R. Prove that the following do not hold, in general

$$f^1(A) \subset f^1(B) \to (A \subset B)$$
$$f^{-1}(M) \subset f^{-1}(N) \to M \subset N$$

where A and B are any two subsets of D, and M and N are any two subsets of R.

8. ONE-TO-ONE CORRESPONDENCE

Let f be a function from D into R. If f maps distinct elements of D into distinct elements of R, then f is called a *one-to-one* function (or mapping) from D into R.

Diagrammatically, $f : D \to R$ is a one-to-one mapping if from every element of D one and only one arrow emanates, and at no point of R two arrows terminate.

For instance, Figure 22 represents a one-to-one mapping from D into R.

Clearly, a relation f is a one-to-one function if distinct elements of f have distinct first and second coordinates. Thus, if a, b, c, m, p and q are distinct

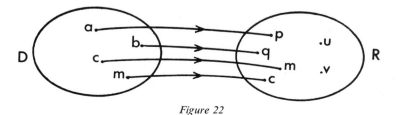

Figure 22

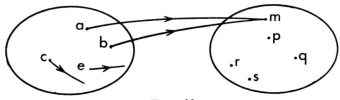

Figure 23

sets, then

$$\{(a,p), (b,q), (c,m), (m,c)\}$$

is the one-to-one function represented by Figure 22.

The main feature of a one-to-one mapping (also written: 1-1 mapping) consists in the fact that a *function f, whose domain is D, is a one-to-one mapping if and only if $y \in f^1(D)$ implies that there is one and only one $x \in D$ such that $y = f(x)$*. In other words, $f : D \to R$ is a one-to-one mapping if and only if for no two distinct elements a and b of D does a situation such as that shown in Figure 23 occur.

In view of the above considerations, it is easily proved that *a function*

$$f : D \to R$$

is a one-to-one mapping if and only if any one of the following holds:

(63) $f^{-1}(f^1(X)) = X$ *for every* $X \subset D$

(64) $(f(x) \in f^1(X)) \leftrightarrow (x \in X)$

for every $x \in D$ and every $X \subset D$.

(65)
$$(X \subset Y) \leftrightarrow (f^1(X) \subset f^1(Y))$$
$$f^1(X \cap Y) = (f^1(X) \cap f^1(Y))$$
$$f^1(X \smallsetminus Y) = (f^1(X) \smallsetminus f^1(Y))$$
$$f^1(X \oplus Y) = (f^1(X) \oplus f^1(Y))$$

for every $X \subset D$ and every $Y \subset D$.

The proofs of the above are straightforward. To illustrate, we shall prove (63).

By (60), for every $X \subset D$, we have:

$$f^{-1}(f^1(X)) \supset X$$

Now, if there exists an $x \in f^{-1}(f^1(X))$ such that $x \notin X$, then a situation such as that shown in Figure 23 must occur which will contradict the one-to-oneness of f. Hence, (63) is true.

A one-to-one function f is also called a *one-to-one correspondence between the domain and the range of f*. Thus, if f is a one-to-one function from D onto H, then it is customary to say that f is a *one-to-one correspondence between D and H* (in that order) and that *D and H are in one-to-one correspondence*.

Clearly, a function f is a one-to-one correspondence between D and H if and only if f_{-1} (the converse of f) is a function from H onto D. Naturally, in this case f_{-1} is also a one-to-one correspondence between H and D.

Also, it can be easily proved that *f is a one-to-one correspondence between D and H if and only if*

(66) $f^{-1}(f^1(X)) = X$ and $f^1(f^{-1}(Y)) = Y$

for every $X \subset D$ and every $Y \subset H$.

A one-to-one correspondence between D and H is also called an *equipollence* between D and H. Moreover, if there exists an equipollence between D and H, then D is called *equipollent* to H or *of the same power as H*.

If f is an equipollence between D and H, then, as mentioned above, f_{-1} is also an equipollence between H and D. Thus, we may say that D and H are two *equipollent* sets (or of the *same power*).

To indicate the fact that D and H are equipollent sets, we write:

(67) $D \cong H$

According to Figure 22, we see at once that

$$\{a,b,c,m\} \cong \{p,q,m,c\}$$

Moreover,

$$\{0,2,5\} \cong \{3,4,1\}$$

since, for instance, $\{(0,3), (2,1), (5,4)\}$ is an equipollence between $\{0,2,5\}$ and $\{3,4,1\}$.

Furthermore,

$$2 \cong 5 \frown 3$$

since $2 = \{0,1\}$ and $5 \frown 3 = \{3,4\}$ and $\{(0,3), (1,4)\}$ is an equipollence between 2 and $\{3,4\}$.

The equipollence of sets will be treated in Chapter VI. However, let us mention here that the equipollence between sets is used to give a precise set-theoretical definition of a *finite* and of an *infinite* set. The reader is advised to set aside all his intuitive feelings concerning infinite sets and to adopt the concept of an infinite set strictly according to the definition given below. Undoubtedly, up to a certain point our intuition serves to motivate our definition; however, once a definition is made, for the sake of consistency we must adhere to it.

It is reasonable to define a finite set in such a way that a set such as, say, $\{0,1,2\}$ falls in the category of finite sets. Let us examine all the subsets of $\{0,1,2\}$. They are the following: $\varnothing$, $\{0\}$, $\{1\}$, $\{2\}$, $\{0,1\}$, $\{0,2\}$, $\{1,2\}$, $\{0,1,2\}$.

We see at once that $\{0,1,2\}$ cannot be equipollent to any of its *proper* subsets. Motivated by this fact, we introduce:

Definition 7.   *A set is called infinite if it has a proper subset that is equipollent to the set itself.*

Accordingly, the empty set $\varnothing$ is not an infinite set since it has no proper subset to begin with.

Definition 8.   *A set is called finite if it is not infinite.*

Accordingly, the empty set $\varnothing$ is a finite set.

Clearly, a set is finite if and only if it is the empty set $\emptyset$ or it is a nonempty set that has no proper subset equipollent to the set itself.

The axiom of Infinity ensures the existence of an infinite set in the Theory of Sets, namely, the set ω of all natural numbers. To prove that ω is an infinite set, it is enough to observe that

$$f = \{(x,y) \mid (x \in \omega) \wedge (y = x^+)\}$$

is an equipollence between

$$\omega = \{0, 1, 2, 3, \ldots\}$$

and its proper subset $\{1, 2, 3, \ldots\}$. Clearly,

$$f = \{(0,1), (1,2), (2,3), \ldots\}$$

Infinite sets will be treated in detail in Chapter VI.

EXERCISES

1. Let f be a function from D into D such that $f(f(x)) = x$, for every $x \in D$. Prove that f is a one-to-one correspondence in D and that $f_{-1}(x) = f(x)$, for every $x \in D$.

2. Let f be a function from D into D such that $f(f(f(x))) = x$, for every $x \in D$. Prove that f is a one-to-one correspondence in D and that $f_{-1}(x) = f(f(x))$, for every $x \in D$.

3. Prove that the function $y = 1 - x$, defined in the set of all real numbers, satisfies the conditions of Problem 1.

4. Prove that the function $y = \dfrac{1}{1-x}$, defined in the set of all real numbers except 0 and 1, satisfies the conditions of Problem 2.

5. Prove that the function $h(x,y) = x + y$, defined for every real number x and every real number y, is expressible as

$$g(x,g(g(x,x),y))$$

where $g(x,y) = x - y$, for every real number x and every real number y.

6. Prove that there are $n! = 1 \cdot 2 \cdot 3 \cdots n$ distinct one-to-one correspondences in any set of n natural numbers.

7. Prove that each of the following functions establishes a one-to-one correspondence in the set of all real numbers

(i) $y = x + 3$

(ii) $y = \dfrac{x}{|x| + 1}$

where $|x|$ is the usual *absolute value of* x.

Describe the converse function of each of these functions.

8. Prove that the function

$$h(m,n) = 2^{m-1}(2n - 1)$$

defined from the Cartesian product $N \times N$ into N (the set of all positive natural numbers) is a one-to-one correspondence.

9. Prove that there exists a one-to-one correspondence between the power-set $\mathscr{P}S$ of a set S and the set of all functions $f(x)$, each mapping S into 2 (where, naturally, $2 = \{0,1\}$).

10. Represent graphically a one-to-one correspondence between the points of any two line segments.

11. Establish a one-to-one correspondence between the set of all points in a plane different from a given point p and the set of all straight lines on the same plane not passing through the point p.

12. Let f be a function from D into R. Prove that f is an onto mapping if and only if

$$\complement_R(f^1(X)) \subset f^1(\complement_D X)$$

for every subset X of D.

13. Let f be a function from D into R. Prove that f is a one-to-one correspondence between D and R if and only if

$$f^1(\complement_D X) = \complement_R(f^1(X))$$

for every subset X of D.

14. Prove (64), (65) and (66).

15. Let f be a function from D into R. Prove that if f is an onto mapping, then $f^1 \cdot f^{-1}$ is the identity mapping in $\mathscr{P}(R)$.

9. FAMILIES OF SETS

Consider the function

(68) $$F = \{(a,m), (b,n), (c,m), (e,p)\}$$

According to notation (50), we have:

$$m = F(a), \qquad n = F(b), \qquad m = F(c), \qquad p = F(e)$$

Sometimes it is more convenient to write this in the following indexed form:

$$m = F_a, \qquad n = F_b, \qquad m = F_c, \qquad p = F_e$$

in which case the function F, given by (68), is written as:

$$F = \{(a,F_a), (b,F_b), (c,F_c), (e,F_e)\}$$

When a function is expressed in the above form, it is called a *family* or a *family of sets* or, more precisely, a *family of indexed sets*. The domain of a family is called an *index set* and an element of the domain, an *index*. Moreover, the value, denoted by F_i, of the family at an index i, is called a *term* of the family. Clearly, a term of a family is an element of the range of the family.

Thus, a family of sets is nothing but a function. With this new terminology, a new notation is introduced. A family F whose index set is I, is denoted by:

$$(F_i)_{i \in I}$$

Thus,

$$(F_i)_{i \in I} = \{(i, F(i)) \mid i \in I\}$$

where $F_i = F(i)$, for every $i \in I$.

The *union of a family* $(F_i)_{i \in I}$, denoted by $\underset{i \in I}{\cup} F_i$, *is defined as the sum-set of the range of the family*, i.e.,

(69) $$\underset{i \in I}{\cup} F_i = \{x \mid (\exists i)((i \in I) \wedge (x \in F_i))\}$$

The *intersection of a family* $(F_i)_{i \in I}$, denoted by $\underset{i \in I}{\cap} F_i$, *is defined as the intersection-set* (the *meet-set*) *of the range of the family*, i.e.,

(70) $$\underset{i \in I}{\cap} F_i = \{x \mid (x \in \underset{i \in I}{\cup} F_i) \wedge (\forall i)((i \in I) \rightarrow (x \in F_i))\}$$

When there is no ambiguity as far as the index set is concerned or when the index set is not relevant, the family, its union and its intersection are denoted respectively by:

$$(F_i), \qquad \underset{i}{\cup} F_i, \qquad \underset{i}{\cap} F_i$$

We see from (70) that for every family (F_i), we have:

$$\underset{i}{\cap} F_i \subset \underset{i}{\cup} F_i$$

Moreover, from (69) and (70), it follows that:

(71) $$\underset{i \in \varnothing}{\cup} F_i = \varnothing = \underset{i \in \varnothing}{\cap} F_i$$

Let us give an example. If $I = 3 = \{0,1,2\}$, and $F_0 = \{a,b,c\}$, $F_1 = \{a,m,n\}$ and $F_2 = \{a,u,v\}$, where distinct letters are distinct sets, then

$$\underset{i \in 3}{\cup} F_i = F_0 \cup F_1 \cup F_2 = \{a,b,c,m,n,u,v\}$$

and

$$\underset{i \in 3}{\cap} F_i = F_0 \cap F_1 \cap F_2 = \{a\}$$

Let us observe that every set can be expressed as the union or as the intersection of a family of indexed sets. For instance, for every set S, we have:

$$S = \underset{i \in S}{\cup} X_i = \underset{i \in S}{\cap} X_i \qquad \text{where} \quad X_i = S \quad \text{for every} \quad i \in S$$

Now, if the index set I of a family $(X_i)_{i \in I}$ is itself the union of a family $(K_j)_{j \in J}$, i.e.,

(72) $$I = \underset{j \in J}{\cup} K_j$$

then

$$(73) \qquad \bigcup_{i \in I} X_i = \bigcup_{j \in J} \left(\bigcup_{i \in K_j} X_i \right) \qquad \text{(associativity of } \cup)$$

and, if $K_j \neq \varnothing$, for every $j \in J$, then

$$(74) \qquad \bigcap_{i \in I} X_i = \bigcap_{j \in J} \left(\bigcap_{i \in K_j} X_i \right) \qquad \text{(associativity of } \cap)$$

To prove (73), let x be an element of $\bigcup_{i \in I} X_i$; then by (69) there exists $i \in I$ such that $x \in X_i$. Hence, by (72), there exists $j \in J$ such that $i \in K_j$. Consequently, x is an element of $\bigcup_{i \in K_j} X_i$, and therefore x is also an element of $\bigcup_{j \in J} \left(\bigcup_{i \in K_j} X_i \right)$. Conversely, if x is an element of the latter, then by (69) there exists $j \in J$ such that x is an element of $\bigcup_{i \in K_j} X_i$. Hence, there exists $i \in K_j$, and by (72) $i \in I$ such that $x \in X_i$. Therefore, $x \in \bigcup_{i \in I} X_i$. If $J = \varnothing$ or $K_j = \varnothing$, for every $j \in J$, then the proof of (73) follows also from (71).

The proof of (74) is also easily established by means of (70), (72) and (71).

DeMorgan laws (3) and (4) (page 124) can be now generalized as follows: *For every family $(X_i)_{i \in I}$, with $I \neq \varnothing$, and every set M, the following hold:*

$$(75) \qquad \complement_M \left(\bigcup_{i \in I} X_i \right) = \bigcap_{i \in I} (\complement_M X_i)$$

$$(76) \qquad \complement_M \left(\bigcap_{i \in I} X_i \right) = \bigcup_{i \in I} (\complement_M X_i)$$

where $\complement_M S$ *stands for the complement of S with respect to M, or, which is the same, $M - S$.*

The distributivity laws given by (15) and (16) (page 128) can now be generalized as follows:

Let $(X_i)_{i \in I}$ and $(Y_j)_{j \in J}$ be two families of sets; then

$$(77) \qquad \left(\bigcap_{i \in I} X_i \right) \cup \left(\bigcap_{j \in J} Y_j \right) = \bigcap_{(i,j) \in I \times J} (X_i \cup Y_j) \qquad \text{with } I \times J \neq \varnothing$$

$$(78) \qquad \left(\bigcup_{i \in I} X_i \right) \cap \left(\bigcup_{j \in J} Y_j \right) = \bigcup_{(i,j) \in I \times J} (X_i \cap Y_j)$$

where $I \times J$ is the set of all ordered pairs (i,j), with $i \in I$ and $j \in J$.

Also, we have the following distributivity formulas:

$$(79) \qquad \left(\bigcup_{i \in I} X_i \right) \times \left(\bigcup_{j \in J} Y_j \right) = \bigcup_{(i,j) \in I \times J} (X_i \times Y_j)$$

$$(80) \qquad \left(\bigcap_{i \in I} X_i \right) \times \left(\bigcap_{j \in J} Y_j \right) = \bigcap_{(i,j) \in I \times J} (X_i \times Y_j)$$

Now, let f be a function from D into R and let $(A_i)_{i \in I}$ be a family of subsets of D (i.e., $A_i \subset D$ for every $i \in I$) and $(M_j)_{j \in J}$ be a family of subsets of R (i.e., $M_j \subset R$ for every $j \in J$). Then we have the following, which are generalizations of some of (44), (56) and (65):

$$f^1\left(\bigcup_i A_i\right) = \bigcup_i f^1(A_i)$$

$$f^1\left(\bigcap_i A_i\right) \subset \bigcap_i f^1(A_i)$$

(81)

$$f^{-1}\left(\bigcup_j M_j\right) = \bigcup_j f^{-1}(M_j)$$

$$f^{-1}\left(\bigcap_j M_j\right) = \bigcap_j f^{-1}(M_j)$$

and if f is a one-to-one mapping, then

(82)
$$f^1\left(\bigcap_i A_i\right) = \bigcap_i f^1(A_i)$$

EXERCISES

1. Let $I = \{1,2,3\}$, $X_1 = \{0,5\}$, $X_2 = \{3,4\}$ and $X_3 = \{0,3,7\}$. Moreover, let $J = \{4,5\}$, $K_4 = \{1,2\}$ and $K_5 = \{1,2,3\}$. Form $\bigcup_{i\in I} X_i$ and $\bigcup_{j\in J}\left(\bigcup_{i\in K_j} X_i\right)$ and show that they are equal. Similarly, form $\bigcap_{i\in I} X_i$ and $\bigcap_{j\in J}\left(\bigcap_{i\in K_j} X_i\right)$ and show that they are equal.

2. Prove (74), (75) and (76).

3. Prove (77), (78), (79) and (80).

4. Prove (81) and (82).

5. Let $(A_i)_{i\in I}$ be a family of sets and let f be a function from J onto I. Prove that

$$\bigcup_{j\in J} A_{f(j)} = \bigcup_{i\in I} A_i \quad \text{and} \quad \bigcap_{j\in J} A_{f(j)} = \bigcap_{i\in I} A_i$$

6. For every set A and every family $(X_i)_{i\in I}$ with $I \neq \varnothing$, prove the following:

$$A \cup \left(\bigcup_{i\in I} X_i\right) = \bigcup_{i\in I} (A \cup X_i)$$

$$A \cap \left(\bigcap_{i\in I} X_i\right) = \bigcap_{i\in I} (A \cap X_i)$$

7. Prove that if $J \subset I$, then $\bigcup_{i\in J} X_i \subset \bigcup_{i\in I} X_i$; moreover, if $J \neq \varnothing$, then $\bigcap_{i\in I} X_i \subset \bigcap_{i\in J} X_i$.

8. Prove that for every two families $(X_i)_{i\in I}$ and $(Y_i)_{i\in I}$ we have:

$$\left(\bigcap_{i\in I} X_i\right) \times \left(\bigcap_{i\in I} Y_i\right) = \bigcap_{i\in I} (X_i \times Y_i)$$

10. CARTESIAN PRODUCTS

Let $(X_i)_{i \in I}$ be a family of sets. We define the Cartesian product of $(X_i)_{i \in I}$, denoted by $\prod_{i \in I} X_i$, as *the set of all functions f from I into $\cup_{i \in I} X_i$ such that $f(i) \in X_i$ for every $i \in I$.*

For instance, if $I = \{1,2,3\}$ and

$$X_1 = \{a,b\}, \qquad X_2 = \{m,n\}, \qquad X_3 = \{u\}$$

then

$$\prod_{i \in I} X_i = \{\{(1,a), (2,m), (3,u)\}, \{(1,a), (2,n), (3,u)\},$$
$$\{(1,b), (2,m), (3,u)\}, \{(1,b), (2,n), (3,u)\}\}$$

When there is no ambiguity as far as the index set I is concerned or when the index set I is not relevant, the Cartesian product $\prod_{i \in I} F_i$ is denoted simply by

$$\prod_i F_i$$

Now, since each function is a family of sets, we may say that $\prod_{i \in I} X_i$ is the set of all families $(x_i)_{i \in I}$ such that $x_i \in X_i$, for every $i \in I$.

Inasmuch as $\prod_{i \in I} X_i$ is a set of functions from I into $\cup_{i \in I} X_i$, our axioms ensure the existence of $\prod_{i \in I} X_i$ which is a subset of the power-set $P = \mathscr{P}\left(I \times \cup_{i \in I} X_i\right)$.

Formally, we have:

$$\prod_{i \in I} X_i = \{(x_i)_{i \in I} \mid ((x_i)_{i \in I} \in P) \wedge (\forall i)((i \in I) \to (x_i \in X_i))\}$$

where $P = \mathscr{P}\left(I \times \cup_{i \in I} X_i\right)$.

Theorem 4. *The Cartesian product of a family is equal to the empty set if and only if the empty set is a term of the family*, i.e.,

$$\left(\prod_{i \in I} X_i = \varnothing\right) \leftrightarrow (\exists i)((i \in I) \wedge (X_i = \varnothing))$$

PROOF. If one of the terms of the family $(X_i)_{i \in I}$ is the empty set, then there is no function f whose domain is I such that $f(i) \in X_i$, for every $i \in I$. Therefore, the set of all such functions f is $\varnothing$. Consequently, $\prod_{i \in I} X_i = \varnothing$. On the other hand, let $\prod_{i \in I} X_i = \varnothing$ and assume $X_i \neq \varnothing$ for every $i \in I$. Then, by the General Principle of Choice (page 117), there exists a function F from the rng (X_i) into $\cup X_i$ such that $F(X_i) \in X_i$ for every $i \in I$. Now, consider the function $f = F \cdot g$, where $g : I \to$ rng (X_i) such that $g(i) = X_i$ for every $i \in I$. Then f is a function from I into $\cup X_i$ such that $f(i) \in X_i$ for every $i \in I$. This contradicts $\prod_{i \in I} X_i = \varnothing$. Hence, our assumption is false and indeed there exists an $i \in I$ such that $X_i = \varnothing$.

Let us call Theorem 4 the *Multiplicative Principle*. The above proof establishes the equivalence of the Multiplicative Principle and the General Principle of Choice. However, the latter is equivalent to the axiom of Choice (Theorem 25 on page 118). Hence, we have:

Corollary 2. *The axiom of Choice is equivalent to the Multiplicative Principle.*

Next, let $(X_i)_{i \in I}$ be such that $X_i = S$, for every $i \in I$. Then we see at once that $\prod_{i \in I} X_i$ is the set of all functions from I into S which, according to (54), is denoted by S^I. Also, we know that

$$S^{\varnothing} = \{\varnothing\} \quad \text{for every set } S$$

and

$$(S^E = \varnothing) \leftrightarrow ((S = \varnothing) \wedge (E \neq \varnothing))$$

Therefore,

(83)
$$\prod_{i \in \varnothing} X_i = \{\varnothing\}$$

In Chapter II, Section 9, we introduced the Cartesian product $A \times B$ of two sets A and B as the set of all ordered pairs (x,y) with $x \in A$ and $y \in B$. The following theorem shows the relation between $A \times B$ and the Cartesian product of a family of sets.

Theorem 5. *The Cartesian product $A \times B$ is equipollent to the Cartesian product of the family $(X_i)_{i \in 2}$ with $X_0 = A$ and $X_1 = B$.*

In connection with Theorem 5, let us mention that sometimes $A \times B$ is defined as $\prod_{i \in 2} X_i$ with $X_0 = A$ and $X_1 = B$. However, as usual we will continue to consider $A \times B$ as the set of all ordered pairs (x,y) with $x \in A$ and $y \in B$.

· Motivated by the definition of the Cartesian product of a family, we introduce the definition of the Cartesian product of a set S as follows:

Definition 9. *The Cartesian product of a set S, denoted by ΠS, is the set of all functions f from S into $\cup S$ such that $f(s) \in s$, for every $s \in S$.*

The existence and uniqueness of ΠS follows immediately from our axioms and the definition of equality between sets.

Thus, for instance, if

$$S = \{1,2\}$$

where $1 = \{0\}$ and $2 = \{0,1\}$, we have:

$$\Pi S = \{\{(1,0), (2,0)\}, \{(1,0), (2,1)\}\}$$

As in the case of Theorem 4, here also, in view of the axiom of Choice, we have:

Theorem 6. *The Cartesian product ΠS of a set S is equal to the empty set if and only if the empty set is an element of S.*

Here also, as in the case of (83), we have:

(84) $$\Pi \varnothing = \{\varnothing\}$$

EXERCISES

1. Let $(X_i)_{i \in \{2,3\}}$ be a family of sets such that $X_i = i$, for every $i \in \{2,3\}$. Construct

$$\prod_{i \in \{2,3\}} X_i$$

2. Prove that if $(X_i)_{i \in I}$ is a family of sets such that $\cup_{i \in I} X_i \subset S$, then

$$\prod_{i \in I} X_i \subset S^I$$

3. Using notations introduced by (54) and (67), prove that for every u, v and w

$$(u \times v)^w \simeq u^w \times v^w \qquad \text{and} \qquad (u^v)^w \simeq u^{v \times w}$$

4. Prove that if $(X_i)_{i \in I}$ and $(Y_i)_{i \in I}$ are two families of sets (with the same index set I) and if $X_i \subset Y_i$ for every $i \in I$, then

$$\prod_{i \in I} X_i \subset \prod_{i \in I} Y_i$$

Prove also that if $\prod_{i \in I} X_i \subset \prod_{i \in I} Y_i$ and if $X_i \neq \varnothing$ for every $i \in I$, then $X_i \subset Y_i$ for every $i \in I$.

5. Prove Theorems 5 and 6 and (84).

6. Let $(X_i)_{i \in I}$ and $(Y_i)_{i \in I}$ be two families of sets indexed by the same set I. Prove that

$$\left(\prod_{i \in I} X_i \right) \cap \left(\prod_{i \in I} Y_i \right) = \prod_{i \in I} (X_i \cap Y_i)$$

7. Let $(X_{i,j})_{(i,j) \in I \times J}$ be a family of sets indexed by the Cartesian product $I \times J$. Prove that if $J \neq \varnothing$, then

$$\bigcap_{j \in J} \left(\prod_{i \in I} X_{(i,j)} \right) = \prod_{i \in I} \left(\bigcap_{j \in J} X_{(i,j)} \right)$$

11. SEQUENCES OF SETS

A family of sets $(S_i)_{i \in I}$ is called a *finite sequence* if the index set I is a natural number. Thus,

$$(S_i)_{i \in 0}, \qquad (S_i)_{i \in 3}, \qquad (S_i)_{i \in 4}$$

are examples of finite sequences. Clearly, the terms of, say, $(S_i)_{i \in 3}$ are S_0, S_1 and S_2.

A family of sets $(S_i)_{i \in I}$ is called a *sequence*, or more precisely, an *infinite sequence*, if the index set I is the set ω of all natural numbers. Thus, the terms of the sequence $(S_i)_{i \in \omega}$ are

$$S_0, S_1, S_2, S_3, \ldots$$

Sometimes in speaking about a sequence $(S_i)_{i \in \omega}$, it is customary to refer to it as the sequence $S_0, S_1, S_2, \ldots$.

In what follows, (S_n) will stand for $(S_n)_{n \in \omega}$.

The *limit superior* of a sequence (S_n), denoted by

$$\overline{\lim_{n \to \infty}} \, S_n$$

is the set of all those sets that are elements of *infinitely many* terms of (S_n).

For instance, if a, b, c and e are distinct sets and if (S_n) is given by

$$S_0 = \{b,c,e\}, \quad S_1 = \{a,b\}, \quad S_2 = \{a,c\}, \quad S_3 = \{a,b\}, \quad S_4 = \{a,c\}, \quad \cdots$$

then we see that

$$\overline{\lim_{n \to \infty}} \, S_n = \{a,b,c\}$$

The *limit inferior* of a sequence (S_n), denoted by

$$\underline{\lim_{n \to \infty}} \, S_n$$

is the set of all those sets that are elements of *all but finitely many terms* of (S_n). Thus, for the example given above, we have:

$$\underline{\lim_{n \to \infty}} \, S_n = \{a\}$$

Again, if (E_n) is a sequence given by

(85) $E_0 = \{1\}, \quad E_2 = \{2\}, \quad E_3 = \{1\}, \quad E_4 = \{2\}, \ldots$

then

$$\overline{\lim_{n \to \infty}} \, E_n = \{1,2\} \quad \text{and} \quad \underline{\lim_{n \to \infty}} \, E_n = \varnothing$$

The reader is urged to note the difference between the two expressions: *x belongs to infinitely many terms of a sequence*, and *y belongs to all but finitely many terms of a sequence*. In the former, x, while belonging to infinitely many terms of the sequence, may also not belong to infinitely many terms of that sequence. In the latter, however, y must belong to infinitely many terms of the sequence and not belong to at most a finite number of terms of that sequence.

Clearly, for every sequence (S_n), we have:

(86) $$\underline{\lim_{n \to \infty}} \, S_n \subset \overline{\lim_{n \to \infty}} \, S_n$$

Let us observe that our axioms ensure the existence and the uniqueness of the limit superior and the limit inferior of any sequence (S_n).

A sequence (S_n) is called *convergent* if

$$\overline{\lim_{n \to \infty}} \, S_n = \underline{\lim_{n \to \infty}} \, S_n$$

and in this case the common limit is denoted by

$$\lim_{n \to \infty} S_n$$

and is called the limit of the convergent sequence (S_n). A sequence that is not convergent is called *divergent*.

For instance, if (S_n) is given by

$$S_0 = \{1,0\}, \qquad S_1 = \{1,1\}, \qquad S_2 = \{1,2\}, \qquad S_3 = \{1,3\}, \qquad \ldots$$

then it is convergent, since

$$\overline{\lim_{n \to \infty}} \, S_n = \underline{\lim_{n \to \infty}} \, S_n = \lim_{n \to \infty} S_n = \{1\}$$

On the other hand, the sequence given by (85) is divergent.

Let (S_n) be a sequence; then it is customary to introduce the following notations

$$\bigcup_{n=0}^{\infty} S_n, \qquad \bigcap_{n=0}^{\infty} S_n, \qquad \bigcup_{n=m}^{\infty} S_n, \qquad \bigcap_{n=m}^{\infty} S_n$$

respectively for

$$\bigcup_{n \in \omega} S_n, \qquad \bigcap_{n \in \omega} S_n, \qquad \bigcup_{n \in (\omega \smallsetminus m)} S_n, \qquad \bigcap_{n \in (\omega \smallsetminus m)} S_n$$

Thus, by abusing notation, we write

$$\bigcup_{n=0}^{\infty} S_n = S_0 \cup S_1 \cup S_2 \cup \cdots$$

and

$$\bigcup_{n=m}^{\infty} S_n = S_m \cup S_{m+1} \cup S_{m+2} \cup \cdots$$

Theorem 7. *Let (S_n) be a sequence. Then*

$$\overline{\lim_{n \to \infty}} \, S_n = \bigcap_{n=0}^{\infty} \left(\bigcup_{i=n}^{\infty} S_i \right)$$

and

$$\underline{\lim_{n = \infty}} \, S_n = \bigcup_{n=0}^{\infty} \left(\bigcap_{i=n}^{\infty} S_i \right)$$

PROOF. According to the above, we have to show that

$$\overline{\lim_{n \to \infty}} \, S_n = (S_0 \cup S_1 \cup \cdots) \cap (S_1 \cup S_2 \cup \cdots) \cap (S_2 \cup S_3 \cup \cdots) \cap \cdots$$

Now, if x belongs to infinitely many terms of (S_n), then it must belong to every one of the parentheses on the right side of the above equality. Conversely, if x belongs to every one of the above parentheses, then x must belong to infinitely many terms of (S_n).

Similarly, we prove that

$$\underline{\lim_{n \to \infty}} \, S = (S_0 \cap S_1 \cap \cdots) \cup (S_1 \cap S_2 \cap \cdots) \cup (S_2 \cap S_3 \cap \cdots) \cup \cdots$$

Let us call a sequence (S_n) *nondecreasing* if $S_0 \subset S_1 \subset S_2 \subset \cdots$, and *nonincreasing* if $S_0 \supset S_1 \supset S_2 \supset \ldots$.

If a sequence (E_n) is nondecreasing, then clearly,

$$\overline{\lim_{n \to \infty}} E_n = \lim_{\overline{n \to \infty}} E_n = \bigcup_{n=0}^{\infty} E_n$$

Similarly, if a sequence (P_n) is nonincreasing, then clearly,

$$\overline{\lim_{n \to \infty}} P_n = \lim_{\overline{n \to \infty}} P_n = \bigcap_{n=0}^{\infty} P_n$$

Let us call $\underset{n \in \omega}{\cup} S_n$ the *sum* of the sequence (S_n) and $\underset{n \in \omega}{\cap} S_n$ the *product* of the sequence (S_n). In view of the above, we have:

Theorem 8. *A nondecreasing sequence (E_n) is convergent and its limit is the sum $\bigcup_{n=0}^{\infty} E_n$ of the sequence. A nondecreasing sequence (P_n) is convergent and its limit is equal to the product $\bigcap_{n=0}^{\infty} P_n$ of the sequence.*

With every sequence (S_n), we associate the sequence (E_n) of *partial sums* of (S_n), where

$$E_n = \bigcup_{i \in n^+} S_i$$

Thus,

$$E_0 = S_0, \qquad E_1 = S_0 \cup S_1, \qquad E_2 = S_0 \cup S_1 \cup S_2, \qquad \ldots$$

Similarly, with every sequence (S_n), we associate the sequence (P_n) of *partial products* of (S_n), where

$$P_n = \bigcap_{i \in n^+} S_i$$

Thus,

$$P_0 = S_0, \qquad P_1 = S_0 \cap S_1, \qquad P_2 = S_0 \cap S_1 \cap S_2, \qquad \ldots$$

Clearly, the sequence of partial sums of a sequence is nondecreasing and hence convergent. Also, the sequence of partial products of a sequence is nonincreasing and hence convergent. Moreover, we have:

Theorem 9. *The sum $\bigcup_{i=0}^{\infty} S_n$ of a sequence (S_n) is the limit of the sequence of partial sums of (S_n). The product $\bigcap_{n=0}^{\infty} S_n$ is the limit of the sequence of partial products of (S_n).*

The above theorem bears a great resemblance to a theorem (of the classical analysis) stating that the sum of a sequence of real numbers (defined later) is equal to the limit of the sequence of its partial sums and that the product of a sequence of real numbers is equal to the limit of the sequence of its partial products.

The reader should note also that for every sequence of sets, the sequence of its partial sums and similarly the sequence of its partial products are convergent sequences. However, not every sequence of partial sums or partial products of a given sequence of real numbers is convergent (in the sense of the classical analysis).

Let us recall that two sets M and N are called disjoint if $M \cap N = \varnothing$.

Theorem 10. *For every sequence (S_n), there exists a sequence (D_n) whose distinct terms are pairwise disjoint and such that the sums of the two sequences are equal, i.e., $\bigcup\limits_{n=0}^{\infty} S_n = \bigcup\limits_{n=0}^{\infty} D_n$.*

PROOF.   In view of the fact that

$$S_0 \cup S_1 \cup S_2 \cup \cdots = S_0 \cup (S_1 \smallsmile S_0) \cup (S_2 \smallsmile (S_0 \cup S_1)) \cup \cdots ,$$

it is enough to choose the terms of the desired sequence (D_n) as follows:

$$D_0 = S_0, \qquad D_1 = S_1 \smallsmile S_0, \qquad D_2 = S_2 \smallsmile (S_0 \cup S_1), \qquad \cdots$$

Theorem 11. *For every sequence (S_n) and every set M,*

$$\complement \varlimsup_{n\to\infty} S_n = \varliminf_{n\to\infty} \complement S_n \qquad and \qquad \complement \varliminf_{n\to\infty} S_n = \varlimsup_{n\to\infty} \complement S_n$$

where $\complement x$ represents the complement of x with respect to M.

PROOF.   Since

$$\varlimsup_{n\to\infty} S_n = \bigcap_{n=0}^{\infty} \left(\bigcup_{i=n}^{\infty} S_i \right)$$

then by (75) and (76), we have:

$$\complement \varlimsup_{n\to\infty} S_n = \complement \bigcap_{n=0}^{\infty} \left(\bigcup_{i=n}^{\infty} S_i \right) = \bigcup_{n=0}^{\infty} \left(\bigcap_{i=n}^{\infty} \complement S_i \right) = \varliminf_{n\to\infty} \complement S_n$$

Similarly, by (75) and (76), we have:

$$\complement \varliminf_{n\to\infty} S_n = \complement \bigcup_{n=0}^{\infty} \left(\bigcap_{i=n}^{\infty} S_i \right) = \bigcap_{n=0}^{\infty} \left(\bigcup_{i=n}^{\infty} \complement S_i \right) = \varlimsup_{n\to\infty} \complement S_n$$

Thus, Theorem 11 is proved.

EXERCISES

1. Prove (86) and show that if $\varlimsup\limits_{n\to\infty} S_n = \varnothing$, then (S_n) is convergent.

2. Prove that if $S_n = A$ for every $n \in \omega$, then (S_n) is convergent.

3. Prove Theorems 8 and 9.

4. Let (X_i) and (Y_i) be two infinite sequences. Prove that

$$\overline{\lim_{n \to \infty}} (X_n \cup Y_n) = \overline{\lim_{n \to \infty}} X_n \cup \overline{\lim_{n \to \infty}} Y_n$$

$$\lim_{n \to \infty} (X_n \cap Y_n) = \lim_{n \to \infty} X_n \cap \lim_{n \to \infty} Y_n$$

$$\lim_{n \to \infty} (X_n \cup Y_n) \supset \lim_{n \to \infty} X_n \cup \lim_{n \to \infty} Y_n$$

$$\overline{\lim_{n \to \infty}} (X_n \cap Y_n) \subset \overline{\lim_{n \to \infty}} X_n \cap \overline{\lim_{n \to \infty}} Y_n$$

$$\overline{\lim_{n \to \infty}} (X_n \smallsetminus Y_n) \subset \overline{\lim_{n \to \infty}} X_n \smallsetminus \lim_{n \to \infty} Y_n$$

$$\lim_{n \to \infty} (X_n \smallsetminus Y_n) \supset \lim_{n \to \infty} X_n \smallsetminus \overline{\lim_{n \to \infty}} Y_n$$

5. Using the above results, prove that if the sequences (X_n) and (Y_n) are convergent and their limits are equal respectively to $\lim_{n \to \infty} X_n$ and $\lim_{n \to \infty} Y_n$, then

$$\lim_{n \to \infty} (X_n \cup Y_n) = \lim_{n \to \infty} X_n \cup \lim_{n \to \infty} Y_n$$

$$\lim_{n \to \infty} (X_n \cap Y_n) = \lim_{n \to \infty} X_n \cap \lim_{n \to \infty} Y_n$$

$$\lim_{n \to \infty} (X_n \smallsetminus Y_n) = \lim_{n \to \infty} X_n \smallsetminus \lim_{n \to \infty} Y_n$$

6. Let (X_n) and (Y_n) be two sequences. Prove that

$$\bigcup_{n=0}^{\infty} X_n \cap \bigcup_{n=0}^{\infty} Y_n = \bigcup_{n=0}^{\infty} ((X_0 \cup X_1 \cup \cdots \cup X_n) \cap (Y_0 \cup Y_1 \cup \cdots \cup Y_n))$$

and

$$\bigcap_{n=0}^{\infty} X_n \cup \bigcap_{n=0}^{\infty} Y_n = \bigcap_{n=0}^{\infty} ((X_0 \cap X_1 \cap \cdots \cap X_n) \cup (Y_0 \cap Y_1 \cap \cdots \cap Y_n))$$

12. SUMMARY

Relations play an essential role in all of mathematics. In fact a specific relation may give rise to an entire theory. The central idea is that of an ordered pair (x,y), itself defined as the set $\{\{x\}, \{x,y\}\}$. After the notion of an ordered pair is introduced, a relation is defined as a set of ordered pairs.

In Section 6, a function is defined as a relation whose distinct elements have distinct first coordinates. Moreover, in Section 8, a one-to-one correspondence is defined as a relation whose distinct elements have distinct first and distinct second coordinates, i.e., as a function whose distinct elements have distinct second coordinates. As shown in that section, a one-to-one correspondence is used to define finite and infinite sets.

In Section 9, families of sets are defined as functions, and in Section 10 the Cartesian product of a family and the Cartesian product of a set are defined as certain sets of functions.

In Section 11, sequences of sets are defined as a special kind of function—namely, functions with ω (the set of all natural numbers) as their domains.

In the sequel, relations will be used constantly, especially those relations that are defined in a set, i.e., a subset of the Cartesian product of a set with itself. To this category of relations belong the various kinds of order and equivalence relations.

Chapter IV

ORDER AND ZORN'S LEMMA

1. PARTIALLY ORDERED SETS

In this chapter, we shall study various order relations defined in sets. Specifically, we shall study *partially ordered*, *simply ordered* and *well ordered* sets. As we know, any relation in a set S is a subset R of the Cartesian product $S \times S$. Various restrictions imposed on R will yield various order relations in S.

Our motivation for the definition of a partial order is based on the usual properties of the relation "*is smaller than or equal to*," in connection with the intuitive notion of the size of objects. For example, we usually agree that *sizewise:*

(i) Every object is smaller than or equal to itself.

(ii) If each of two objects is smaller than or equal to the other, then they are equal.

(iii) If one object is smaller than or equal to a second and the latter is smaller than or equal to a third, then the first object is smaller than or equal to the third object.

Motivated by (i), (ii) and (iii) above, we introduce:

Definition 1. *A subset P of the Cartesian product $S \times S$ is called a partial order in the set S if the following three conditions are satisfied:*

(i) $(x,x) \in P$, *for every element x of S.*

(ii) *If* $(x,y) \in P$ *and* $(y,x) \in P$, *then* $x = y$, *for every two elements x and y of S.*

(iii) *If* $(x,y) \in P$ *and* $(y,z) \in P$, *then* $(x,z) \in P$, *for every three elements x, y and z of S.*

Conditions (i), (ii) and (iii) state respectively that a partial order is a *reflexive* *antisymmetric* and *transitive* relation.

Remark 1. For the sake of convenience in giving examples, let us agree that in what follows different letters are different sets.

Let us give an example of a partial order in a set.

Let $S = \{a,b,c\}$ and let

(1) $$P = \{(a,a), (a,b), (b,b), (c,c)\}$$

Clearly, P is a partial order in S, since for every $x \in \{a,b,c\}$, we have $(x,x) \in P$; also, conditions (ii) and (iii) are obviously satisfied in P. Hence, P is reflexive, antisymmetric and transitive. Consequently, P is a partial order in S.

It is easily seen that conditions (i), (ii) and (iii) are mutually independent in the sense that none is a logical consequence of the other two. To see this, it is enough to exhibit three relations in S: one that is reflexive and antisymmetric but not transitive, another that is antisymmetric and transitive but not reflexive and a third that is transitive and reflexive but not antisymmetric. For instance, in the set $S = \{a,b,c\}$, the relation

$$\{(a,a),\ (b,b),\ (c,c),\ (a,b),\ (b,c)\}$$

is reflexive and antisymmetric but not transitive since (a,c) does not belong to it. On the other hand,

$$\{(a,a),\ (a,b),\ (b,c),\ (a,c)\}$$

is an antisymmetric and transitive relation in S, but it is not reflexive since (b,b) does not belong to it. Finally,

$$\{(a,a),\ (b,b),\ (c,c),\ (a,b),\ (b,a)\}$$

is a transitive and reflexive relation in S but it is not antisymmetric since $a \neq b$ (see Remark 1).

Let us observe that the converse of a partial order relation in a set is again a partial order in that set. Thus, the converse of the partial order P above is

$$P_{-1} = \{(a,a),\ (b,a),\ (b,b),\ (c,c)\}$$

which is obviously a partial order in S.

Clearly, in the same set $S = \{a,b,c\}$, we may have many different partial orders. For instance, besides (1), the following are also partial orders in S:

(2)
$$Q = \{(a,a),\ (b,b),\ (c,c)\}$$
$$R = \{(a,a),\ (b,b),\ (c,c),\ (a,c)\}$$
$$M = \{(a,a),\ (b,b),\ (c,c),\ (a,b),\ (b,c),\ (a,c)\}$$

The symbol $\leq$ is frequently used to denote an arbitrary partial order in a set. Thus, $\leq$ may stand for P given by (1), i.e.,

$$\leq\ =\ \{(a,a),\ (b,b),\ (c,c),\ (a,b)\}$$

In this connection, if (x,y) is an element of a partial order, then this fact is denoted by:

$$\leq(x,y) \quad \text{or} \quad \geq(y,x) \quad \text{or} \quad x \leq y \quad \text{or} \quad y \geq x$$

Thus, for (1), we have:

$$a \leq a, \quad b \leq b, \quad c \leq c, \quad a \leq b$$

Definition 2. *An ordered pair* $(S,\leq)$ *is called a partially ordered set if* $\leq$ *is a partial order in the set* S.

Thus,

$$(\{a,b,c\},\ \{(a,a),\ (b,b),\ (c,c),\ (a,c)\})$$

is a partially ordered set.

In practice however, instead of calling $(S,\leq)$ a partially ordered set, we call S *a partially ordered set*, or to be more precise, we say:

S is a set partially ordered by $\leq$

For instance, if $S = \{a,b,c\}$ and Q, R and M are given as in (2), then (S,Q), (S,R), (S,M) are partially ordered sets. However, it is customary to refer to them respectively as: "*S is partially ordered by Q*," "*S is partially ordered by R*," and "*S is partially ordered by M*."

Let $(S,\leq)$ be a partially ordered set. If for two elements x and y of S it is true that $x \leq y$, i.e., if $(x,y) \in (\leq)$, then x and y are called *comparable*. Moreover, $x \leq y$ may be read: "*x is less than or equal to y*," or "*x is smaller than or equal to y*," or "*x is equal to or precedes y*," or "*y is greater than or equal to x*," or "*y is larger than or equal to x*," or "*y is equal to or succeeds x*," or "*y is equal to or exceeds x*."

If two elements x and y of a partially ordered set $(S,\leq)$ are not comparable, we write $x \nleq y$ and $y \nleq x$.

In view of the reflexivity of a partial order, if S is a partially ordered set, then every element is comparable to itself. However, neither (i) nor (ii) nor (iii) implies that in a partially ordered set every two elements are comparable.

For instance, when $S = \{a,b,c\}$ is partially ordered by Q as given in (2), then no two distinct elements of S are comparable.

Let us give some classical examples of partially ordered sets. If for every two elements x and y of a set S, we write:

$$x \leq y \quad \textit{if and only if} \quad x \subset y$$

then we see at once that for every set S

$$(S,\subset)$$

is a partially ordered set. Thus, we may say that *every set is partially ordered by* $\subset$.

Likewise, if for every two elements x and y of a set S, we write:

$$x \leq y \quad \textit{if and only if} \quad x = y$$

then we see at once that for every set S

$$(S,=)$$

is a partially ordered set. Thus, we may say that *every set is partially ordered by* $=$.

On the other hand, it is obvious that in general $(S,\in)$ is not a partially ordered set. However, in view of Theorem 16 and Corollary 4 of Chapter II (page 106), if for every two elements x and y of a natural number n, we write

(3) $x \leq y \quad \textit{if and only if} \quad (x \in y) \vee (x = y)$

then we see at once that for every natural number n,

$$(n, (\in \text{ or } =))$$

is a partially ordered set. Similarly, the set ω of all natural numbers is partially ordered by (3). This is called the *natural partial order* of the set ω of all natural numbers.

Closely related to a partial order relation is an *order* relation. Our motivation in the definition of an order is based on the usual properties that the relation "*is smaller than*" possesses (say, in connection with the size of objects).

Definition 3. *A subset E of the Cartesian product $S \times S$ is called an order in a set S if the following conditions are satisfied:*
(iv) *$(x,x) \notin E$ for every element x of S.*
(v) *If $(x,y) \in E$ and $(y,z) \in E$, then $(x,z) \in E$, for every three elements x, y and z of S.*

Conditions (iv) and (v) state respectively that an order is an *irreflexive* and *transitive* relation.

For instance, $E = \{(a,b), (c,d)\}$ is an order in the set $\{a,b,c,d\}$.

The symbol $<$ is frequently used to denote an arbitrary order in a set. Thus, $<$ may stand for the above order E in the set $\{a,b,c,d\}$, i.e.,

$$< \,= \{(a,b), (c,d)\}$$

Here also, an ordered pair $(S,<)$ is called *an ordered set* if $<$ is an order in the set S. However, here also, instead of calling $(S,<)$ an ordered set, we call *S an ordered set*, or more precisely we say S is a *set, ordered* by $<$.

Let $(S,<)$ be an ordered set. If for two elements x and y of S, it is the case that $(x,y) \in (<)$, then this fact is denoted by

$$<(x,y) \qquad \text{or} \qquad >(y,x) \qquad \text{or} \qquad x < y \qquad \text{or} \qquad y > x$$

and in this connection we say that in the set S ordered by $<$, the elements x and y are *comparable*. Moreover, $x < y$ may be read: "*x is less than y*," or "*x is smaller than y*," or "*x precedes y*," or "*y is greater than x*," or "*y is larger than x*," or "*y succeeds x*," or "*y exceeds x*."

If two elements x and y of an ordered set $(S,<)$ are not comparable, we write $x \not< y$ and $y \not< x$.

Lemma 1. *Let $(S,<)$ be an ordered set. Then, for every two elements x and y of S,*

$$(x < y) \rightarrow (y \not< x)$$

i.e., *order is an asymmetric relation.*

PROOF. Assume the contrary, that $x < y$ and $y < x$. Then in view of the transitivity of $<$, we must have $x < x$ which contradicts the irreflexivity of $<$. Thus, Lemma 1 is proved.

The connection between a partial order and an order in a set is given by:

Lemma 2. *Let* $(S, \leq)$ *be a partially ordered set. For every two elements* x *and* y *of* S, *write*

$$x < y \quad \textit{if and only if} \quad (x \leq y) \wedge (x \neq y)$$

Then $(S, <)$ *is an ordered set.*

Lemma 3. *Let* $(S, <)$ *be an ordered set. For every two elements* x *and* y *of* S, *write*

$$x \leq y \quad \textit{if and only if} \quad (x < y) \vee (x = y)$$

Then $(S, \leq)$ *is a partially ordered set.*

In view of the above and (3), clearly $(n, \in)$ is an ordered set for every natural number n. Moreover, $(\omega, \in)$ is an ordered set. Thus, the set ω of all natural numbers is ordered by $\in$. This is called the *natural order* of the set ω of all natural numbers.

Remark 2. *For the sake of convenience in giving examples, let us agree that a configuration such as*

(4) $\{\ldots, (\ldots; a; b; \ldots; c; \ldots), (\ldots; m; n; \ldots), \ldots\}$

will represent the partially ordered set $(S, \leq)$ *where*

(5) $S = \{\ldots, a, b, \ldots, c, \ldots, m, n, \ldots\}$

and where

  $x \leq y$ *if and only if* x *and* y *are contained in the same pair of parentheses and* x *is not written to the right of* y.

In view of Lemma 2 and Remark 1, configurations such as (4) will represent the ordered set $(S, <)$ where

  $x < y$ *if and only if* x *and* y *are contained in the same pair of parentheses and* x *is written to the left of* y.

Consequently, in a configuration such as (4), those elements of (5) that are contained in the same pair of parentheses are comparable and the elements belonging to different pairs of parentheses are not comparable.

Thus, according to notation (4), the partial order given by (1) is represented as:

$$\{(a; b), (c)\}$$

Let us observe that configurations such as (4) give information concerning both the set S and the partial order $\leq$ (or the order $<$) in S. Clearly, whenever we say: *consider the partially ordered set*

$$A = \{(a; b), (c; d)\}$$

we mean the set $A = \{a, b, c, d\}$ and the partial order

$$\{(a, a), (b, b), (c, c), (d, d), (a, b), (c, d)\}$$

Definition 4. *Let* $(S, \leq)$ *be a partially ordered set. An element* $a \in S$ *is called a minimal element of* S *if*

$$x \leq a \textit{ implies } x = a \qquad \textit{for every } x \in S$$

On the other hand, an element $m \in S$ is called a maximal element of S if

$$m \leq x \text{ implies } m = x \qquad for\ every \quad x \in S$$

In other words, a is a *minimal element of S if no element of S precedes a.* On the other hand, m is a *maximal element of S if no element of S exceeds m.* Partially ordered sets may or may not have minimal (maximal) elements. When minimal (maximal) elements exist they may or may not be unique.

Let us give some examples.

(6)
$$A = \{(a)\}$$
$$B = \{(a;b), (d;e)\}$$
$$C = \{(\ldots; a_2; a_1; b_1; b_2; \ldots)\}$$
$$D = \{(\ldots; a_2; a_1; \ldots; b_2; b_1; c_1; c_2; \ldots; d_2; d_1), (a;b;c)\}$$
$$E = \{(a;b), (c; \ldots; d_2; d_1; e_1; e_2; \ldots; h), (\ldots; m_2; m_1)\}$$
$$F = \{(\ldots; a_2; a_1; b_1; b_2; \ldots), (\ldots; c_2; c_1; e_1; e_2; \ldots)\}$$

In the above, C and F have no minimal elements. Each of A and D has one minimal element. Each of B and E has two minimal elements. On the other hand, C and F have no maximal elements. Each of B and D has two maximal elements and E has three maximal elements, whereas A has one maximal element.

Definition 5. *Let $(S, \leq)$ be a partially ordered set. An element $p \in S$ is called the least (smallest, first, minimum) element of S if*

$$p \leq x \qquad for\ every \quad x \in S$$

On the other hand, an element $g \in S$ is called the greatest (largest, last, maximum) element of S if

$$x \leq g \qquad for\ every \quad x \in S$$

Let us observe immediately that if in S there exists an element p such that $p \leq x$ for every $x \in S$, then p is unique. Indeed, if $q \in S$ is such that $q \leq x$ for every $x \in S$, then on the one hand, $p \leq q$ and on the other hand, $q \leq p$. However, in view of the transitivity of $\leq$, the last two statements imply $p = q$. Thus, p is unique and we are justified in calling p (in Definition 5) *the least* element of S. Similarly, a partially ordered set can have at most one greatest element.

Definition 5 implies that the least (minimum) and the greatest (maximum) elements of a partially ordered set S must be comparable to every element of S. On the other hand, as Definition 4 shows, it is not required that minimal and maximal elements of a partially ordered set S be comparable to every element of S.

In (6), A has a least and a greatest element which is a. However, B, C, D, E and F have no least and no greatest elements. On the other hand, the partially ordered set

(7)
$$\{(a_1; a_2; a_3; \ldots; b_3; b_2; b_1)\}$$

has a least element a_1 and a greatest element b_1.

Definition 6. *Let* $(S, \leq)$ *be a partially ordered set. An element* $w \in S$ *is called a lower bound of a subset* A *of* S *if*

$$w \leq x \quad \text{for every} \quad x \in A$$

On the other hand, an element $u \in S$ *is called an upper bound of a subset* A *of* S *if*

$$x \leq u \quad \text{for every} \quad x \in A$$

Let us observe that it is not required that a lower bound or an upper bound of a subset A of a partially ordered set belong to A. For instance, in (7), each of $a_1, a_2, a_3, \ldots$ is a lower bound of the set $B = \{b_1, b_2, b_3, \ldots\}$; however, none of them is an element of B. On the other hand, c and h in (6) are respectively a lower and an upper bound of the subset $H = \{c, h, e_1, d_1, e_2, d_2, \ldots\}$ of E, and c and h belong to H. Let us observe that a subset of a partially ordered set may have no or many lower and upper bounds [see (6)].

Definition 7. *If a subset* A *of a partially ordered set has a lower bound, then* A *is called bounded below. If* A *has an upper bound, then* A *is called bounded above. Finally, if* A *has a lower and an upper bound, then* A *is called a bounded subset.*

It may happen that the set L of all lower bounds of a subset A of a partially ordered set S possesses a greatest element g. Clearly, g is unique, and consequently it is appropriate to call it *the greatest lower bound* of A. Naturally, $g \in L$; however, g need not belong to A.

The greatest lower bound of a subset A of a partially ordered set S is also called the *infimum* of A and is customarily denoted by:

$$\text{glb}_S \, A \quad \text{or} \quad \text{inf}_S \, A$$

When there is no ambiguity as to what partially ordered set the set A is considered to be a subset of, then we simply write:

$$\text{glb} \, A \quad \text{or} \quad \text{inf} \, A$$

Similarly, it may happen that the set U of all upper bounds of a subset A of a partially ordered set S possesses a least element v. Clearly, v is unique and consequently it is appropriate to call it *the least upper bound* of A. Naturally, $v \in U$; however, v need not belong to A.

The least upper bound of a subset A of a partially ordered set S is also called the *supremum* of A and is customarily denoted by:

$$\text{lub}_S \, A \quad \text{or} \quad \text{sup}_S \, A$$

When there is no ambiguity as to what partially ordered set the set A is considered to be a subset of, then we simply write:

$$\text{lub} \, A \quad \text{or} \quad \text{sup} \, A$$

Consider the subset $A = \{b_1, c_1, b_2, c_2, \ldots\}$ of the partially ordered set D given in (6). Although A is bounded above, it has no least upper bound. On the other hand,

$$\text{glb } A = \text{inf } A = a_1$$

Clearly, $a_1 \notin A$. Next, consider the subset $B = \{b_1, b_2, \ldots\}$ of the partially ordered set given by (7). Although B is bounded below, it has no greatest lower bound. On the other hand,

$$\text{lub } B = \text{sup } B = b_1$$

Clearly, $b_1 \in B$.

Theorem 1. *A partially ordered set $(S, \leq)$ has a least element if and only if the empty set $\varnothing$ has a least upper bound in S.*

PROOF. First, let us observe that every element $x \in S$ is an upper bound of $\varnothing$. Indeed, if $x \in S$, then

$$(\forall y)(y \in \varnothing \rightarrow y \leq x)$$

is true since the antecedent of this implication is false. Now, if S has a least element v, then v is the least of all upper bounds of $\varnothing$ and consequently v is the least upper bound of $\varnothing$. Conversely, since every element $x \in S$ is an upper bound of $\varnothing$, it follows that if $\varnothing$ has a least upper bound, say v, then v must be the least element of S.

Remark 3. As mentioned previously, the converse P_{-1} of every partial order P in a set S is again a partial order in the set S. Moreover, $(P_{-1})_{-1} = P$. It is customary to call the partially ordered set (S, P_{-1}) and the partial order P_{-1} respectively the *dual* of (S, P) and that of P. Clearly, (S, P) and (S, P_{-1}) are duals of each other.

Now, let (S, P) be a partially ordered set and (S, P_{-1}) its dual. In view of Definitions 4, 5 and 6, we see at once that a *distinguished* element, i.e., a *minimal*, a *maximal*, the *least* and the *greatest* element of S with respect to (S, P), as well as a *distinguished* element, i.e., a *lower bound*, an *upper bound*, the *greatest lower bound* and the *least upper bound* of a subset A of S with respect to (S, P), becomes respectively its *counterpart*, i.e., a *maximal*, a *minimal*, the *greatest* and the *least* element of S with respect to (S, P_{-1}), as well as an *upper bound*, a *lower bound*, the *least upper bound* and the *greatest lower bound* of the subset A of S with respect to (S, P_{-1}).

Let us call the above-mentioned counterpart of a distinguished element of a subset of a partially ordered set, the *dual* of that distinguished element. Then in view of the above considerations, we have:

Lemma 4. *Let (S, P) be a partially ordered set. Then the distinguished elements of a subset A of S with respect to (S, P), become their duals for A with respect to (S, P_{-1}).*

Thus, glb A in (S, P) becomes lub A in (S, P_{-1}), and so forth.

Now, in view of Lemma 4 and the fact that $(P_{-1})_{-1} = P$, we have:

Theorem 2 (*Duality theorem*). *Let a statement $\mathcal{T}$ be a theorem in every partially ordered set $(S, \leq)$. If in $\mathcal{T}$ every distinguished element is changed to its dual,* *and $\leq$ to $\geq$, then the statement thus obtained is again a theorem (called the dual of $\mathcal{T}$) in every partially ordered set.*

In view of the above, we have the following theorem which is the dual of Theorem 1.

Theorem 3. *A partially ordered set has a greatest element if and only if the empty set $\varnothing$ has a greatest lower bound in it.*

Theorem 4. *Let $(S, \leq)$ be a partially ordered set and let h be the least upper bound of the set L of all lower bounds of a subset A of S. Then*

$$h \in L \qquad and \qquad h = \text{lub } L = \text{glb } A$$

PROOF. Since every element of A is an upper bound of L, we see that $h \leq x$, for every $x \in A$. Therefore, h is a lower bound of A and as such $h \in L$. On the other hand, since h is greater than or equal to every lower bound of A, we see that $h = \text{glb } A$.

The dual of Theorem 4 is given below.

Theorem 5. *Let $(S, \leq)$ be a partially ordered set and let k be the greatest lower bound of the set U of all upper bounds of a subset A of S. Then*

$$k \in U \qquad and \qquad k = \text{glb } U = \text{lub } A$$

Theorem 6. *Let $(S, \leq)$ be a partially ordered set. Every nonempty subset of S that is bounded above has a least upper bound if and only if every nonempty subset of S that is bounded below has a greatest lower bound.*

PROOF. Assume every nonempty subset of S that is bounded above has a least upper bound. Let A be a nonempty subset of S that is bounded below. Let L be the nonempty set of all lower bounds of A. By our assumption lub L exists and by Theorem 4, lub $L = \text{glb } A$. The converse follows from Theorem 2.

A partially ordered set in which every nonempty subset that is bounded above has a least upper bound (and therefore, in which every nonempty subset that is bounded below has a greatest lower bound) is called a *conditionally complete* partially ordered set.

As a corollary of Theorem 6 we have:

Theorem 7. *Let $(S, \leq)$ be a partially ordered set. Every subset of S has a least upper bound if and only if every subset of S has a greatest lower bound.*

A partially ordered set in which every subset has a least upper bound (and therefore every subset has a greatest lower bound) is called a *complete* partially ordered set or a *complete lattice*. Clearly, a complete lattice has a greatest (inf $\varnothing$) and a least (sup $\varnothing$) element.

In closing this section, let us observe that if $\leq$ is a partial order in a set S then it induces in a natural way a partial order $\leq$ in every subset A of S. Specifically, $x \leq y$ for every two elements of A, if and only if $x \leq y$ with respect to $\leq$ in S. Clearly, in this case when speaking, say, about lub H of a subset H of A, one has to specify whether lub H is considered with respect to $(A, \leq)$ or

$(S, \leq)$. Obviously, it may happen that lub H exists in one case and does not exist in the other; or if they exist, they may not be equal. Consider, for instance,

$$S = \{(a_1; a_2; a_3; \ldots; b_1; b_2; b_3; \ldots; c_3; c_2; c_1)\}$$

Let $A = \{a_1, a_2, a_3, \ldots\}$ and $H = \{a_3, a_4, a_5, \ldots\}$. Then we see that $\text{lub}_S H = b_1$. However, $\text{lub}_A H$ does not exist. Also, if $B = \{c_2, b_1, b_2, b_3, \ldots\}$ and $D \stackrel{.}{=} \{b_1, b_2, b_3, \ldots\}$, then $\text{lub}_B D = c_2$. However, $\text{lub}_S D$ does not exist. Finally, let $E = \{b_2, a_1, a_2, a_3, \ldots\}$ and $G = \{a_1, a_2, a_3, \ldots\}$; then $\text{lub}_E G = b_2$ and $\text{lub}_S G = b_1$. However, $b_1 \neq b_2$.

EXERCISES

1. Let $S = \{a,b,c\}$, where a, b and c are three distinct elements. Discuss each of the following relations for reflexivity, antisymmetry and transitivity in S.

$$\{(a,a), (b,b), (a,c)\}, \qquad \{(b,a), (a,c), (a,d)\}, \qquad \{(a,a)\},$$
$$\{(a,a), (b,c), (c,b)\}, \qquad \{(a,a), (b,b), (c,c), (a,b)\},$$
$$\{(a,c), (c,a)\}, \qquad \{(a,c), (c,b), (a,a), (b,a)\},$$
$$\{(a,a), (b,b), (c,c), (a,b), (b,c), (a,c)\}$$

2. Let $S = \{a,b,c\}$, where a, b and c are distinct elements. Determine which of the following are partial orders in S, which are orders in S and which are neither.

$$\{(a,b)\}, \qquad \{(a,a), (b,b), (c,c), (a,c)\}, \qquad \{(b,c), (a,c)\},$$
$$\{(b,c), (c,a)\}, \qquad \{(a,a), (b,b), (a,c)\}, \qquad \{(a,b), (b,c), (a,c)\},$$
$$\{(c,b), (b,b)\}, \qquad \{(a,a), (b,b), (c,c), (a,c), (c,b)\}, \qquad \{(a,a)\}$$

3. How many distinct partial orders and how many distinct orders are there in a set having three distinct elements?

4. Prove that $x \leq y$ defined as: x *divides* y introduces a partial order in the set ω of all natural numbers.

5. Prove that $x \leq y$ introduces a partial order in the set ω of all natural numbers if $x \leq y$ is defined as follows:
   (i) x is less than or equal (in the usual sense) to y and x and y have the same parity.
   (ii) x is even, and x and y have different parities.

6. Prove that $x < y$ introduces an order in the set ω of all natural numbers if $x < y$ is defined as follows:
   (i) Upon the division of x and y by 5, x yields the smaller remainder.
   (ii) In the above division, x and y yield the same remainder and x is smaller than y.

7. Prove that the set of all triples (three-termed sequences) (x_1, x_2, x_3) of natural numbers is partially ordered by *the principle of first differences* (i.e., *lexicographically*), where

$$(a_1, a_2, a_3) \leq (b_1, b_2, b_3)$$

if $a_1 \leq b_1$, and if $a_1 = b_1$ then $a_2 \leq b_2$, and if $a_1 = b_1$ and $a_2 = b_2$ then $a_3 \leq b_3$, where $x \leq y$ means x is less than or equal to y in the usual sense.

8. Motivated by Problem 7, define partial ordering in the set of all triples of natural numbers by the *principle of last differences*.

Generalize the results of Problems 7 and 8 to the case of the set of all n-tuples of natural numbers ($n = 1, 2, \ldots$). Also, define ordering in the set of all n-tuples of natural numbers by the principle of first or last differences.

9. Give an example of a partially ordered set having three minimal and two maximal elements and neither a minimum nor a maximum.

10. Give an example of a partially ordered set in which every nonempty subset has a least upper bound but not necessarily a lower bound.

11. Give an example of a partially ordered set in which every nonempty subset bounded above has a least upper bound and in which not every subset has a lower bound.

12. A partially ordered set, every two-element subset of which has a glb and lub, is called a *lattice*. How many different lattices are there in a set of three elements?

13. For every set S, is $(S, \subseteq)$ a complete or a conditionally complete partially ordered set?

14. Is $(\omega, (\in \text{ or } =))$ a complete or a conditionally complete partially ordered set?

15. Give an example of a conditionally complete, partially ordered set that is not a complete partially ordered set.

2. SOME THEOREMS ON PARTIALLY ORDERED SETS

We recall that in every partially ordered set S, lub $\varnothing$ exists if and only if S has a least (minimum) element and glb $\varnothing$ exists if and only if S has a greatest (maximum) element. Moreover,

(8) $$\text{lub } \varnothing = \text{minimum of } S$$

and

(9) $$\text{glb } \varnothing = \text{maximum of } S$$

Theorem 8. *Consider the partially ordered set $(S, \subseteq)$. Let X be any subset of S. If $\cup X$ is an element of S, then*

$$\text{lub } X = \cup X$$

Moreover, if X is not empty and $\cap X$ is an element of S,

$$\text{glb } X = \cap X$$

Furthermore, if $X = \varnothing$ and $\cup S$ is an element of S, then

$$\text{glb } \varnothing = \cup S$$

PROOF.   Since $x \subset \cup X$ for every $x \in X$, we see that $\cup X$ is an upper bound of X. On the other hand, if V is an upper bound of X, then $y \in V$ for every $y \in \cup X$. Consequently, $\cup X \subset V$ and thus, lub $X = \cup X$.

Similar reasoning shows that if X is not empty and $\cap X$ is an element of S, then glb $X = \cap X$.

If $X = \varnothing$ and $\varnothing$ is an element of S, then clearly,

$$\text{lub } \varnothing = \cup \varnothing = \varnothing$$

in which case $\varnothing$ [in accordance with (8)] is the minimum of S.

Furthermore, if $X = \varnothing$ and $\cup S$ is an element of S, then, in accordance with (9),

$$\text{glb } \varnothing = \cup S = \text{maximum of } S$$

and, as expected, $\cap \varnothing = \varnothing \neq \text{glb } \varnothing$, unless $S = \{\varnothing\}$.

As previously defined, a partially ordered set is *complete* if every subset of it has a least upper bound. By Theorem 7, every subset of a complete partially ordered set has a greatest lower bound.

In view of Theorem 8, we see that if $\cup X$ of every subset X of a set S is an element of S, then $(S, \subset)$ is a complete partially ordered set. Consequently, we have:

Corollary 1.   *For every set S, $(\mathscr{P}(S), \subset)$ is a complete partially ordered set where $\mathscr{P}(S)$ is the power-set of S.*

Corollary 2.   *For every natural number n, $(n, \subset)$ is a complete partially ordered set.*

As previously defined, a partially ordered set is *conditionally complete* if every nonempty subset of it that is bounded above has a least upper bound. By Theorem 6, in a conditionally complete partially ordered set, every nonempty subset that is bounded below has a greatest lower bound.

Clearly, every complete partially ordered set is conditionally complete.

In view of Theorem 8, we have:

Corollary 3.   *The set $(\omega, \subset)$ is a conditionally complete partially ordered set where ω is the set of all natural numbers.*

Definition 8.   *Let $(P, \leq)$ be a partially ordered set. A subset L of P is called a lower cut of P if*

   (i) *L is a nonempty proper subset of P.*
   (ii) *L has no last element.*
   (iii) *If x is an element of L, then every element y of P such that $y \leq x$ is also an element of L.*

Theorem 9.   *Let D be the set of all lower cuts of a partially ordered set $(P, \leq)$. Then $(D, \subset)$ is a conditionally complete partially ordered set.*

PROOF. Let D_1 be a nonempty subset of D and let D_1 be bounded above. This means that there exists a lower cut L of P such that every element of D_1 is a subset of L. Now, consider the union of all elements of D_1, i.e., consider $\cup D_1$. We claim that $\cup D_1$ is a lower cut of P. Clearly, $\cup D_1$ is a nonempty subset of P. Moreover, since every element of D_1 is a subset of L, we see that $\cup D_1 \subset L$, and since L is a proper subset of P so is $\cup D_1$. Consequently $\cup D_1$ satisfies condition (i) of Definition 8.

Now it is easily seen that $\cup D_1$ has no last element. Indeed, if m were the last element of $\cup D_1$, then m would be the last element of an element of D_1. However, this is impossible since every element of D_1 is a lower cut of P, and consequently m cannot be the last element of any element of D_1. Therefore $\cup D_1$ has no last element and thus satisfies condition (ii) of Definition 8.

Finally let x be an element of $\cup D_1$ and let $y \in P$ be such that $y \leq x$. Since $\cup D_1$ is the union of all elements of D_1 there exists a lower cut L_1 of P such that $L_1 \subset \cup D_1$ and $x \in L_1$. However by (iii) if $x \in L_1$ and $y \leq x$, then $y \in L_1$ and therefore $y \in \cup D_1$. Consequently, $\cup D_1$ satisfies condition (iii) of Definition 8.

Thus, we see that $\cup D_1$ is a lower cut of P and therefore $\cup D_1 \in D$. However, in view of Theorem 8, the least upper bound of D_1 is $\cup D_1$. Thus the least upper bound of an arbitrary nonempty subset D_1 of D that is bounded above exists. Therefore, the set D of all lower cuts of a partially ordered set $(P, \leq)$ is conditionally complete with respect to $\subset$. Hence Theorem 9 is proved.

Let $(P, \leq)$ be a partially ordered set. A function f from P into P is called *nondecreasing* if for every two elements u and v of P,

$$(10) \qquad u \leq v \quad implies \quad f(u) \leq f(v)$$

Theorem 10. *Let $(P, \leq)$ be a conditionally complete partially ordered set and f a nondecreasing function from P into P. If P has two elements a and b such that*

$$(11) \qquad a \leq f(a) \leq f(b) \leq b$$

then there exists an element c of P such that

$$a \leq c \leq b \quad and \quad f(c) = c$$

Thus, P has at least one fixed point under f.

PROOF. Let $S \subset P$ be defined as follows:

$$(12) \qquad S = \{x \mid a \leq x \leq b \text{ and } x \leq f(x)\}$$

i.e., S is the set of all the elements x of P such that $a \leq x \leq b$, and such that they are less than or equal to their respective mates under the mapping f.

By (11), $a \in S$, and therefore S is nonempty. Moreover, S is bounded above by b. Let

$$c = \text{lub } S$$

which exists in view of the hypothesis of the theorem. Obviously,

$$(13) \qquad a \leq c \leq b$$

We show that $f(c) = c$.

Since $x \leq c$ for every $x \in S$, and since f is nondecreasing, in view of (10) and (12) we have $x \leq f(x) \leq f(c)$ for every $x \in S$. Therefore, $f(c)$ is an upper bound of S and consequently,

(14) $$c \leq f(c)$$

On the other hand, since f is nondecreasing, in view of (13) and (11), we have:

$$a \leq f(a) \leq f(c) \leq f(b) \leq b$$

Also, from (14), we derive $f(c) \leq f(f(c))$, which in view of the above inequalities implies $f(c) \in S$. Since $c = \text{lub } S$, we have $f(c) \leq c$, which by (14) yields $f(c) = c$, as desired.

Corollary 4. *If f is a nondecreasing function from a complete partially ordered set P into itself, then P has at least one fixed point under f.*

PROOF. Since P is a complete partially ordered set, obviously P has a least (lub $\varnothing$) element a and a greatest (lub P) element b. In view of the fact· that f is nondecreasing and maps P into itself, we have:

$$a \leq f(a) \leq f(b) \leq b$$

Thus, P and f satisfy all the conditions of Theorem 10, and therefore there exists an element $c \in P$, such that:

$$a \leq c \leq b \qquad \text{and} \qquad f(c) = c$$

i.e., c is left fixed by f.

Let $(P, \leq)$ be a partially ordered set. For every two elements x and y of P we write:

(15) $$x < y \quad \text{if and only if} \quad x \leq y \quad \text{and} \quad x \neq y$$

and we say that x *is less than,* or *is smaller than,* or *precedes y,* or y *is greater than,* or *is larger than,* or *succeeds,* or *exceeds x.*

Definition 9. *Let $(P, \leq)$ be a partially ordered set. For every element a of P, the set of all elements x of P such that $x < a$ is denoted by $I(a)$ and is called the initial segment of P determined by a. If $I(a)$ is nonempty, then $I(a)$ is called a proper initial segment of P.*

In short, using notation (15),

$$I(a) = \{x \mid (x \in P) \wedge (x < a)\}$$

For instance, in the partially ordered set

$$\{(a;b;c), (m;n;p), (r;s;t)\}$$

we have:

$$I(c) = \{a,b\}, \qquad I(n) = \{m\}, \qquad I(r) = \varnothing$$

Definition 10. *A partially ordered set $(P, \leq)$ is called dense if for every two elements a and b of P such that $a < b$, there exists an element c of P such that $a < c < b$.*

Theorem 11. *Let $(P, \leq)$ be a dense partially ordered set. If an initial segment $I(b)$ is nonempty, then $I(b)$ is a lower cut of P.*

PROOF. For an element $b \in P$, let $I(b)$ be the nonempty initial segment determined by b. We show that $I(b)$ is a lower cut of P. First of all, by assumption $I(b)$ is nonempty and since $b \notin I(b)$, we see that $I(b)$ is a proper subset of P. Secondly, $I(b)$ has no last element. Indeed, if a were the last element of $I(b)$, then in view of the denseness of P, there would exist an element $c \in P$ such that $a < c < b$. However, the latter would imply that c is an element of $I(b)$, which in turn would contradict the fact that a is the last element of $I(b)$. Finally, if $x \in I(b)$ and $y \leq x$, then clearly $y \leq x < b$ and hence $y \in I(b)$. Thus, indeed $I(b)$ is a lower cut of P.

Definition 11. *Let $(P, \leq)$ be a partially ordered set. For every two elements a and b of P, the set of all elements x of P such that $a \leq x \leq b$ is called a closed interval and is denoted by $[a,b]$, and the set of all elements x of P such that $a < x < b$ is called an open interval and is denoted by (a,b).*

In short,

$$[a,b] = \{x \mid (x \in P) \wedge (a \leq x \leq b)\}$$
$$(a,b) = \{x \mid (x \in P) \wedge (a < x < b)\}$$

If a and b are not comparable or $b < a$, then $[a,b] = (a,b) = \varnothing$. Thus, in every nonempty partially ordered set the empty set is an open interval. Moreover, in every partially ordered set having more than one element, the empty set is an open as well as a closed interval. Clearly, in a partially ordered set, a singleton $\{a\}$ is always a closed interval since $\{a\} = [a,a]$.

Theorem 12. *If $(P, \leq)$ is a partially ordered set in which every lower cut that is bounded above has a least upper bound, then for every sequence of non-empty closed intervals of P each term of which contains the next one, there exists a nonempty closed interval $[a,b]$ that is contained in every interval of the sequence.*

PROOF. Let $[a_1,b_1]$, $[a_2,b_2]$, $[a_3,b_3]$, . . . be the sequence under consideration so that $a_1 \leq a_2 \leq a_3 \leq \cdots$ and $b_1 \geq b_2 \geq b_3 \geq \cdots$. Moreover,

$$(16) \qquad\qquad a_n \leq b_k \qquad n, k = 1, 2, 3, \ldots$$

First, let us assume that there exists no positive natural number p such that

$$(17) \qquad a_p = a_{p+1} = a_{p+2} = \cdots \qquad \text{and} \qquad b_p = b_{p+1} = b_{p+2} = \cdots$$

so that, for every a_m, there exists a natural number $n > m$ such that $a_n > a_m$; also, for every b_m, there exists a natural number $q > m$ such that $b_q < b_m$.

Naturally, in this case, (16) becomes

$$(18) \qquad\qquad a_n < b_k \qquad n, k = 1, 2, 3, \ldots$$

Consider the set L of all elements x of P such that $x \in L$ if and only if there exists an a_i, $i = 1, 2, 3, \ldots$ such that $x \leq a_i$. We claim that L is a lower cut of P. Obviously, L is nonempty, and in view of (18) since $b_k \notin L$ we see that L is a proper subset of P and L is bounded above. Also, L cannot have a last element. Indeed, if t were the last element of L then $t = a_m$, for some natural number m, contrary to the assumption that for every a_m there exists a natural number $n > m$ such that $a_n > a_m$. Similarly, it is easily seen that if $x \in L$ and $y \le x$, then $y \in L$. Consequently, L is a lower cut of P and L is bounded above. However, by hypothesis, sup L exists. Let $a = \sup L$. Clearly, $a_n \le a$ for $n = 1, 2, 3, \ldots$ and in view of (18) we have $a \le b_k$ for $k = 1, 2, 3, \ldots$. Therefore, a is such that

$$(19) \qquad\qquad a \in [a_n, b_n] \qquad \text{for} \quad n = 1, 2, 3, \ldots$$

Now, consider the set E of all elements x of P such that $x \in E$ if and only if $x \le b_i$ for every $i = 1, 2, 3, \ldots$. We claim that E has a last element. Indeed, if E did not have a last element, then, by reasoning similar to the above, it could be shown that E would be a lower cut of P. However, since E is bounded above, lub E would be the last element of E. Thus, indeed E has a last element. Let b be the last element of E. Clearly, $b < b_n$ for $n = 1, 2, 3, \ldots$ and $a \le b$. Therefore, $b \in [a_n, b_n]$ for $n = 1, 2, 3, \ldots$ and consequently, in view of (19), we derive $[a, b] \subset [a_n, b_n]$ for $n = 1, 2, 3, \ldots$.

Thus, when (17) occurs, the theorem is proved.

Now, consider the case in which for some positive natural number p,

$$(20) \qquad\qquad a_p = a_{p+1} = a_{p+2} = \cdots$$

or

$$(21) \qquad\qquad b_p = b_{p+1} = b_{p+2} = \cdots$$

If (20) occurs and (21) does not occur, then $[a_p, b]$ is the desired closed interval. If (20) and (21) both occur, then $[a_p, b_p]$ is the desired closed interval. If (21) occurs and (20) does not occur, then $[a, b_p]$ is the desired closed interval.

Therefore, the theorem is proved.

A sequence of intervals each term of which contains the next one is called a sequence of *nested* intervals.

Clearly, it may happen that, corresponding to cases (17), (20) or (21), we may have $a = b$, $a_p = b$, $a_p = b_p$ or $a = b_p$, in which cases the desired closed intervals reduce to singletons. In any event, we always have:

Corollary 5. *If P is a partially ordered set in which every lower cut that is bounded above has a least upper bound, then for every sequence of nonempty nested closed intervals there exists at least one element of P that is common to all intervals of the sequence.*

Theorem 12 does not hold for every sequence of nonempty nested open intervals. For instance, in the partially ordered set

$$Q = \{(a_1; a_2; a_3; a_4; \ldots; m_1; m_2; m_3)\}$$

the sequence of nonempty nested open intervals

$$(a_n, m_1), \qquad n = 1, 2, 3, \ldots$$

is such that there exists no element of Q common to all intervals of that sequence. Naturally, it may happen that for a particular sequence of nested open intervals of Q there exists an element of Q common to all intervals of that sequence. For instance, (a_n, m_2) is such a sequence.

Let us observe that Theorem 12 is also valid when $(P, \leq)$ is a conditionally complete partially ordered set.

EXERCISES

1. Let f map A into B and g map B into A. Prove that there exists a subset C of A such that

$$C = g(f(C))$$

2. Let f map A into B and g map B into A. Prove that there exists a subset S of A such that

$$S = C_A(g(C_B f(S)))$$

3. Using Definition 8, define an *upper cut* in a nonempty partially ordered set as the dual of a lower cut. Prove that the set of all upper cuts of a partially ordered set is a conditionally complete partially ordered set.

4. Prove that no subset of ω is a lower cut when ω is partially ordered by its natural order.

5. Partial order the set ω of all natural numbers so that it becomes a complete partially ordered set.

6. Partial order the set ω of all natural numbers so that it possesses at least two lower cuts.

7. Partial order the set $\omega \times \omega$ so that it possesses infinitely many lower cuts.

8. Partial order the set $\omega \times \omega$ so that it possesses no lower cuts.

3. SIMPLY ORDERED SETS

Neither a partial order nor an order in a set S ensures the comparability of every two elements of S.

For example, in the partially ordered set

$$\{(a;b), (m;n), (p;q)\}$$

none of the elements inside a pair of parentheses is comparable with an element inside another pair of parentheses.

Definition 12. *A partial order $\leq$ in a set S is called a simple (or linear, or total) order in S, if*

$$x \leq y \qquad or \qquad y \leq x$$

for every two elements x and y of S.

Accordingly, a partially ordered set $(S, \leq)$ is called a *simply* (or *linearly*, or *totally*) *ordered* set if $\leq$ is a *simple* (or *linear*, or *total*) *order* in S.

Thus, *a simply ordered set is a partially ordered set in which every two elements are comparable.*

Equivalently, and in view of notation (15), a partially ordered set $(S, \leq)$ is a simply ordered set in which

$$x \leq y \quad \text{or} \quad y < x \quad \text{for every two elements } x \text{ and } y \text{ of } S$$

which is the same as:

$$x < y \quad \text{or} \quad y < x \quad \text{for every two } distinct \text{ elements } x \text{ and } y \text{ of } S$$

Clearly, as usual, $x < y$ means $x \leq y$ and $x \neq y$.

For instance,

$$\{(a,a), (b,b), (c,c), (c,b), (b,a), (c,a)\}$$

is a *simple order* in the set $\{a,b,c\}$ and consequently,

$$(\{a,b,c\}, \{(a,a), (b,b), (c,c), (c,b), (b,a), (c,a)\})$$

is a simply ordered set, which according to Remark 2, can be written as: $\{(c;b;a)\}$.

Clearly, the natural partial order $\leq$ given by (3) is a simple order in any natural number n, as well as in the set ω of all natural numbers. Let us observe however that in general, $(S, \subset)$ is not a simply ordered set.

Lemma 5. *Let L be a lower cut of a simply ordered set $(S, \leq)$. If $y \in (S \smallsetminus L)$, then $x < y$, for every $x \in L$. Moreover, if $m = \text{lub } L$ exists, then $L = I(m)$.*

PROOF. Since S is simply ordered, $x < y$ or $y \leq x$. However, $y \leq x$ is impossible, because this (in view of the fact that L is a lower cut of S) would imply $y \in L$. Moreover, if $m = \text{lub } L$ and $x < m$, then $x \in L$, since otherwise $x \geq m$, contradicting $x < m$. Thus, indeed $L = I(m)$.

Theorem 13. *Let D be the set of all lower cuts of a simply ordered set $(S, \leq)$. Then $(D, \subset)$ is a conditionally complete simply ordered set.*

PROOF. The conditional completeness of $(D, \subset)$ is ensured by Theorem 9. Let L and L_1 be two lower cuts of S. Assume $L_1 \not\subset L$. Therefore, there exists an element $y \in S$ such that $y \in L_1$ and $y \notin L$. Let x be any element of L. Since $y \notin L$, by Lemma 5 we have $x \leq y$. However, since $y \in L_1$ we see that $x \in L_1$. Thus, $L \subset L_1$ and Theorem 13 is proved.

Theorem 14. *Let $(S, \leq)$ be a simply ordered set. Then the set of all the initial segments of S is simply ordered by $\subset$.*

PROOF. Assume the contrary. Hence there exists $c \in S$ such that $c \in I(a)$ and $c \notin I(b)$. Also, there exists $e \in S$ such that $e \notin I(a)$ and $e \in I(b)$. However, $c \leq e$ or $e \leq c$, implying respectively $c \in I(b)$ or $e \in I(a)$ which is impossible.

Theorem 15. *A simply ordered set $(S, \leq)$ is dense if and only if every non-empty initial segment of S is a lower cut of S.*

PROOF.   The necessity is secured by Theorem 11. Now, let a and b be two elements of S such that $a < b$. Clearly, $I(b)$ is not empty. Assume $I(b)$ is a lower cut of S. Since $a \in I(b)$ and since $I(b)$ has no last element and since S is simply ordered, there must exist an element $c \in S$ such that $a < c < b$. Thus, $(S, \leq)$ is dense, as desired.

Definition 13.   *A simply ordered set $(S, \leq)$ is called continuous if S is dense and conditionally complete.*

Theorem 16.   *Let $(S, \leq)$ be continuous. A subset L of S is a lower cut of S if and only if L is a proper initial segment of S.*

PROOF.   The necessity is ensured by Lemma 5 and the sufficiency by Theorem 11.

Theorem 17.   *Let D be the set of all lower cuts of a dense simply ordered set $(S, \leq)$. Then $(D, \subset)$ is continuous.*

PROOF.   From Theorem 13 it follows that $(D, \subset)$ is a conditionally complete simply ordered set. We must prove that $(D, \subset)$ is dense. Now, let D_1 and D_2 be two distinct lower cuts of S such that $x \in D_2$ and $x \notin D_1$. Since x cannot be the last element of D_2, there exists $y \in D_2$ such that $x < y$. But then by Theorem 15 we see that $I(y)$ is a lower cut of S such that $D_1 \subset I(y) \subset D_2$. Thus, $(D, \subset)$ is dense and the theorem is proved.

EXERCISES

1. Let $(P, \leq)$ be a dense partially ordered set and let a and b be two elements of P such that $a < b$. Prove that there exist infinitely many distinct elements x of P such that $a < x < b$.

2. Let $(P, \leq)$, a and b be given as in Problem 1. Using the axiom of Choice, prove that there exists an infinite sequence (x_n) of distinct elements of P such that $a < x_n < b$ for $n = 1, 2, 3, \ldots$.

3. Prove that a simply ordered set S is dense if and only if no element of S has an immediate successor.

4. Give examples of sequences of distinct nonempty nested open intervals in a continuous set S such that:
   (i) There exists no element of S common to all intervals of that sequence.
   (ii) There exists precisely one element of S common to all intervals of that sequence.
   (iii) There exists a nonempty open interval common to all intervals of that sequence.

5. Give an example of a sequence of distinct nested closed intervals in a continuous set S such that there exists precisely one element of S common to all intervals of that sequence.

6. Give an example of a simply ordered set every initial segment of which contains finitely many elements.

7. Is the set of all initial segments of a simply ordered set, ordered by $\subset$, conditionally complete?

8. Give an example of a set such that the set of all its initial segments, ordered by $\subset$, is a complete simply ordered set.

9. Prove that in a simply ordered set, if an initial segment $I(x)$ is a subset of an initial segment $I(y)$, then $I(x)$ is an initial segment of $I(y)$.

10. Let $I(x)$ be an initial segment of a simply ordered set S. If $I(y)$ is an initial segment of $I(x)$, prove that $I(y)$ is also an initial segment of S.

11. Let $(D, \subset)$ be the set of all the lower cuts of a dense partially ordered set. Is $(D, \subset)$ dense?

4. WELL ORDERED SETS

Partially ordered sets as well as simply ordered sets lack a property of considerable importance. In general, it is not true that a nonempty partially or simply ordered set has a *smallest* (*least* or *first*) element. Nor is it true that every nonempty subset of a partially or simply ordered set has a *smallest* (*least* or *first*) element.

For instance, the partially ordered set

$$\{(\ldots\, ; a_3; a_2; a_1), (\ldots\, ; b_3; b_2; b_1; \ldots\, ; c_3; c_2; c_1)\}$$

has no first element. Also, none of the simply ordered subsets $\{a_1, a_2, a_3, \ldots\}$, $\{b_1, b_2, b_3, \ldots\}$ or $\{c_1, c_2, c_3, \ldots\}$ has a first element.

On the other hand, there are partially ordered sets every nonempty subset of which has a first element. For example, one such is the partially ordered set $\{(a_1; a_2; a_3; \ldots)\}$. As we shall see in the sequel, partially ordered sets every nonempty subset of which has a first element, play a significant role. They are called *well ordered* sets. Thus, we introduce:

Definition 14. *A partially ordered set, every nonempty subset of which has a first element, is called a well ordered set.*

Thus, every nonempty well ordered set has a first element. Also,

Lemma 6. *Every well ordered set is a simply ordered set.*

PROOF.   Let $(W, \leq)$ be a well ordered set. To prove that $(W, \leq)$ is a simply ordered set, we only have to show that if $a \in W$ and $b \in W$, then $a \leq b$ or $b \leq a$. Now, consider the subset $\{a,b\}$ of W. By definition, $\{a,b\}$ must have a first element. Thus, if a is the first element of $\{a,b\}$, then $a \leq b$ and if b is the first element of $\{a,b\}$, then $b \leq a$.

It is clear that a first element of a subset S of a partially ordered set is unique, and this is the reason for calling it *the first* element of S.

A most significant example of a well ordered set is the set ω of all natural numbers where, according to (3), we write:

(i) $\qquad\qquad\qquad m \leq n \quad$ *if and only if* $\quad (m \in n) \vee (m = n)$

for every two natural numbers m and n.

The above condition, in view of Theorem 14 of Chapter II (page 105), is equivalent to:

(ii) $\qquad\qquad\qquad m \leq n \quad$ *if and only if* $\quad m \subset n$

for every two natural numbers m and n.

As mentioned previously, the order introduced by either of equivalent conditions (i) or (ii) is called *the natural order* of the set ω of all natural numbers.

The fact that ω is well ordered by its natural order is ensured by Theorem 21 on page 110.

In a partially ordered set $(P, \leq)$, an element b is called an *immediate successor* of a if $a < b$ and if there is no element c such that $a < c < b$. If b is an immediate successor of a, then a is called an *immediate predecessor* of b. Clearly, as usual, $x < y$ means $x \leq y$ and $x \neq y$.

Lemma 7. *In a well ordered set W every element other than the last element of W has a unique immediate successor. Moreover, an element of a well ordered set has at most one immediate predecessor. Furthermore, every well ordered set is conditionally complete.*

PROOF. Let $(W, \leq)$ be a well ordered set. If a is not the last element of W, then a has successors. Let S be the set of all successors of a. Since S is a nonempty subset of W it has a first element. Let b be the first element of S. Clearly, b is an immediate successor of a, since $a < c < b$ would contradict the choice of b. Furthermore, b is unique, since if b and e were two distinct immediate successors of a, say, with $b < e$, then $a < b < e$ would contradict the fact that e is an immediate successor of a.

Moreover, $a \in W$ cannot have two distinct immediate predecessors g and h, say, with $g < h$, since $g < h < a$ would contradict the fact that a is the immediate successor of g.

Finally, let S be a nonempty subset of W and let S be bounded above. Consider the set U of all the upper bounds of S. Since U is a nonempty subset of W, it has a first element. Clearly, the latter is the least upper bound of S. Hence, every well ordered set is conditionally complete.

To show that in a well ordered set an element need not have an immediate predecessor, it is enough to consider the well ordered set $\{(a_1; a_2; a_3; \dots; b_1; b_2)\}$. Clearly, in this set b_1 has no immediate predecessor.

Now, let us consider the set ω of all natural numbers ordered by its natural order, i.e., $(\omega, \leq)$, where $\leq$ is given by (i) or (ii) above. It is easy to verify that the immediate successor (as defined above) of a natural number n in the well ordered set $(\omega, \leq)$, coincides with the immediate successor n^+ of n, as defined on page 102. According to that definition,

$$n^+ = n \cup \{n\}$$

Indeed, we show that there exists no natural number c such that $n < c < n \cup \{n\}$. Clearly, in order that these relations hold, in view of (i) it must be the case that $n \in c$ and $c \in (n \cup \{n\})$. This means that

$$n \in c \quad \text{and} \quad c \in n, \qquad \text{or} \qquad n \in c \quad \text{and} \quad c = n$$

However, any one of the above cases, in view of the fact that $(\omega, \le) = (\omega, (\in \text{ or } =))$ is a well ordered set, leads to a contradiction. Thus, indeed, in the well ordered set $(\omega, \le)$, where $\le$ is given by (i) or (ii), the immediate successor of a natural number n is precisely $n \cup \{n\}$, and, as usual, is denoted by n^+.

Let us also observe that the initial segment $I(n)$ determined by a natural number n in the set ω of all natural numbers ordered by its natural order, is the set of all natural numbers less than n, i.e.,

$$I(n) = \{x \mid (x \in \omega) \wedge (x < n)\}$$

Clearly, in view of (i) we have:

$$I(n) = \{x \mid (x \in \omega) \wedge (x \in n)\} = n$$

Thus, *the initial segment $I(n)$ determined by the natural number n in the set of all natural numbers ω ordered by its natural order, is equal to n.*

Since every nonempty well ordered set has a first element, the empty set is an initial segment of every nonempty well ordered set. Thus, if a is the first element of a well ordered set W, then $\varnothing = I(a)$.

Also, let us note that every subset of a well ordered set is again a well ordered set. However, the converse of a well order in a set is not necessarily a well order in that set.

For example, $W = \{(a_1; a_2; a_3; \ldots)\}$ is a well order in the set

$$S = \{a_1, a_2, a_3, \ldots\}$$

however,

$$W_{-1} = \{(\ldots ; a_3; a_2; a_1)\}$$

is not a well order in the set S, since for instance W_{-1} itself fails to have a first element.

Lemma 8. *Let I be the set of all the initial segments of a well ordered set W; then $(I, \subset)$ is a well ordered set.*

PROOF. By Theorem 14, $(I, \subset)$ is simply ordered. Now, let $\{I(a), I(b), I(c), \ldots\}$ be a nonempty subset of I. Consider the nonempty subset $\{a, b, c, \ldots\}$ of W. As such $\{a, b, c, \ldots\}$ has a first element. Let c be the first element of $\{a, b, c, \ldots\}$. Clearly, $I(c)$ is the first element of $\{I(a), I(b), I(c), \ldots\}$. Thus, indeed the set $(I, \subset)$ is well ordered.

One of the significant features of well ordered sets is that *if the fact that every element of an initial segment $I(x)$ satisfies a property implies that x satisfies that property, then every element of the well ordered set under consideration satisfies that property.* This provides a convenient device for proving that a property is satisfied by every element of a well ordered set.

In view of its resemblance to the theorem of Finite (or Mathematical) Induction (see page 105), the above feature is called the theorem (or principle) of *Transfinite Induction*.

Clearly, an initial segment $I(x)$ of a partially ordered (or in particular, of a well ordered) set is the set of all predecessors of x. Thus, we may formulate the theorem of Transfinite Induction as follows.

The Theorem of Transfinite Induction. *Let W be a well ordered set and V a subset of W which, for every element $x \in W$, satisfies the following condition:*

if every predecessor of x belongs to V, then x belongs to V

Then $V = W$.

PROOF. Assume $V \neq W$. Therefore, $H = W \smallsetminus V$ is not empty. Let x be the first element of H. Clearly, $x \notin V$. Since H is the set of all those elements of W not belonging to V and since x is the first such element, every predecessor of x belongs to V. But then by hypothesis x must belong to V. However, this contradicts the fact that $x \notin V$. Hence, our assumption is false and therefore $V = W$.

The reader should note that the condition stated in the theorem of Transfinite Induction implies that the first element (if it exists) of W must belong to V. Indeed, if a is the first element of W, it has no predecessors and therefore every predecessor of a belongs to V. Hence, in view of the above condition, a must belong to V.

It can be readily seen that the theorem of Transfinite Induction in reference to the set ω (ordered by its natural order) is equivalent to the theorem of Finite Induction. However, since in general not every element which is not the first element of a well ordered set has an immediate predecessor, the theorems of Finite and Transfinite Induction are not equivalent. This is in the sense that, if W is an arbitrary well ordered set and if a subset V of W satisfies the conditions stated in the theorem of Finite Induction, then V is not necessarily equal to W.

EXERCISES

1. Prove the equivalence of the theorems of Finite and Transfinite Induction, in reference to the set ω of all natural numbers ordered by its natural order.

2. Give an example of a well ordered set with respect to which the theorems of Finite and Transfinite Induction are not equivalent.

3. Well order the set of all natural numbers so that five of its elements do not have immediate predecessors.

4. Which of the following sets are well orders in the set $\{a,b,c\}$?

$$\{(a,a), (b,b), (c,c), (a,b), (a,c), (b,c)\} \quad \checkmark$$
$$\{(a,a), (b,b), (c,c), (c,b), (c,a), (b,a)\} \quad \checkmark$$
$$\{(a,a), (b,b), (c,c), (c,b), (a,c)\}$$
$$\{(a,a), (b,b), (a,b), (a,c), (b,c)\}$$

5. Prove that the converse of a well order in a set having finitely many elements is again a well order in that set.

6. Prove that any union and any intersection of a family of initial segments of a well ordered set are again initial segments of that well ordered set.

7. How many distinct well orders are there in the set $\{a,b,c,d\}$?

8. Prove that any simply ordered set having finitely many elements is a well ordered set.

9. Let A and B be two well ordered sets. Well order $A \cup B$ and $A \times B$ by making judicious use of the well orderings of A and B.

5. ZORN'S LEMMA

A partially ordered set in which every nonempty well ordered subset has a least upper bound is of particular interest to us. Clearly, not every partially ordered set is of this type. For example,

$$\{(a_1; a_2; a_3; \ldots), (m_1; m_2; m_3; \ldots)\}$$

is not of the type mentioned above, since for instance neither of its well ordered subsets, $\{a_1, a_2, a_3, \ldots\}$ or $\{m_1, m_2, m_3, \ldots\}$ has a least upper bound.

The importance of a partially ordered set $(P, \leq)$ in which every nonempty well ordered subset has a least upper bound, lies in the fact that for *any element p* of *P* and *any mapping f from P into P with $x \leq f(x)$ (for every $x \in P$)*, it is possible to construct a well ordered subset $W(p)$ of P such that $f(\text{lub } W(p)) = \text{lub } W(p)$.

Before proving the theorem asserting the existence of a well ordered set such as $W(p)$, we introduce the following definitions and lemmas:

Definition 15. *Let $(P, \leq)$ be a partially ordered set every nonempty well ordered subset of which has a least upper bound in P. Moreover, let f be a mapping from P into P with $x \leq f(x)$ for every $x \in P$. Furthermore, let p be any element of P. Corresponding to p, we define a subset of P, called a p-chain, denoted by $C(p,r)$, and satisfying the following conditions:*

(22) $C(p,r)$ *is well ordered with p its first and r its last element.*

(23)   *The immediate successor in $C(p,r)$ of an element x of $C(p,r)$, except of course r, is $f(x)$.*

(24)   *The least upper bound (in P) of every nonempty subset of $C(p,r)$, which in view of the hypothesis of the definition exists, belongs to $C(p,r)$.*

Let $W(p)$ denote the set of all $r \in P$ for which there exists a p-chain $C(p,r)$. Then we have:

Lemma 9.   *Every p-chain $C(p,r)$ is a subset of $W(p)$.*

PROOF.   If $x \in C(p,r)$, the set of all elements of $C(p,r)$ which are $\leq x$ is clearly a p-chain and hence $x \in W(p)$. Thus, the lemma is proved.

Lemma 10.   *If* $x \in W(p)$, *then* $f(x) \in W(p)$. ⟨a well ordered subset of P⟩

PROOF.   The set $C(p,x) \cup \{f(x)\}$ is obviously a p-chain and hence $f(x) \in W(p)$.

Lemma 11.   *If* $r, s \in W(p)$, *then either* $s \in C(p,r)$ *or else* $r < s$.

PROOF.   Let $S = C(p,r) \cap C(p,s)$. Clearly, S is a well ordered set since it is a subset of both well ordered sets $C(p,r)$ and $C(p,s)$. Moreover, by (22) $S \neq \varnothing$, and hence by (24) $x = \text{lub } S$ belongs simultaneously to $C(p,r)$ and $C(p,s)$, and therefore $x \in S$. Now, assume $s \notin C(p,r)$, hence $x \neq s$. If also $x \neq r$, then by (23) the immediate successor $f(x)$ of x belongs to S, contrary to the fact that $x = \text{lub } S$. Hence, $s \notin C(p,r)$ implies that $x = r$ so that $r \in C(p,s)$, and since $r \neq s$, we see by (22) that $r < s$. On the other hand, since by (22) $s \in C(p,r)$ and $r < s$ cannot both hold, the proof of the lemma follows.

Lemma 12.   *If* $r \in W(p)$, *there is a unique* $C(p,r)$ *equal to the set of all elements* s *of* $W(p)$ *such that* $s \leq r$.

PROOF.   By Lemma 9 $C(p,r) \subset W(p)$ and by Lemma 11 if $s \in W(p)$ and $s \leq r$, then $s \in C(p,r)$. Thus, Lemma 12 is proved.

Now, we prove the main theorem.

Theorem 18.   *Let* $(P, \leq)$ *be a partially ordered set every nonempty well ordered subset of which has a least upper bound in P. Moreover, let f be a mapping from P into P with* $x \leq f(x)$ *for every* $x \in P$. *Furthermore, let p be an element of P. Then* $W(p)$ *is a well ordered set such that*

$$(25) \qquad \text{lub } W(p) \in W(p)$$

and if we denote lub $W(p)$ *by m, then*

$$(26) \qquad f(m) = m$$

The proof is based on the fact that $W(p)$ turns out to be a p-chain $C(p,m)$. Hence, by Lemma 10, $f(m) \in W(p)$. Moreover, since m is the last element of $W(p)$, it follows that $f(m) \leq m$. However, $f(m) \geq m$, by the definition of f. Consequently, $f(m) = m$, as desired.

PROOF.   Our aim is to prove that $W(p)$ is a p-chain $C(p,m)$, where $m = \text{lub } W(p)$. Therefore, according to Definition 15, we have to show that $W(p)$ is well ordered with p its first and m its last element, i.e., (22) is valid for $W(p)$. Moreover, we have to show that (23) and (24) are also valid for $W(p)$.

Now, let H be a nonempty subset of $W(p)$ and $r \in H$. Since $r \in H \cap C(p,r)$, condition (22) implies that $H \cap C(p,r)$ has a first element which, by virtue of Lemma 12, is the first element of H. Since H is an arbitrary nonempty subset of $W(p)$, we conclude that $W(p)$ is a well ordered set. By Lemma 9, every $C(p,r)$ is a subset of $W(p)$. Hence, we conclude that $p \in W(p)$. Moreover, by condition (22), if $r \in W(p)$ then $p \leq r$. Hence, p is the first element of $W(p)$. Since $W(p)$ is well ordered, by the hypothesis of Theorem 18, lub $W(p)$ exists. Let $m = \text{lub } W(p)$.

Next, consider $V = W(p) \cup \{m\}$. We show that V is a p-chain. Since $W(p)$ is well ordered, V is well ordered too with p its first and m its last element. Thus, condition (22) is satisfied by V. Now, let $z \in V$ and $z \neq m$. Then, $z \in W(p)$ and since $z \neq m$, we see that z has an immediate successor r in $W(p)$, and hence also in V. By Lemma 12, z and r are the last two elements of $C(p,r)$. Hence, by (23) applied to z as an element of $C(p,r)$, we see that $f(z) = r$. Thus, condition (23) is also satisfied by V.

To prove that condition (24) holds for V, let U be any nonempty subset of V. Obviously, m is an upper bound of U. If there is no element of $W(p)$ that exceeds every element of U, then since $W(p)$ is well ordered, any upper bound of U is also an upper bound of $W(p)$ and hence is not exceeded by m. This implies that $m = \text{lub } U$. Thus, lub $U \in V$. If there is an element $r \in W(p)$ that exceeds every element of U, then $U \subset W(p)$ and by Lemma 12, $U \subset C(p,r)$. Hence by (24), lub U exists and is in $C(p,r)$. Therefore, by Lemma 9, lub $U \in W(p)$. Thus, again lub $U \in V$. Consequently, condition (24) is also satisfied by V. Therefore, V is indeed a p-chain with m its last element. However, $W(p)$ is the set of all last elements of p-chains; therefore, $m \in W(p)$ and $W(p) = V$. Thus, indeed $W(p)$ is a p-chain $C(p,m)$. Hence, our aim is accomplished. On the other hand, since $m \in W(p)$, by Lemma 10 we derive that $f(m) \in W(p)$. Moreover, since m is the last element of $W(p)$ we see that $f(m) \leq m$. However, by the hypothesis of the theorem, $f(m) \geq m$. Consequently, $f(m) = m$.

In short, we have proved that $W(p)$ is well ordered, and that $m = \text{lub } W(p)$ is an element of $W(p)$, i.e., (25) is valid for $W(p)$; furthermore, $f(m) = m$, i.e., (26) is also valid for $W(p)$. Consequently, Theorem 18 is proved.

Let us recall that in a partially ordered set $(P, \leq)$, an element h is called *maximal* if h is not succeeded by any of the elements of P. Accordingly, to prove that an element h is a maximal element of a partially ordered set P, it is enough to show that the set of all successors of h is empty.

Motivated by the above and in view of Theorem 18, we prove:

Theorem 19. *Let $(P, \leq)$ be a nonempty partially ordered set every nonempty well ordered subset of which has a least upper bound. Then P has at least one maximal element.*

PROOF. Assume the contrary, so that the set of all successors of every element of P is nonempty. For every element a of P, let $S(a)$ denote the set of all successors of a. By the axiom of Choice, there exists a set C such that C contains one element s_a from each of the sets $S(a)$. Now, consider the mapping f from P onto C (which obviously is a mapping from P into P) such that $f(a) = s_a$ for every element a of P. Since s_a is a successor of a, we have $a < f(a)$. From Theorem 18, it follows that there exists an element $m \in P$ such that $m = f(m)$, i.e., $m = s_m$, which contradicts the fact that $m < s_m$. Hence, our assumption is false and therefore there exists an element $h \in P$ such that the set of all successors of h is empty. But this means that h is a maximal element of P. Hence, the theorem is proved.

Let us observe that in the proof of the above theorem we used the axiom of Choice, which is one of the axioms of our theory.

Before proving the next theorem, we show that the set Q of all well ordered subsets of a partially ordered set $(P,\leq)$ can be partially ordered by:

(27) $(u \lessgtr v) \equiv (u$ is an initial segment of v or $u = v)$

for every two elements u and v of Q.

Clearly, $\lessgtr$ is reflexive since $u \lessgtr u$ for every element u of Q. Also, if $u \lessgtr v$ and $v \lessgtr u$, then $u = v$. To see this, let us assume on the contrary that $u \neq v$. In that case $u \lessgtr v$ would mean that $u = I(b)$, where $b \in v$ and $v \lessgtr u$ would mean $v = I(a)$, where $a \in u$. But then a would be a predecessor of b; i.e., $a < b$ and b would be a predecessor of a; i.e., $b < a$, which is impossible. Thus, $\lessgtr$, as introduced in (27), is antisymmetric. The transitivity of $\lessgtr$ is obvious. Hence, $\lessgtr$, as given by (27), is indeed a partial order in the set Q of all well ordered subsets of a partially ordered set $(P,\leq)$.

Now, we prove:

Lemma 13.   *If the set Q of all well ordered subsets of a partially ordered set $(P,\leq)$ is partially ordered by $\lessgtr$, as given in (27), then every simply ordered subset of Q has a least upper bound.*

PROOF.   Let $S = \{u, v, \ldots\}$ be a nonempty simply ordered subset of $(Q,\lessgtr)$. Consider the sum-set $w = \cup S = \cup\{u, v, \ldots\}$. We claim that $(w,\leq)$ is a well ordered subset of $(P,\leq)$. Let s be a nonempty subset of w. Therefore, among the sets $u, v, \ldots$ there exists at least one that contributes to s. Let u be such a set. Since $(u,\leq)$ is a well ordered set, $u \cap s$ has a first element. Let a be the first element. We show that a is the first element of $(s,\leq)$. Consider an element $b \in s$ that is distinct from a. We prove that $a < b$. This will prove that a is indeed the first element of s. Now, since $b \in s$, there exists an element v of S such that $b \in v$. However, since S is simply ordered by $\lessgtr$, then either $v \lessgtr u$ or $u \lessgtr v$. If $v \lessgtr u$, then in view of the definition of a it is obvious that $a < b$. If $u \lessgtr v$, then $b < a$ is impossible, since otherwise $b \in u$, which contradicts the fact that a is the first element among all those elements of u that are also elements of s. Hence, again $a < b$. Thus, indeed $(W,\leq)$ is a well ordered set and hence $w \in Q$. The proof of the fact that $w = \text{lub } S$ is straightforward and is left to the reader. If $S = \varnothing$, then lub $S = \varnothing$ (clearly, $\varnothing \in Q$).

Now, let us call a well ordered subset w of a partially ordered set P, a *maximal well ordered subset of P if w is not an initial segment of any well ordered subset of P.*

With the above definition of a maximal well ordered set, we prove the following:

Theorem 20.   *Every partially ordered set has a maximal well ordered subset.*

PROOF.   Consider the set Q of all well ordered subsets of a partially ordered set P. Partial order Q by $\lessgtr$, as given in (27). Since by Lemma 13 every well ordered subset of $(Q,\lessgtr)$ has a least upper bound, in view of Theorem 19, we conclude that $(Q,\lessgtr)$ has a maximal element which is obviously a maximal well ordered subset of P.

Theorem 21. *Let P be a nonempty partially ordered set every well ordered subset of which has an upper bound. Then P has at least one maximal element.*

PROOF. By Theorem 20, P has a maximal well ordered subset w. Let m be an upper bound of w, which by the hypothesis of the theorem exists. Clearly, $m \in w$, as otherwise $w \cup \{m\}$ would be a well ordered subset of P and $w = I(m)$, which would contradict the maximality of w. Also, m cannot be exceeded by any element x of P, because in that case $w \cup \{x\}$ would be a well ordered subset of P, contradicting again the maximality of w. Thus, m is a maximal element of P and the theorem is proved.

Theorem 22 (*Zorn's lemma*). *Let P be a nonempty partially ordered set every simply ordered subset of which has an upper bound. Then P has at least one maximal element.*

PROOF. Since every well ordered subset of P is a priori a simply ordered subset of P, Theorem 22 follows immediately from Theorem 21.

Theorem 22 is also called Kuratowski's lemma.

Lemma 14. *The set S of all simply ordered subsets of a partially ordered set $(P, \leq)$ when partially ordered by $\subset$ is such that every simply ordered subset of S has a least upper bound.*

PROOF. Let $R = \{u, v, \ldots\}$ be a nonempty simply ordered subset of $(S, \leq)$. Consider the sum-set $r = \cup R = \cup \{u, v, \ldots\}$. We claim that r is a simply ordered subset of $(P, \leq)$. This is because if a and b are any two distinct elements of r such that, say, $a \in u$ and $b \in v$, then since $(R, \subset)$ is a simply ordered set, $u \subset v$ or $v \subset u$. Therefore, a and b are both elements of v or of u, and since $(u, \leq)$ and $(v, \leq)$ are both simply ordered sets, $a \leq b$ or $b \leq a$. Thus, r is indeed a simply ordered subset of P. Moreover, r is obviously the least upper bound of $(R, \subset)$. If $R = \varnothing$, then lub $R = \varnothing$ (clearly, $\varnothing \in S$).

Before proving the next theorem, we introduce the following definition. We shall say that a simply ordered subset s of a partially ordered set P is a *maximal simply ordered subset* of P if s is not a proper subset of any simply ordered subset of P.

Theorem 23. *Every partially ordered set has a maximal simply ordered subset.*

PROOF. Consider the set S of all simply ordered subsets of a partially ordered set P. Partial order S by $\subset$. Since by Lemma 14, every simply ordered subset of S has a least upper bound, in view of Theorem 22 we conclude that S has a maximal element, which is obviously a maximal simply ordered subset of P. Thus, Theorem 23 is proved.

Given a set, say, $S = \{a, b, c, d, \ldots\}$, its subsets can be well ordered in many different ways. For instance,

$$\{(a;b;c)\}, \qquad \{(c;b;a)\}, \qquad \{(a;c;b)\}$$

are three different well orderings of the subset $\{a,b,c\}$ of the set S.

The above shows that given any set S, we can well order some of its subsets. The question of whether the set S itself can be well ordered is answered positively by the following *well ordering theorem*.

Theorem 24.   *Every set can be well ordered.*

PROOF.   Let E be a set. Consider the set W of all those subsets of E that can be well ordered. Partial order W by $\exists$, i.e., according to (27). By Theorem 23, the set W has a maximal simply ordered subset S. We claim that $\cup S$ is well ordered and $\cup S = E$. The proof that $\cup S$ is well ordered is similar to that given in the proof of Lemma 13 where $w = \cup S$ is shown to be well ordered.

To prove that $\cup S = E$, let us assume that there exists an element $y \in E$ such that $y \notin \cup S$. Now, $\cup S \cup \{y\}$ can be well ordered by considering y to be the last element of $\cup S$. But then

$$S \cup \{\cup S \cup \{y\}\}$$

is a simply ordered subset of W containing S properly, thus contradicting the maximality of S. Thus, indeed $\cup S = E$ and since $\cup S$ is well ordered, so is E and the theorem is proved. This theorem is called the *well ordering theorem*.

Theorem 25.   *The well ordering theorem implies the axiom of Choice.*

PROOF.   Let $S = \{u, v, w, \ldots\}$ be a set whose elements are nonempty sets. Using Theorem 24, we prove that there exists a choice function f from S into $\cup S$, i.e., a function such that $f(u) \in u$, $f(v) \in v$, ... In short, $f(x) \in x$ for every element $x \in S$. To this end, let us observe that according to Theorem 24 we can well order $\cup S$. Hence, consider a well ordering of $\cup S$. The elements of S, being nonempty subsets of $\cup S$, are also well ordered and hence each possesses a first element. Define the mapping f from S into $\cup S$ by:

$$f(x) = \textit{the first element of } x$$

for every $x \in S$. Clearly, $f(x)$ is a choice function and the theorem is proved.

Remark 4.   At the end of the proof of Theorem 19 we mentioned that it is a consequence of the axiom of Choice. Also, in the above, each of the Theorems 20–25 is derived from its predecessor. Therefore, in view of Theorem 25, we have:

Theorem 26.   *Each of the Theorems 19–25 is equivalent to the axiom of Choice.*

It is worth mentioning that Theorem 19 can be stated as follows:

Theorem 27.   *Let $(P, \leq)$ be a nonempty partially ordered set every nonempty well ordered subset of which has a least upper bound and let a be an element of P. Then P has a maximal element m such that $a \leq m$.*

The proof of the above theorem parallels that of Theorem 19, with the difference that P is replaced by the partially ordered set P', where P' is the subset of P that consists of all those elements of P that are comparable with a.

Similarly, Theorem 20 can be stated as:

Theorem 28.   *Let   W be a well ordered subset of a partially ordered set P. Then there exists a maximal well ordered subset W' of P such that W $\mathrel{\text{-}3}$ W'.*

The proof of the above theorem parallels that of Theorem 20 with the difference that Q is replaced by the set Q', where Q' is the set of all well ordered subsets of P such that every element of Q' is comparable (with respect to $\mathrel{\text{-}3}$) with W.

Likewise, Theorems 21, 22 and 23 can be stated respectively as:

Theorem 29.   *Let $(P, \leq)$ be a nonempty partially ordered set every well ordered subset of which has an upper bound and let a be an element of P. Then P has a maximal element m such that $a \leq m$.*

Theorem 30 (*Zorn's lemma*).   *Let $(P, \leq)$ be a nonempty partially ordered set every simply ordered subset of which has an upper bound and let a be an element of P. Then P has a maximal element m such that $a \leq m$.*

Theorem 31.   *Let S be a simply ordered subset of a partially ordered set P. Then there exists a maximal simply ordered subset S' of P such that $S \subset S'$.*

Remark 5.   The applications of Zorn's lemma are numerous.   Zorn's lemma is probably one of the most powerful and convenient methods often used in proving the validity of a property in a set S.   The method consists of the following steps: first, in exhibiting a subset A of S in which the property under consideration holds; second, in considering the set $\{A, B, C, \ldots\}$ of all the subsets A, B, C, $\ldots$ of S in each of which the property holds, and in partial ordering $\{A, B, C, \ldots\}$ in such a way that every simply ordered subset of $\{A, B, C, \ldots\}$ has an upper bound in $\{A, B, C, \ldots\}$; and third, in asserting (by Zorn's lemma) the existence of a maximal element M of $\{A, B, C, \ldots\}$ and then in attempting to prove that $M = S$.   This last equality shows that the property under consideration holds for the entire set S.

Remark 6.   The dual of Zorn's lemma is obtained by considering the converse of the partial order mentioned in Theorems 22 and 30.   Thus, we have:

Theorem 32.   *Let P be a nonempty partially ordered set every simply ordered subset of which has a lower bound. Then P has at least one minimal element.*

Theorem 33.   *Let $(P, \leq)$ be a nonempty partially ordered set every simply ordered subset of which has a lower bound and let a be an element of P. Then P has a minimal element m such that $m \leq a$.*

EXERCISES

1. Let us call a family of sets $F = \{A, B, \ldots\}$ of *finite character* if $X \in F$ is equivalent to: *every finite subset of X is a member of F*. Prove that in a family of finite character there exists (with respect to $\subset$) a maximal member.

2. Prove that in every family of nonempty sets there exists (with respect to $\subset$) a maximal subfamily of pairwise disjoint sets.

3. Let us call a family of sets monotonic if, for every two members of that family, one is a subset of the other. Prove that in every family of nonempty sets there exists a maximal monotonic subfamily.

4. Prove Theorems 29, 30 and 31.

6. SUMMARY

In this chapter, various order relations in a set were discussed. Many fundamental questions in mathematics are directly related to the notion of order. Consequently, the study of the general properties of ordered sets is of capital importance. Let us recall that a partial order in a set S is defined as a certain subset—say, $\leq$ of $S \times S$, and that $(S, \leq)$ is called a partially ordered set. Nevertheless, we have used and will continue to use expressions such as: *let S be a set partially ordered by $\leq$*.

As pointed out in this chapter, with the notion of partial order in a set S, the concepts of an upper bound, lower bound, least upper bound, greatest lower bound, the least element (minimum), the greatest element (maximum), a maximal element and a minimal element of subsets of S are readily introduced.

Also, we have mentioned that not every partially ordered set S is such that every nonempty bounded above subset of it has a least upper bound. Partially ordered sets having this property are especially important and are called conditionally complete partially ordered sets. It was shown that the set of all lower cuts of a partially ordered set is a conditionally complete partially ordered set. Among partially ordered sets, we have singled out two special types: simply ordered and well ordered sets. A simply ordered set is a partially ordered set in which every two elements are comparable. A well ordered set is a partially ordered set in which every nonempty subset has a first element.

Special importance was given to those partially ordered sets in which every nonempty well ordered subset has a least upper bound. For this particular type of partially ordered sets, Theorem 18 was proved. Theorem 18 paved the way for proving the various theorems equivalent to the axiom of Choice. Among these theorems, Zorn's lemma (Theorem 22), because of the convenience and broad scope of its application, deserves special attention. This point was made in Remark 5.

Chapter V

EQUIVALENCE CLASSES
THE REAL NUMBERS

1. EQUIVALENCE RELATION

In many cases we do not distinguish between two sets if they possess certain properties pertinent to our objective. If, for instance, our objective is to classify sets according to the numbers of their elements, then relative to this objective the three sets $\{a,b\}$, $\{c,d\}$ and $\{k,h\}$ are alike since each has two elements.

Now, let us consider the set:

$$S = \{\{a,b\}, \{m,n,p\}, \{c,d\}, \{e,p,q\}, \{g\}, \{k,h\}, \{t\}\}$$

where, according to our previous convention, distinct letters are distinct sets.

If our interest in the elements of S is solely in the numbers of their elements, then we see that for this purpose the three elements $\{a,b\}$, $\{c,d\}$ and $\{k,h\}$ of S are alike. Similarly, for this purpose, the two elements $\{m,n,p\}$ and $\{e,p,q\}$ are alike. Likewise, for this purpose, the two elements $\{g\}$ and $\{t\}$ are alike.

Now, let us consider the following three subsets of the above-mentioned set S:

$$A = \{\{a,b\}, \{c,d\}, \{k,h\}\},$$

$$B = \{\{m,n,p\}, \{e,p,q\}\} \quad \text{and} \quad C = \{\{g\}, \{t\}\}$$

where any two elements of each subset have the same number of elements.

Thus, with respect to the property "*having the same number of elements,*" the elements of the set S are partitioned into three subsets A, B and C.

Let us observe that

$$S = A \cup B \cup C$$

and

$$A \cap B = \varnothing, \quad A \cap C = \varnothing, \quad B \cap C = \varnothing$$

i.e., A, B and C are pairwise disjoint subsets of S.

Motivated by the above, let us introduce:

Definition 1. *A partition of a nonempty set S is a set of nonempty subsets of S whose sum-set is equal to S and in which every two distinct elements are disjoint. Every element of a partition is called an equivalence class.*

Thus, for instance, given the set

$$S = \{a,b,c\}$$

then

(1) $\{\{a,b\}, \{c\}\}$

is a partition of S having two *equivalence classes* $\{a,b\}$ and $\{c\}$.

Partition (1) of S can also be written as

(2) $E = \{(a,a), (b,b), (a,b), (b,a), (c,c)\}$

where both elements of each ordered pair belong to the same equivalence class.

Obviously, the above set is a relation in S since it is a subset of $S \times S$. Moreover, the above relation is *reflexive*, *symmetric* and *transitive*.

Motivated by the above, we introduce:

Definition 2. *For every set S a subset E of the Cartesian product $S \times S$ is called an equivalence relation in the set S if the following three conditions are satisfied:*

(i) $(x,x) \in E$, *for every element x of S.*
(ii) *If $(x,y) \in E$, then $(y,x) \in E$, for every two elements x and y of S.*
(iii) *If $(x,y) \in E$ and $(y,z) \in E$, then $(x,z) \in E$, for every three elements x, y and z of S.*

The first condition states than an equivalence relation is reflexive. The second and third conditions state respectively that an equivalence relation is symmetric and transitive.

Thus, in the set $\{a,b,c\}$, the relation

(3) $Q = \{(a,a), (b,b), (a,c), (c,a), (c,c)\}$

is an equivalence relation, whereas

$$\{(a,a), (c,c)\}$$

is not an equivalence relation in $\{a,b,c\}$ since it fails to be reflexive, although it is symmetric and transitive.

Similarly, the relation $\{(a,a), (b,b), (c,c), (a,c)\}$ is not an equivalence relation in the set $\{a,b,c\}$ since it fails to be symmetric, although it is reflexive and transitive.

Finally, the relation

$$\{(a,a), (b,b), (c,c), (a,c), (c,a), (c,b), (b,c)\}$$

is not an equivalence relation in the set $\{a,b,c\}$ since it fails to be transitive, although it is reflexive and symmetric.

The above examples show that reflexivity, symmetry and transitivity of a relation in a set are mutually independent conditions.

The connection between a partition of a nonempty set S and an equivalence relation in the set S consists in the fact that every partition of S gives rise to an equivalence relation in S and vice versa. For instance, the partition given by (1) of the set $S = \{a,b,c\}$ gives rise to the equivalence relation E (in the set S) given by (2). As one can see, $(x,y) \in E$ if and only if x and y are elements of the same element of the partition given by (1). Conversely, with the equivalence relation, say, Q given by (3), we may associate the partition

$$P = \{\{a,c\}, \{b\}\}$$

where $X \in P$ and $u \in X$ and $v \in X$ if and only if $(u,v) \in Q$.

In general, we have:

Theorem 1. *A relation E in a nonempty set S is an equivalence relation in S if and only if the family $(P_i)_{i\in I}$ is a partition of S provided:*

(4)   *$(x,y) \in E$ if and only if there exists an $i \in I$ with $x \in P_i$ and $y \in P_i$. Moreover, for every $j \in I$, if $(x,y) \in E$ and $x \in P_j$, then $y \in P_j$. Furthermore, P_i is nonempty for every $i \in I$.*

PROOF.   Let E be an equivalence relation in S. We shall prove that $(P_i)_{i\in I}$ is a partition of S provided (4) is satisfied.

First, let us observe that since E is a relation in S, in view of (4), for every $i \in I$, every element of P_i is an element of S. Indeed, if $x \in P_i$, then by (4) we have $(x,x) \in E$, and since E is a relation in S we see that $x \in S$. Now, let P_i and P_j be two distinct terms of $(P_i)_{i\in I}$. We shall show that $P_i \cap P_j = \varnothing$. Since P_i and P_j are distinct, there exists an element $y \in S$ such that, say,

(5) $y \in P_i$ and $y \notin P_j$

Assume on the contrary that $P_i \cap P_j \neq \varnothing$. Thus there must exist an element $x \in S$ such that $x \neq y$ and $x \in P_j$ and $x \in P_i$. However, the latter, in view of (5) and (4), implies that $(x,y) \in E$, which in turn, in view of (4) and the fact that $x \in P_j$, implies that $y \in P_j$, contradicting (5). Hence, indeed $P_i \cap P_j = \varnothing$.

Next, we show that $\cup_{i\in I} P_i = S$. Since every element of P_i is an element of S, it is enough to show that if $x \in S$, then $x \in P_i$ for some $i \in I$. Now, since E is an equivalence relation, for every $x \in S$ we have $(x,x) \in E$. However, in view of (4), the latter implies that there exists a P_i such that $x \in P_i$. Consequently, $x \in \cup_{i\in I} P_i$ and therefore $\cup_{i\in I} P_i = S$.

Recalling that P_i is nonempty for every $i \in I$, we see that $(P_i)_{i\in I}$ is indeed a partition of S in accordance with Definition 1.

Now, let $(P_i)_{i\in I}$ be a partition of S. We show that the set E of all ordered pairs (x,y) satisfying (4) is an equivalence relation in S. In view of the fact that $(P_i)_{i\in I}$ is a partition of S, every element $x \in S$ must belong to a P_i. Thus, for every element $x \in S$, it is true that $(x \in P_i) \wedge (x \in P_i)$ for an $i \in I$. But this in view of (4) implies that $(x,x) \in E$ for every $x \in S$. Thus, E is reflexive. Next, let $(x,y) \in E$. Then by (4) for every $i \in I$ if $(x \in P_i) \wedge (y \in P_i)$, then

$(y \in P_i) \wedge (x \in P_i)$, which in view of (4) implies that $(y,x) \in E$. Thus, E is symmetric. Finally, let $(x,y) \in E$ and $(y,z) \in E$. Accordingly, there exists a P_i such that $(x \in P_i) \wedge (y \in P_i)$ and there exists a P_j such that $(y \in P_j) \wedge (z \in P_j)$. Since two distinct equivalence classes are disjoint, in view of the last two conjunctions, we conclude that $P_i = P_j$. Hence, $x \in P_i$ and $z \in P_i$, and consequently by (4) we have $(x,z) \in E$. Thus, E is transitive. Hence, E is indeed an equivalence relation in S and the theorem is proved.

Since the distinct elements (equivalence classes) of a partition are pairwise disjoint, a single element of an equivalence class characterizes that equivalence class. By this we mean that if a is an element of an equivalence class, corresponding to an equivalence relation E in a set S, then the equivalence class to which a belongs is given by:

$$\{x \mid (x \in S) \wedge (a,x) \in E\}$$

The equivalence class to which the element a belongs is usually represented by

(6) $[a]$ or a/E (read a modulo E)

and the set of all equivalence classes is represented by

$$S/E \quad \text{(read } S \text{ modulo } E\text{)}$$

In (6), the element a is called a *representative* of the equivalence class $[a]$. For example, let us consider the following partition

$$\{\{a,b\}, \{m,n,p\}\}$$

of the set $\{a,m,b,p,n\}$. This partition gives rise to the equivalence relation

$$\{(a,a), (b,b), (m,m), (n,n), (p,p), (a,b), (b,a), (m,n), (n,m), (m,p), (n,p), (p,m), (p,n)\}$$

in the set $\{a,m,b,p,n\}$. Naturally, there are two equivalence classes:

$$[a] = [b] = \{a,b\}$$

and

$$[m] = [n] = [p] = \{m,n,p\}$$

Let S be a set and E an equivalence relation in S. Then the mapping f from S onto S/E defined by

$$f(x) = [x] = x/E$$

for every element x of S, is called the *canonical map* from S onto S/E. In other words, the canonical map maps an element x of S into the equivalence class to which x belongs.

Let us observe that the equivalence relation

$$E = \{(a,a), (b,b), (c,c)\}$$

in the set $\{a,b,c\}$ is the usual equality relation in the set $\{a,b,c\}$. The equivalence classes in this case are singletons $[a] = \{a\}$, $[b] = \{b\}$ and $[c] = \{c\}$.

An important application of the notion of equivalence class will be given in connection with the definitions of the integers, rational numbers and real numbers.

EXERCISES

1. Discuss the reflexivity, symmetry and transitivity of the following relations in the set $\{a,b,c\}$:

$$\{(a,a), (b,b)\}, \qquad \{(a,a), (a,b), (b,a), (b,b)\}, \qquad \{(c,c), (c,b)\}$$
$$\{(a,a), (b,b), (c,c)\}, \qquad \{(a,a), (b,b), (c,c), (a,b), (b,a)\}$$
$$\{(a,a), (b,b)(c,c), (a,b), (b,c)\}, \qquad \{(a,b), (b,a), (a,a)\}$$

2. Prove that the set $S \times S$ is an equivalence relation in the set S. Determine the equivalence classes of this equivalence relation.

3. Determine in the set $\{a,b,c,d,e\}$ an equivalence relation such that the range of the corresponding canonical map has three elements.

4. How many distinct equivalence relations are there in the set $\{a,b,c,d\}$ where, as usual, distinct letters are distinct sets?

5. Determine a necessary and sufficient condition that the canonical map corresponding to an equivalence relation in a set be a one-to-one mapping.

2. THE ARITHMETIC OF NATURAL NUMBERS

In Chapter II, Section 8, the natural numbers 0, 1, 2, . . . were defined as the elements of the set ω. The purpose of this section is to define the usual operations of *addition, multiplication* and *exponentiation* in the set ω of all natural numbers. Clearly, we would like these operations to possess all the usual and familiar arithmetical properties. Naturally, in the Theory of Sets each of these operations must be defined as a set. Moreover, as usual, a definition of a set S must be justified by a proof (based on our axioms given in Chapter II) of the existence of S. In view of this and motivated by the familiar sum $n + m$ of two natural numbers n and m, it would be quite appropriate to define addition in the set ω as being the set A, where:

$$A = \{(0, (0, 0 + 0)), \quad (0, (1, 0 + 1)), \quad (0, (2, 0 + 2)), \quad (0, (3, 0 + 3)), \ldots$$
$$(1, (0, 1 + 0)), \quad (1, (1, 1 + 1)), \quad (1, (2, 1 + 2)), \quad (1, (3, 1 + 3)), \ldots$$
$$(2, (0, 2 + 0)), \quad (2, (1, 2 + 1)), \quad (2, (2, 2 + 2)), \quad (2, (3, 2 + 3)), \ldots$$
$$\cdot \quad \cdot \quad \cdot \quad \cdot \quad \cdot \quad \cdot \quad \cdot \quad \cdot \quad \cdot \quad \cdot \quad \cdot \quad \cdot \quad \cdot \quad \cdot \quad \cdot \quad \cdot \quad \cdot \quad \cdot \quad \cdot \quad \cdot \}$$

In short
$$A = \{(n, (x, n + x)) \mid \cdots\}$$
where x and n are natural numbers and $n + x$ is the usual sum of n and x.

However, as mentioned above, in order to accept the definition of addition in ω as being the set A, we must prove the existence of A (in the Theory of Sets).

To prove the existence of A it is enough to prove that for every $n \in \omega$, there exists a set S_n, where:

$$S_n = \{(x, n + x) \mid \cdots\}$$

Indeed, the existence of S_n for every $n \in \omega$ will then (in view of the axioms of Replacement and Sum-Set) imply the existence of A, since:

$$A = \bigcup_{n \in \omega} (\{n\} \times S_n)$$

Thus, we see that the proof of the existence of A is reduced to that of the existence of S_n for every $n \in \omega$.

Now, let us observe that in order to prove that S_n exists for every $n \in \omega$, it is enough to prove that for every $n \in \omega$ there exists a mapping (function) S_n from ω into ω such that $S_n(x) = s$, where s is made to coincide with the usual sum $n + x$ of n and x. As we shall see shortly, the proof of the existence of such a mapping S_n is a direct consequence of the Finite Recursion Theorem given below.

Remark 1.   Despite the above discussion, in what follows, we shall substitute the definition of addition in the set ω of all natural numbers by giving the definition of the sum (in this order) $n + m$ of two natural numbers n and m as the image of m under the mapping S_n. Similar considerations will apply to the definitions of multiplication and exponentiation in the set ω.

The Finite Recursion Theorem.   *Let $p(x,y)$ be a binary predicate, functional in x, such that for every x there exists a (and therefore unique) y, denoted by $p(x)$, such that $p(x,p(x))$ is true. Then for every set s there exists a unique function g defined on the set ω of all natural numbers such that:*

(i) $g(0) = s$ *and* $g(m^+) = p(g(m))$ *for every* $m \in \omega$

PROOF.   Let us recall that m^+ in the above is the immediate successor $m \cup \{m\}$ of the natural number m where ω is ordered (and hence well ordered) by its natural order $\leq$, i.e., where for every two natural numbers m and n:

(ii) $m \leq n$ *if and only if* $m \subset n$

Let us recall also that every natural number is well ordered by $\subset$.

To prove the theorem, first we show that there exists at most one function g satisfying (i). Assume on the contrary that there exist two distinct functions g and h each satisfying (i). Since $g(0) = s = h(0)$ we see that g and h cannot differ on the first element 0 of ω. Since $(\omega, \leq)$ is a well ordered set, there must exist a first nonzero natural number m such that

(iii) $g(m) \neq h(m)$

and

(iv) $g(m^-) = h(m^-)$ with $m > 0$

where m^- is the immediate predecessor of m in $(\omega, \leq)$, i.e., $(m^-)^+ = m$. However, in view of (i) and (iv) we have

$$g(m) = p(g(m^-)) = p(h(m^-)) = h(m)$$

which contradicts (iii). Thus, our assumption is false. Consequently, if there exists a function g satisfying (1), then g is unique.

Next, we prove that there exists a function g defined on ω and satisfying (i).

Let us observe that there exist natural numbers n and corresponding functions g_n such that g_n is defined on the natural number n^+ and satisfies

(v) $g_n(0) = s$ and $g_n(m^+) = p(g_n(m))$ for every $m^+ \in n^+$

for instance, the natural number 0 and the function:

$$g_0 = \{(0,s)\}$$

Moreover, for every natural number n there exists at most one function g_n satisfying (v). This fact is proved (since every natural number is well ordered by $\subset$) as one proves the uniqueness of g in the earlier argument. Furthermore, for every two such functions g_n and g_m, in view of the uniqueness, (ii) and (v), we have:

(vi) $g_n|_{m^+} = g_m$ with $m \leq n$

where the left side of the equality in (vi) is the restriction of the function g_n to m^+.

Now, we prove that for every natural number n there exists a function g_n defined on n^+ and satisfying (v). Assume the contrary, and let $h > 0$ (since g_0 exists) be the smallest natural number for which this fails. But then motivated by (vi) we define

$$g_h = g_{h^-} \cup \{(h, p(g_{h^-}(h^-)))\}$$

which in view of the existence of g_{h^-} exists. But this in turn shows that there exists a function g_h defined on h^+ and satisfying (v). Thus, our assumption is false, and hence for every $n \in \omega$ there exists a function g_n defined on n^+ and satisfying (v).

Finally, consider the set

$$G = \{g_n \mid n \in \omega\}$$

of all functions g_n such that g_n is defined on the natural number n^+ and satisfies (v). The set G exists in view of the axiom of Sum-Set.

Since every function g_n is a set of ordered pairs, in view of (vi) we see that

$$g = \cup G$$

is a function such that

$$\text{dom } g = \cup\{\text{dom } g_n \mid g_n \in G\} = \cup\{n^+ \mid n^+ \in \omega\} = \omega$$

Thus, $g = \cup G$ is a function defined on the set of all natural numbers ω. Moreover, in view of (vi) and (v), the function g satisfies (i). Hence, the existence of the function g is established and the Finite Recursion Theorem is proved.

An immediate consequence of the Finite Recursion Theorem is the following theorem, which is also called the Finite Recursion Theorem.

Theorem 2 (Finite Recursion Theorem). *Let e be an element of a set E and f a mapping from E into E. Then there exists a unique mapping g from ω into E such that*

$$g(0) = e \quad \text{and} \quad g(m^+) = f(g(m)) \quad \text{for every} \quad m \in \omega$$

PROOF. Let us take in the hypothesis of the Finite Recursion Theorem

$$p(x,y) \equiv ((x \in E) \wedge (y = f(x))) \vee ((x \notin E) \wedge (y = 0))$$

where f is the mapping from E into E given in the hypothesis of Theorem 2. Then we see at once that with the above choice of the binary predicate $p(x,y)$, the proof of Theorem 2 follows from that of the Finite Recursion Theorem.

✦ **Theorem 3.** *For every natural number n there exists a unique mapping S_n from ω into ω such that:*

$$S_n(0) = n \quad \text{and} \quad S_n(x^+) = (S_n(x))^+$$

PROOF. It is enough to take in the hypothesis of Theorem 2, $E = \omega$, $e = n$, $g = S_n$ and f as the function from ω into ω such that $f(y) = y^+$, for every $y \in \omega$. Then clearly Theorem 2 yields Theorem 3.

✦ **Definition 3 (Addition).** *Let n and m be two natural numbers and S_n the mapping mentioned in Theorem 3. We define $n + m$ as the image of m under the mapping S_n, i.e.,*

$$n + m = S_n(m)$$

Now, since by Theorem 3, $S_n(0) = n$ and $S_n(x^+) = (S_n(x))^+$, we have:

(7) $$n + 0 = n$$

and

(8) $$n + m^+ = (n + m)^+$$

Thus, the sum $n + m$ of every two natural numbers n and m is defined and is a natural number.

Let us mention again that the above definition of addition is justified in view of the Finite Recursion Theorem (Theorem 2). A definition which is based on the Recursion Theorem is called *definition by recursion*.

Lemma 1. *For every two natural numbers n and m:*

(9) $$m^+ + n = (m + n)^+$$

PROOF. We shall prove (9) by induction on n.
Let us observe that in view of (7),

$$m^+ + 0 = m^+ = (m + 0)^+$$

Next, assume $(m^+ + n) = (m + n)^+$. But then by (8), $(m^+ + n^+) = (m^+ + n)^+$, and since by our assumption $(m^+ + n) = (m + n)^+$, we see that $(m^+ + n^+) = ((m + n)^+)^+$. However, by (8), $(m + n)^+ = m + n^+$. Thus,

$$(m^+ + n^+) = (m + n^+)^+$$

Therefore, the set N of all natural numbers n satisfying (9) is such that $0 \in N$, and $n^+ \in N$ whenever $n \in N$. Thus, by the Finite Induction Theorem, $N = \omega$. Hence, Lemma 1 is proved.

Theorem 4. *Addition of natural numbers is associative and commutative, i.e.,*

(10) $$(m + n) + k = m + (n + k)$$

and

(11) $$m + n = n + m$$

for every three natural numbers m, n and k.

PROOF. The proof of (10) is by induction on k. Let us observe that since by (7), $(m + n) + 0 = m + n$ and $(n + 0) = n$, we see that $(m + n) + 0 = m + (n + 0)$. Next, assume $(m + n) + k = m + (n + k)$; then by (8)

$$(m + n) + k^+ = ((m + n) + k)^+$$

and since $(m + n) + k = m + (n + k)$, we see that:

$$(m + n) + k^+ = (m + (n + k))^+$$

But then by (8), $(m + (n + k))^+ = m + (n + k)^+ = m + (n + k^+)$. Therefore, $(m + n) + k^+ = m + (n + k^+)$ and (10) is proved.

The proof of (11) is by induction on n. Let us observe that in view of (9), $m + 0 = 0 + m$. Next, assume $m + n = n + m$. Then by (8), $m + n^+ = (m + n)^+$, and since $m + n = n + m$, we see that $(m + n^+) = (n + m)^+$. But then in view of (9), $(n + m)^+ = n^+ + m$. Therefore, $m + n^+ = n^+ + m$ and (11) is proved.

In view of (10), for every three natural numbers m, n and k the expression $m + n + k$ can now be used to mean either of $(m + n) + k$ or $m + (n + k)$.

Among various properties of addition of natural numbers, we mention the following *law of cancellation for addition.*

For any three natural numbers m, n and k, if $m + n = m + k$, then $n = k$. The proof of this law is by induction on m and is left as an exercise.

As mentioned previously, the set ω of all natural numbers is well ordered by $\subset$. Also, for every two natural numbers x and y we write as usual $x \leq y$ whenever $x \subseteq y$, and we write $x < y$ whenever $x \in y$.

Theorem 5. *For every natural number n the mapping S_n mentioned in Theorem 3, is such that:*

$$x \leq S_n(x) \qquad \text{for every} \quad x \in \omega$$

PROOF. By induction on x.

Theorem 6. *For every natural number n the mapping S_n mentioned in Theorem 3, is a one-to-one mapping from the set of all natural numbers ω onto the set of all natural numbers not less than n.*

PROOF.   Use Theorem 5.

Theorem 7. *For every two natural numbers m and n if $m \leq n$ then there exists a unique natural number d such that:*

$$m + d = n$$

PROOF.   Use Theorem 6.

Theorem 8. *For every two natural numbers m and n, $m \leq n$ if and only if there exists a natural number d such that:*

$$m + d = n$$

PROOF.   Use Theorem 7.

★   **Theorem 9.** *For every natural number n there exists a unique mapping P_n from ω into ω such that:*

$$P_n(0) = 0 \quad and \quad P_n(x^+) = P_n(x) + n$$

PROOF.   It is enough to take in the hypothesis of Theorem 2, $E = \omega$, $e = 0$, $g = P_n$ and f as the function from ω into ω such that $f(y) = y + n$. Then clearly Theorem 2 yields Theorem 9.

✳   **Definition 4 (Multiplication).** *Let n and m be two natural numbers and P_n the mapping mentioned in Theorem 9. We define $n \cdot m$ as the image of m under the mapping P_n, i.e.,*

$$n \cdot m = P_n(m)$$

Now, since by Theorem 9, $P_n(0) = 0$ and $P_n(x^+) = P_n(x) + n$, we have:

$$n \cdot 0 = 0 \quad and \quad n \cdot m^+ = n \cdot m + n$$

Thus, the product $n \cdot m$ of every two natural numbers n and m is defined and is a natural number. Very often the product $n \cdot m$ is denoted simply by nm.

Theorem 10. *Multiplication of natural numbers is associative and commutative. Moreover, multiplication is distributive with respect to addition, i.e., for every three natural numbers n, m and k, we have:*

$$(nm)k = n(mk), \quad nm = mn, \quad n(m + k) = nm + nk$$

The proof of Theorem 10 parallels that of Theorem 4 and is left as an exercise. Also, one can easily prove that $1x = x1 = x$ for every $x \in \omega$.

In short, addition and multiplication of natural numbers (defined in this section) have all the usual properties of addition and multiplication of natural numbers in ordinary arithmetic.

In view of the associativity of multiplication, for every three natural numbers m, n and k the expression mnk can now be used to mean either of $(mn)k$ or $m(nk)$.

Here again, we mention the *law of cancellation for multiplication* according to which, for every three natural numbers m, n and k with $m \neq 0$,

$$\text{if} \quad mn = mk \quad \text{then} \quad n = k$$

Theorem 11. *For every natural number n there exists a unique mapping H_n from ω into ω such that:*

$$H_n(0) = 1 \quad \text{and} \quad H_n(x^+) = H_n(x) \cdot n$$

PROOF. It is enough to take in the hypothesis of Theorem 2, $E = \omega$, $e = 1$, $g = H_n$ and f as the function from ω into ω such that $f(y) = y \cdot n$. Then clearly Theorem 2 yields Theorem 11.

Definition 5 (Exponentiation). *Let n and m be two natural numbers and H_n the mapping mentioned in Theorem 11. We define n^m as the image of m under the mapping H_n, i.e.,*

$$n^m = H_n(m)$$

Now, since by Theorem 11, $H_n(0) = 1$ and $H_n(x^+) = H_n(x) \cdot n$, we have:

$$n^0 = 1 \quad \text{and} \quad n^{m^+} = n^m \cdot n$$

Thus, the m-th power of n, where m and n are any two natural numbers, is defined and is a natural number.

EXERCISES

1. Explain why we had to use the Recursion Theorem in defining addition for natural numbers.

2. Is it possible to obtain the function S_n, mentioned in Theorem 3, as a result of the direct application of the theorem of Separation to the set $\omega \times \omega$?

3. Prove Theorems 5, 6, 7, 10 and 11.

4. Prove the following laws of exponentiation of natural numbers

$$m^n \cdot m^k = m^{n+k}$$
$$m^n \cdot p^n = (mp)^n$$
$$(m^n)^k = m^{nk}$$

for every four natural numbers k, m, n and p.

5. Prove that for every three natural numbers m, n and k, if $n < k$, then

$$m + n < m + k$$

6. Prove that for every three natural numbers m, n and k, if $n + m = k + m$, then $n = k$.

7. Prove that for every two natural numbers m and n, if $m \cdot n = 0$, then $m = 0$ or $n = 0$.

8. Prove that for every three natural numbers m, n and k,

   (i) If $m \neq 0$ and if $n < k$, then $mn < mk$.
   (ii) If $n \leq k$, then $mn \leq mk$.
   (iii) If $m \neq 0$ and if $mn = mk$, then $n = k$.
   (iv) If $mn < mk$, then $n < k$.

9. Prove that for every natural number n

$$2(1 + 2 + 3 + \cdots + n) = n + n^2$$

10. Prove that for every three natural numbers a, n and r, if $r > 1$, then

$$(r - 1)(a + ar + ar^2 + \cdots + ar^n) = a(r^{n+1} - 1),$$

where $x - 1$ stands for the immediate predecessor of x.

11. Prove that there exists no natural number x such that:

   (i) $3 + x = 1$ or   (ii) $5x = 7$ or   (iii) $2^x = 9$

12. Prove that for every natural number n:

$$n^1 = n, \qquad 1^n = 1$$

and if $n > 0$, then $0^n = 0$.

13. Prove that for every two natural numbers m and n, if $m < n$ then there exists a unique natural number d such that $m + d = n$.

14. Prove that for every two natural numbers m and n, $m < n$ if and only if there exists a natural number $d > 0$ such that $m + d = n$.

15. Prove that for every nonzero natural number n, the mapping P_n mentioned in Theorem 7 is a one-to-one mapping from the set ω of all natural numbers *into* ω.

16. For every natural number n, is the mapping H_n mentioned in Theorem 11 a one-to-one mapping from ω *onto* ω? Is it a one-to-one *into* mapping?

17. Prove that for every two nonzero natural numbers m and n, if $m \geq n$ then there exist two natural numbers q and r such that $r < n$ and $m = nq + r$. Are q and r uniquely determined by m and n?

3. THE INTEGERS AND THEIR ARITHMETIC

In this section, we shall introduce *the set of all integers* $+0$, $+1$, -1, $+2$, -2, $+3$, -3, ... We have deliberately prefixed 0, 1, 2, 3, ... with $+$ or $-$ in order to distinguish an *integer* from a *natural number*. Later, we shall indicate that for all arithmetical purposes, $+0$, $+1$, $+2$, ... are identified respectively with the natural numbers 0, 1, 2, ... For this reason, the set of all integers (denoted by I) is called an extension of the set ω of all natural numbers.

As expected, in the Theory of Sets an integer is defined as a special set.

The question arises as to how to define an integer as a set. Perhaps prior to giving a formal definition, we should give some motivation.

Informally speaking, we wish that, say, -3 represent the result of subtracting 5 from 2, i.e., $2-5$ or $1-4$ or $0-3$, etc. But then $2-5$ or $1-4$ or $0-3$ etc., suggest that we represent them as ordered pairs of natural numbers $(2,5)$ or $(1,4)$ or $(0,3)$, etc. Thus, we see that any one of the ordered pairs $(2,5)$, $(1,4)$, $(0,3)$, etc., is a reasonable candidate for representing the integer -3. Consequently, it would be quite reasonable to consider the entire set

(12) $\{(2,5), (1,4), (0,3), \ldots\}$

as a definition of the integer -3.

We note that there is a definite relation among the elements of (12). Namely, if (x_1, x_2) and (y_1, y_2) are elements of (12), then $x_1 + y_2 = x_2 + y_1$. Thus, we may insert further elements in (12) according to the above-mentioned rule and write:

$$-3 = \{(2,5), (1,4), (0,3), (3,6), (4,7), \ldots\}$$

Similarly,

$$-2 = \{(0,2), (3,5), (2,4), (1,3), \ldots\}$$

Motivated by the above, we write:

$$+2 = \{(2,0), (5,3), (4,2), (3,1), \ldots\}$$
$$+0 = \{(0,0), (3,3), (2,2), (4,4), \ldots\}$$

Considering the above-mentioned sets $-3, -2, +2, +0$, we see first of all that each is a subset of $\omega \times \omega$. Secondly, they are pairwise disjoint. Thirdly, there is enough evidence to indicate that the union of all sets such as $\ldots$, $-2, -1, +0, +1, +2, \ldots$ is equal to $\omega \times \omega$.

These considerations suggest the following.

Lemma 2. *Let R be the relation in $\omega \times \omega$ given by*

$$((x_1, x_2), (y_1, y_2)) \in R \leftrightarrow (x_1 + y_2 = x_2 + y_1)$$

Then R is an equivalence relation in $\omega \times \omega$.

PROOF. R is reflexive since for every two natural numbers x_1 and x_2 we have:

$$x_1 + x_2 = x_2 + x_1 \quad \text{and hence} \quad ((x_1, x_2), (x_1, x_2)) \in R$$

R is symmetric since for every four natural numbers x_1, x_2, y_1 and y_2 we have:

$$\text{if} \quad x_1 + y_2 = x_2 + y_1 \quad \text{then} \quad y_1 + x_2 = y_2 + x_1$$

R is transitive since for every six natural numbers x_1, x_2, y_1, y_2, z_1 and z_2 we have:

if $x_1 + y_2 = x_2 + y_1 \quad \text{and} \quad y_1 + z_2 = y_2 + z_1,$

then

$$x_1 + z_2 = x_2 + z_1$$

Thus, indeed R is an equivalence relation in $\omega \times \omega$. Naturally, R is a subset of $(\omega \times \omega) \times (\omega \times \omega)$. Clearly, the existence of R is secured by our axioms. Motivated by the above, we introduce:

Definition 6. *An integer is an equivalence class of the partition associated with the equivalence relation R in the set $\omega \times \omega$, given by:*

$$((x_1,x_2), (y_1,y_2)) \in R \leftrightarrow (x_1 + y_2 = x_2 + y_1)$$

According to notation (6), the set I of all integers is denoted by $\omega \times \omega/R$ and an integer by $(m,n)/R$ or by

$$[(m,n)]$$

where m and n are any two natural numbers. Usually, instead of writing $[(m,n)]$, we write $[m,n]$.

Thus,

$$[3,5] = \{(0,2), (7,9), (8,10), (3,5), \ldots\}$$
$$[6,2] = \{(5,1), (4,0), (8,4), (9,5), \ldots\}$$

In view of Definition 6, for every two integers $[x_1,x_2]$ and $[y_1,y_2]$, we have:

(13) $$([x_1,x_2] = [y_1,y_2]) \leftrightarrow (x_1 + y_2 = x_2 + y_1)$$

Clearly,

$$[3,5] = [0,2] = [7,9] = \cdots \quad \text{and} \quad [0,0] = [3,3] = [1,1] = \cdots$$

Addition and multiplication of integers are defined based on the addition and multiplication of natural numbers.

The *sum* of any two integers $[a,b]$ and $[c,d]$ is defined by

(14) $$[a,b] + [c,d] = [(a + c), (b + d)]$$

where $a + c$ and $b + d$ are respectively the sums of the natural numbers a, c and b, d.

The *product* of any two integers $[a,b]$ and $[c,d]$ is defined by

(15) $$[a,b] \cdot [c,d] = [(ac + bd), (ad + bc)]$$

where the natural numbers $ac + bd$ and $ad + bc$ are uniquely determined in terms of the natural numbers a, b, c and d.

To accept (14) and (15) as valid definitions, we have to prove the so-called *uniqueness* of the sum and the uniqueness of the product. In other words, we have to prove that the sum of two integers is independent of the choice of their representatives, i.e., if

$$[a,b] = [A,B] \quad \text{and} \quad [c,d] = [C,D]$$

then

$$[a,b] + [c,d] = [A,B] + [C,D] \quad \text{and} \quad [a,b] \cdot [c,d] = [A,B] \cdot [C,D]$$

The proof of the above equalities is left to the reader.

Addition and multiplication of integers have all the properties of the addition and multiplication of natural numbers. Addition and multiplication of integers are associative and commutative. Moreover, multiplication is distributive with respect to addition. However, integers possess a property not shared by natural numbers. Consider the two natural numbers 8 and 5. It is not possible to find a natural number x such that $8 + x = 5$, because no matter what natural number x we choose, we always have $5 \in (8 + x)$, i.e., $5 < 8 + x$. Hence, for no natural number x is it true that $8 + x = 5$. This deficiency of the natural numbers is not shared by the integers. Thus we have:

Theorem 12. *For every two integers* [a,b] *and* [c,d], *there exists a unique integer* [x,y] *such that:*

(16) $[a,b] + [x,y] = [c,d]$

PROOF.   To satisfy (16) it is enough to choose $[x,y] = [(b + c), (a + d)]$. To prove the uniqueness of the solution, it is enough to prove that if $[x,y]$ is such that it satisfies (16), then $[x,y] = [(b + c), (a + d)]$. Now, if $[x,y]$ satisfies (16), then in view of (13) and (14) we have:

$$a + x + d = b + y + c$$

On the other hand, by (13) the above equality implies that

$$[x,y] = [(b + c), (a + d)]$$

as desired.

The integer $[0,0] = [1,1] = [2,2] = \cdots$ has a neutral role with respect to addition. It is easily seen that

$$[a,b] + [m,m] = [a + m, b + m] = [a,b]$$

i.e., the addition of $[m,m]$ to any integer $[a,b]$ yields the same integer $[a,b]$. In other words, with respect to the addition of integers, the integer $[0,0]$ behaves in the same way as the natural number 0 (zero) with respect to the addition of natural numbers. This is why the integer $[0,0]$ is also called the *zero integer*.

Similarly, the integer $[1,0] = [2,1] = [3,2] = \cdots$ has a neutral role with respect to multiplication. It is readily seen that

$$[a,b] \cdot [(m + 1),m] = [(am + bm + a), (am + bm + b)] = [a,b]$$

i.e., the multiplication of any integer $[a,b]$ by $[(m + 1),m]$ yields the same integer $[a,b]$. In other words, with respect to the multiplication of integers, the integer $[1,0]$ behaves in the same way as the natural number 1 (unit) with respect to the multiplication of natural numbers. This is why the integer $[1,0]$ is also called the *unit integer*.

It is easily proved that the product of two natural numbers is equal to zero if and only if at least one of them is equal to zero. This property is usually expressed by saying that ω has no *divisors of zero*. The same property holds in the case of integers. *The product of two integers* [m,n] *and* [p,q] *is equal to* [0,0] *if and only if at least one of* [m,n] *or* [p,q] *is equal to* [0,0]. Thus, the set I of all integers has no divisors of zero.

It is customary to refer to the set I of all integers as an *integral domain*. This is because in I there are defined two associative and commutative operations, namely addition and multiplication, having the following properties.

Multiplication is distributive with respect to addition. Moreover, for every two integers a and b there is an integer c such that $a + c = b$. Furthermore, there exists an integer e such that $xe = x$ for every integer x. Finally, there are no divisors of zero.

Besides addition and multiplication, a third operation (*subtraction*) can be introduced in the set I of all integers.

Let us define the difference (in the following order) between any two integers $[a,b]$ and $[c,d]$ as the integer $[(a + d), (b + c)]$, i.e.,

✶ (17) $$[a,b] - [c,d] = [(a + d), (b + c)]$$

It is easy to show that if $[a,b] = [A,B]$ and $[c,d] = [C,D]$, then

$$[a,b] - [c,d] = [A,B] - [C,D]$$

This ensures that (17) is a valid definition.

We observe easily that *subtraction*, defined by (17), is neither an associative nor a commutative operation in the set I of all integers.

The following are some examples of subtraction:

$$[3,5] - [7,9] = [12,12] = [0,0]$$
$$[1,0] - [0,1] = [2,0]$$

EXERCISES

1. Write three elements of each of the following sets:

$$[1,0], \quad [0,1], \quad [3,4], \quad [5,2], \quad [5,5], \quad [2,5]$$

2. Is an element of an integer an integer?
Is a proper subset of an integer an integer?
Is the union of two integers an integer?
Is the intersection of two integers an integer?

3. Is an integer a subset of $\omega \times \omega$ or a subset of $(\omega \times \omega) \times (\omega \times \omega)$?

4. Is an integer an equivalence class associated with the partition of an equivalence relation in ω or in $\omega \times \omega$?

5. Is a natural number an integer?
Is an integer a natural number?

6. Solve the following equations:

$$[7,4] + [x,y] = [5,7]$$
$$[x,y] + [5,9] = [4,2]$$
$$[9,3] - [x,y] = [7,2]$$
$$[x,y] - [5,8] = [0,3]$$

7. Solve the following equations:

$$[5,2] \cdot [x,y] = [12,3]$$
$$[1,3] \cdot [x,y] = [9,11]$$
$$[x,y] \cdot [3,8] = [0,10]$$

8. Prove that there is no integer $[x,y]$ such that:

$$[6,3] \cdot [x,y] = [4,2]$$

9. Prove that if the product of two integers is equal to $[0,0]$, then at least one of them must be equal to $[0,0]$.

10. Prove that for every integer $[x,y]$:

$$[x,y] \cdot [0,1] = [y,x]$$

11. Prove that for every two integers $[x,y]$ and $[u,v]$:

$$[x,y] \cdot [u,v] = [1,0]$$

if and only if $[x,y] = [u,v] = [1,0]$ or $[x,y] = [u,v] = [0,1]$.

12. Prove that for every two integers $[x,y]$ and $[u,v]$:

$$[x,y] \cdot [u,v] = [y,x] \cdot [v,u]$$

13. Prove that the set of all integers when ordered according to the natural order is not dense.

4. THE NATURAL ORDER AMONG INTEGERS

In the set I of all integers, let us introduce the relation $\leq$ given by the following definition.

Definition 7. *For every two integers* $[m,n]$ *and* $[p,q]$, *we define:*

(18) $$[m,n] \leq [p,q] \leftrightarrow (m + q \leq n + p)$$

The right side of the equivalence sign in (18) is a familiar expression involving the two natural numbers $m + q$ and $n + p$ and the natural order $\leq$ of the natural numbers given by (3) of Chapter IV (page 172).

Let us observe that (18) is a valid definition since if

$$[m,n] = [M,N] \quad \text{and} \quad [p,q] = [P,Q]$$

then:

$$([m,n] \leq [p,q]) \leftrightarrow ([M,N] \leq [P,Q])$$

Moreover, it is easily seen that $\leq$ (read *less than or equal*), defined by (18), is a partial order relation in the set I of all integers (i.e., $\leq$ is reflexive, anti-symmetric and transitive). This partial order is called the *natural partial order*, or simply the *natural order* in the set I of all integers.

According to our general convention, if

$$[m,n] \leq [p,q] \quad \text{and} \quad [m,n] \neq [p,q]$$

then we write

$$[m,n] < [p,q]$$

and we say that the integer $[m,n]$ is less than the integer $[p,q]$.

In view of (18), we have:

$$[m,n] < [p,q] \leftrightarrow (m + q < n + p)$$

Definition 7 implies that the set I of all integers is a simply ordered set. This follows from the fact that, as we know, for every two natural numbers $m + q$ and $n + p$, it is always the case that either $m + q \leq n + p$ or $m + q \geq n + p$. Consequently, for every two integers $[m,n]$ and $[p,q]$, it is always the case that either $[m,n] \leq [p,q]$ or $[p,q] \leq [m,n]$. Hence, we have:

The set I of all integers is a simply ordered set with respect to its natural order given by (18).

Let us observe that for every integer $[m,n]$ there exists an integer less than $[m,n]$. For instance, $[m,n + 1]$ is such an integer. It follows therefore that *the set I of all integers* [ordered according to (18)] *is not a well ordered set with respect to the natural order.*

Lemma 3.   *For every integer $[m,n]$ there exist unique positive natural numbers p and q such that one and only one of the following three cases holds:*

$$[m,n] = [p,0] \quad or \quad [m,n] = [0,q] \quad or \quad [m,n] = [0,0]$$

PROOF.   Since m and n are natural numbers, by Theorem 19 of Chapter II (page 110), one and only one of the three cases

$$m > n \quad or \quad m < n \quad or \quad m = n$$

must hold.

If $m > n$, then by Theorem 8 there exists a unique natural number p, which is necessarily positive, such that $m = n + p$. But then by (13) we have $[m,n] = [p,0]$.

If $m < n$, then by Theorem 8 there exists a unique natural number q, which is necessarily positive, such that $m + q = n$. But then by (13) we have $[m,n] = [0,q]$.

If $m = n$, then by (13) $[m,n] = [0,0]$.

Thus, the lemma is proved.

According to Lemma 3, every integer $[m,n]$ can be written in one and only one of the three forms $[p,0]$ or $[0,q]$ or $[0,0]$, where p and q are nonzero (positive) natural numbers.

Definition 8.   *If p and q are positive (nonzero) natural numbers, then the integers $[p,0]$, $[0,q]$ and $[0,0]$ are called respectively a positive, a negative and the zero integer. Moreover, $[p,0]$ is denoted by $+p$, $[0,q]$ by $-q$ and $[0,0]$ by $+0$.*

Remark 2.   Although no integer is equal to a natural number, for all arithmetical purposes the nonnegative integers $+0, +1, +2, \ldots$ can be identified respectively with the natural numbers $0, 1, 2, \ldots$. Indeed, between the two sets $\{+0, +1, +2, \ldots\}$ and $\{0, 1, 2, \ldots\}$, there exists a one-to-one correspondence f given by

$$f(+p) = p$$

which also preserves addition, multiplication and order, i.e.,

$$f((+p) + (+q)) = f(+p) + f(+q) = p + q$$
$$f((+p) \cdot (+q)) = f(+p) \cdot f(+q) = p \cdot q$$
$$+p \le +q \leftrightarrow f(+p) \le f(+q) \leftrightarrow p \le q$$

This kind of one-to-one correspondence is called an *isomorphism* between $\{+0, +1, +2, \ldots\}$ and $\{0, 1, 2, \ldots\}$, and the latter sets are called *isomorphic*. Hence, we have:

Lemma 4. *The set of all nonnegative integers is isomorphic to the set of all natural numbers.*

In view of the above considerations, we say that the set I of all integers is an extension of the set ω of all natural numbers. Therefore, we may abandon the set ω and instead deal with the set I. To indicate this, we shall denote the integers $+0, +1, +2, \ldots$ simply by $0, 1, 2, \ldots$.

Thus, according to our notational convention, we shall represent the set I of all integers by

$$I = \{(\ldots; -3; -2; -1; 0; 1; 2; 3; \ldots)\}$$

which also indicates the natural order in the set I.

EXERCISES

1. Determine which of the following inequalities are true.

$$[3,5] \le [2,7], \qquad [5,8] \le [2,1], \qquad [3,0] \le [5,2]$$
$$[8,3] \le [1,2], \qquad [1,2] \le [8,3], \qquad [3,5] \le [0,2]$$

2. Express the following integers in one of the forms $[m,0]$ or $[0,m]$, where m is a natural number.

$$[7,8], \qquad [1,6], \qquad [7,9], \qquad [3,2], \qquad [4,6]$$
$$[3,4], \qquad [3,3], \qquad [2,5], \qquad [1,9], \qquad [9,1]$$

3. Prove that the set of all integers (with respect to the natural order) is a conditionally complete, simply ordered set.

4. Prove that every integer (with respect to the natural order) has an immediate successor and an immediate predecessor.

5. Prove that the set of all integers I (with respect to the natural order) is not dense.

6. Prove that the set of all integers I (with respect to the natural order) is not continuous.

7. Define the exponentiation of an integer by a nonnegative integer in such a way that it coincides with the usual exponentiation. Derive some of the usual properties of exponentiation.

8. Introduce an order in the set I of all integers so that I becomes a well ordered set.

9. Prove that no integer is equal to a natural number.

10. Prove that the product of a negative and a positive integer is a negative integer. Prove the corresponding statements for all other cases.

5. THE RATIONAL NUMBERS AND THEIR ARITHMETIC

In this section, we shall introduce *the set of all rational numbers* $\frac{2}{3}$, $-\frac{1}{4}$, $\frac{3}{1}$, $-\frac{6}{3}$, $\frac{7}{2}$, $-\frac{8}{2}$, ... Later, we shall indicate that for all arithmetical purposes rational numbers such as $\frac{3}{1}$, $-\frac{6}{3}$, $-\frac{8}{2}$, ... are identified respectively with the integers 3, −2, −4, ... For this reason, the set of all rational numbers (denoted by Q) is called an extension of the set I of all integers.

As expected, in the Theory of Sets a rational number is defined as a special set.

The question arises as to how to define a rational number as a set. Perhaps prior to giving a formal definition, we should give some motivation.

Informally speaking, we wish that $-\frac{2}{3}$ represent the result of dividing −2 by 3, i.e., −2:3 or 2:−3 or 4:−6 or −8:12, etc. But then −2:3 or 2:−3 or 4:−6, etc., suggest that we represent them as ordered pairs of integers (−2,3) or (2,−3) or (4,−6), etc. Thus, we see that any one of the ordered pairs (−2,3), (2,−3), (4,−6) etc., is a reasonable candidate for representing the rational number $-\frac{2}{3}$. Consequently, it would be quite reasonable to consider the entire set

(19) $$\{(-2,3), (2,-3), (4,-6), \ldots\}$$

as a definition of the rational number $-\frac{2}{3}$.

We note that there is a definite relation among the elements of (19). Namely, if (x_1,x_2) and (y_1,y_2) are elements of (19), then $x_1 \cdot y_2 = x_2 \cdot y_1$. Thus, we may insert further elements in (19) according to the above-mentioned rule and write:

$$-\tfrac{2}{3} = \{(-2,3), (2,-3), (4,-6), (-8,12), (10,-15), \ldots\}$$

Similarly,

$$-\tfrac{2}{1} = \{(-2,1), (2,-1), (4,-2), (-4,2), \ldots\}$$
$$\tfrac{0}{3} = \{(0,1), (0,-3), (0,4), (0,-5), \ldots\}$$
$$\tfrac{1}{1} = \{(3,3), (2,2), (-1,-1), (-5,-5), \ldots\}$$
$$-\tfrac{1}{1} = \{(-3,3), (2,-2), (1,-1), (-1,1), \ldots\}$$

Considering the above-mentioned sets $-\frac{2}{3}$, $-\frac{2}{1}$, $\frac{0}{3}$, $\frac{1}{1}$, $-\frac{1}{1}$ we see first of all that each is a subset of $I \times (I \smallsetminus \{0\})$. Secondly, they are pairwise disjoint. Thirdly, there is enough evidence to indicate that the union of all sets such as $-\frac{2}{3}$, $-\frac{2}{1}$, $\frac{0}{3}$, $\frac{1}{1}$, $-\frac{1}{1}$, ... is equal to $I \times (I \smallsetminus \{0\})$.

These considerations suggest the following:

Lemma 5. *Let R be the relation in $I \times (I \smile \{0\})$ given by:*

$$((x_1,x_2), (y_1,y_2)) \in R \leftrightarrow (x_1 \cdot y_2 = x_2 \cdot y_1)$$

Then R is an equivalence relation in $I \times (I \smile \{0\})$.

In the above, I is the set of all integers and $I - \{0\}$ is the set of all nonzero integers.

PROOF. R is reflexive since for every two integers x_1 and x_2, we have:

$$x_1 \cdot x_2 = x_2 \cdot x_1 \quad \text{and hence} \quad ((x_1,x_2), (x_1,x_2)) \in R$$

R is symmetric since for every four integers x_1, x_2, y_1 and y_2 we have:

$$\text{if} \quad x_1 \cdot y_2 = x_2 \cdot y_1, \quad \text{then} \quad y_1 \cdot x_2 = y_2 \cdot x_1$$

R is transitive since for every six natural numbers x_1, x_2, y_1, y_2, z_1 and z_2 we have:

$$\text{if} \quad x_1 \cdot y_2 = x_2 \cdot y_1 \quad \text{and} \quad y_1 \cdot z_2 = y_2 \cdot z_1, \quad \text{then}$$
$$x_1 \cdot y_2 \cdot y_1 \cdot z_2 = x_2 \cdot y_1 \cdot y_2 \cdot z_1 \quad \text{and hence} \quad x_1 \cdot z_2 = x_2 \cdot z_1$$

Thus, indeed R is an equivalence relation in $I \times (I \smile \{0\})$. Naturally, R is a subset of:

$$(I \times (I \smile \{0\})) \times (I \times (I \smile \{0\}))$$

Motivated by the above, we introduce:

Definition 9. *A rational number is an equivalence class of the partition associated with the equivalence relation R in the set $I \times (I \smile \{0\})$ given by:*

$$((x_1,x_2), (y_1,y_2)) \in R \leftrightarrow (x_1 \cdot y_2 = x_2 \cdot y_1)$$

Our axioms secure the existence of the set Q of all rational numbers. According to notation (6), the set of all rational numbers is denoted by $I \times (I \smile \{0\})/R$ and a rational number by $(m,n)/R$ or by

$$[(m,n)]$$

where m and n are any two integers with $n \neq 0$. Usually, instead of writing $[(m,n)]$, we write $[m,n]$.

Thus,

$$[2,3] = \{(2,3), (4,6), (-2,-3), (-4,-6), \ldots\}$$
$$[4,-1] = \{(4,-1), (-4,1), (8,-2), (-2,8), \ldots\}$$

In view of Definition 9, for every two rationals $[x_1,x_2]$ and $[y_1,y_2]$ we have:

(20) $$\underline{([x_1,x_2] = [y_1,y_2]) \leftrightarrow (x_1 \cdot y_2 = x_2 \cdot y_1)}$$

Thus,

$$[2,3] = [4,6] = [-2,-3] = \cdots \quad \text{and} \quad [-4,3] = [4,-3] = [8,-6] = \cdots$$

The first integer m appearing in the rational number $[m,n]$ is called the *numerator* of $[m,n]$, and the second integer n is called the *denominator* of $[m,n]$.

Let us observe that *there exists no rational number whose denominator is the zero integer.*

Addition and multiplication of rational numbers are defined based on the addition and multiplication of integers.

The *sum* of any two rational numbers [a,b] and [c,d] is defined by

(21) $[a,b] + [c,d] = [(ad + bc), bd]$

where ad, bc and bd are respectively the products of the integers a and d, b and c, and b and d, and where ad + bc is the sum of the two integers ad and bc.

The *product* of any two rational numbers [a,b] and [c,d] is defined by

(22) $[a,b] \cdot [c,d] = [ac,bd]$

where ac is the product of the integers a and c, and bd that of the integers b and d.

To accept (21) and (22) as valid definitions, we have to prove the *uniqueness* of the sum and the uniqueness of the product. However, one can easily see that if

$$[a,b] = [A,B] \quad \text{and} \quad [c,d] = [C,D]$$

then

$$[a,b] + [c,d] = [A,B] + [C,D] \quad \text{and} \quad [a,b] \cdot [c,d] = [A,B] \cdot [C,D]$$

Both of the above equalities are easily proved by virtue of (20), (21) and (22) and in view of the rules of the arithmetic of integers.

Addition and multiplication of rationals are associative and commutative operations; moreover, multiplication is distributive with respect to addition. These properties are easily proved.

The rational number

$$[0,-1] = [0,1] = [0,2] = [0,-2] = [0,m] = \cdots$$

where m is any nonzero integer, has a neutral role with respect to addition, since

$$[a,b] + [0,m] = [(am, b \cdot 0), b,m] = [am,bm] = [a,b]$$

i.e., the addition of [0,m] to any rational number [a,b] yields the same rational [a,b]. Thus, [0,m] where m is any nonzero integer, can be called the *zero rational number.*

Similarly, the rational number

$$[-1,-1] = [1,1] = [-2,-2] = [2,2] = [m,m] = \cdots$$

where m is any nonzero integer, has a neutral role with respect to multiplication, since

$$[a,b] \cdot [m,m] = [am,bm] = [a,b]$$

i.e., the multiplication of any rational number [a,b] by [m,m] yields the same rational [a,b]. Thus, [m,m] where m is any nonzero integer, can be called the *unit rational* number.

One can easily verify that rationals do not have divisors of zero, i.e., if the product of two rational numbers is the zero rational number [0,*m*], then at least one of them must be equal to the zero rational number.

In short, *the set Q of all rational numbers, like the set I of all integers, is an integral domain.*

However, rationals do possess a property not shared by the integers. Consider the two integers 3 and 2. It is not possible to find an integer x such that $3x = 2$. Indeed, no matter what positive integer x we choose, we always have $3x > 2$, i.e., $3x \neq 2$. This deficiency of the integers is not shared by the rational numbers. Thus, we have:

*✳ **Theorem 13.*** *For every two rational numbers [a,b] and [c,d] with [a,b] ≠ [0,m], there exists a unique rational number [x,y] such that:*

(23) $$[a,b] \cdot [x,y] = [c,d]$$

PROOF. Let us observe that in [*a,b*] the integer *a* is different from 0 and in [*c,d*] the integer *d* is also different from 0; hence the configuration [*bc,ad*] is a rational number. Now, it is enough to choose [*x,y*] = [*bc,ad*] in order to satisfy (23). To prove the uniqueness of the solution, it is enough to prove that if [*x,y*] is such that it satisfies (23), then [*x,y*] = [*bc,ad*]. Now, if [*x,y*] satisfies (23), then in view of (22) and (20) we have:

$$axd = byc$$

On the other hand, by (20) the above equality implies that [*x,y*] = [*bc,ad*], as desired.

Two rational numbers [*m,n*] and [*p,q*] are called *multiplicative inverses of each other* or simply *inverses of each other* or *reciprocals of each other*, if:

(24) $$[m,n] \cdot [p,q] = [1,1]$$

By Theorem 13, if [*m,n*] ≠ [0,*t*], then there exists a unique rational number [*p,q*] such that (24) is satisfied. Clearly, [*p,q*] = [*n,m*]. Hence:

Lemma 6. *Every nonzero rational number [m,n] has a unique multiplicative inverse, namely [n,m].*

An integral domain, every nonzero element of which has a multiplicative inverse, is called a *field*. Thus:

The set Q of all rational numbers is a field.

Besides addition and multiplication, two more operations can be introduced in the set *Q* of all rational numbers. These two operations are *subtraction* and *division*.

Let us define the *difference* (in the following order) between any two rationals [*m,n*] and [*p,q*] as the rational number [*mq − np, nq*], where *mq − np* is the difference between the two integers *mq* and *np*, given by (17). Thus,

(25) $$[m,n] - [p,q] = [mq - np, nq]$$

It is easily verified that (25) is a valid definition in the sense that it does not depend on the choice of the representatives for the rationals [*m,n*] and [*p,q*].

Also, we observe that *subtraction*, defined by (25), is neither an associative nor a commutative operation in the set Q of all rational numbers.

Similarly, we define the *quotient* of a rational number $[m,n]$ by a nonzero rational number $[p,q]$ as the rational number $[mq,np]$, i.e.,

⁎ (26) $$[m,n]:[p,q] = [mq,np]$$

It is easily verified that (26) with $p \neq 0$ is also a valid definition.

We observe that *division*, defined by (26), is neither an associative nor a commutative operation in the set Q of all rational numbers.

The following are some examples of subtraction and division of rational numbers.

$$[2,-3] - [-5,2] = [-11,-6], \qquad [-1,3] - [1,3] = [0,6]$$
$$[2,-3]:[-5,2] = [4,15], \qquad\qquad [-1,3]:[1,3] = [-3,3]$$

EXERCISES

1. Write three elements of each of the following sets:

$$-\tfrac{3}{2}, \qquad -\tfrac{4}{1}, \qquad \tfrac{0}{3}, \qquad \tfrac{7}{2}, \qquad -\tfrac{5}{1}$$

2. Is a rational number an element of the set:

$$\mathscr{P}(\omega \times \omega) \times \mathscr{P}(\omega \times \omega)?$$

3. Is a rational number a subset of $(\omega \times \omega) \times (\omega \times \omega)$?

4. Is a rational number an equivalence class corresponding to an equivalence relation in I, or in $I \times I$, or in $I \times (I \frown \{0\})$?

5. Is every element of every rational number a rational number?
Is every proper subset of every rational number a rational number?
Is the union of every two rational numbers a rational number?
Is the intersection of every two rational numbers a rational number?

6. Solve the following equations involving rational numbers:

$$[-7,3] + [x,y] = [-5,-6], \qquad [-3,1] + [x,y] = [0,-1]$$
$$[-4,-5] - [x,y] = [-3,1], \qquad\quad [x,y] - [-2,3] = [0,5]$$

7. Solve the following equations involving rational numbers:

$$[4,-5] \cdot [x,y] = [3,2], \qquad [-1,3] \cdot [x,y] = [-1,3]$$
$$[x,y]:[-2,4] = [0,7], \qquad\quad [2,-3]:[x,y] = [1,7]$$

8. Prove that the set of all nonzero rational numbers is a commutative group under multiplication.

9. Is the set of all rational numbers a group under subtraction?

10. Is the set of all nonzero rational numbers a group under division?

11. Write down the reciprocals of:

$$[3,-5], \qquad [-7,-2], \qquad [1,-3], \qquad [-4,2]$$

12. Prove that $[a,b] = [c,b]$ if and only if $a = c$.

13. Prove that if $a \neq 0$, then $[a,b] = [a,d]$ if and only if $b = d$.

14. Prove that the product of every two rational numbers is equal to the zero rational number if and only if at least one of the two rational numbers is equal to the zero rational number.

15. Prove that the cancellation law holds for addition and multiplication of rational numbers, i.e., if:

$$[a,b] + [c,d] = [e,f] + [c,d], \qquad \text{then} \quad [a,b] = [e,f]$$

Also, if:

$$[a,b] \cdot [c,d] = [e,f] \cdot [c,d] \quad \text{and} \quad c \neq 0, \qquad \text{then} \quad [a,b] = [e,f]$$

6. THE NATURAL ORDER AMONG RATIONAL NUMBERS

In the set Q of all rational numbers, let us introduce the relation $\leq$ given by the following definition.

Definition 10.   *For every two rational numbers* $[m,n]$ *and* $[p,q]$, *we define:*

(27) $$[m,n] \leq [p,q] \leftrightarrow (mq - np)nq \leq 0$$

The right side of the equivalence sign in (27) is a familiar expression involving the four integers mq, np, nq, 0 and the natural order $\leq$ among the integers as given by (18).

Accordingly, $[-3,2] \leq [1,5]$ since $(-15 - 2)(10) = -170 \leq 0$.

Let us observe that (27) is a valid definition in the sense that if $[m,n] = [M,N]$ and $[p,q] = [P,Q]$, then $[m,n] \leq [p,q]$ if and only if $[M,N] \leq [P,Q]$.

Also, it is easy to verify that $\leq$ (read *less than or equal*), defined by (27), is a partial order in the set Q of all rationals (in other words, $\leq$ is reflexive, anti-symmetric and transitive in Q). This partial order is called *the natural partial order*, or simply *the natural order* in the set Q of all rationals.

In Section 4 we mentioned that the natural order in the set I of all integers is a simple order. Hence, for the two integers $(mq - np)nq$ and 0, it is always the case that $(mq - np)nq \leq 0$ or $(mq - np)nq \geq 0$. But in view of (27), this simply means that for every two rational numbers $[m,n]$ and $[p,q]$, it is always the case that:

$$[m,n] \leq [p,q] \qquad \text{or} \qquad [p,q] \leq [m,n]$$

Thus, we have:

The set Q *of all rational numbers* [ordered according to (27)] *is a simply ordered set with respect to the natural order.*

If, as usual, we write $[m,n] < [p,q]$ when $[m,n] \le [p,q]$ and $[m,n] \ne [p,q]$, then in view of the above, we have:

✗ **Lemma 7.** *For every two rational numbers $[m,n]$ and $[p,q]$, one and only one of the following three cases must hold:*

$$[m,n] < [p,q] \quad \text{or} \quad [m,n] = [p,q] \quad \text{or} \quad [m,n] > [p,q]$$

Thus, for every rational number $[m,n]$ one and only one of the following three cases must hold:

$$[m,n] < [0,q] \quad \text{or} \quad [m,n] = [0,q] \quad \text{or} \quad [m,n] > [0,q]$$

If the first of these three cases holds, then $[m,n]$ is called a *negative* rational number. If the second holds, then, as we already know, $[m,n]$ is called the *zero* rational number. If the third holds, then $[m,n]$ is called a *positive* rational number. Thus, we have:

✗ **Corollary 1.** *For every rational number $[m,n]$, one and only one of the following three cases holds:*

$$[m,n] \quad \text{is positive,} \quad [m,n] \quad \text{is zero,} \quad [m,n] \quad \text{is negative}$$

Moreover, one can easily verify that:

✗ **Corollary 2.** *A rational number $[m,n]$ is positive, zero or negative if and only if $mn > 0$, $mn = 0$ or $mn < 0$ respectively.*

Theorem 14. *If the rational number $[m,n]$ is such that $[m,n] < [p,q]$, then there exists a unique positive rational number $[s,t]$ such that:*

$$[m,n] + [s,t] = [p,q]$$

PROOF. The existence of a unique rational number $[s,t]$ satisfying the above equality follows from the fact that the set Q of all rational numbers is an integral domain. Also, we know that:

$$[s,t] = [(np - mq), nq]$$

However, the hypothesis of the theorem implies that $(mq - np)nq < 0$, which (by virtue of the properties of the arithmetic of integers) implies that $(np - mq)\, nq > 0$. But the latter, in view of Corollary 2, implies that $[s,t]$ is positive.

Theorem 15. *Let $[m,n]$ be a rational number and $[p,q]$ a negative rational number. Then:*

$$[m,n] + [p,q] < [m,n]$$

PROOF. By the hypothesis, $pq < 0$. On the other hand, $[m,n] + [p,q] = [(mq + np), nq]$. According to (27), to prove the theorem we have to show that $((mq + np)n - nqm)nqn < 0$. However, $((mq + np)n - nqm)nqn = n^4 pq$, and since $pq < 0$, we conclude that the above inequality holds.

From the above theorem it follows that for every rational number $[m,n]$ there always exists another rational number less than $[m,n]$. Hence:

Corollary 3.   *The set Q of all rational numbers is not a well ordered set with respect to the natural order.*

Lemma 8.   *For every two rational numbers $[m,n]$ and $[p,q]$ if $[m,n] < [p,q]$ then there exists a rational number $[s,t]$ such that:*

$$[m,n] < [s,t] < [p,q]$$

PROOF.   It is enough to take, for instance:

$$[s,t] = [1,2][(mq + np), nq]$$

In Section 4, we mentioned that the set I of all integers, in its natural order, is not a well ordered set. However, for every integer i, with respect to the natural order, there is an immediate predecessor $i - 1$ and an immediate successor $i + 1$. In view of Lemma 8, this property of integers is not shared by the rational numbers. Consequently, there is no rational number which, with respect to the natural order, is immediately prior to or immediately after a given rational number.

In view of Lemma 8 we have:

The set Q of all rational numbers is a dense simply ordered set with respect to the natural order.

Although no integer is equal to a rational number, for all arithmetical purposes every integer i can be identified with the rational number $[i,1]$. Thus, for instance, the integers -2, -1, 0, 1 and 2 can be identified respectively with the rational numbers $[-2,1]$, $[-1,1]$, $[0,1]$, $[1,1]$ and $[2,1]$. This identification is justified because between the set I of all integers and the set of all rational numbers whose denominators are equal to the integer 1, there exists a one-to-one correspondence g given by

$$g(i) = [i,1]$$

which also preserves addition, multiplication and order, i.e.,

$$g(i + j) = g(i) + g(j) = [i + j,1]$$
$$g(i \cdot j) = g(i) \cdot g(j) = [ij,1]$$
$$(i \le j) \leftrightarrow ([i,1] \le [j,1])$$

for every two integers i and j. In view of this we have:

✗ **Lemma 9.**   *The set of all integers is isomorphic to the set of all rational numbers whose denominators are the integer 1.*

In view of the above considerations, we say that the set Q of all rational numbers is an extension of the set I of all integers. Therefore, we may abandon the set I and instead deal with the set Q. To indicate this, we shall denote the rational number $[i,1]$ simply by i. Thus, according to this notational convention, we shall represent, say, the rational numbers $[-4,1]$, $[2,1]$, $[0,1]$, $[-5,1]$ and $[1,1]$ by -4, 2, 0, -5 and 1 respectively.

Also, we shall abandon the representation of a rational number by a symbol such as $[m,n]$, and instead we shall denote it as usual by the symbol $\dfrac{m}{n}$. For obvious reasons $[-m,n]$ and $[m,-n]$ both will be represented by the symbol $-\dfrac{m}{n}$. Thus, $[-3,2]$, $[7,-2]$, $[5,3]$ and $[3,-2]$ will be denoted respectively by $-\frac{3}{2}$, $-\frac{7}{2}$, $-\frac{5}{3}$ and $-\frac{3}{2}$.

Also, as usual, for every rational number a, the product of a and -1 will be denoted by $-a$.

We observe that the set of all *positive rational* numbers has the following properties:

(28)   The sum of two positive rational numbers is a positive rational number.

(29)   The product of two positive rational numbers is a positive rational number.

Moreover, in view of Corollary 1, for every rational number q one and only one of the following cases must hold.

(30) $q > 0, \qquad q = 0, \qquad -q > 0$

i.e., either q is positive, or $q = 0$, or $-q$ is positive.

Definition 11. *A field is called ordered if the property of positiveness satisfying conditions* (28), (29) *and* (30) *is defined for its elements.*

According to the above definition, the set Q of all rational numbers is an ordered field.

In every ordered field, and in particular in the set Q of all rational numbers, we define the *absolute value* $|a|$ of an element a to be equal to a if $a \geq 0$, and to be equal to $-a$ if $a < 0$. Thus,

$$|\tfrac{3}{2}| = \tfrac{3}{2}, \qquad |0| = 0, \qquad |-\tfrac{1}{2}| = \tfrac{1}{2}$$

Note that the absolute value of every rational number is always a non-negative rational number.

The absolute value has the following properties.

(31) $|a + b| \leq |a| + |b|$

(32) $|a - b| \geq \big||a| - |b|\big| \geq |a| - |b|$

(33) $|a \cdot b| = |a| \cdot |b|$

for every two rational numbers a and b.

EXERCISES

1. Prove that $\leq$ defined by (27) is reflexive, antisymmetric and transitive in the set Q of all rationals.

2. Prove the validity of the definition given by (27).

3. Prove that if $[m,n] > [p,q]$, then $[m,n] - [p,q]$ is a positive rational number.

4. Prove that if $[m,n] > [p,q]$ and if $[s,t]$ is a positive rational number, then:

$$[m,n] + [s,t] > [p,q]$$
$$[m,n] + [s,t] > [p,q] + [s,t]$$
$$[m,n] + [s,t] > [p,q] - [s,t]$$
$$[m,n] - [s,t] > [p,q] - [s,t]$$

5. Prove that every positive rational number is greater than every negative rational number.

6. Prove that if $[m,n] > [p,q]$, then:

$$[m,n][-1,1] < [p,q][-1,1]$$

7. Prove that for every rational number $[m,n]$

$$[m,n] \cdot [m,n] \geq [0,1]$$

and if $[m,n] \neq [0,1]$, then $[m,n] \cdot [m,n] > [0,1]$.

8. Prove that if $[m,n]$ is a positive rational number, then

$$[m,n][1,2] < [m,n], \qquad [m,n][1,3] < [m,n], \qquad [m,n][1,4] < [m,n]$$

What are the corresponding conclusions if $[m,n]$ is a negative rational number?

9. Prove that if $[a,b] < [c,d]$ and $[e,f] < [g,h]$, then $[a,b] + [e,f] < [c,d] + [g,h]$.

10. Prove (31), (32) and (33).

11. Prove Corollary 2.

12. Prove that $|a - b| = |b - a|$ for every two rational numbers a and b.

13. For every rational number a, prove that $|a^2| = a^2$.

14. For every two rational numbers a and b, prove that $|a - b| \geq |a| - |b|$.

15. Given a rational number a and a positive rational number p, determine explicitly the set of all rational numbers x corresponding to each of the following inequalities:

$$|x - a| < p, \qquad |x - a| \leq p, \qquad |x - a| > p, \qquad |x - a| \geq p$$

16. Prove that for every rational number a and every positive rational number p, there exists a positive rational number q such that $|a - q| < p$.

7. TERMINATING DECIMALS

A rational number the denominator of which is of the form 10^n, where $n = 0, 1, 2, 3, \ldots$ is called a *terminating decimal*.
Thus

$$[3,1], \qquad [-53,10], \qquad [-65,100], \qquad [-42,1000], \qquad [7452,10]$$

are examples of terminating decimals. In the usual notation these terminating decimals are denoted respectively by:

$$3, \quad -\tfrac{53}{10}, \quad -\tfrac{65}{100}, \quad -\tfrac{42}{1000}, \quad \tfrac{7452}{10}$$

As the reader knows, it is customary to represent the same terminating decimals by their *decimal representation*, given respectively as:

$$3, \quad -5.3, \quad -0.65, \quad -0.042, \quad 745.2$$

Clearly, every integer m is a terminating decimal since by our convention:

$$m = [m,1] = [m,10^0]$$

Also, in view of the fact that, say

$$[3,1] = [30,10] = [300,100] = \cdots$$

we have:

$$3 = 3.0 = 3.00 = 3.000 = \cdots$$

Similarly,

$$0 = 0.0 = 0.00 = 0.000 = \cdots$$

We also agree that:

$$0 = \pm 0 = \pm 0.0 = \pm 0.00 = \pm 0.000 = \cdots$$

In view of the above considerations, we may say that a configuration of the form

$$\pm m \cdot d_1 d_2 d_3 \cdots d_n$$

represents a terminating decimal if m is the usual symbol for a natural number and d_i, for $i = 1, 2, 3, \cdots, n$, is the usual symbol for a natural number less than 10. In the above, $\pm m$ is called the *integral part* and $\pm 0 \cdot d_1 d_2 d_3 \cdots d_n$ is called the *decimal part* and d_i is called the *digit in the i-th decimal place*, or simply, the *i-th decimal coordinate* of the terminating decimal $\pm m \cdot d_1 d_2 d_3 \cdots d_n$.

Clearly, our axioms secure the existence of the set D of all terminating decimals. The set D can be obtained from the set Q of all rational numbers via the theorem of Separation.

The set D of all terminating decimals as a subset of the set Q of all rational numbers is a simply ordered set with respect to the natural order among rationals. However, as the reader knows, the same natural order in D can be established by comparing any two terminating decimals t_1 and t_2 in an obvious manner—i.e., by first comparing the integral parts of t_1 and t_2, and in the case of equal integral parts by comparing the decimal parts of t_1 and t_2 place by place, that is to say, *coordinatewise*. Clearly, obvious precautions must be taken when t_1 and t_2 are both negative terminating decimals. Thus, we have $4.23 < 4.24$ and $-53.252 < -53.251$.

We can easily verify that for every two terminating decimals m and n if $m < n$ then there exists a terminating decimal p such that $m < p < n$. Thus, *the set D of all terminating decimals* (with respect to the natural order) *is a dense simply ordered set.*

Let us observe, however, that the set D of all terminating decimals is not conditionally complete (with respect to the natural order) and hence D is not a continuous set. To see this, it is enough to consider the following bounded set of terminating decimals:

$$B = \{3, 3.3, 3.33, 3.333, 3.3333, \ldots\}$$

Although every element of B is a terminating decimal, there is no terminating decimal that can serve as the least upper bound of B. The only reasonable candidate which somewhat resembles a terminating decimal is the *nonterminating decimal* 3.33333 . . . , which of course cannot be the least upper bound of B since it is not even an element of D.

Clearly, the sum and the product of two terminating decimals are again terminating decimals. Moreover, it can be easily verified that the set D of all terminating decimals is an integral domain. Furthermore, since the property of positiveness for the elements of the set D satisfies conditions (28), (29) and (30), we may say that the set D of all terminating decimals is an *ordered integral domain*.

Lemma 10. *For every two rational numbers p and q if $p < q$, then there exists a terminating decimal t such that $p < t < q$.*

The proof of the above lemma is left to the reader.

EXERCISES

1. Prove that the following rational numbers are terminating decimals and represent them according to the standard representation of terminating decimals.

$$\tfrac{3}{2}, \quad -\tfrac{15}{4}, \quad \tfrac{7}{525}, \quad -\tfrac{354}{800}, \quad \tfrac{71}{16}, \quad -\tfrac{83}{62500}$$

2. Prove that the following rational numbers are not terminating decimals:

$$\tfrac{1}{3}, \quad -\tfrac{15}{144}, \quad \tfrac{25}{6}, \quad -\tfrac{3}{7}, \quad -\tfrac{1}{10001}$$

3. Give a necessary and sufficient condition that the denominator of a rational number q must satisfy in order that q be a terminating decimal.

4. Prove that the set of all terminating decimals is an ordered integral domain.

5. Prove that the set of all terminating decimals is a dense simply ordered set (with respect to the natural order).

6. Prove that the set of all terminating decimals is not conditionally complete (with respect to the natural order).

7. Prove Lemma 10.

8. Prove that between (with respect to the natural order) any two distinct rational numbers there exists a rational number that is not a terminating decimal.

9. Prove that the set of all terminating decimals is not a well ordered set (with respect to the natural order).

10. Prove that the set D of all terminating decimals is not a field (with respect to the usual addition and multiplication in D).

8. THE REAL NUMBERS AND THEIR ARITHMETIC

As shown in the previous section, the set Q of all rational numbers, with respect to its natural order, is a dense simply ordered set. However, as shown below, Q is not conditionally complete (and hence not continuous) with respect to its natural order. To see this, it is enough to exhibit a nonempty subset P of Q such that P is bounded above and has no least upper bound. Let P be the set of all rational numbers u such that $u \cdot u \le 2$, i.e., $u^2 \le 2$. Thus

$$P = \{u \mid (u \in Q) \wedge (u^2 \le 2)\}$$

where $\le$ is the natural order in the set Q of all rationals.

We shall prove first that there exists no rational number s such that $s^2 = 2$. For this purpose, let us assume on the contrary that there exists a rational number $\dfrac{p}{q}$, where p and q are two nonzero integers having no divisor $(\ne 1)$ in common and such that $\dfrac{p^2}{q^2} = 2$. Thus, in particular, we may assume that p and q are not even integers. Now, since $p^2 = 2q^2$, the nonzero integer p must be even, since otherwise p^2 cannot be equal to the nonzero even integer $2q^2$. Hence, $p = 2k$, for some nonzero integer k. But then since $p = 2k$, we must have $p^2 = (2k)^2 = 4k^2 = 2q^2$, which yields $2k^2 = q^2$. However, the last equality implies that q must be a nonzero even integer. Consequently, $\dfrac{p^2}{q^2} = 2$ implies that p and q are both nonzero even integers, contradicting our assumption. Hence, there is no rational number s such that $s^2 = 2$.

Next, let us observe that P cannot have a least upper bound. Indeed, if the rational number m were the least upper bound of P, then in view of the above either $m^2 > 2$ or $m^2 < 2$. Now, if $m^2 > 2$, then, as can be easily shown, in view of the denseness of the set Q of all rational numbers, there would exist a rational number n such that $n < m$ and $n^2 > 2$, contradicting the fact that m was the least upper bound of P. Similarly, if $m^2 < 2$, then there would exist a rational number h such that $m < h$ and $h^2 < 2$, again contradicting the fact that m was the least upper bound of P.

To construct a set R having (as we shall see shortly) all the arithmetical properties of the set Q of all rationals and in addition being conditionally complete, we make use of Theorem 17 of Chapter IV (page 188), according to which *the set R of all the lower cuts of a dense simply ordered set $(Q, \le)$ is such that $(R, \subset)$ is a conditionally complete dense simply ordered set. In other words, $(R, \subset)$ is continuous.*

prove thm.

Motivated by the above, we introduce:

✳ **Definition 12.** *A lower cut of the set Q of all rational numbers is called a real number.*

Our axioms ensure the existence of the set R of all the real numbers. Clearly, every real number is a subset of Q and R is a subset of the power-set $\mathscr{P}(Q)$ of the set Q of all rational numbers.

Now, let us consider the set R of all real numbers.

The relation of equality in R is the usual set-theoretical equality, and as expected for *the natural order* (denoted by $\leq$) in R we shall take the usual set-theoretical inclusion, $\subset$.

Thus, a real number r, i.e., the lower cut r of Q, is called *less than or equal to* a real number s, i.e., to the lower cut s of Q, if r is a subset of s. In other words

$$(34) \qquad\qquad (r \leq s) \leftrightarrow (r \subset s)$$

Similarly, a real number r is called *less than* a real number s, if r is a proper subset of s. In other words,

$$(35) \qquad\qquad (r < s) \leftrightarrow ((r \subset s) \wedge (r \neq s))$$

Let us observe that in view of Theorem 11 of Chapter IV (page 184), for every rational number q, the initial segment $I(q)$, i.e., the set of all rational numbers less than q, is a lower ~~number~~ cut of the set Q of all rationals and hence is a real number. Thus, some examples of real numbers are given by $I(-1)$, $I(0)$, $I(\frac{2}{3})$, and so forth, which are the sets:

$$I(-1) = \{\ldots, -150, \ldots, -10, \ldots, -1.1, \ldots, -1.01, \ldots, -1.001, \ldots\}$$
$$I(0) = \{\ldots, -15, \ldots, -0.1, \ldots, -0.001, \ldots, -0.0001, \ldots, -0.00001, \ldots\}$$
$$I(\tfrac{2}{3}) = \{\ldots, -12, \ldots, 0.4, \ldots, 0.65, \ldots, 0.666, \ldots, 0.6666, \ldots\}$$

These examples are given to impress upon the reader the fact that a real number is first of all a set. Naturally, according to Definition 12 a real number is a special set, namely a lower cut of the set Q of all rational numbers. Incidentally, according to (35) we see that:

$$I(-1) < I(0) < I(\tfrac{2}{3})$$

In view of Definition 12, and in view of Theorem 17 of Chapter IV (page 188), we have:

✳ **Corollary 4.** *Let R be the set of all real numbers. Then $(R, \subset)$ is a conditionally complete dense simply ordered set.*

Accordingly, since the natural order $\leq$ in R is defined by (34), we see that $(R, \leq)$ is a continuous set.

Corollary 5. *The set R of all real numbers is a continuous set with respect to its natural order.*

⌐ dense ¬
conditionally complete

Thus, every nonempty bounded above subset S of real numbers has a least upper bound. Moreover, by Theorem 8 of Chapter IV (page 180), we have:

$$(36) \qquad\qquad \text{lub } S = \cup S$$

Similarly, every nonempty bounded below subset H of real numbers has a greatest lower bound given by:

$$(37) \qquad\qquad \text{glb } H = \cap H$$

Now, if K is any set of rational numbers such that lub K or glb K is a rational number, then in view of (36) and (37) we have:

$$(38) \qquad \text{lub } \{I(x) \mid x \in K\} = \cup \{I(x) \mid x \in K\} = I(\text{lub } K)$$

$$(39) \qquad \text{glb } \{I(x) \mid x \in K\} = \cap \{I(x) \mid x \in K\} = I(\text{glb } K)$$

The reader should observe that although every initial segment of the set Q of all rationals is a real number, not every real number is an initial segment of Q. This is because not every lower cut of Q is an initial segment of Q. For instance, the set of all negative rationals, together with all rationals u such that $u^2 \leq 2$, is a lower cut of Q and hence a real number; however, the same set is not an initial segment of Q.

The arithmetic of the real numbers is developed based on the arithmetic of the rational numbers and on the fact that *every element of a real number is a rational number*.

We define *addition* in the set R of all reals by defining the *sum* of two real numbers r and s as follows

$$(40) \qquad\qquad r + s = \{x + y \mid (x \in r) \wedge (y \in s)\}$$

where x and y are rational numbers which are respectively elements of the reals r and s, and where $x + y$ is the familiar sum of the two rationals x and y.

In order to validate the definition given by (40), we have to prove that for every two lower cuts r and s of the set Q of all rationals, $r + s$ given by (40) is again a lower cut of Q. To this end, it is enough to observe that since r and s are lower cuts of Q, according to Definition 8 of Chapter IV (page 181), $r + s$ as given by (40) is a nonempty proper subset of Q. Moreover, $r + s$ cannot have a last element since neither r nor s has a last element. Finally, let

$$(x_1 + y_1) \in (r + s),$$

with $x_1 \in r$ and $y_1 \in s$, and let q be a rational number such that $q < (x_1 + y_1)$. Then by Theorem 14 there exists a positive rational number p such that $q = x_1 + y_1 - p$. However, since $(y_1 - p) < y_1$ and since s is a lower cut of Q, we see that $(y_1 - p) \in s$ and consequently, $q \in (r + s)$. Thus, indeed $r + s$ is a lower cut of Q.

Now, if two real numbers m and n are respectively equal to the initial segments $I(a)$ and $I(b)$ of Q, then in view of (40) it can be easily proved that:

$$(41) \qquad\qquad m + n = I(a) + I(b) = I(a + b)$$

Moreover, as we know,

(42) $$(m \leq n) \leftrightarrow (I(a) \leq I(b))$$

The real number $I(0)$, i.e., the initial segment $I(0)$ of the set Q of all rationals, where 0 is the zero rational number, has a neutral role with respect to addition. Thus,

$$I(0) + r = r + I(0) = r \qquad \text{for every real number} \quad r$$

Clearly, we shall call $I(0)$ *the zero real number*, and as expected we shall call a real number r *positive* if $r > I(0)$, and *negative* if $r < I(0)$.

Next, we introduce the notion of *the negative of a real number* r, denoted by $-r$, as follows:

(43)   If $r = I(a)$, where a is a rational number, then

$$-r = -I(a) = I(-a)$$

where $-a$ is the negative of the rational number a, and

(44)   If $r \neq I(a)$, where a is a rational number, then

$$-r = \{-x \mid x \in (Q \smallsetminus r)\}$$

where Q is the set of all rational numbers and $-x$ is the negative of the rational number x.

It is easily verified that $-r$, given by (43) and (44), is a real number. Moreover,

$$-I(0) = I(0)$$

and

(45) $-(-r) = r$ for every real number r

We define *multiplication* in the set R of all real numbers by defining the *product* of two nonnegative real numbers m and n, denoted by $m \cdot n$ (or simply by mn), as follows

(46) $m \cdot n = Q \smallsetminus \{x \cdot y \mid (x \in (Q \smallsetminus m)) \wedge (y \in (Q \smallsetminus n))\}$

where $x \cdot y$ is the familiar product of the two rationals x and y and Q is the set of all rational numbers. It is readily verified that $m \cdot n$ given by (46) is a real number.

The product $r \cdot s$ of any two real numbers r and s is defined by employing (46) and the following equalities:

(47) $r \cdot s = (-r) \cdot (-s) = -((-r) \cdot s) = -(r \cdot (-s))$

Now, if the real numbers m and n are respectively equal to the initial segments $I(a)$ and $I(b)$ of the set Q of all rationals, then in view of (46) and (47) we have:

(48) $m \cdot n = I(a) \cdot I(b) = I(a \cdot b)$

The real number $I(1)$, where 1 is the unit rational number, has a neutral role with respect to multiplication. Thus

$$I(1) \cdot r = r \cdot I(1) = r \qquad \text{for every real number} \quad r$$

Clearly, we shall call $I(1)$, *the unit real number*.

We define *subtraction* in the set R of all reals by defining the *difference* between (in the following order) two real numbers r and s, denoted by $r - s$, as follows:

$$r - s = r + (-s)$$

where $-s$ is the negative of the real number s, given by (43) and (44).

Clearly, if the real numbers m and n are respectively equal to the initial segments $I(a)$ and $I(b)$ of Q, then:

(49) $$m - n = I(a) - I(b) = I(a - b)$$

The *multiplicative inverse* of a *nonzero* real number s, denoted by $1:s$ or by $\frac{1}{s}$, is defined as follows:

(i) If $s = I(a)$, where a is a nonzero rational number, then

$$1:s = 1:I(a) = I(1:a)$$

where $1:a$ is the multiplicative inverse of the nonzero rational number a. Otherwise,

(ii) $$1:s = \{1:x \mid x \in (Q \smallsetminus s)\} \cup I(0) \cup \{0\} \qquad \text{if} \quad s > 0$$

where Q is the set of all rational numbers; and

(iii) $$1:s = -(1:(-s)) \qquad \text{if} \quad s < 0$$

We define *division* (except by $I(0)$) in the set of all real numbers by defining the *quotient* of a real number r by a nonzero real number s, denoted by $r:s$ or by $\frac{r}{s}$, as follows:

$$r:s = r \cdot (1:s)$$

Clearly, if the real numbers m and n are respectively equal to the initial segments $I(a)$ and $I(b)$ of Q, then:

(50) $$m:n = I(a):I(b) = I(a:b) \qquad \text{provided} \quad n \neq I(0)$$

With addition and multiplication defined by (41), (46) and (47), the set R of all real numbers becomes a field. Moreover, the property of positiveness for real numbers satifies conditions (28), (29) and (30). Consequently, in view of Corollary 5, we have:

Corollary 6. *The set of all real numbers is a continuous ordered field.*

Let us verify the existence of a real number s such that $s \cdot s = s^2 = I(2)$. To this end we observe that the set of all negative rationals together with all rationals u such that $u^2 < 2$ is a lower cut s of the set Q of all rationals. Also, it is evident that $s \cdot s = I(2)$ since every element of $s \cdot s$ is an element of $I(2)$ and vice versa.

Although no rational number is equal to a real number, for all arithmetical purposes each rational number q can be identified with the real number $I(q)$, i.e., with the initial segment $I(q)$ of the set Q of all rationals. This is justified by virtue of (41), (48) and (42), according to which between the set Q of all rationals and the set of all initial segments of Q there exists a one-to-one correspondence h given by

$$h(q) = I(q)$$

preserving addition, multiplication and order, i.e.,

$$h(p + q) = h(p) + h(q) = I(p + q)$$
$$h(p \cdot q) = h(p) \cdot h(q) = I(p \cdot q)$$
$$(p \le q) \leftrightarrow (I(p) \le I(q))$$

for every two rationals p and q. In view of this, we have:

Lemma 11. *The set Q of all rationals is isomorphic to the set of all initial segments of Q.*

In view of the above considerations, we say that the set R of all reals is an extension of the set Q of all rationals. Therefore, we may abandon the set Q and instead deal with the set R. To indicate this, we shall denote the real number $I(q)$ simply by q. Thus, we shall denote, say, the real numbers $I(-3.21)$, $I(-2)$, $I(0)$, $I(1)$ and $I(\frac{7}{3})$ by -3.21, -2, 0, 1 and $\frac{7}{3}$, respectively.

According to the previous sections and this one, the set R of all real numbers is an extension of the set Q of all rational numbers, which in turn is an extension of the set I of all integers, which in turn is an extension of the set ω of all natural numbers. Moreover, according to our notational convention, a symbol such as, say, 5 may stand for the natural number 5, or for the integer [5,0], or for the rational number $[+5, +1]$, or for the real number $I(\frac{5}{1})$.

EXERCISES

1. Prove that there exists no rational number q such that $q^2 = 3$.

2. Prove that there exists a real number s such that $s^2 = 3$ (i.e., $s^2 = I(3)$). Prove also that s is not an initial segment of the set of all rational numbers.

3. Prove (38) and (39).

4. Prove (41), (42), (45) and (48).

5. Prove that (43), (44), (46) and (47) are valid definitions.

6. Prove (49) and (50).

7. Prove Corollary 6.

8. Motivated by the definition of the absolute value of a rational number given in Section 6 (page 228), define the absolute value $|r|$ of a real number r and prove properties (31), (32) and (33).

9. REPRESENTATION OF THE REAL NUMBERS

The representation of the real numbers as *nonterminating decimals* or as *infinite decimals* is based on the following:

✗ **Theorem 16.** *Two real numbers are equal if and only if they have the same terminating decimals as elements.*

PROOF.   Let r and s be two real numbers, i.e., two lower cuts of the set Q of all rationals.

Now, if $r = s$, then if t is a terminating decimal (a priori, t is a rational number) such that $t \in r$ (or $t \in s$), then $t \in s$ (or $t \in r$). Consequently, r and s have the same terminating decimals as their elements.

Next, assume that r and s have the same terminating decimals as elements. We shall prove that $r = s$. To this end it is enough to show that if p is a rational number such that $p \in r$, then $p \in s$ and vice versa. However, since r is a lower cut of Q, we see that p is not the last element of Q and there exists a rational q such that $q \in r$ and $p < q$. But then in view of Lemma 10 there exists a terminating decimal t such that $p < t < q$, and since $q \in r$ we see that $t \in r$. From this, in view of our hypothesis it follows that $t \in s$. However, since s is a lower cut of Q and $t \in s$ and $p < t$, we see that $p \in s$. Similarly, we can prove that if a rational number p is such that $p \in s$, then $p \in r$. Consequently, $r = s$, as desired.

In view of Theorem 16, a real number r is completely characterized by the set of all terminating decimals belonging to r. This, as explained below, is the key to the representation of any real number as a nonterminating decimal.

First, we shall describe the representation of a positive real number r. Let A be the subset of r consisting of all the terminating decimals belonging to r. Since r is a lower cut of the set Q of all rational numbers, A is nonempty and is bounded above. Let A_0 be the nonempty subset of A consisting of those elements having the largest integral part p. Consider the symbol:

$$p.$$

Since r has no last element, neither A nor A_0 has a last element; consequently, we may consider the nonempty subset A_1 of A_0, consisting of those elements of A_0 having the *largest* digit a_1 in the first decimal place. Consider the symbol:

$$p \cdot a_1$$

Again, in view of the fact that A_1 has no last element, we may consider the nonempty subset A_2 of A_1, consisting of those elements of A_1 having the largest digit a_2 in the second decimal place. Consider the symbol:

$$p \cdot a_1 a_2$$

Since r has no last element, the above process continues *without terminating* to yield a nonterminating symbol

(51) $$p \cdot a_1 a_2 a_3 \cdots a_n \cdots$$

where, for every natural number k

$$p \cdot a_1 a_2 a_3 \cdots a_k$$

represents the unique greatest terminating decimal in the set of all the terminating decimals obtained by limiting or *truncating* the elements of the set A (the set consisting of all the terminating decimals belonging to r) up to and including the k-th decimal place.

In view of Theorem 16 and the above considerations, we see that representation (51) of a positive real number is unique. Moreover, since at each stage of our construction above there are terminating decimals belonging to r greater than the terminating decimal produced, there can be no unending succession of zeros in (51). Thus, we have:

Lemma 12. *Every positive real number has a unique nonterminating decimal representation in which there is no infinite succession of zeroes.*

Accordingly, we have the following representations:

$$3 = I(3) \qquad \text{is represented as} \qquad 2.99999999 \cdots$$

$$12.58 = I(12.58) \quad \text{is represented as} \quad 12.579999999999 \cdots$$

$$\tfrac{9}{7} = I(\tfrac{9}{7}) \qquad \text{is represented as} \qquad 1.285428542854 \cdots$$

It is customary to identify a positive real number with its nonterminating decimal representation. Thus, we have:

$$1 = 0.9999999 \cdots \qquad \text{and} \qquad \tfrac{90}{11} = 8.181818181818 \cdots$$

Next, we describe the representation of a nonpositive real number s. Let B be the subset of s consisting of all the terminating decimals belonging to s. Since s is a lower cut of the set Q of all rational numbers, B is nonempty and is bounded above. Let B_0 be the nonempty subset of B consisting of those elements of B having the largest integral part $-q$, where q is a nonnegative integer. Consider the symbol:

$$-q.$$

Since s has no last element, neither B nor B_0 has a last element and we may consider the nonempty subset B_1 of B_0, consisting of those elements of B_0 having the *smallest* digit b_1 in the first decimal place. Consider the symbol:

$$-q \cdot b_1$$

Again, in view of the fact that B_1 has no last element, we may consider the nonempty subset B_2 of B_1, consisting of those elements of B_1 having the smallest digit b_2 in the second decimal place. Consider the symbol:

$$-q \cdot b_1 b_2$$

In view of the fact that s has no last element, the above process continues *without terminating* to yield a nonterminating symbol

$$(52) \qquad\qquad -q \cdot b_1 b_2 b_3 \cdots b_n \cdots$$

where, for every natural number k

$$-q \cdot b_1 b_2 b_3 \cdots b_k$$

represents the unique greatest terminating decimal in the set of all terminating decimals obtained by limiting or truncating the elements of the set B (the set consisting of all the terminating decimals of s) up to and including the k-th decimal place.

In view of Theorem 16 and the above considerations, we see that representation (52) of a nonpositive real number is unique. Moreover, since at each stage of our construction in the above there are terminating decimals belonging to s greater than the terminating decimal produced, there can be no unending succession of nines in (52). Thus, we have:

Lemma 13.   *Every nonpositive real number has a unique nonterminating decimal representation in which there is no infinite succession of nines.*

Accordingly, we have the following representations:

$$0 = I(0) \qquad \text{is represented as} \quad -0.00000000 \cdots$$
$$-5 = I(-5) \qquad \text{is represented as} \quad -5.00000000 \cdots$$
$$-3.45 = I(-3.45) \quad \text{is represented as} \quad -3.4500000000 \cdots$$
$$-\tfrac{9}{7} = I(-\tfrac{9}{7}) \qquad \text{is represented as} \quad -1.285428542854 \cdots$$

According to the custom of identifying a nonpositive real number with its nonterminating decimal representation, we have:

$$-1 = -1.00000000 \cdots \qquad \text{and} \qquad -\tfrac{120}{99} = -1.212121212 \cdots$$

Next, based solely on the nonterminating representation, we define addition, subtraction, multiplication and division of the real numbers and compare the results with those obtained in Section 8 of this chapter.

Let $h_0 \cdot h_1 h_2 h_3 \cdots$ and $k_0 \cdot k_1 k_2 k_3 \cdots$ be two nonterminating decimals representing respectively the two real numbers r and s. For a natural number m, let

$$u_0 \cdot u_1 u_2 u_3 \cdots u_m = h_0 \cdot h_1 h_2 h_3 \cdots h_m + k_0 \cdot k_1 k_2 k_3 \cdots k_m$$

where the right side is the familiar sum of two terminating decimals. Let us call $u_0 \cdot u_1 u_2 u_3 \cdots u_m$, appearing above, the *m-th truncated sum* of r and s.

Thus, corresponding to every natural number n, there is a unique n-th truncated sum of r and s. Let A be the set of all n-th truncated sums of r and s and let

$$a_0 \cdot a_1 a_2 a_3 \cdots$$

be the nonterminating decimal, where a_0 is the integral part of all but a finite number of the elements of A, and where in general a_i is the digit occurring in the i-th decimal place of all but a finite number of the elements of A (the existence of such an a_i can be easily proved). We shall call $a_0 \cdot a_1 a_2 a_3 \cdots$ the sum of $h_0 \cdot h_1 h_2 h_3 \cdots$ and $k_0 \cdot k_1 k_2 k_3 \cdots$ obtained by the process of forming the n-th truncated sums.

Subtraction, multiplication and division of the real numbers can be similarly developed based on the nonterminating decimal representation of the real numbers and on the notion of the *n-th truncated differences, products and quotients.*

Let us observe that, for every two positive real numbers r and s, if $r + s$ is first obtained according to (40) and then represented as a nonterminating decimal, the latter will coincide with the nonterminating decimal representation of

$r + s$ obtained by the above-mentioned process of forming the n-th truncated sums of r and s. However, in general this is not the case for addition, multiplication, subtraction or division of two real numbers.

For instance, according to (48) and Lemma 12, we have:

(53) $(-3) \cdot (-1) = I(-3) \cdot I(-1) = 2.99999 \cdots$

On the other hand, applying the method of the n-th truncated products to

$$(-3.00000 \cdots) \cdot (-1.00000 \cdots)$$

we obtain:

(54) $3.00000 \cdots$

The above considerations suggest the identification of (53) with (54), i.e.,

$$2.99999 \cdots = 3.00000 \cdots$$

and in general the identification

(55) $e_0 \cdot e_1 e_2 \cdots e_n 9999 \cdots = e_0 \cdot e_1 e_2 \cdots (e_n + 1)0000 \cdots$

where $e_n \neq 9$, if $n > 0$. Furthermore, equating the difference between the left and the right sides of $=$ in (55) with the difference between the right and the left sides of $=$ in (55), we obtain:

(56) $-0.000000 \cdots = 0.000000 \cdots$

Thus, according to (55), we have:

$$-2.17000 \cdots = -2.16999 \cdots \quad \text{and} \quad 2.3999 \cdots = 2.4000 \cdots$$

Thus, in view of (55) we see that a real number that is a terminating decimal has two (*dual*) nonterminating decimal representations, one containing an unending succession of zeroes, and the other containing an unending succession of nines.

Hence, in view of Lemmas 12 and 13 and (55), we have:

Lemma 14. *Every real number that is not a terminating decimal has a unique nonterminating decimal representation. Every real number that is a terminating decimal has a dual nonterminating decimal representation.*

Now, in view of (55) and Lemma 14, it is easy to see that the sum, the product, the difference and the quotient of two real numbers r and s, as defined in Section 8 of this chapter, agree respectively with the sum, the product, the difference and the quotient of r and s, obtained by the method of the n-th truncated sums, products, differences and quotients of r and s.

We close this section by observing that if a real number h is equal to the initial segment $I(t)$, where t is a terminating decimal, then for all arithmetical purposes the nonterminating decimal representation of h can be identified with the usual terminating decimal representation of t. Thus,

$$0.000 \cdots = 0, \quad -7.8999 \cdots = -7.9 \quad \text{and} \quad 1.6000 \cdots = 1.6$$

EXERCISES

1. Determine which real number is represented by each of the following *periodic* nonterminating decimals:

$$21.35353535 \cdots, \qquad -2.10101010 \cdots, \qquad -0.62626262 \cdots$$

2. Represent the following real numbers as nonterminating decimals and in each case indicate the *period*:

$$I(\tfrac{2}{7}) = \tfrac{2}{7}, \qquad I(\tfrac{3}{8}) = \tfrac{3}{8}, \qquad I(-\tfrac{15}{9}) = -\tfrac{15}{9}, \qquad I(-\tfrac{31}{14}) = -\tfrac{31}{41}$$

3. Prove that a necessary and sufficient condition for a nonterminating decimal representation of a real number r to have a period is that r be equal to an initial segment of the set of all rational numbers.

4. Determine the third truncated sum, product, difference and quotient of

$$3.96666 \cdots \qquad \text{and} \qquad 7.89898989 \cdots$$

5. Let B be a bounded set of real numbers, given in their nonterminating decimal representation. Describe an algorithm for obtaining the nonterminating decimal representation of the lub B and glb B.

6. Prove (56).

7. Let $[a_1, b_1], [a_2, b_2], \ldots, [a_n, b_n], \ldots$ be a sequence of nested nonempty closed intervals of real numbers. Using the nonterminating decimal representation of a_n and b_n, determine a nonterminating decimal representation of a real number belonging to every element of the sequence under consideration.

8. Prove that $4 - 3.9999 \cdots = 0$, by using the method of the n-th truncated differences.

10. SUMMARY

In this chapter the arithmetic of the natural numbers was developed strictly from the set-theoretical point of view. The development was based on the Finite Recursion Theorem.

Similarly, in this chapter an integer, a rational number and a real number were introduced strictly from the set-theoretical point of view. An integer was defined as a special subset of $\omega \times \omega$, where ω is the set of all natural numbers. A rational number was defined as a special subset of $I \times \{I - \{0\}\}$, where I is the set of all integers. Finally, a real number was defined as a special subset of the set Q of all rational numbers. The existence of the sets I, Q and R (the set of all reals) was ensured by our axioms.

It was shown that although the set Q of all rationals is a dense simply ordered set (with respect to the natural order), nevertheless Q fails to be continuous. On the other hand, the set R of all reals is continuous.

Although no natural number is equal to an integer, no integer is equal to a rational number and no rational number is equal to a real number, it was agreed (for arithmetical purposes) to identify natural numbers, integers and rational numbers with certain real numbers.

The nonterminating decimal representation of a real number was based on the fact that two real numbers are equal if and only if they contain the same terminating decimals (which are, a priori, rational numbers). Also, with the notions of the n-th truncated sums, products, differences and quotients of two real numbers, the arithmetic of the reals was reduced to the arithmetic of the nonterminating decimals.

Chapter VI

EQUIPOLLENCE OF SETS

1. FINITE AND INFINITE SETS

In Chapter III, Section 8, a one-to-one correspondence between two sets D and H was defined as a one-to-one function from D onto H, i.e., as a function whose domain is D, whose range is H and whose distinct elements have distinct first and distinct second coordinates.

Thus, if, as usual, distinct letters represent distinct sets, then

$$\{(a, m), (b, n), (c, p)\}$$

is a one-to-one correspondence between $\{a, b, c\}$ and $\{m, n, p\}$. *one to one cor. equivalent*

Also, as mentioned in Chapter III, Section 8, D is called *equipollent* to H or *of the same power as H*, if there exists an equipollence between D and H. Moreover, as indicated by (67) of Chapter III (page 155), the fact that D is equipollent to H is written:

$$D \cong H$$

Clearly, the converse f_{-1} of an equipollence f between x and y is an equipollence between y and x. Also, if f is an equipollence between x and y and g is an equipollence between y and z, then the composite $g \cdot f$ [see Definition 6 of Chapter III (page 147)] is an equipollence between x and y.

In view of the above, we have

(1)	$x \cong x$	(reflexivity of $\cong$)
(2)	*if $x \cong y$, then $y \cong x$*	(symmetry of $\cong$)
(3)	*if $x \cong y$ and $y \cong z$, then $x \cong z$*	(transitivity of $\cong$)

for every three sets x, y and z.

Thus, in view of (1) every set is equipollent to itself. Moreover, in view of (2) and (3) if x is equipollent to y and y is equipollent to z, then we can say that x, y and z are *equipollent sets* or are of the same power.

In Chapter III, Section 6, we saw how the notion of equipollence is used to give set-theoretical definitions of a *finite* and of an *infinite* set. According to Definitions 7 and 8 of Chapter III (page 155), we have:

A set is called infinite if it has a proper subset that is equipollent to the set itself.

Moreover:

A set is called finite if it is not infinite.

Thus, $\{0, 1\}$ is a finite set since it is impossible to establish a one-to-one correspondence between $\{0, 1\}$ and any of its three proper subsets $\varnothing$, $\{0\}$ and $\{1\}$.

On the other hand, the set ω of all natural numbers is infinite since

(4) $\qquad\qquad \{(0, 1), (1, 2), (2, 3), (3, 4), \ldots\}$

is a one-to-one correspondence between ω and its proper subset $\{1, 2, 3, \ldots\}$ of all positive natural numbers. Similarly

(5) $\qquad\qquad \{(0, 0), (1, 2), (2, 4), (3, 6), \ldots\}$

is a one-to-one correspondence between ω and its proper subset $\{0, 2, 4, \ldots\}$ of all even natural numbers.

Let us observe that since the empty set $\varnothing$ is a finite set, *every infinite set is nonempty*.

In view of the fundamental importance of the set ω of all natural numbers, ω is taken as a prototype of sets of a certain type called *denumerable* sets. More precisely:

Definition 1. *A set equipollent to the set of all natural numbers is called denumerable.*

Countable

Thus, in view of (1), the set ω is denumerable. Similarly, in view of (4) and (5), the set of all positive natural numbers and the set of all even natural numbers are denumerable. Similarly, it is easy to verify that the set of all odd natural numbers and the set of all natural numbers greater than a natural number n are denumerable.

In view of (3) and Definition 1, we have:

Corollary 1. *A set is denumerable if and only if it is equipollent to the set of all positive natural numbers $\{1, 2, 3, \ldots\}$.*

Remark 1. According to Definition 1, if E is a denumerable set, then there exists a one-to-one correspondence between the elements of E and the elements of the set $\{0, 1, 2, 3, \ldots\}$. This correspondence assigns to every element of E a natural number, such that two distinct elements of E have distinct natural numbers assigned to them, and such that every natural number is assigned to some element of E. Equivalently, we may say that every element of E is indexed by a unique natural number. Consequently, if E is a denumerable set, then all its elements can be enumerated or can be arranged in an infinite sequence

$$e_0, e_1, e_2, \ldots$$

of distinct terms; the converse is obviously true. Moreover, in view of Corollary 1, the elements of any denumerable set E can also be arranged in an infinite sequence

$$a_1, a_2, a_3, \ldots$$

of distinct terms.

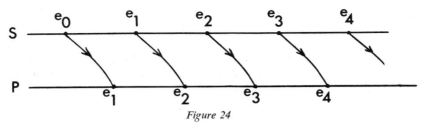

Figure 24

Now, we prove a very important theorem.

Theorem 1. *A set is infinite if and only if it contains a denumerable subset.*

PROOF. First we give some motivation for the proof of the sufficiency.
Let S be an infinite set and let f be a one-to-one correspondence between S
and a proper subset P of S. Since P is a proper subset of S, we see that $S \smallsetminus P \neq$
$\varnothing$, and therefore there exists an element $e_0 \in (S \smallsetminus P)$. Let $e_1 = f(e_0)$. Since
$e_1 \in P$, we see that $e_0 \neq e_1$. However, $e_1 \in S$, and therefore under f it has an
image $f(e_1)$ which belongs to P. Let $e_2 = f(e_1)$. Since f is one-to-one, $e_1 \neq e_2$,
and since $e_0 \notin P$, we see that e_0, e_1 and e_2 are three distinct elements of S. Without loss of generality, we may represent the elements of S as points on the straight
line S and the elements of P as points on the straight line P (Figure 24). To
emphasize the fact that P is a subset of S, we shall represent the same elements of
S and P on the same vertical line. Thus, it appears that we can obtain an
infinite sequence e_0, e_1, e_2, ... of distinct elements of S. If this is so, then in
view of Remark 1 we can conclude that any infinite set S contains a denumerable
subset.

The rigorous proof of the sufficiency runs as follows. In view of Theorem 2
(Finite Recursion Theorem) of Chapter V (page 208), there exists a unique
mapping g from ω into S, such that

(6) $g(0) = e_0$ and $g(m^+) = f(g(m))$

where m^+, as usual, is the immediate successor of the natural number m. In (6),
f is the above-mentioned one-to-one correspondence between the infinite set S
and its proper subset P, and e_0 is the above-mentioned element of $S \smallsetminus P$.

Now, to prove the sufficiency, it is enough to show that g is a one-to-one
correspondence between ω and a subset of S. Since g is a mapping from ω into
S, we need only prove that g is one-to-one.

We recall that every nonzero element m of ω has a unique immediate predecessor m^-, with respect to the natural order (which is a well order) in ω.

Assume on the contrary that g is not one-to-one, and (since ω is well ordered)
let n be the smallest natural number such that:

(7) $g(n) = g(k)$ with $n \neq k$

Clearly, $k > n$. Moreover, $n > 0$ since $g(0) \in (S \smallsetminus P)$ and $g(m) \in P$ for
every $m > 0$. Thus, $k > n > 0$. But then in view of (6) and (7) we have:

$$g(n) = f(g(n^-)) = f(g(k^-)) = g(k)$$

However, since f is a one-to-one mapping, the above and (7) imply

$$g(n^-) = g(k^-) \qquad \text{with} \quad n^- \neq k^-$$

contradicting the choice of n. Thus, our assumption is false, and indeed g is a one-to-one correspondence between ω and a subset of S. Consequently, if S is an infinite set, then S contains a denumerable subset.

Next, we prove the necessity, i.e., we prove that if S has a denumerable subset E, then S is an infinite set.

According to Remark 1, we may assume:

$$E = \{e_0, e_1, e_2, \ldots\}$$

Consider the proper subset $S \smallsetminus \{e_0\}$ of S. Clearly, there exists a function f from S into $S \smallsetminus \{e_0\}$ such that $f(x) = x$ for every $x \in (S \smallsetminus E)$ and $f(e_m) = e_{m+1}$ for $m = 0, 1, 2, \ldots$. Obviously, f is a one-to-one correspondence between S and its proper subset $S \smallsetminus \{e_0\}$. Hence, by Definition 7 of Chapter III (page 155), S is an infinite set.

Thus, Theorem 1 is proved.

In view of Theorem 1, we see that the set ω of all natural numbers, the set I of all integers, the set Q of all rational numbers and the set R of all real numbers are infinite sets, since each contains a subset isomorphic to ω (see Chapter V).

From Theorem 1, we have:

Corollary 2.   *A set which is equipollent to an infinite set is itself an infinite set.*

PROOF.   If $S \cong V$ and V is infinite, then S contains a denumerable set.

Corollary 3.   *A set containing an infinite subset is itself an infinite set.*

PROOF.   If $P \subset S$ and P is infinite, then P as well as S has a denumerable subset. Thus, S is infinite.

In view of Corollary 3, we have:

Corollary 4.   *The union of every two sets one of which is infinite is again an infinite set.*

Corollary 5.   *A set equipollent to a finite set is itself a finite set.*

PROOF.   Let $A \cong B$ and B be finite. If A is not finite, i.e., if A is infinite, then in view of Corollary 2, B is also infinite, a contradiction.

Corollary 6.   *Every subset of a finite set is finite.*

PROOF.   Let $A \subset B$ and B be finite. If A is infinite, then by Corollary 3, B is also infinite, a contradiction.

Since $A \smallsetminus X$ and $A \cap X$ are always subsets of A, in view of Corollary 6 we have:

Corollary 7.   *For every finite set A and every set X*

$$A \smallsetminus X \qquad \text{and} \qquad A \cap X$$

are finite sets.

Lemma 1.   *For every infinite set S and every set a, $S \smile \{a\}$ is an infinite set.*

PROOF.   In view of Theorem 1, S contains an infinite sequence

(8) $e_0, e_1, e_2, \ldots$

of distinct terms. If, for no natural number n, it is the case that $a = e_n$, then $S \smile \{a\}$ contains sequence (8), and hence in view of Theorem 1, $S \smile \{a\}$ is an infinite set. If, however, for some natural number n, $a = e_n$, then the set $S \smile \{a\}$ contains the denumerable set $\{e_{n+1}, e_{n+2}, \ldots\}$, and hence again in view of Theorem 1, $S \smile \{a\}$ is infinite.

Theorem 2.   *A set is finite if and only if it is equipollent to a natural number.*

PROOF.   Let S be a finite set. If S is empty, then it is equal to the natural number 0 and hence equipollent to it. Next, let S be a nonempty finite set. By Theorem 24 of Chapter IV (page 198), the set S can be well ordered. Consider a well ordering of S and let, as usual, x^+ denote the immediate successor of an element x of S if x is not the last element of S. Furthermore, consider the mapping f from S into S given by:

$$f(x) = x^+ \qquad \text{if } x \text{ is not the last element of } S$$

and

$$f(x) = x \qquad \text{if } x \text{ is the last element of } S$$

Now, assume on the contrary that S is not equipollent to any natural number. By Theorem 2 (Finite Recursion Theorem) of Chapter V (page 208), there exists a unique mapping g from the set ω of all natural numbers into S such that

$$g(0) = e \qquad \text{and} \qquad g(m^+) = f(g(m))$$

where e is the first element of S and m^+ is the immediate successor of the natural number m.

Since, by our assumption, S is not equipollent to any natural number, for every two natural numbers m and n, we see that $m \neq n$ implies $g(m) \neq g(n)$.

Consequently, the function g is a one-to-one mapping from ω into S. Thus, S must have a denumerable subset, contradicting the fact that S is finite. Hence, our assumption is false, and therefore *if S is finite, then it must be equipollent to a natural number.*

Now, we prove that if S is equipollent to a natural number, then S is finite. To this end, in view of Corollary 5 it is enough to prove that every natural number is a finite set. The proof is by induction. The natural number 0, being equal to the empty set $\varnothing$, is finite. Now, supposing that the natural number n is finite, let us prove that $n^+ = n \cup \{n\}$ is finite. Assume that $n \cup \{n\}$ is infinite; then by Lemma 1, $(n \cup \{n\}) \smile \{n\} = n$ is infinite, contradicting our assumption that n is finite. Hence our assumption is false, and therefore $n \cup \{n\}$ must be finite. Consequently, every natural number is finite.

Thus, Theorem 2 is proved.

Corollary 8.   *Every natural number is a finite set.*

Remark 2.   In view of Theorem 2, to say that a set P is finite is the same as saying that P is equipollent to a natural number. Similarly, to say that a set S is infinite is the same as saying that S is not equipollent to any natural number.

In view of Theorem 2, we introduce:

Definition 2.   *A set is said to have n elements if it is equipollent to the natural number n.*

Remark 3.   In view of the above, a set which is equipollent to the natural number n can be represented as a finite sequence of elements indexed by the natural numbers $0, 1, 2, \ldots, n - 1$, or by the natural numbers $1, 2, 3, \ldots, n$.

Lemma 2.   *Let A be disjoint from B and M disjoint from N. If $A \cong M$ and $B \cong N$, then:*
$$A \cup B \cong M \cup N$$

PROOF.   Let f be a one-to-one correspondence between A and M and g be a one-to-one correspondence between B and N. Define the mapping h from $A \cup B$ into $M \cup N$ such that $h = f$ on A and $h = g$ on B. Clearly, h establishes a one-to-one correspondence between $A \cup B$ and $M \cup N$. Thus, $A \cup B \cong M \cup N$, as desired.

Lemma 3.   *The union of two finite disjoint sets is a finite set.*

PROOF.   Let A and B be two finite sets such that $A \cap B = \varnothing$. By Theorem 2 the set A is equipollent to a natural number, say, m. Similarly, B is equipollent to a natural number, say, n. But then it can be easily shown that $A \cup B$ is equipollent to the natural number $m + n$. Hence, by Theorem 2, $A \cup B$ is finite.

Lemma 4.   *The union of two finite sets is a finite set.*

PROOF.   Let H and K be two finite sets. Clearly, $H \cup K = H \cup (K \smallsetminus H)$. By Corollary 7, $K \smallsetminus H$ is finite, and since H and $K \smallsetminus H$ are disjoint their union is finite.

Remark 4.   In view of Lemma 4, if each one of the sets $A_1, A_2, A_3, \ldots, A_n$ is finite, then
$$A_1 \cup A_2 \cup \cdots \cup A_n$$
is also a finite set (proof by induction on n).

Lemma 5.   *If S is an infinite set and A is a finite set, then $S \smallsetminus A$ is an infinite set. Moreover,*
$$S \smallsetminus A \cong S \qquad and \qquad S \cup A \cong S$$

PROOF.   Assume that $S \smallsetminus A$ is finite. Then, in view of Corollary 7 and Lemma 4, $(S \smallsetminus A) \cup (S \cap A) = S$ would also be finite, contradicting the fact that S is infinite. Hence, $S \smallsetminus A$ is an infinite set.

Now, we shall establish a one-to-one correspondence between S and $S \smallsetminus A$. Since A is finite, by Corollary 7, $S \cap A$ is a finite set. We pass over the trivial case: $S \cap A = \varnothing$.

In view of Remark 3, we have

$$S \cap A = \{a_1, a_2, \ldots, a_n\}$$

where n is a natural number. On the other hand, since $S \smallsetminus A$ is an infinite set, by Theorem 1 the set $S \smallsetminus A$ has a denumerable subset E where, according to Remark 1, we have:

$$E = \{e_1, e_2, e_3, \ldots\}$$

Now, clearly,

$$S = ((S \smallsetminus A) \smallsetminus E) \cup \{e_1, e_2, \ldots\} \cup \{a_1, a_2, \ldots, a_n\}$$

and

$$S \smallsetminus A = ((S \smallsetminus A) \smallsetminus E) \cup \{e_1, e_2, \ldots\}$$

Define the mapping f from S into $S \smallsetminus A$ as follows:

f is the identity map on $(S \smallsetminus A) \smallsetminus E$,
$$f(a_i) = e_i \quad \text{and} \quad f(e_j) = e_{j+n}$$

It is easy to verify that f establishes a one-to-one correspondence between S and $S \smallsetminus A$. Thus, $S \cong S \smallsetminus A$.

Next, let us observe that:

$$S \cup A = S \cup (A \smallsetminus S)$$

However, since S is an infinite set and $A \smallsetminus S$ is a finite set,

$$(S \cup (A \smallsetminus S)) \smallsetminus (A \smallsetminus S) \cong S \cup (A \smallsetminus S)$$

Consequently, $S \cong S \cup A$, as desired.

Lemma 6. *The union of two disjoint denumerable sets is a denumerable set.*

PROOF. Let $A = \{a_1, a_2, a_3, \ldots\}$ and $B = \{b_1, b_2, b_3, \ldots\}$ be two disjoint denumerable sets. The mapping

$$f(0) = a_1, \quad f(2) = a_2, \quad f(4) = a_3, \ldots$$
$$f(1) = b_1, \quad f(3) = b_2, \quad f(5) = b_3, \ldots$$

establishes a one-to-one correspondence between ω and $A \cup B$. Hence, $A \cup B$ is a denumerable set.

From Lemma 6, we obtain immediately:

Corollary 9. *The union of a finite number (≥ 1) of pairwise disjoint denumerable sets is a denumerable set.*

[In view of (71) of Chapter III (page 158), we may say that the union of no sets is $\varnothing$.]

Theorem 3. *A set of natural numbers is infinite if and only if it is unbounded.*

PROOF. Let S be an infinite set of natural numbers. Assume S is bounded. Hence, there exists a natural number n such that n is greater than every element of S. Consequently, every element of S is an element of n, and therefore $S \subset n$. However, by Theorem 2, n is a finite set. Therefore, by Corollary 6 the set S is also finite, contradicting our hypothesis. Hence, our assumption is false and S is unbounded.

Next, let S be an unbounded set of natural numbers. We shall prove that S is infinite. Consider the function f from ω into S such that

$$(9) \qquad\qquad f(n) = m$$

where m is the smallest natural number belonging to S and such that $n < m$. In view of the fact that S is unbounded, mapping (9) exists.

By Theorem 2 (Finite Recursion Theorem) of Chapter V (page 208), there exists a function g from ω into S such that:

$$g(0) = f(0)$$
$$g(n^+) = f(g(n))$$

It is obvious that g is one-to-one, since according to (9), $g(n) < g(n^+)$. Consequently, the mapping g establishes a one-to-one correspondence between ω and a subset of S. Thus, S has a denumerable subset and hence is infinite.

Theorem 4.   *A set is infinite if and only if for every natural number n it contains a subset equipollent to n.*

PROOF.   Let S be an infinite set. By Theorem 1 it contains a denumerable subset $D = \{e_0, e_1, e_2, \ldots\}$. For every natural number n, that subset of D consisting of those elements of D whose indices are less than n, is a subset of S and equipollent to the natural number n.

Next, let us assume that for every natural number n, a set S has a subset equipollent to n. Let us prove that S is infinite. Assume on the contrary that S is finite. Then by Theorem 2, S is equipollent to a natural number n. However, by hypothesis, S must contain a subset equipollent to $n + 1$. Thus, n must contain a subset equipollent to $n + 1$. In other words, $n + 1$ must be equipollent to a subset of n. However, every subset of n is a proper subset of $n + 1$. Consequently, $n + 1$ must be equipollent to a proper subset of $n + 1$. But this, in view of Corollary 8, contradicts the fact that $n + 1$, as a natural number, is a finite set. Hence, our assumption is false and S is infinite.

EXERCISES

1. Prove that a set S is infinite if and only if S is equipollent to the set $S \cup \{a\}$ where $a \notin S$.

2. Prove that a set S is infinite if and only if it is equipollent to the set obtained by adjoining to S the elements of any finite set.

3. Prove that if $P \cong S$, then it is not necessarily true that $(P \smile S) \cong (S \smile P)$.

4. Prove that if $P \cong S$ and $M \cong N$, then it is not necessarily true that $(P \cap S) \cong (M \cap N)$.

5. Prove that a set of natural numbers is finite if and only if it is bounded.

6. Prove that a set is finite if and only if its power-set is finite.

7. Prove that if the union of two sets is infinite, then at least one of them must be infinite.

8. Prove that for every two sets P and S it is true that:

$$(P \times S) \cong (S \times P)$$

9. Prove that for every three sets P, Q and S it is true that:

$$(P \times Q) \times S \cong P \times (Q \times S)$$

10. Prove that if $(M \smallsetminus N) \cong (N \smallsetminus M)$, then $M \cong N$.

11. Prove that if $B \subset A$ and $B \cong (B \cup C)$, then $A \cong (A \cup C)$.

12. Let A, B, C and D be four sets such that:

$$(A \cap B) = (C \cap D) = \varnothing$$

and

$$A \cong B, \qquad C \cong D, \qquad (A \cup B) \cong (C \cup D)$$

Prove that $A \cong C$.

13. Let p and q be two distinct points in a plane. Prove that the set of all straight lines in the plane passing through p is equipollent to the set of those passing through q.

14. Prove that the set of all positive rational numbers is equipollent to the set of all negative rational numbers.

15. Prove that the set of all natural numbers divisible by 3 is equipollent to the set of all natural numbers divisible by 9.

2. CANTOR'S THEOREMS

There are several important theorems concerning the equipollence of sets. We shall consider them after the introduction of the following lemmas.

Lemma 7. *Let f be a mapping from a set A into a set B and g a mapping from B into A. Then there exists a subset C of A such that*

$$\complement_A g(\complement_B f(C)) = C$$

where, as usual, $\complement_M N$ stands for the complement of N with respect to M, i.e., $M \smallsetminus N$.

PROOF. Consider the mapping h from the power-set $\mathscr{P}(A)$ of A into $\mathscr{P}(A)$ given by

$$h(X) = \complement_A g(\complement_B f(X))$$

for every element X of $\mathscr{P}(A)$.

Clearly, $h(X)$ is a nondecreasing function from $\mathscr{P}(A)$ into $\mathscr{P}(A)$. Indeed, if $X \subset Y \subset A$, then $f(X) \subset f(Y)$ and consequently, $\complement_B f(Y) \subset \complement_B f(X)$, from which it follows that

$$g(\complement_B f(Y)) \subseteq g(\complement_B f(X))$$

which in turn implies:

$$\complement_A g(\complement_B f(X)) \subseteq \complement_A g(\complement_B f(Y))$$

Therefore, $X \subset Y$ implies $h(X) \subset h(Y)$. Thus, h is indeed a nondecreasing function from $\mathscr{P}(A)$ into $\mathscr{P}(A)$. However, $(\mathscr{P}(A), \subseteq)$ is a complete partially ordered set and hence by Corollary 4 of Chapter IV (page 183), there exists a subset C of A that is fixed under h, i.e., $h(C) = C$. Hence, $\complement_A g(\complement_B f(C)) = C$. Thus, the lemma is proved.

Now, consider the subset $f(C)$ of B. Let $M = f(C)$. Then in view of Lemma 7 we have:

$$g(B \smallsetminus M) = (A \smallsetminus C)$$

Consequently, we have the following:

Lemma 8. *Let f be a mapping from a set A into a set B and g a mapping from B into A. Then there exists a subset C of A and a subset M of B such that:*

$$f(C) = M$$
$$(A \smallsetminus C) = g(B \smallsetminus M)$$

Theorem 5 (Cantor-Bernstein). *Two sets of which each is equipollent to a subset of the other are equipollent.*

PROOF. Let A be a set equipollent to a subset of a set B and B be equipollent to a subset of A. This means that there exists a one-to-one mapping f from A into B and a one-to-one mapping g from B into A. We shall show that $A \simeq B$.

According to Lemma 8, there exists a subset C of A and a subset M of B such that:

$$f(C) = M$$
$$(A \smallsetminus C) = g(B \smallsetminus M)$$

Since g is a one-to-one mapping from $(B \smallsetminus M)$ onto $(A \smallsetminus C)$, its converse g_{-1} is a one-to-one mapping from $(A \smallsetminus C)$ onto $(B \smallsetminus M)$. In view of this, we may define a mapping h from A into B given by:

$$h = f \quad\quad \text{on} \quad\quad C$$
$$h = g_{-1} \quad\quad \text{on} \quad\quad A \smallsetminus C$$

Obviously, h is a one-to-one mapping from A onto B. Hence, $A \simeq B$. Thus, Theorem 5 is proved.

Remark 5. We may give the following informal but illuminating proof of Theorem 5.

Let us observe that if two sets A and B are equipollent, then they can be considered in a sense as photographic images of each other.

Now, let us assume, as in Theorem 5, that a set A is equipollent to a subset of B (i.e., B contains a photographic image of A) and that B is equipollent to a subset of A (i.e., A contains a photographic image of B).

Let us represent A by a disc and B by a square (Figure 25).

Figure 25

Since A contains a photographic image of B, inside A we must see a square B_1. Similarly, since B contains a photographic image of A, inside B we must see a disc A_1 (Figure 26).

Figure 26

However, B_1 is a photographic image of B; hence, inside B we must see a disc A_2. But, since A_2 is a photographic image of A, inside A_2 we must see a photographic image B_2 of B. Similarly, inside B_2 we must see a photographic image A_3 of A, and so on. Thus, A is represented as in Figure 27.

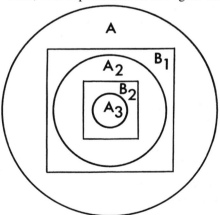

Figure 27

As Figure 27 shows,

$$A \supset B_1 \supset A_2 \supset B_2 \supset A_3 \cdots$$

Let $M = A \cap B_1 \cap A_2 \cap B_2 \cap A_3 \cap \cdots$
It is easy to see that:

$$A = M \cup (A \smallsetminus B_1) \cup (B_1 \smallsetminus A_2) \cup (A_2 \smallsetminus B_2) \cup (B_2 \smallsetminus A_3) \cup \cdots$$
$$B_1 = M \cup (A_2 \smallsetminus B_2) \cup (B_1 \smallsetminus A_2) \cup (A_3 \smallsetminus B_3) \cup (B_2 \smallsetminus A_3) \cup \cdots$$

From the above, we see at once that $A \simeq B_1$, and since $B_1 \simeq B$ we have $A \simeq B$, as desired.

As a corollary to Theorem 5, we have:

Corollary 10. *If a set A is equipollent to a subset B of A and if C is a subset of A and contains B, then A is equipollent to C.*

PROOF. Since $B \subset C$ and $A \simeq B$, we see that A is equipollent to a subset of C. However, since $C \subset A$, we see that C is equipollent to a subset of A (namely, C). Therefore, in view of Theorem 5, $A \simeq C$.

Corollary 11. *A subset of a denumerable set is finite or denumerable.*

PROOF. Let S be a denumerable set and H an infinite subset of S. By Theorem 1, H contains a denumerable subset E. Thus, $E \subset H \subset S$ and $E \simeq S$. Consequently, in view of Corollary 10, $H \simeq S$.

Corollary 12. *If S is an infinite set and E a finite or a denumerable set, then:*

$$S \cup E \simeq S$$

PROOF. The case where E is finite is taken care of by Lemma 5. Now, let E be denumerable. Since

$$S \cup E = S \cup (E \smallsetminus S)$$

we see that if $E \smallsetminus S$ is finite, then by Lemma 5, $S \cup (E \smallsetminus S) \simeq S$. Hence, $S \cup E \simeq S$, as desired. However, if $E \smallsetminus S$ is not finite, then by Corollary 11, $E \smallsetminus S$ is denumerable. Let:

$$E \smallsetminus S = \{e_1, e_2, e_3, \ldots\}$$

Also, since S is infinite, S has a denumerable subset $D = \{d_1, d_2, d_3, \ldots\}$. Thus,

$$S \cup (E \smallsetminus S) = (S \smallsetminus D) \cup \{d_1, d_2, d_3, \ldots\} \cup \{e_1, e_2, e_3, \ldots\}$$

and
$$S = (S \smallsetminus D) \cup \{d_1, d_2, d_3, \ldots\}$$

Define the mapping f from $S \cup (E \smallsetminus S)$ into S as follows:

f is the identity map on $S \smallsetminus D$

$$f(d_i) = d_{2i} \qquad \text{and} \qquad f(e_i) = d_{2i-1}$$

Clearly, f is a one-to-one correspondence between $S \cup (E \smallsetminus S)$ and S. Hence, indeed $S \cup E \simeq S$, as desired.

An immediate consequence of Corollary 12 is:

Corollary 13. *The union of finitely (≥ 1) many denumerable sets is a denumerable set.*

Theorem 6 (Diagonal Theorem). *Let f be a mapping of a set S into the power-set $\mathscr{P}(S)$ of S. Then the subset*

$$P = \{x \mid (x \in S) \wedge (x \notin f(x))\}$$

of S does not belong to the range of f.

PROOF. We have to show that for no element $y \in S$ is it the case that $f(y) = P$. Assume the contrary and let $y \in S$ be such that $f(y) = P$. Now, either $y \in P$ or $y \notin P$. If $y \in P$, then in view of our definition of P we have $y \notin f(y)$, and since $f(y) = P$ we see that $y \notin P$, a contradiction. Next, if $y \notin P$, then in view of our definition of P we have $y \in f(y)$, and since $f(y) = P$ we see that $y \in P$, a contradiction. Since in both of the above cases we arrive at a contradiction, we conclude that our assumption is false. Thus, for no $y \in S$ is it the case that $f(y) = P$.

Hence, the theorem is proved.

Theorem 7 (Cantor's Theorem). *No set is equipollent to its power-set.*

PROOF. Let us assume the contrary and let f be a one-to-one mapping of a set S onto the power-set $\mathscr{P}(S)$ of S. Clearly, the subset

$$\{x \mid (x \in S) \wedge (x \notin f(x))\}$$

of S is an element of $\mathscr{P}(S)$ which, by virtue of Theorem 6, cannot be the mate of any element of S. This contradicts the fact that f is a one-to-one correspondence between S and $\mathscr{P}(S)$. Hence, our assumption is false and the theorem is proved.

So far we have seen only examples of denumerable infinite sets—for instance, the set ω, the set of all even natural numbers, the set of all odd natural numbers, and so forth. There is no reason to assume that every infinite set is denumerable. As a matter of fact, the above theorem ensures the existence of infinite sets which are not denumerable. For instance, by virtue of the above theorem, the power-set $\mathscr{P}(\omega)$ of the set ω of all natural numbers is an infinite set which is not denumerable.

EXERCISES

1. Give three examples of infinite sets which are not denumerable.

2. Let f be a mapping from the power-set $\mathscr{P}(S)$ of a set S onto $\mathscr{P}(S)$ such that $X \subset f(X)$, for every subset X of S. Is it true that for every finite subset E of S, it is the case that $f(E) = E$?

3. Let f be a nondecreasing mapping from the power-set $\mathscr{P}(S)$ of a set S into $\mathscr{P}(S)$ such that $f(H) \subset H$ for a certain subset H of S. Prove that there exists a subset C of S such that $f(C) = C$.

4. Prove that if $S \cong P$, then there exist four sets A, B, C and D such that:

$$S \smallsetminus P = A \cup B, \qquad\qquad P \smallsetminus S = C \cup D,$$
$$A \cap B = C \cap D = \varnothing, \qquad A \cong C,$$

and

$$(B \cup (S \cap P)) \cong (S \cap P) \cong (D \cup (S \cap P))$$

5. Prove that for every two sets there exists a mapping that maps one onto the other.

6. Prove that for every set S there exists a set H such that S is equipollent to a subset of H and that H is not equipollent to any subset of S.

7. Prove that if $A \subset B$ and $A \cong (A \cup C)$, then $B \cong (A \cup B \cup C)$.

3. COMPARABILITY OF THE POWERS OF SETS

As mentioned earlier, two sets A and B are called of the same power if they are equipollent, i.e., if $A \cong B$. In this connection, it is natural to introduce:

Definition 3. *If X is equipollent to a subset of Y, then X is said to be of power less than or equal to that of Y. In symbols:*

$$X \preccurlyeq Y$$

Moreover, if X is equipollent to a subset of Y and X is not equipollent to Y, then X is said to be of smaller power than Y. In symbols:

$$X \prec Y$$

In view of the above definition, for every two sets X and Y,

(10) $\qquad\qquad$ if $\;\; X \subset Y \qquad$ then $\;\; X \preccurlyeq Y$

and

(11) $\qquad\qquad$ if $\;\; X \prec Y \qquad$ then $\;\; X \preccurlyeq Y$

Also, in view of (1) and (3), we have

(12) $\qquad\qquad\qquad X \preccurlyeq X \qquad$ for every set $\;\; X$

and for every three sets X, Y and Z,

(13) $\qquad\qquad$ if $\;\; X \preccurlyeq Y \qquad$ and $\;\; Y \preccurlyeq Z \qquad$ then $\;\; X \preccurlyeq Z$

Furthermore, in view of Theorem 5, for every two sets X and Y,

$\qquad\qquad$ if $\;\; X \preccurlyeq Y \qquad$ and $\qquad Y \preccurlyeq X \qquad$ then $\;\; X \cong Y$

Consequently, for every two sets X and Y,

(14) $\qquad\qquad\qquad$ if $\;\; X \preccurlyeq Y \preccurlyeq X \qquad$ then $\;\; X \cong Y$

Similarly, in view of Definition 3,

(15) $\qquad\qquad\qquad X \nprec X \qquad$ for every set $\;\; X$

Also, for every two sets X and Y

(16) $\qquad\qquad\qquad$ if $\;\; X \prec Y \qquad$ then $\;\; Y \nprec X$

because otherwise, in view of (11), $X \preccurlyeq Y$ and $Y \preccurlyeq X$, which implies $X \cong Y$, contradicting the fact that $X \prec Y$.

Moreover, for every three sets X, Y and Z

(17)   if $X \prec Y$ and $Y \prec Z$,   then $X \prec Z$

because in view of (11) and (13), $X \leq Z$ and if $X \nprec Z$, then $X \cong Z$, which in view of (14) contradicts the fact that $X \prec Y$.

Similarly, it is easy to verify that for every three sets X, Y and Z:

(18)   if $X \cong Y$ and $X \prec Z$ then $Y \prec Z$

(19)   if $X \leq Y$ and $Y \prec Z$ then $X \prec Z$

(20)   if $X \prec Y$ and $Y \leq Z$ then $X \prec Z$

Lemma 9.   *For every two sets X and Y*

$$X \prec Y$$

if and only if $X \leq Y$ and Y is not equipollent to any subset of X.

PROOF.   Let $X \prec Y$ and assume $Y \leq X$. Thus, in view of (11), $X \leq Y$ and then by (14), $X \cong Y$, contradicting the fact that $X \prec Y$. On the other hand, if $X \leq Y$ and Y is not equipollent to any subset of X, then in particular $X \ncong Y$, and consequently $X \prec Y$, as desired.

Let us observe that none of the above statements states that for any two sets X and Y, either $X \leq Y$ or $Y \leq X$. However, this is the case as shown by:

Theorem 8.   *For every two sets, one is equipollent to a subset of the other.*

PROOF.   Let A and B be any two sets and suppose that A is not equipollent to any subset of B. We shall prove that B is equipollent to a subset of A.

Clearly, there are subsets of B equipollent to some subsets of A, for instance, the empty set $\varnothing$.

Let $\{(S, s) \mid \cdots\}$ be the set of all ordered pairs (S, s) such that S is a subset of B and s is a one-to-one mapping from S into A.

Partial order $\{(S, s) \mid \cdots\}$ by $\leq'$ where, for every two elements (G, g) and (H, h) of $\{(S, s) \mid \cdots\}$

$$(G, g) \leq' (H, h)$$

if the restriction of h to G is equal to g, i.e., $g \subset h$. If $(G, g) \leq' (H, h)$ and $(G, g) \neq (H, h)$ then we write $(G, g) \prec' (H, h)$.

It is easy to show that every simply ordered subset of $\{(S, s) \mid \cdots\}$ has a least upper bound in $\{(S, s) \mid \cdots\}$. To this end, let Z be a simply ordered subset of $\{(S, s) \mid \cdots\}$. Let K be the union of the first coordinates of all the elements of Z, and let k be the union of the second coordinates of all the elements of Z. (Naturally, every second coordinate of an element of Z is a function which in turn is a set of ordered pairs.)

Clearly, (K, k) is an element of $\{(S, s) \mid \cdots\}$, and moreover (K, k) is the least upper bound of Z.

In view of the above, and by virtue of Zorn's lemma (page 199), it follows that $\{(S, s) \mid \cdots\}$ has a maximal element (M, m) where, according to our definition, m is a one-to-one mapping from M into A.

Let us observe that in view of our supposition the set A is not equipollent to any subset of B, and hence $m^1(M) \neq A$. Therefore, there exists an element a such that $a \in A$ and $a \notin m^1(M)$.

Next, we show that $M = B$. Let us assume on the contrary that there exists an element y such that $y \in B$ and $y \notin M$. Consider the ordered pair

$$(M \cup \{y\}, m^*)$$

where m^* is a mapping from $M \cup \{y\}$ into A such that $m^* = m$ on M, and $m^*(y) = a$, where a is the above-mentioned element of A. Clearly, m^* is one-to-one. Thus, $(M \cup \{y\}, m^*) \in \{(S, s) \mid \cdots\}$. Moreover, $(M, m) \prec' (M \cup \{y\}, m^*)$, a fact which contradicts the maximality of (M, m). Hence our assumption is false, and therefore $M = B$.

From this it follows that m is a one-to-one mapping from B into A, and hence B is equipollent to a subset of A.

Thus, the theorem is proved.

Corollary 14. *For every two sets X and Y,*

$$X \preceq Y \quad or \quad Y \preceq X$$

In view of Theorems 5 and 8, we have:

Theorem 9 (Comparability Theorem). *Two sets are equipollent or one and only one of them is equipollent to a subset of the other.*

PROOF. Let us assume that A and B are two nonequipollent sets. Then by Theorem 8 at least one of the sets A and B is equipollent to a subset of the other. However, in view of our assumption only one of the sets A and B can be equipollent to a subset of the other, since otherwise, by virtue of Theorem 5, they would be equipollent.

Thus, we have:

Corollary 15. *For every two sets X and Y, one and only one of the following three cases must hold:*

$$X \prec Y \quad or \quad Y \prec X \quad or \quad X \cong Y$$

Next, we prove the following important theorem.

Theorem 10. *If A and B are two disjoint infinite equipollent sets, then:*

$$A \cup B \cong A$$

PROOF. Let g be a one-to-one correspondence between the two disjoint infinite equipollent sets A and B.

Clearly, there exist subsets V and W of A and B respectively such that $g^1(V) = W$ (hence, $V \cong W$) and such that $V \cup W \cong V$. To see this, it is enough to take $V = W = \varnothing$.

Consider the set

(21) $\{V, W, f) \mid \cdots\}$

of all ordered triplets (V, W, f) where $V \subset A$, $W \subset B$, $g^1(V) = W$ (hence, $V \cong W$) and such that f is a one-to-one correspondence between $V \cup W$ and V (hence, $V \cup W \cong V$).

Obviously, (21) is not empty since $(\varnothing, \varnothing, \varnothing)$ is an element of (21).

Partial order $\{(V, W, f) \mid \cdots\}$ by $\preceq'$ where

$$(V, W, f) \preceq' (K, L, h)$$

if the restriction of h to $V \cup W$ is equal to f, i.e., $f \subset h$.

It is easy to show that every simply ordered subset of (21) has a least upper bound in (21). For let Z be a simply ordered subset of (21). Consider the ordered triplet (X, Y, q) where X is the union of the first coordinates of all the elements of Z, Y is the union of the second coordinates of all the elements of Z, and q is the union of the third coordinates of all the elements of Z (naturally, every third coordinate of an element of Z is a function which in turn is a set of ordered pairs).

Clearly, in view of the definition of q, we see at once that $X \subset A$, $Y \subset B$, $g^1(X) = Y$ (hence, $X \cong Y$) and q is a one-to-one correspondence between $X \cup Y$ and X (hence, $X \cup Y \cong X$).

In view of the above considerations, (X, Y, q) is an element of (21). Moreover, (X, Y, q) is the least upper bound of Z.

Thus, every simply ordered subset of (21) has a least upper bound in (21), and therefore, by Zorn's lemma, (21) has a maximal element (M, N, m). This means that

(22) $M \cup N \cong M$ and $g^1(M) = N$

and that there exists no element (V, W, f) of $\{(V, W, f) \mid \cdots\}$ such that M is a proper subset of V (or N is a proper subset of W) and such that $m \subset f$.

We shall show that $M \cong A$ and $N \cong B$.

Assume on the contrary that $M \not\cong A$. Then, $A \smallsetminus M$ must be infinite. Indeed, if $A \smallsetminus M$ were finite, then since A is infinite and $M \subset A$, by Lemma 5 we would have

$$A \smallsetminus (A \smallsetminus M) = M \cong A$$

contrary to our assumption that $M \not\cong A$.

Now, in view of Theorem 1, let D be a denumerable subset of $A \smallsetminus M$. Let $g^1(D) = H$. Since $g^1(M) = N$, we see that H is a denumerable subset of $B \smallsetminus N$.

Since D and H are two denumerable sets, by Corollary 9, $D \cup H \cong D$. Let c be a one-to-one mapping from $D \cup H$ onto D.

Consider the ordered triplet

(23) $(M \cup D, \text{N} \cup H, k)$

where k is a mapping from $(M \cup D) \cup (N \cup H)$ into $M \cup D$, defined as follows:

$$k = m \quad \text{on} \quad M \cup N$$
$$k = c \quad \text{on} \quad D \cup H$$

Obviously, k is a one-to-one correspondence between $(M \cup D) \cup (N \cup H)$ and $(M \cup D)$. Moreover, $g^1(M \cup D) = N \cup H$.

Thus, clearly (23) is an element of (21), which contradicts the maximality of (M, N, m). Consequently, our assumption is false, and therefore indeed $M \cong A$. But since $M \cong N$ and $A \cong B$, it follows that $N \cong B$. However, on the one hand A and B and on the other hand M and N are disjoint sets. Therefore, in view of Lemma 1 and (22) we conclude that:

$$A \cup B \cong A$$

Thus, Theorem 10 is proved.

Corollary 16. *For every infinite set S and every set P if $P \preceq S$ then $S \cup P \cong S$.*

PROOF. Let S_1 be a set equipollent to S and such that $P \cap S_1 = \varnothing$. Let g be a one-to-one mapping from P into S_1. And let $g^1(P \smile S) = H$.
Clearly,

(24) $$S \cup P \cong S \cup H$$

Also, $S \subset S \cup H \subset S \cup S_1$, and hence by (10),

$$S \preceq S \cup H \preceq S \cup S_1$$

However, in view of Theorem 10, we have $S \cong S \cup S_1$, and hence by (14) we obtain $S \cup H \cong S$. The latter, in view of (24), yields $S \cup P \cong S$, as desired.

Corollary 17. *Let $S_1, S_2, \ldots, S_n$ be a finite number of sets and S an infinite set. If, for $i = 1, 2, \ldots, n$*

$$S_i < S \quad then \quad S_1 \cup S_2 \cup \cdots \cup S_n < S$$

Moreover, if for $i = 1, 2, \ldots, n$

$$S_i \leq S \quad then \quad S_1 \cup S_2 \cup \cdots \cup S_n \leq S$$

PROOF. If S_i for $i = 1, 2, \ldots, n$ is a finite set, then the proof of the corollary is trivial. We prove the first part of the theorem. The proof of the second part is along similar lines.
Without loss of generality, let us assume that S_i for $i = 1, 2, \ldots, n$ is an infinite set. In view of Corollary 14 we have $S_1 \preceq S_2$ or $S_2 \preceq S_1$. Thus, in view of Corollary 16, $$S_1 \cup S_2 \preceq S_1 \quad or \quad S_1 \cup S_2 \preceq S_2$$

However, in either case, in view of (19) and the hypothesis of the corollary, $S_1 \cup S_2 \prec S$.
Similarly, we prove that $S_1 \cup S_2 \cup \cdots \cup S_n \prec S$.

Theorem 11. *If S is an infinite set and P a set such that $P \prec S$, then $S \smile P \cong S$.*

PROOF. Clearly, $S \smile P \preceq S$. Assume $S \smile P \not\cong S$. Then by Corollary 15, $S \smile P \prec S$. But then since $P \prec S$, by Corollary 17 we derive $(S \smile P) \cup P \prec S$, contradicting (15). Thus, our assumption is false and $S \smile P \cong S$, as desired.

Theorem 12. *Let A be a set simply ordered by set-theoretical inclusion $(\subset)$, and let S be a set such that $x \prec S$ for every $x \in A$. Then $\cup A \preceq S$.*

PROOF. If $A = \varnothing$ or S is finite, then the proof of the theorem is trivial. Thus, in what follows we let A be nonempty and S be infinite.

Consider the set

(25) $B = \{y \mid (z \in \mathscr{P}(A)) \wedge (y = \cup z)\}$

whose existence is ensured by the axioms of Power-Set, Sum-Set and Replacement. Clearly, the elements of B are unions of the elements of A.

Let us observe that as (25) shows every element of A is an element of B. Hence, in view of the hypothesis, there exist elements of B which are equipollent to some subsets of S.

Consider the set

(26) $C = \{(G,g) \mid \cdots\}$

of all ordered pairs (G,g), where G is an element of B and g is a one-to-one correspondence between G and a subset of S. In view of our above observation, C is not empty. Partial order C by $\preceq'$ where

(27) $(G,g) \preceq' (H,h)$

if $g \subset h$. It is easy to show that every simply ordered subset of C has a least upper bound in C. For let Z be a simply ordered subset of C. Consider the ordered pair (K,k) where K is the union of the first coordinates of all the elements of Z and k is the union of the second coordinates of all the elements of Z. Clearly, (K,k) is an element of C [as given by (25)] and is the least upper bound of Z. Thus, by Zorn's lemma, C has a maximal element (M,m).

We claim that $M = \cup A$. Assume on the contrary that $M \neq \cup A$. But then there must exist an element N of A such that $N \not\subseteq M$. However, since A is simply ordered by $\subset$, we see that:

(28) $M \subset N$ and $M \neq N$

Since by the hypothesis $N \prec S$, in view of (28) we have:

$$M \prec S \quad \text{and} \quad m^1(M) \prec S$$

But then, by Theorem 11, we derive:

(29) $S \sim m^1(M) \cong S$

Since $N \prec S$ we see that $N \sim M \prec S$. Therefore, in view of (29), there exists a one-to-one mapping t from $N \sim M$ into $S \sim m^1(M)$. Consider the ordered pair (N,h) where:

$$h = m \quad \text{on} \quad M$$
$$h = t \quad \text{on} \quad N \sim M$$

Clearly, (N,h) is an element of C, which in view of (27) and (28) contradicts the maximality of (M,m). Hence our assumption is false and $M = \cup A$. But then m is a one-to-one correspondence between $\cup A$ and a subset of S. Thus, $\cup A \preceq S$, as desired.

Corollary 18. *Let A be a set simply ordered by set-theoretical inclusion ($\subset$). If P is a set such that $P \prec \cup A$, then there exists an element a of A such that $P \preceq a$.*

PROOF. Assume on the contrary that $P \npreceq x$ for every $x \in A$. Then by Corollary 15 we have $x \prec P$ for every $x \in A$. But then by Theorem 12 we derive $\cup A \preceq P$, contradicting the hypothesis $P \prec \cup A$. Thus, indeed there must exist an element a of A such that $P \preceq a$.

Theorem 13. *There is no infinite decreasing sequence*

$$\cdots \prec S_3 \prec S_2 \prec S_1$$

of subsets S_1, S_2, $S_3 \cdots$ of any set S.

PROOF. If S is a finite set, then the proof is trivial. Let S be an infinite set. Clearly, there is a subset H_j of S such that there is no infinite decreasing sequence

$$(30) \qquad\qquad \cdots \prec H_{j3} \prec H_{j2} \prec H_{j1}$$

of subsets H_{j1}, H_{j2}, $H_{j3} \cdots$ of H_j. To see this, it is enough to take any finite subset of S. Let

$$(H_j)_{j \in b}$$

be the family of all subsets H_j of S such that for every H_j, with $j \in b$, there is no infinite decreasing sequence of type (30).

Partial order $(H_j)_{j \in b}$ by set-theoretical inclusion. Let $(H_i)_{i \in a}$ be a simply ordered subset of $(H_j)_{j \in b}$. We claim that $\cup_{i \in a} H_i$ is an element of $(H_j)_{j \in b}$. Indeed, if (without loss of generality)

$$(31) \qquad\qquad \cdots \prec M \prec N \prec P \prec \underset{i \in a}{\cup} H_i$$

were an infinite decreasing sequence of subsets of $\underset{i \in a}{\cup} H_i$, then by Corollary 18 there would exist an element H_k of $(H_i)_{i \in a}$ such that $P \preceq H_k$.

However, since there is no infinite decreasing sequence of type (30) of the subsets of H_k, there is no infinite decreasing sequence such as is given by (31).

In view of the above, every simply ordered (by set-theoretical inclusion) subset of $(H_j)_{j \in b}$ has a least upper bound. Hence, by Zorn's lemma, $(H_j)_{j \in b}$ has a maximal element H_m. We claim $H_m = S$. Assume $H_m \neq S$ and let $u \in S$ and $u \notin H_m$. If H_m is finite, then so is $H_m \cup \{u\}$, and if H_m is infinite, then according to Lemma 5, $H_m \cup \{u\} \cong H_m$. In either case, since there is no infinite decreasing sequence of the subsets of H_m, there is no infinite decreasing sequence of the subsets of $H_m \cup \{u\}$. Thus, $H_m \cup \{u\}$ is an element of $(H_j)_{j \in b}$, contradicting the maximality of H_m. Thus, our assumption is false and indeed $S = H_m$ and the theorem is proved.

Corollary 19. *There is no infinite decreasing sequence*

$$\cdots \prec a_3 \prec a_2 \prec a_1$$

of elements a_1, a_2, a_3, ... of any set A.

PROOF. Since $a_1, a_2, a_3, \ldots$ are subsets of $\cup A$, the proof of the corollary follows from that of Theorem 13.

Definition 4. *An element m of a set S is called a minimal element of S if $m \preceq x$ for every element x of S.*

Next, we prove the fundamental theorem.

Theorem 14. *Every nonempty set has a minimal element.*

PROOF. Let a_1 be an element of a nonempty set A. If a_1 is not a minimal element of A, then by Corollary 15 there must exist an element a_2 of A such that $a_2 \prec a_1$. Thus, if A has no minimal element, then (by reasoning analogous to the above) there must exist an infinite decreasing sequence

$$(32) \qquad \cdots \prec a_3 \prec a_2 \prec a_1$$

of elements of A. However, the existence of a sequence such as is given by (32) contradicts Corollary 19. Hence, every nonempty set must have a minimal element.

Theorems 8, 10, 11, 12, 13 and 14 have numerous applications, some of which may be found in the exercises below.

EXERCISES

1. Prove the second part of Corollary 17.

2. Let R be a relation in the set S defined by

$$R(x,y) \equiv (x \cong y)$$

for every two elements x and y of S. Prove that R is an equivalence relation in S.

3. Consider the equivalence relation R in S, as described in Problem 2. Let $\bar{x}$ denote the equivalence class to which the element x of S belongs. Let P be the set of all equivalence classes. Define

$$(\bar{\bar{x}} \leq \bar{\bar{y}}) \equiv (x \leq y)$$

where $x \leq y$ is in the sense of Definition 3. Prove that $(P, \leq)$ is a well ordered set.

4. Let S be a set. Prove that there exists a set P such that $S \prec P$ (in the sense of Definition 3).

5. Prove that there exists no set of all sets.

6. Does the set of all sets equipollent to a given set exist?

7. Let H be a nonempty subset of a set S such that there exists an element s of S with $x \leq s$ (in the sense of Definition 3) for every $x \in H$. Prove that there exists an element u of S with $x \leq u$ for every $x \in H$ such that $u \leq v$ for every $v \in S$ with $x \leq v$ for every $x \in H$. Is u unique?

4. THEOREMS ON THE EQUIPOLLENCE OF SETS

In Lemma 2 we proved that if A is disjoint from B and M is disjoint from N and if $A \cong M$ and $B \cong N$, then $A \cup B \cong M \cup N$.

The above can be generalized to the case of two disjointed sets. We recall that a set E is called disjointed if the elements of E are pairwise disjoint sets.

Theorem 15. *Let f be a one-to-one correspondence between a disjointed set E and a disjointed set S such that:*

$$X \cong f(X) \quad \text{for every} \quad X \in E$$

Then:

$$\cup E \cong \cup S$$

PROOF. For every element X of E, let Y denote the mate of X under f, i.e., $Y = f(X) \cong X$.

Let $(F_i(X, Y))_{i \in \alpha}$ represent the family of all one-to-one correspondences between X and Y. Next, consider the family

(33) $$((F_i(X, Y))_{i \in \alpha})_{X \in E}$$

each of whose elements is the family of all one-to-one correspondences between an element X of E and its mate Y under f. The family given by (33) is a disjointed set, since two distinct elements $(F_i(X_1, Y_1))_{i \in \alpha_1}$ and $(F_j(X_2, Y_2))_{j \in \alpha_2}$ of (33) are respectively subsets of $\mathscr{P}(X_1 \times Y_1)$ and $\mathscr{P}(X_2 \times Y_2)$, where X_1 and X_2 are disjoint.

By the axiom of Choice there exists a family

$$(F(X, Y))_{X \in E}$$

containing one and only one element from each of the elements of the family given by (33).

Now, consider:

(34) $$\underset{X \in E}{\cup} F(X, Y)$$

In view of the fact that f is a one-to-one correspondence between E and S and in view of the disjointedness of E and S, we see at once that the set given by (34) is a one-to-one correspondence between $\underset{X \in E}{\cup} X$ and $\underset{Y \in S}{\cup} Y$, as desired.

Let us observe that the following theorem, which somewhat resembles Theorem 15, can be proved without the use of the axiom of Choice.

Theorem 16. *Let A be a function from the set I such that $A(i) \cap A(j) = \varnothing$, for $i \in I, j \in I$ and $i \neq j$. Also, let B be a function from I such that $B(i) \cap B(j) = \varnothing$, for $i \in I, j \in I$ and $i \neq j$. Finally, let g be a function from I such that $g(k)$ is a one-to-one correspondence between $A(k)$ and $B(k)$ for $k \in I$. Then:*

$$\underset{i \in I}{\cup} A(i) \cong \underset{i \in I}{\cup} B(i)$$

The proof of this theorem is straightforward and is left to the reader.

Lemma 10. *Let $A \cong P$ and $B \cong S$; then:*

$$(A \times B) \cong (P \times S)$$

PROOF. Let f be a one-to-one correspondence between A and P, and g between B and S. Then there exists a mapping given by $h((a,b)) = (f(a), g(b))$ which is a one-to-one correspondence between $A \times B$ and $P \times S$, as desired.

Lemma 11. *For every three sets A, B and C,*

$$(A \times B) \times C \cong A \times (B \times C) \qquad \text{and} \qquad (A \times B) \cong (B \times A)$$

PROOF. Clearly, the mapping f given by $f(((a,b), c)) = (a, (b,c))$ is an equipollence (i.e., a one-to-one correspondence) between $(A \times B) \times C$ and $A \times (B \times C)$. Also, the mapping g given by $g((a,b)) = (b,a)$ is an equipollence between $A \times B$ and $B \times A$.

In view of Lemma 11, any two Cartesian products arising from insertion of parentheses in

$$A_1 \times A_2 \times A_3 \times \cdots \times A_n$$

are equipollent.

Theorem 17. *The Cartesian product $A \times B$ is equipollent to the sum-set of any family $(A_b)_{b \in B}$, with $A_b \cong A$ and $A_b \cap A_c = \varnothing$, for $b \in B$, $c \in B$ and $b \neq c$.*

PROOF. As in the proof of Theorem 15, in view of the axiom of Choice and our hypothesis, there exists a family $(f_b)_{b \in B}$ of one-to-one correspondences f_b such that:

$$f_b : A \to A_b \qquad \text{for every} \quad b \in B$$

Let $f_b(a) = a_b$, for $a \in A$ and $b \in B$. Then there exists a mapping g from $A \times B$ into $\underset{b \in B}{\cup} A_b$ such that $g((a,b)) = a_b$ for every ordered pair $(a,b) \in A \times B$. In view of the fact that $A_b \cap A_c = \varnothing$, for $b \in B$, $c \in B$ and $b \neq c$, it is easily seen that g is a one-to-one correspondence between $A \times B$ and the sum-set $\underset{b \in B}{\cup} A_b$ of the family $(A_b)_{b \in B}$.

Remark 6. The above theorem shows that a Cartesian product is equipollent to a repeated union.

The extension of Lemma 10 to any set of factors is given below.

Let us recall that given a set S, its Cartesian product denoted by

$$\Pi S$$

is defined (see Definition 9 of Chapter III, page 162) as the set of all functions g such that g maps every element X of S into an element x of X. With this definition in mind we prove:

Theorem 18. *Let f be a one-to-one correspondence between E and S such that:*

$$X \cong f(X) = Y \qquad \text{for every} \quad X \in E$$

Then the Cartesian product ΠE is equipollent to the Cartesian product ΠS.

PROOF. As in the proof of Theorem 15, by virtue of the axiom of Choice there exists a family

(35) $(F(X,Y))_{X \in E}$

which, for every $X \in E$, has as an element one and only one one-to-one correspondence between X and $Y = f(X)$.

As we know, ΠE is the set of all functions g such that g maps E into $\cup E$ and assigns to every element X of E an element x of X, i.e.,

$$x = g(X) \quad \text{with} \quad x \in X \qquad \text{for every} \quad X \in E$$

Thus,

$$\Pi E = \{ g \mid \cdots \}$$

Now, consider such a function g. It is a certain set of ordered pairs (X,x) with $x \in X$, for every $X \in E$. Let:

$$g = ((X,x))_{X \in E}$$

By our hypothesis, there is a one-to-one correspondence f, given by $Y = f(X)$, between E and S that assigns to every $X \in E$ an equipollent element $Y \in S$. Also, in view of (35) there exists a one-to-one correspondence $F(X, Y)$, given by $y = F(X)$, between X and Y that assigns to every $x \in X$ an element $y \in Y$.

Consider

$$H = \{ (f(X), F(x))_{X \in E} \mid \cdots \}$$

where $f(X)$ and $F(X)$ are those given above; and where X and x are respectively the first and the second coordinates of an element of g given above.

It is easy to see that

(36) $$H = \Pi S$$

where ΠS is the set of all functions h such that h maps S into $\cup S$ and assigns to every element Y of S an element y of Y.

Finally, in view of the fact that f and $F(X, Y)$ are one-to-one correspondences, ΠE and H are equipollent. Consequently, by virtue of (36), ΠE and ΠS are equipollent, as desired.

Here again we observe that the following theorem, which somewhat resembles Theorem 18, can be proved without the use of the axiom of Choice.

Theorem 19. *Let A, B and g be three functions from the set I such that for every $i \in I$ the function $g(i)$ is a one-to-one correspondence between $A(i)$ and $B(i)$. Then*:

$$\prod_{i \in I} A(i) \cong \prod_{i \in I} B(i)$$

In the above, $\prod_{i \in I} A(i)$ is given according to the definition on page 161.

The proof of Theorem 19 is straightforward and is left to the reader.

Let us consider a special case of the Cartesian product of a family $(X_i)_{i \in I}$ where all the factors X_i are equal sets, i.e., $X_i = S$, for every $i \in I$. As mentioned on page 162, in this case

$$\prod_{i \in I} X_i = S^I$$

where S^I [according to (54) of Chapter III (page 146)] represents the set of all functions from I into S.

It is appropriate to call S^I the I-*th power of the set S. We consider the above equality involving S^I as the definition for exponentiation of sets.*

Now, we shall prove some theorems concerning exponentiation of sets.

Theorem 20. *If $A \cong P$ and $B \cong S$, then $A^B \cong P^S$.*

PROOF. Let f be a one-to-one correspondence between A and P, and g between B and S.

We shall prove the existence of a one-to-one correspondence between A^B and P^S.

An element of A^B is a function from B into A. As such, it is a certain set of ordered pairs (b,a) with $b \in B$ and $a \in A$. Let $\{(b,a) \mid \cdots\}$ represent an element of A^B. There exists a mapping h from A^B into P^S given by:

$$h(\{(b,a) \mid \cdots\}) = \{(g(b), f(a)) \mid \cdots\}$$

In view of the fact that f and g are one-to-one correspondences, it is clear that h is a one-to-one correspondence between A^B and P^S.

Theorem 21. *Let A, B and C be sets such that $B \cap C = \varnothing$. Then:*

$$A^{B \cup C} \cong A^B \times A^C$$

PROOF. An element of $A^{B \cup C}$ is a function from $B \cup C$ into A. As such, it is a certain set of ordered pairs (m,a) with $m \in B$ or $m \in C$ and $a \in A$. Since $B \cap C = \varnothing$, an element of $A^{B \cup C}$ is given by

$$\{(b,a) \mid \cdots\} \cup \{(c,a) \mid \cdots\}$$

where $\{(b,a) \mid \cdots\}$ and $\{(c,a) \mid \cdots\}$ are respectively functions from B into A and from C into A. Thus, $\{(b,a) \mid \cdots\}$ and $\{(c,a) \mid \cdots\}$ are respectively elements of A^B and A^C. From this it follows that an element of $A^B \times A^C$ is given by the ordered pair:

$$(\{(b,a) \mid \cdots\}, \{(c,a) \mid \cdots\})$$

Now, there exists a function h from $A^{B \cup C}$ into $A^B \times A^C$ such that:

$$h(\{(b,a) \mid \cdots\} \cup \{(c,a) \mid \cdots\}) = (\{(b,a) \mid \cdots\}, \{(c,a) \mid \cdots\})$$

Since $B \cap C = \varnothing$, it is easily seen that h is a one-to-one correspondence between $A^{B \cup C}$ and $A^B \times A^C$.

Remark 7. The above theorem shows that a power of a set is equipollent to a repeated Cartesian product.

Theorem 22. *For every three sets A, B and C,*

$$(A \times B)^C \cong A^C \times B^C$$

PROOF. An element of $(A \times B)^C$ is a function from C into $A \times B$. As such, it is a certain set of ordered pairs $(c, (a,b))$ where $a \in A$, $b \in B$ and $c \in C$. Thus, an element of $(A \times B)^C$ is given by a set such as $\{(c, (a,b)) \mid \cdots\}$.

On the other hand, an element of $A^C \times B^C$ is an ordered pair of sets

$\{(c,a) \mid \cdots\}$ and $\{(c,b) \mid \cdots\}$. Thus, an element of $A^C \times B^C$ is given by a set such as:

$$(\{(c,a) \mid \cdots\}, \{(c,b) \mid \cdots\})$$

There exists a function h from $(A \times B)^C$ into $A^C \times B^C$ such that:

$$h(\{(c, (a,b)) \mid \cdots\}) = (\{(c,a) \mid \cdots\}, \{(c,b) \mid \cdots\})$$

It is easy to verify that h is a one-to-one correspondence between $(A \times B)^C$ and $A^C \times B^C$.

Theorem 23. *For every three sets A, B and C,*

$$(A^B)^C \simeq A^{B \times C}$$

PROOF. Clearly, an element of $(A^B)^C$ is a certain set of ordered pairs $\{(c, \{(b,a) \mid \cdots\}) \mid \cdots\}$ where $a \in A$, $b \in B$ and $c \in C$.

On the other hand, an element of $A^{B \times C}$ is also a certain set of ordered pairs $\{((b,c), a) \mid \cdots\}$ where $a \in A$, $b \in B$ and $c \in C$.

There exists a mapping h from $(A^B)^C$ into $A^{B \times C}$ such that:

$$h(\{(c, \{(b,a) \mid \cdots\}) \mid \cdots\}) = \{((b,c), a) \mid \cdots\}$$

Obviously, h is a one-to-one correspondence between $(A^B)^C$ and $A^{B \times C}$.

EXERCISES

1. Prove Theorems 16 and 19.

2. Prove that if A, B, C and D are such that $B \subset D$, $C \subset A$ and $A \cup B \simeq B$, then $C \cup D \simeq D$.

3. Prove that if A, B, C, D, E and F are such that

$$B \subset C, \qquad D \subset E, \qquad F \subset A,$$
$$A \simeq B, \qquad C \simeq D \qquad \text{and} \qquad E \simeq F$$

then

$$A \simeq E \qquad \text{and} \qquad A \simeq C$$

4. Prove that if A, B, C and D are such that

$$A \cap C = \varnothing, \qquad B \cap D = \varnothing, \qquad A \simeq C, \qquad B \simeq D \qquad \text{and}$$
$$A \cup C \simeq B \cup D, \qquad \text{then} \quad A \simeq B.$$

5. Let $(X_i)_{i \in I}$ and $(Y_i)_{i \in I}$ each be a family of pairwise disjoint sets such that $X_i \simeq A_i$ and $Y_i \simeq B_i$ for every $i \in I$ where each of $(A_i)_{i \in I}$ and $(B_i)_{i \in I}$ is a family of pairwise disjoint sets. Prove that:

$$\left(\bigcup_{i \in I} X_i\right) \times \left(\bigcup_{i \in I} Y_i\right) \simeq \bigcup_{(i,j) \in I \times J} (A_i \times B_j)$$

5. THEOREMS ON DENUMERABLE SETS

In previous sections we proved many theorems involving finite and denumerable sets. In this section we prove additional theorems concerning denumerable sets.

Lemma 12.   *The sum-set of a denumerable family whose terms are pairwise disjoint finite sets is finite or denumerable.*

PROOF.   Clearly, the above sum-set is finite if and only if all but a finite number of the pairwise disjoint sets under consideration are empty. Otherwise, without loss of generality and in view of Theorem 15, we may consider a denumerable family whose terms are particular pairwise disjoint nonempty finite sets. Let:

$$P_1 = \{2, 2^2, 2^3, \ldots, 2^{k_1}\}$$
$$P_2 = \{3\cdot2, 3\cdot2^2, 3\cdot2^3, \ldots, 3\cdot2^{k_2}\}$$
$$\cdots$$
$$P_n = \{(2n-1)2, (2n-1)2^2, (2n-1)2^3, \ldots, (2n-1)2^{k_n}\}$$
$$\cdots$$

Clearly, $\{P_1, P_2, \ldots\}$ is a denumerable family whose terms are pairwise disjoint nonempty finite sets.

It is obvious that $S = P_1 \cup P_2 \cup \cdots$ is an infinite subset of the denumerable set ω, and hence, by Corollary 11, S is denumerable.

It is customary to rephrase Lemma 12 as follows:

A denumerable union of pairwise disjoint finite sets is finite or denumerable.

Lemma 13.   *The sum-set of a denumerable set is always equal to the sum-set of a denumerable set whose elements are pairwise disjoint.*

PROOF.   Let $\{P_1, P_2, P_3, \ldots\}$ be a denumerable set. Clearly,

$$P_1 \cup P_2 \cup P_3 \cup \cdots$$
$$= P_1 \cup (P_2 \smallsmile P_1) \cup (P_3 \smallsmile (P_1 \cup P_2)) \cup (P_4 \smallsmile (P_1 \cup P_2 \cup P_3)) \cup \cdots$$

Also, it is easily observed that

$$\{P_1, (P_2 \smallsmile P_1), (P_3 \smallsmile (P_1 \cup P_2)), \ldots\}$$

is a denumerable set whose elements are pairwise disjoint.

Theorem 24.   *A denumerable union of finite sets is finite or denumerable.*

PROOF.   In view of Lemma 13 and the fact that every subset of a finite set is finite, it follows that the above union is equal to a denumerable union of pairwise disjoint finite sets, and hence (in view of Lemma 12) is finite or denumerable.

Lemma 14.   *A denumerable union of pairwise disjoint denumerable sets is denumerable.*

PROOF. In view of Theorem 15, we may give the proof of this theorem for a denumerable family whose terms are particular pairwise disjoint denumerable sets. Let:

$$P_1 = \{2, 2^2, 2^3, \ldots\}$$
$$P_2 = \{3 \cdot 2, 3 \cdot 2^2, 3 \cdot 2^3, \ldots\}$$
$$\cdots$$
$$P = \{(2n - 1)2, (2n - 1)2^2, (2n - 1)2^3, \ldots\}$$
$$\cdots$$

Clearly, $\{P_1, P_2, P_3, \ldots\}$ is a denumerable family whose terms are pairwise disjoint denumerable sets.

On the other hand, again it is obvious that $S = P_1 \cup P_2 \cup \cdots$ is an infinite subset of the denumerable set ω. Hence, by Corollary 11, S is denumerable.

Theorem 25. *A denumerable union of finite or denumerable sets is finite or denumerable.*

PROOF. In view of Lemma 13 and the fact that every subset of a finite or denumerable set is finite or denumerable, it follows that the above union is equal to a denumerable union of pairwise disjoint finite or denumerable sets, and hence (in view of Lemmas 12 and 14) is finite or denumerable.

Remark 8. Lemma 14 can be used to decompose a denumerable set into a denumerable set of pairwise disjoint denumerable sets. Consequently, as a corollary we have:

Corollary 20. *Every denumerable set is the sum-set of a denumerable set of pairwise disjoint denumerable sets.*

Theorem 26. *The set of all finite sequences of a denumerable set is denumerable.*

PROOF. In view of Theorem 15, it is enough to consider the set S of all finite sequences of positive natural numbers. Now, to each finite sequence of positive natural numbers

$$n_1, n_2, \ldots, n_k$$

let us assign the natural number:

$$2^{n_1-1} + 2^{n_1+n_2-1} + \cdots + 2^{n_1+n_2+\cdots+n_k-1}$$

The above assignment is a one-to-one mapping from the set S of all finite sequences of positive natural numbers onto an infinite subset of ω. Thus, in view of Corollary 11, S is denumerable.

Let us observe that any finite subset of the set of all positive natural numbers can be made into a finite sequence of its elements by writing them, say, in ascending order. Thus, the set of all finite subsets of positive natural numbers is an infinite subset of the set of all finite sequences of positive natural numbers. Consequently, in view of Corollary 11 and Theorem 26 we have:

Corollary 21. *The set of all finite subsets of a denumerable set is denumerable.*

Next, we prove some standard theorems concerning the Cartesian products of finite and denumerable sets.

Lemma 15.   *The Cartesian product of two finite sets is finite.*

PROOF.   In view of Theorem 17, the Cartesian product of any two finite sets is equipollent to a certain finite union of finite sets, and hence is finite.

Theorem 27.   *The Cartesian product of a finite and a denumerable set is denumerable or empty.*

PROOF.   In view of Theorem 17, the Cartesian product of a nonempty finite and a denumerable set is equipollent to a certain union of a finite number (≥ 1) of denumerable sets, and hence is denumerable. If the finite set under consideration is empty, then the above Cartesian product is empty.

Theorem 28.   *The Cartesian product of two denumerable sets is denumerable.*

PROOF.   In view of Theorem 17, the Cartesian product of two denumerable sets is equipollent to a certain denumerable union of denumerable sets, and hence is denumerable.

From Theorem 28, we derive immediately:

Corollary 22.   *The Cartesian product of a finite number (≥ 1) of denumerable sets is denumerable.*

[In view of (83) of Chapter III (page 162), we may say that the Cartesian product of no sets is $\{\varnothing\}$ and therefore is finite.]

Theorem 29.   *If A is a denumerable set and B a nonempty finite set, then A^B is denumerable.*

PROOF.   In view of Remark 7, A^B is equipollent to the Cartesian product of a finite number (≥ 1) of certain denumerable sets, and hence is denumerable. If $B = \varnothing$, then, as we know, $A^B = \{\varnothing\}$ and hence is finite.

Let us give some examples of denumerable sets.

Theorem 30.   *The set of all rational numbers is denumerable.*

PROOF.   First, we shall prove that the set P of all positive rational numbers is denumerable. According to the notation introduced on page 221, a positive rational number is represented as $[m,n]$ where m and n are nonnegative integers with $n \neq 0$. Clearly, P is an infinite set since it contains the denumerable set $\{[1,2], [1,3], [1,4], \ldots\}$.

Also, it is clear that the set P of all positive rational numbers is a subset of the table:

$$[1,1], \quad [1,2], \quad [1,3], \quad \cdots$$
$$[2,1], \quad [2,2], \quad [2,3], \quad \cdots$$
$$[3,1], \quad [3,2], \quad [3,3], \quad \cdots$$
$$\cdots$$

However, the above table can be looked at as a denumerable union of denumerable sets; hence, by Theorem 25, the set whose elements are the elements of the above table is denumerable. Thus, P is an infinite subset of a denumerable set, and therefore P is denumerable. On the other hand, the set N of all negative rational numbers is equipollent to P. Hence, by virtue of Corollary 13 we assert that $P \cup N$ is denumerable. Consequently, in view of Lemma 5, $P \cup N \cup \{0\}$, which is the set of all rational numbers, is denumerable.

We note that the same theorem is an immediate corollary of Theorem 26.

Theorem 31. *The set of all algebraic numbers is denumerable.*

PROOF. Let us recall that an algebraic number is a root of a polynomial in one variable with integer coefficients. Obviously, the set of all algebraic numbers is an infinite set since every rational number is an algebraic number. For instance, the rational number $\frac{p}{q}$ is the root of the polynomial $qx - p$, where q and p are integers with $q \neq 0$.

Now, let us consider a polynomial in one variable of the degree n (n is a positive natural number) with integer coefficients.

$$a_n x^n + a_{n-1} x^{n-1} + \cdots + a_1 x + a_0, \qquad a_n \neq 0$$

With such a polynomial, let us associate the finite sequence of integers:

$$(a_n, a_{n-1}, \ldots, a_1, a_0)$$

The above association shows that there exists a one-to-one mapping from the infinite set $\{P(x) \mid \cdots\}$ of all polynomials in one variable with integer coefficients, into the set of all finite sequences of integers. However, by Theorem 26, the latter set is denumerable. Thus, the set $\{P(x) \mid \cdots\}$ is also denumerable. On the other hand, every polynomial in one variable has a finite number of distinct roots. Hence, by Lemma 12 the set of all algebraic numbers is denumerable.

Theorem 32. *Every infinite set of pairwise nonoverlapping intervals of real numbers each having more than one element is denumerable.*

PROOF. Let us recall that if a and b are two real numbers, then the set of all real numbers x such that $a < x < b$ or $a \leq x < b$, or $a \leq x \leq b$, or $a < x \leq b$ is called an interval. Two intervals are called nonoverlapping if they have no element in common, except perhaps their end points (when these exist). It is clear that if an interval of real numbers contains more than one real number, then it contains a rational number. With this in mind, the proof of the theorem follows from the fact that the set of all rational numbers is denumerable.

EXERCISES

1. Prove that a set is denumerable if and only if it is equipollent to each of its infinite subsets.

2. Prove that an infinite set is equipollent to a set obtained by adjoining to it a denumerable set, or by removing from it a certain denumerable set.

3. Prove that the set of all prime numbers is denumerable.

4. Prove that the set of all rational numbers x, such that $0 \leq x \leq 1$, is denumerable.

5. Prove that every infinite set of real numbers for which the natural order is a well ordering, is denumerable.

6. Prove that the set of all finite sequences of algebraic numbers is denumerable.

7. Prove that the set of all straight lines in a plane, each passing through two distinct points with rational coordinates, is denumerable.

8. Consider the table:

$$(1,1), \quad (1,2), \quad (1,3), \quad \cdots$$
$$(2,1), \quad (2,2), \quad (2,3), \quad \cdots$$
$$\cdots$$

With the element (r,c) of the above table, associate the natural number:

$$n = \tfrac{1}{2}(r + c - 1)(r + c) + 1 - r$$

Is this association a one-to-one correspondence between the set whose elements are the elements of the above table and the set ω of all natural numbers?

6. FURTHER THEOREMS ON THE EQUIPOLLENCE OF SETS

According to Corollary 16, if S is an infinite set and if P is a set equipollent to a subset of S (i.e., $P \preceq S$), then $S \cup P \cong S$. In this section, we shall prove an analogous result for the Cartesian product (i.e., that under the same hypothesis) $S \times P \cong S$. However, prior to the proof of the latter we prove:

Theorem 33.   *If for a natural number $n \geq 1$*

$$S_1 \cong S_2 \cong \cdots \cong S_n$$

and if S_1 is an infinite set, then:

$$S_1 \cup S_2 \cup \cdots \cup S_n \cong S_1$$

PROOF. Employing the notation introduced in Definition 3, clearly, $S_1 \preceq S_1 \cup S_2 \cup \cdots \cup S_n$. On the other hand, by Corollary 17 we have $S_1 \cup S_2 \cup \cdots \cup S_n \preceq S_1$. Therefore, in view of (14),

$$S_1 \cup S_2 \cup \cdots \cup S_n \cong S_1$$

as desired.

Theorem 34.   *If S is an infinite set and P is a subset of S not equipollent to S, then there exists a subset E of $S \smallsetminus P$ such that $E \cong P$.*

PROOF.   Since P is a subset of S, we see that $P \preceq S$. On the other hand, since P is not equipollent to S, by Corollary 15, $P \prec S$. But then by Theorem 11, $S \smallsmile P \cong S$. Consequently, $S \smallsmile P$ must contain a subset E such that $E \cong P$.
Next, we prove:

Theorem 35.   *If A is an infinite set, then:*

$$A \times A \cong A$$

PROOF.   Let D be a denumerable subset of A. By Theorem 28, $D \times D \cong D$. Consequently, our theorem holds for the subset D of A. Let f be a one-to-one correspondence between $D \times D$ and D.
Consider the set

(37) $\{(V,g) \mid \cdots\}$

of all ordered pairs (V,g) where $D \subset V \subset A$ and g is an equipollence between $V \times V$ and V.
Clearly, the set given by (37) is not empty since (D,f) is an element of it. Partial order $\{(V,g) \mid \cdots\}$ by $\preceq'$, where

$$(V,g) \preceq' (K,h)$$

if $V \subset K$ and the restriction of h to $V \times V$ is equal to g, i.e., $g \subset h$.
It is easy to verify that every simply ordered subset of (37) has a least upper bound in (37), and hence by Zorn's lemma $\{(V,g) \mid \cdots\}$ has a maximal element (M,m). This means that

(38) $M \times M \cong M$

$D \subset M \subset A$ and there exists no element (V,g) of $\{(V,g) \mid \cdots\}$ such that M is a proper subset of V and $(M,m) \preceq' (V,g)$.
We shall prove that:

(39) $M \cong A$

Assume on the contrary that M is not equipollent to A. Since A is infinite and $M \subset A$, and since M is not equipollent to A, by Theorem 34 there exists a set E such that:

(40) $E \cong M$ and $E \subset A \smallsmile M$

Observe that:

(41) $(M \cup E) \times (M \cup E) = (M \times M) \cup (M \times E) \cup (E \times M) \cup (E \times E)$

Now, in view of (40), (38) and Lemma 11, we have

$$(M \times E) \cong (E \times M) \cong (E \times E) \cong E$$

and therefore, by Theorem 33, we derive:

$$(M \times E) \cup (E \times M) \cup (E \times E) \cong E$$

Consequently, there exists a one-to-one correspondence t between

$$(M \times E) \cup (E \times M) \cup (E \times E)$$

and E.

Now, define a mapping h from

$$(42) \hspace{2cm} (M \times M) \cup (M \times E) \cup (E \times M) \cup (E \times E)$$

into $M \cup E$ as follows:

$$h = m \hspace{1cm} \text{on} \hspace{1cm} M \times M$$
$$h = t \hspace{1cm} \text{on} \hspace{1cm} (M \times E) \cup (E \times M) \cup (E \times E)$$

Clearly, in view of the definitions of m and t, the mapping h is a one-to-one correspondence between (42) and $M \cup E$.

However, (41) shows that (42) is equal to $(M \cup E) \times (M \cup E)$. Hence, h is a one-to-one mapping from $(M \cup E) \times (M \cup E)$ onto $(M \cup E)$. Also, it is clear that $((M \cup E), h)$ is an element of (37). On the other hand, as an infinite set E is not empty, and since by (40), $E \subset A \smile M$, we see at once that M is a proper subset of $M \cup E$. In view of this and the obvious fact that $(M,m) \preceq'$ $((M \cup E), h)$, we arrive at a contradiction regarding the maximality of (M,m). Hence, our assumption is false and M is indeed equipollent to A. Thus, (39) is established. From (39) and (38), we derive $A \times A \cong A$, as desired.

Theorem 35 has many applications. We shall encounter them in connection with the arithmetic of cardinal numbers.

From Theorem 35, in view of Remark 7, we have:

Corollary 23. *If A is an infinite set and N is a nonempty finite set, then $A^N \cong A$.*

Corollary 24. *If A is an infinite set and B is a nonempty set equipollent to a subset of A (i.e., $B \preceq A$), then:*

$$A \times B \cong A$$

PROOF. Employing the notation introduced in Definition 3, we see that $A \times \{b\} \preceq A \times B \preceq A \times A$, where $b \in B$. However, $A \times \{b\} \cong A$, and hence, in view of Theorem 35,

$$A \preceq A \times B \preceq A$$

Consequently, by (14) we have $A \times B \cong A$, as desired.

Corollary 25. *If A is an infinite set and D is a denumerable set, then:*

$$A \times D \cong A$$

EXERCISES

1. Prove that if A is an infinite set and C is a set equipollent to a subset of A, then $A \cup C \cong A$.

2. Prove that if A is an infinite set such that $A = B \cup C$, then $A \cong B$ or $A \cong C$.

3. Prove that if an infinite set A is the union of a finite number of sets, then at least one of these sets is equipollent to A.

4. Prove Corollaries 23 and 25.

5. Let S be an infinite set such that $S_i \preceq S$ for $i = 1, 2, \ldots, n$. Prove that:

$$S_1 \times S_2 \times \cdots \times S_n \cong \prod_{i=1}^{n} S_i \preceq S$$

6. Let S be an infinite set such that $S_i \prec S$ for $i = 1, 2, \ldots, n$. Prove that:

$$S_1 \times S_2 \times \cdots \times S_n \cong \prod_{i=1}^{n} S_i \prec S$$

7. Let S_i be an infinite set with $S_i \cong S$ for $i = 1, 2, \ldots, n$. Prove that:

$$S_1 \times S_2 \times \cdots \times S_n \cong \prod_{i=1}^{n} S_i \cong \bigcup_{i=1}^{n} S_i \cong S$$

7. NONDENUMERABLE SETS

As mentioned in Section 2, Theorem 7 asserts the existence of infinite sets that are not denumerable. For instance, the power-set $\mathscr{P}(\omega)$ of the set ω of all natural numbers is an example of an infinite set that is not denumerable.

Definition 5.   *An infinite set that is not denumerable is called a nondenumerable set.*

We shall prove that the set of all real numbers is nondenumerable. First we prove:

Lemma 16.   *For every infinite sequence of real numbers, there exists a real number different from every element of that sequence.*

PROOF.   Let us recall that every real number can be uniquely represented in the form

$$e \cdot a_1 a_2 a_3 \cdots$$

where e is an integer and where $a_1, a_2, a_3, \ldots$ is an infinite sequence of digital terms in which there is no occurrence of an infinite succession of nines.
    Now, let

$$e_1 \cdot a_1 a_2 a_3 \cdots$$
$$e_2 \cdot b_1 b_2 b_3 \cdots$$
(43)
$$\cdots$$
$$e_n \cdot h_1 h_2 h_3 \cdots$$
$$\cdots$$

be an infinite sequence of real numbers. Consider the real number

(44) $0 \cdot k_1 k_2 k_3 \cdots k_n \cdots$

where:

$$k_1 = 0, \quad \text{if} \quad a_1 \neq 0 \quad \text{and} \quad k_1 = 1, \quad \text{if} \quad a_1 = 0$$
$$k_2 = 0, \quad \text{if} \quad b_2 \neq 0 \quad \text{and} \quad k_2 = 1, \quad \text{if} \quad b_2 = 0$$
$$\cdots$$
$$k_n = 0, \quad \text{if} \quad h_n \neq 0 \quad \text{and} \quad k_n = 1, \quad \text{if} \quad h_n = 0$$

Clearly, $0 \cdot k_1 k_2 k_3 \cdots k_n \cdots$ is a real number in whose decimal part there is no occurrence of an infinite succession of nines. Also, it is easily observed that $0 \cdot k_1 k_2 k_3 \cdots k_n \cdots$ is different from each of the members of sequence (43). Indeed, compared with $e_1 \cdot a_1 a_2 a_3 \cdots$, (44) differs in the first decimal place; compared with $e_2 \cdot b_1 b_2 b_3 \cdots$, (44) differs in the second decimal place, and so on. Thus, Lemma 16 is proved.

Theorem 36. *The set of all real numbers is nondenumerable.*

PROOF. Let R be the set of all real numbers. Assume R is denumerable. Under this assumption, all the elements of R form an infinite sequence such as (43). However, by Lemma 16, no infinite sequence of real numbers can contain every real number. Hence our assumption is false, and consequently R cannot be denumerable. On the other hand, R is obviously infinite (since, for instance, R contains the real numbers $1.000 \ldots$, $2.000 \ldots$, and so on), and consequently R is a nondenumerable set.

In view of the importance of the set of all real numbers in mathematics, we introduce:

Definition 6. *A set that is equipollent to the set of all real numbers is said to be of the power of the continuum.*

A set is either finite or infinite, and an infinite set is either denumerable or nondenumerable. Hence, for every set S, one and only one of the following three cases must hold: S is finite or S is denumerable or S is nondenumerable.

In view of Corollary 16 and Theorem 11, we have:

Lemma 17. *A set of the power of the continuum remains equipollent to itself if we adjoin to it or if we remove from it a finite or a denumerable set.*

In view of the above and Theorem 30, we obtain:

Lemma 18. *The set of all irrational numbers is of the power of the continuum.*

Let us recall that a nonalgebraic real number is called *transcendental*. In view of Lemma 17 and Theorem 31, we obtain:

Lemma 19. *The set of all transcendental numbers is of the power of the continuum.*

Remark 9. Let a and b be two rational numbers such that $a < b$. It is easy to see that the set of all rational numbers x such that $a < x < b$ or $a \leq x < b$ or $a < x \leq b$ or $a \leq x \leq b$ is equipollent to the set Q of all rational numbers. Indeed, each of these sets, being an infinite subset of the denumerable set Q, is in turn a denumerable set and hence equipollent to Q. The corresponding result for the set R of all real numbers is given by the theorem below.

Lemma 20.   *The set of all positive real numbers is of the power of the continuum.*

PROOF.   Let R be the set of all real numbers. Clearly, the set P of all positive real numbers is equipollent to the set N of all negative real numbers. Also, in view of Lemma 17, $R \smallsetminus \{0\} \cong R$, and since $R \smallsetminus \{0\} = P \cup N$, we have $P \cup N \cong R$. On the other hand, in view of Theorem 10 since $P \cong N$, we conclude that $P \cup N \cong R \cong N \cong P$, as desired.

Theorem 37.   *Let a and b be two real numbers such that $a < b$. Then the set of all real numbers x such that $a < x < b$, or $a \leq x < b$ or $a < x \leq b$ or $a \leq x \leq b$ is of the power of the continuum.*

PROOF.   Let us observe that the mapping f given by $f(x) = \dfrac{x}{1 + x}$ establishes a one-to-one correspondence between the set of all positive real numbers and the set of all real numbers x such that $0 < x < 1$. From this, it follows that the set of all negative real numbers is equipollent to the set of all real numbers x such that $-1 < x < 0$. Consequently, the set R of all real numbers is equipollent to the set of all real numbers x such that $-1 < x < 1$. On the other hand, the mapping g given by

$$g(x) = \frac{b - a}{2} x + \frac{b + a}{2}$$

establishes a one-to-one correspondence between the set of all real numbers x such that $-1 < x < 1$ and the set of all real numbers x such that $a < x < b$. Thus, the set of all real numbers is indeed equipollent to the set of all real numbers x such that $a < x < b$. The remaining cases in Theorem 37 are easily obtained by means of Lemma 17.

Theorem 38.   *Let B be the set of all real numbers x such that $0 < x < 1$ and such that in the decimal representation of x only the digits 0 or 1 appear. Then B is of the power of the continuum.*

PROOF.   Let

(45) $$0 \cdot a_1 a_2 a_3 a_4 \cdots$$

be the decimal representation of a real number x such that in (45) there is no occurrence of an infinite succession of nines. Clearly, the set S of all real numbers of type (45) is equal to the set S of all real numbers x such that $0 < x < 1$. Hence, by Theorem 37, S is of the power of the continuum.
    Next, associate with

$$0 \cdot a_1 a_2 a_3 a_4 \cdots$$

the configuration

$$0 \cdot (k_1)\, 0\, (k_2)\, 00\, (k_3)\, 000\, (k_4)\, 0000 \cdots$$

where (k_i) is a succession of a_i copies of the digit 1 if $a_i \neq 0$, and $(k_i) = 0$ if $a_i = 0$.

Thus, for instance, with

$$0.312000000\ldots$$

we associate

$$0.1110100110000000000\ldots$$

and with

$$0.01220310000\ldots$$

we associate:

$$0.001001100011000000000001110000001000000000\ldots$$

Clearly, this association is a one-to-one mapping from S into B. Hence, B contains a subset K of the power of the continuum. Thus, $K \subseteq B \subseteq S$, and since K and S are both of the power of the continuum, we derive from (14) that $B \cong S$. Consequently, the set B is of the power of the continuum, as desired.

Lemma 21. *Let A be a set of two elements. Then*

$$A^S$$

is equipollent to the set of all subsets of the set S.

PROOF. By Theorem 20, A^S is equipollent to $\{0,1\}^S$. On the other hand, $\{0, 1\}^S$ is the set of all functions from S into $\{0, 1\}$. Therefore, to prove the lemma, we have to establish a one-to-one correspondence between the power-set $\mathscr{P}(S)$ of S and the set of all functions from S into $\{0, 1\}$. Now, let E be a subset of S. Associate with E that function from S into $\{0, 1\}$ which maps the elements of E into 1 and the elements of $S \smile E$ into 0. Clearly, this association is a one-to-one correspondence between $\{0, 1\}^S$ and $\mathscr{P}(S)$. Thus, indeed, A^S is equipollent to the set of all subsets of S.

As we know, $\{0, 1\} = 2$, and therefore it follows from the above that:

$$(46) \qquad\qquad 2^S \cong \mathscr{P}(S)$$

Theorem 39. *The power-set of a denumerable set is of the power of the continuum.*

PROOF. Let D be a denumerable set. By (46),

$$\mathscr{P}(D) \cong 2^D$$

By Theorem 20, we may choose for D the set of all positive natural numbers. Hence,

$$\mathscr{P}(D) \cong \{0, 1\}^{\{1,2,3,\ldots\}}$$

Clearly, an element of $\{0, 1\}^{\{1,2,3,\ldots\}}$ is an infinite sequence whose terms are 0's or 1's. Associate with an element, say,

$$0, 0, 1, 0, 1, 1, 0, 0, 1, \ldots$$

of $\{0, 1\}^{\{1,2,3,\ldots\}}$, the real number:

$$0.001011001\ldots$$

It is easily seen that the above association gives rise to a one-to-one correspondence between $\{0, 1\}^{\{1,2,3,\dots\}}$ and the set B of all real numbers x such that $0 < x < 1$ and such that in the decimal representation of x only the digits 0 and 1 appear. However, in view of Theorem 38 the set B is of the power of the continuum. Consequently, the set $\{0, 1\}^{\{1,2,3,\dots\}}$ is also of the power of the continuum. From this, it follows that 2^D as well as the power-set of a denumerable set is of the power of the continuum.

EXERCISES

1. Prove that the union and the Cartesian product of two sets both of the power of the continuum, are again of the power of the continuum.

2. Prove that the set of all points of a finite or a denumerably infinite dimensional real space is of the power of the continuum.

3. Prove that every set of the power of the continuum is a denumerable union of pairwise disjoint sets each of which is of the power of the continuum.

4. Let B be the set of all real numbers x such that $0 < x < 1$ and such that in the decimal representation of x only the digits 0 or 1 or 2 appear. Prove that B is of the power of the continuum.

5. Prove that the set of all subsets of real numbers each of which contains n (a positive natural number) elements is of the power of the continuum.

6. Prove that the set of all finite subsets of the set of all real numbers is of the power of the continuum.

7. Prove that the set of all partitions of the set of all natural numbers is of the power of the continuum. (A partition of a set S is a set of nonempty pairwise disjoint sets whose sum-set is equal to S.)

8. Prove that the set of all infinite sequences of real numbers is of the power of the continuum.

9. Prove that the set of all infinite sequences of natural numbers is of the power of the continuum.

10. Prove that the set of all increasing infinite sequences of natural numbers is of the power of the continuum.

11. Prove that the set of all infinite subsets of natural numbers is of the power of the continuum.

12. Is the set of all denumerable subsets of real numbers of the power of the continuum?

13. Prove that if a set of the power of the continuum is the union of finitely many subsets, then at least one of these subsets must be of the power of the continuum.

8. SUMMARY

This chapter was developed based on the notion of equipollence. Two sets A and B are called equipollent if there exists a one-to-one correspondence between A and B. If A is equipollent to B, we write $A \simeq B$. If A is equipollent to a subset of C, we write $A \preceq C$. If A is equipollent to a subset of E and E is not equipollent to A, we write $A \prec E$.

The definitions of a finite set, an infinite set, a denumerable set, a nondenumerable set and of a set of the power of the continuum are all based on the notion of equipollence.

A set is called infinite if it has a proper subset that is equipollent to the set itself. Otherwise, a set is called finite. As shown, a set is infinite if and only if it contains a denumerable subset, and a set is finite if and only if it is equipollent to a natural number.

It is shown that no set is equipollent to its power-set. Also, if $A \preceq B$ and $B \preceq A$, then $A \simeq B$, for every two sets A and B. Moreover, $A \preceq B$ or $B \preceq A$, for every two sets A and B. Furthermore, there is no infinite decreasing sequence $\ldots \prec s_2 \prec s_1$ of elements $s_1, s_2, \ldots$ of any set S. Thus, every nonempty set S has an element u such that $u \preceq s$, for every $s \in S$.

Also, it is shown that 2^S is equipollent to the power-set $\mathscr{P}(S)$ of S, i.e., $2^S \simeq \mathscr{P}(S)$. Moreover, if D is a denumerable set and C a set of the power of the continuum, then $2^D \simeq C$.

Among the important results obtained in this chapter, let us mention the following ones. If S is an infinite set and A a set such that $A \preceq S$, then $A \cup S \simeq S$ and $A \times S \simeq S$.

Chapter VII

SIMILARITY

1. SIMILAR PARTIALLY ORDERED SETS

In Chapter IV, Section 1, we introduced the notion of a partially ordered set.

A partial order P in a set S is a particular relation in S. As such, P is first of all a subset of $S \times S$. The definition of a partial order P in a set S is given by Definition 1 of Chapter IV (page 170). According to this definition, P is a *reflexive, antisymmetric* and *transitive* relation in S.

As mentioned in Chapter IV, Section 1, if P is a partial order in S, then (S,P) is called a partially ordered set. However, in practice we refer to S as a partially ordered set, or more precisely we say that S is partially ordered by P. If P is a partial order in S, the fact that $(x,y) \in P$ is usually written xPy. The symbol $\leq$ is customarily used to denote an arbitrary partial order in a set S. Accordingly, an arbitrary partially ordered set is denoted by $(S,\leq)$, and the fact that $(x,y) \in \leq$ is denoted by $x \leq y$ or $y \geq x$. Moreover, if $x \leq y$ and $x \neq y$, then we write $x < y$.

If S is partially ordered by $\leq$ and if $x \leq y$, then we say that the elements x and y of S are *comparable* and x is less than or equal to y, or x does not exceed y, and so forth.

If every two elements of a partially ordered set are comparable, then that set is called a *simply ordered* set. Simply ordered sets were treated in Chapter IV, Section 3.

If every nonempty subset of a partially ordered set has a (unique) least (first, smallest) element, then that set is called a *well ordered* set. Well ordered sets were treated in Chapter IV, Section 4.

In the sequel, in connection with partially, simply and well ordered sets, we shall frequently use all the definitions, terminology, notations and results introduced or obtained in Chapter IV.

For instance, if the set $S = \{a,b,c,d\}$ is partially ordered by P, where

$$P = \{(a,a),\ (b,b),\ (c,c),\ (d,d),\ (a,b),\ (b,c),\ (a,c),\ (a,d)\}$$

then we shall represent the partially ordered set (S,P), according to our notational convention [mentioned in Remark 2 of Chapter IV (page 174)], as

$$\{(a;b;c),\ (a;d)\}$$

where $x \leq y$ if and only if x and y are included in the same pair of parentheses and x is not written to the right of y. Moreover, $x < y$ if and only if x and y are included in the same pair of parentheses and x is written to the left of y.

Definition 1. *Let $(A,\leq)$ and $(B,\leq)$ be two partially ordered sets. A mapping f from A into B is called order preserving if for every two elements a and c of A:*

$$a \leq c \quad \text{implies} \quad f(a) \leq f(c)$$

For instance, if $A = \{(a;b;c), (d;e)\}$ and $B = \{(m;n), (r;s)\}$, then

$$f = \{(a,m), (b,m), (c,n), (d,m), (e,n)\}$$

is an order preserving mapping from A into B.

Definition 2. *Let f be a one-to-one order preserving mapping from a partially ordered set P onto a partially ordered set S. If f_{-1} (the converse of f) is order preserving, then f is called a one-to-one order preserving correspondence between P and S.*

For instance, if $P = \{(a;b), (c)\}$ and $S = \{(m;n); (p)\}$, then $\{(a,m), (b,n), (c,p)\}$ is a one-to-one order preserving correspondence between P and S.

However, if $P = \{(a;b), (c)\}$ and $S = \{(m;n;p)\}$, then $f = \{(a,m), (b,n), (c,p)\}$ is not an order preserving correspondence between P and S, even though f is a one-to-one order preserving mapping from P onto S.

Definition 3. *If f is a one-to-one order preserving correspondence between two partially ordered sets P and S, then f is called a similarity between P and S and P is called similar to S.* In symbols:

$$P \simeq S$$

Clearly, every partially ordered set is similar to itself since the identity mapping is an order preserving correspondence between any set and itself. Moreover, if f is a similarity between two partially ordered sets P and S, then f_{-1} is a similarity between S and P. Furthermore, if f and g are similarities between P and S and S and Q respectively, then the composite $g \cdot f$ is a similarity between P and Q.

In view of the above, for every three partially ordered sets x, y and z we have:

(1) $x \simeq x$ (reflexivity of $\simeq$)

(2)   if $x \simeq y$, then $y \simeq x$ (symmetry of $\simeq$)

(3)   if $x \simeq y$ and $y \simeq z$, then $x \simeq z$ (transitivity of $\simeq$)

Thus, if x is similar to y and y is similar to z, then in view of (2) and (3) we can say that x, y and z are similar partially ordered sets. Moreover, we have the obvious:

Lemma 1. *Similarity is an equivalence relation in any set of partially ordered sets.*

In view of Definition 3, we have:

Corollary 1. *Let f be a similarity between two partially ordered sets P and S. Then for every two elements p and q of P*

(4) $p \leq q$ *if and only if* $f(p) \leq f(q)$

or equivalently,

(5) $p < q$ *if and only if* $f(p) < f(q)$

Lemma 2. *Let f be a one-to-one order preserving mapping from a simply ordered set S onto a partially ordered set P. Then f is a similarity between S and P. Moreover, P is simply ordered.*

PROOF. Since f is a one-to-one mapping from S onto P, we see that f_{-1} is a one-to-one mapping from P onto S. Now, let p and q be any two elements of P. We claim:

$$p \leq q \quad \text{implies} \quad f_{-1}(p) \leq f_{-1}(q)$$

Assume on the contrary that $f_{-1}(p) \nleq f_{-1}(q)$. Since S is simply ordered, our assumption implies that $f_{-1}(p) > f_{-1}(q)$. However, since f is order preserving, we derive $f(f_{-1}(p)) > f(f_{-1}(q))$ which, in view of the fact that f is one-to-one, yields $p > q$, contrary to the hypothesis that $p \leq q$. Hence, our assumption is false and indeed $f_{-1}(p) \leq f_{-1}(q)$. Consequently, f_{-1} is a one-to-one order preserving mapping from P onto S. Thus, f is a similarity.

Next, we show that P is simply ordered. Let p and q be any two elements of P. Since S is simply ordered, $f_{-1}(p) \leq f_{-1}(q)$ or $f_{-1}(p) \geq f_{-1}(q)$. However, f is a one-to-one order preserving mapping from P onto S, and consequently if $f_{-1}(p) \leq f_{-1}(q)$, then $f(f_{-1}(p)) \leq f(f_{-1}(q))$, which implies $p \leq q$; and if $f_{-1}(p) \geq f_{-1}(q)$, then $f(f_{-1}(p)) \geq f(f_{-1}(q))$, which implies $p \geq q$. Thus, either $p \leq q$ or $q \geq p$. Hence, P is indeed a simply ordered set.

Lemma 3. *Let f be a mapping from a simply ordered set S onto a partially ordered set P. Then f is a similarity between S and P if and only if*

(6) $u < v$ *implies* $f(u) < f(v)$

for every two elements u and v of S.

PROOF. If f is a similarity, then (6) follows at once. Now, suppose (6) holds. Let u and v be two distinct elements of S. Since S is simply ordered, without loss of generality we may assume $u < v$. But then in view of (6), $f(u) < f(v)$; hence, $f(u) \neq f(v)$. Thus, f is indeed one-to-one. Moreover, (6) implies that f is order preserving. Consequently, by Lemma 2, f is a similarity between S and P.

In view of Lemma 3, similarity is studied mainly in connection with simply ordered sets. Also, as we shall see later, the notion of similarity is most significantly used in connection with well ordered sets.

The fundamental properties of a similarity mapping are embodied in the following theorems.

Theorem 1. *Let f be a similarity mapping between two partially ordered sets P and S and let A be a subset of P.*

  (i) *If w is a lower bound of A, then $f(w)$ is a lower bound of $f^1(A)$.*
  (ii) *If u is an upper bound of A, then $f(u)$ is an upper bound of $f^1(A)$.*
  (iii) *If a is the smallest element of A, then $f(a)$ is the smallest element of $f^1(A)$.*

(iv) *If m is the greatest element of A, then f(m) is the greatest element of* $f^1(A)$.

(v) *If r is the greatest lower bound of A, then f(r) is the greatest lower bound of* $f^1(A)$.

(vi) *If t is the least upper bound of A, then f(t) is the least upper bound of* $f^1(A)$.

In the above, $f^1(A)$ is the image of the subset A of P under f (see page 150).

PROOF. Let w be a lower bound of A. Since $w \leq a$ for every $a \in A$, by (4), $f(w) \leq s$ for every $s \in f^1(A)$. Thus, indeed $f(w)$ is a lower bound of $f^1(A)$.

The proof of (ii) proceeds in an analogous way.

To prove (iii) assume on the contrary that $f(a)$ is not the smallest element of $f^1(A)$. This means that there must exist an element $s \in f^1(A)$ such that $s < f(a)$. But then by (5) we would have $f_{-1}(s) < f_{-1}(f(a))$, i.e., $f_{-1}(s) < a$. However, $f_{-1}(s) \in A$, and therefore $f_{-1}(s) < a$ contradicts the fact that a is the smallest element of A. Hence our assumption is false, and indeed $f(a)$ is the smallest element of $f^1(A)$.

The proof of (iv) proceeds in an analogous way.

To prove (v) let us observe that in view of (i) if B is the set of all lower bounds of A, then $f^1(B)$ is the set of all lower bounds of $f^1(A)$. By (iv), if r is the greatest element of B, then $f(r)$ is the greatest element of $f^1(B)$. This means that if r is the greatest lower bound of A, then $f(r)$ is the greatest lower bound of $f^1(A)$.

The proof of (vi) proceeds in an analogous way.

Theorem 2. *Let f be a similarity between two partially ordered sets P and S. If p is the immediate predecessor and r is the immediate successor of q in P, then* $f(p)$ *and* $f(r)$ *are respectively the immediate predecessor and the immediate successor of* $f(q)$ *in S.*

The proof of Theorem 2 is straightforward and is left to the reader.

Theorem 3. *Let f be a similarity between two partially ordered sets P and S, and L a lower cut of P. Then,* $f^1(L)$ *is a lower cut of S.*

PROOF. According to Definition 8 of Chapter IV (page 181), a lower cut L of P is a nonempty proper subset of P such that L has no last element, and if $x \in L$, $y \in P$ and $y \leq x$, then $y \in L$.

Now, clearly $f^1(L)$ is a nonempty proper subset of S, and by (iv) of Theorem 1, $f^1(L)$ has no last element. Also, if $u \in f^1(L)$, $v \in S$ and $v \leq u$, then $f_{-1}(u) \in L$ and $f_{-1}(v) \in P$ and by (4), $f_{-1}(v) \leq f_{-1}(u)$. Consequently $f_{-1}(v) \in L$, and hence $v \in f^1(L)$. Thus, indeed $f^1(L)$ is a lower cut of S.

Theorem 4. *Let f be a similarity between two partially ordered sets P and S and I(a) the initial segment of P determined by a. Then* $f^1(I(a))$ *is the initial segment of S determined by* $f(a)$.

In view of the definition of an initial segment given by Definition 9 of Chapter IV (page 183), the proof of Theorem 4 is straightforward.

Theorem 5. *If a partially ordered set S is similar to a dense partially ordered set, then S is dense.*

In view of the definition of a dense partially ordered set given by Definition 10 of Chapter IV (page 183), the proof of Theorem 5 is straightforward.

Theorem 6.   *Let P and S be two similar partially ordered sets. If P is conditionally complete or complete, then S is respectively conditionally complete or complete.*

As mentioned in Chapter IV, Section 1, a partially ordered set P is called conditionally complete if every nonempty subset of P that is bounded above has a least upper bound. On the other hand, P is called complete if every subset of P has a least upper bound. In view of these definitions and Theorem 1, the proof of Theorem 6 is straightforward.

Theorem 7.   *If a partially ordered set P is similar to a simply ordered set, then P is simply ordered.*

The proof of this theorem follows from Lemma 2.

Theorem 8.   *If a partially ordered set S is similar to a continuous set P, then S is continuous.*

PROOF.   According to Definition 13 of Chapter IV (page 188), a partially ordered set S is continuous if it is a dense conditionally complete simply ordered set. Now, let f be a similarity between P and S. Then in view of Theorems 5, 6 and 7 we see at once that S is continuous.

Theorem 9.   *If a partially ordered set P is similar to a well ordered set W, then P is well ordered.*

PROOF.   Let f be a similarity between P and W, and let A be a nonempty subset of P. Then $f^1(A)$ is a nonempty subset of W and as such has a first element w. Clearly, in view of (iii) of Theorem 1, $f_{-1}(w)$ is the first element of A. Consequently every nonempty subset of P has a first element, and hence P is a well ordered set.

Remark 1.   It is customary to summarize the conclusions of Theorems 1 to 9 by saying that the notions of *predecessor, successor, immediate predecessor, immediate successor, least, greatest, lower bound, upper bound, greatest lower bound, least upper bound, lower cut, initial segment, denseness, continuity, simple order* and *well order* are invariant under similarity.

EXERCISES

1. Give three different examples of similarities between the set of all integers I and itself, where I is ordered by its natural order.

2. Prove that the set of all rational numbers x with $0 < x < 1$, in their natural order, is similar to the set of all rational numbers also in their natural order.

3. Prove that the set of all real numbers x with $0 < x < 1$, in their natural order, is similar to the set of all real numbers also in their natural order.

4. Prove Lemma 1 and Corollary 1.

5. Prove that the conclusion of Lemma 3 does not hold if S is a partially ordered set.

6. Prove Theorems 2, 4, 5, 6 and 7.

7. Let f be a similarity mapping between two simply ordered sets P and S. Prove that the images under f of closed, open, half-closed and half-open intervals of P are respectively closed, open, half-closed and half-open intervals of S.

2. SIMILARITY BETWEEN SPECIAL SIMPLY ORDERED SETS

In this section we shall characterize the set ω of all natural numbers, the set Q of all rational numbers and the set R of all real numbers from the point of view of order.

As we know, each of the sets ω, Q and R is simply ordered when ordered according to its natural order.

Also, any subset of a simply ordered set is a simply ordered set, ordered by the induced order.

The set ω of all natural numbers, according to our notational convention, is represented as the following simply ordered set, which, as we know, is a well ordered set:

$$\omega = \{(0;1;2;3;4;\ldots)\}$$

Naturally, since every natural number n is a subset of ω we see that n is itself a well ordered set.

For instance

$$6 = \{3,4,2,0,5,1\}$$

is a subset of ω and accordingly, as a well ordered subset of ω, is written as:

$$6 = \{(0;1;2;3;4;5)\}$$

Theorem 10. *If every initial segment of a simply ordered set S is finite, then S is well ordered. Moreover, every element of S other than the first element of S has an immediate predecessor.*

PROOF. To prove that S is well ordered, we have to show that every non-empty subset of S has a first element. Let A be a nonempty subset of S. Assume on the contrary that A has no first element. Let $a \in A$. Since A has no first element and since A is simply ordered, there must exist an element $b \in A$ such that $b < a$. Similarly, since A has no first element, there must exist an element $c \in A$ such that $c < b < a$, and so on. Thus, the initial segment $I(a)$ of S must contain the infinite subset $\{b, c, \ldots\}$, which contradicts the fact that $I(a)$ is finite. Hence our assumption is false, and indeed A has a first element, as desired. By analogous reasoning, one can show that every element of S other than the first element of S has an immediate predecessor.

Theorem 11.   *Every finite simply ordered set is well ordered and, if it is not empty, has a last element.*

PROOF.   Since every initial segment of a finite simply ordered set is finite, by Theorem 10 every finite simply ordered set is well ordered.

Next, let S be a finite nonempty simply ordered set. Assume S has no last element. Let $a \in S$. Since S has no last element, there must exist an element $b \in S$ such that $a < b$. Similarly, since S has no last element, there must exist an element $c \in S$ such that $a < b < c$, and so on. Thus, S must contain the infinite subset $\{a, b, c, \ldots\}$, which contradicts the fact that S is finite. Hence our assumption is false, and indeed S has a last element, as desired.

Theorem 12.   *Two finite simply ordered equipollent sets are similar.*

PROOF.   Let A and B be two finite simply ordered sets such that $A \cong B$. We shall show that $A \simeq B$.

In view of (3) and Theorem 2 of Chapter VI (page 248), we may choose for the set A a natural number n (ordered by its natural order) such that $n \cong A \cong B$.

To prove the theorem, we need only show that, for every natural number n (ordered by its natural order), if a finite simply ordered set B is such that $n \cong B$, then $n \simeq B$.

Since this is a theorem concerning natural numbers, we give a proof by induction.

Clearly, the conclusion of the theorem is true for $n = 0$.

Assume the conclusion of the theorem is true for $n = m$ and let B be a finite simply ordered set such that $m^+ \cong B$.

Since B is equipollent to m^+, it is a nonempty finite simply ordered set; hence, by Theorem 11, B has a last element b.

Obviously, $B \smallsetminus \{b\}$ is equipollent to m, and hence, by our assumption, $B \smallsetminus \{b\}$ is similar to m. Extending the similarity between m and $B \smallsetminus \{b\}$, by assigning to m the element b, we obtain a similarity between m^+ and B.

Hence, the conclusion of the theorem is true for 0 and its truth for m implies its truth for m^+. Consequently, the theorem is proved.

In the sequel, the set ω of all natural numbers is assumed to be ordered by its natural order. As such, as we know, ω is well ordered and hence also simply ordered.

Theorem 13.   *In order that a nonempty simply ordered set S be similar to ω it is necessary and sufficient that S have no last element and that every initial segment of S be finite.*

PROOF.   The necessity is easily established. Indeed, let S be similar to ω. Since ω has no last element, by (iv) of Theorem 1, S has no last element either. Also, since every initial segment $I(n)$ of ω is equal to n, we see that $I(n)$ is finite, and consequently by Theorem 4 every initial segment of S is also finite.

To prove the sufficiency, let S be a nonempty simply ordered set having no last element and such that every initial segment of S is finite. By Theorem 10, S is well ordered. Let a be the first element of S and let s^+ be the immediate successor of an arbitrary element s of S.

Consider the mapping f from ω into S, defined by:

(7) $$f(0) = a \quad \text{and} \quad f(n^+) = (f(n))^+$$

The mapping f exists by virtue of Theorem 2 of Chapter V (page 208) and the fact that S has no last element.

We shall show that f is a similarity between ω and S. To this end, we shall first prove that for every two natural numbers n and m:

(8) $$n < m \quad \text{implies} \quad f(n) < f(m)$$

Clearly, $0 < n$ implies $f(0) < f(n)$ for every natural number n. Indeed, since $0 < n$ we see that n has an immediate predecessor n^-, and hence by (7) we have $f(n) = f((n^-)^+) = (f(n^-))^+$. However, since $f(0) = a$ and a is the first element of S we see that $f(0) < (f(n^-))^+$, which in view of (7) implies that $f(0) < f(n)$, as desired.

Now, let N be the set of all natural numbers n which satisfy (8). In view of the above, $0 \in N$. Let $n \in N$ and $n^+ < k$. But then $n < k^-$ and by (8) we have $f(n) < f(k^-)$. Consequently, $(f(n))^+ < (f(k^-))^+$ which, in view of (7) implies $f(n^+) < f(k)$. In short, $0 \in N$ and $n^+ \in N$ whenever $n \in N$. Thus, by the theorem of Finite Induction, N is equal to the set ω of all natural numbers. Hence, (8) is established.

Next, we show that f maps ω onto S.

Assume on the contrary that there exist elements of S that are not images (under f) of any of the elements of ω. Since S is well ordered, there exists a smallest such element v. Clearly v cannot be the first element of S, since the first element of S is the image of 0. Consequently, by Theorem 10, v has an immediate predecessor u which is the image of an element—say, k of ω. But then by (7) we derive $f(k^+) = (f(k))^+ = u^+ = v$, contradicting the fact that v is not the image of an element of ω. Hence our assumption is false, and f is indeed an onto mapping; and in view of (8) and Lemma 3, f is a similarity between ω and S.

The above theorem gives a characterization of ω (the set of all natural numbers) in terms of order. Moreover, we have:

Corollary 2. *A nonempty simply ordered set having no last element, and such that every initial segment of it is finite, is denumerable.*

Corollary 3. *Every two nonempty simply ordered sets, each of which has no last element, and such that every initial segment of each is finite, are similar.*

Theorem 14. *Let A be a denumerable simply ordered set and B a nonempty dense simply ordered set having no first element and no last element. Then A is similar to a subset of B.*

PROOF. Since A is denumerable, A can be written as an infinite sequence whose elements are indexed by natural numbers. Thus,

$$A = \{a_0, a_1, a_2, \ldots\}$$

Clearly, in the above the order in which the elements of A are written does not necessarily indicate the original simple order defined in A.

Now, let us associate with a_0 an element b_0 of B. Then consider a_1 and associate with a_1 an element b_1 of B which precedes or exceeds b_0, according to whether a_1 precedes or exceeds a_0. Clearly, in view of the fact that B has neither a first nor a last element, such an element b_1 always exists. Next, consider a_2 and associate with a_2 an element b_2 of B which precedes both b_0 and b_1 or exceeds both b_0 and b_1 or is between b_0 and b_1, according to whether a_2 precedes both a_0 and a_1 or exceeds both a_0 and a_1 or is between a_0 and a_1. Clearly, since B has neither a first nor a last element and since B is dense, such an element b_2 always exists. Obviously, this association establishes a similarity between $\{a_0,a_1,a_2\}$ and $\{b_0,b_1,b_2\}$, where the former is a simply ordered set inasmuch as it is a subset of the simply ordered set A, and the latter is a simply ordered set inasmuch as it is a subset of the simply ordered set B.

Now, assume that for a natural number n, by means of the association above a similarity mapping between a subset $\{a_0, a_1, \ldots, a_n\}$ of A and a subset $\{b_0,b_1,\ldots,b_n\}$ of B is established. Then consider the element a_{n+1}, and associate with a_{n+1} an element b_{n+1} of B which precedes each of the elements $b_0, b_1, \ldots, b_n$ or exceeds each of the elements $b_0, b_1, \ldots, b_n$ or is between the pair b_k, b_{k+1} of the elements $b_0, b_1, \ldots, b_n$, according to whether a_{n+1} precedes each of the elements $a_0, a_1, \ldots, a_n$ or exceeds each of the elements $a_0, a_1, \ldots, a_n$ or is between the pair a_k, a_{k+1} of the elements $a_0, a_1, \ldots, a_n$. Clearly, in view of the properties of B, such an element b_{n+1} always exists. By the axiom of Choice and finite induction this association exhausts all of A and thus establishes a similarity between A and a subset of B, as desired.

Corollary 4. *Every nonempty dense simply ordered set having no first and no last element has a subset similar to the set Q of all rational numbers (in their natural order).*

PROOF. Since Q is a denumerable simply ordered set, Corollary 4 follows from Theorem 14, with A replaced by Q.

Corollary 5. *Every denumerable simply ordered set is similar to a subset of the set Q of all rational numbers (in their natural order).*

PROOF. The set Q of all rational numbers (ordered according to its natural order) is obviously nonempty, has no first and no last element and is dense. Hence, Corollary 5 follows from Theorem 14 with B replaced by Q.

Theorem 15. *In order that a simply ordered set S be similar to the set Q of all rational numbers (in their natural order) it is necessary and sufficient that S be denumerable, that S have no first and no last element and that S be dense.*

PROOF. The necessity is easily established. Indeed, the set Q of all rational numbers (in their natural order) is a simply ordered set which is denumerable, which has no first and no last element and which, moreover, is dense. Also, as we know, all these properties are preserved under similarity.

To prove the sufficiency, let S be written as an infinite sequence

(10) $$S = \{s_1, s_2, s_3, \ldots\}$$

and Q as an infinite sequence:

(11) $$Q = \{q_1, q_2, q_3, \ldots\}$$

Let s^1 denote s_1 and q^1 denote q_1. Associate with s^1 the element q^1.

Next, let s^2 denote s_2 and q^2 denote that element of (11) having the lowest index among the indices of elements of Q which have the same position (referring to the natural order in Q) with respect to q^1 that s^2 has (referring to the original order in S) with respect to s^1. Clearly, in view of the hypothesis of the theorem, such an element q^2 always exists. Associate s^2 with q^2.

Next, let q^3 denote that element of (11) having the lowest index among the indices of unused elements of Q. Let s^3 denote that element of (10) having the lowest index among the indices of elements of S which have the same position (referring to the order in S) with respect to s^1 and s^2 that q^3 has (referring to the order in Q) with respect to q^1 and q^2. Clearly, in view of the hypothesis of the theorem, such an element s^3 always exists. Associate q^3 with s^3.

Next, let s^4 denote that element of (10) having the lowest index among the indices of unused elements of S. Let q^4 denote that element of (11) having the lowest index among the indices of elements of Q which have the same position with respect to q^1, q^2 and q^3 that s^4 has with respect to s^1, s^2 and s^3. Such an element q^4 always exists. Associate s^4 with q^4.

Continuing in the manner indicated above, let the elements of the sequence

(12) $$\{s^1, s^2, s^3, \ldots, s^n\}$$

be associated respectively with the elements of the sequence:

(13) $$\{q^1, q^2, q^3, \ldots, q^n\}$$

Clearly, this association is a similarity between (12) and (13).

Now, if n is odd, let s^{n+1} denote that element of (10) having the lowest index not appearing in (12). Let q^{n+1} denote that element of (11) having the lowest index among indices of elements of Q which have the same position with respect to the elements of (13) that s^{n+1} has with respect to the elements of (12). Such an element q^{n+1} always exists. Associate s^{n+1} with q^{n+1}. If n is even, let q^{n+1} denote that element of (11) having the lowest index not appearing in (13). Let s^{n+1} denote that element of (10) having the lowest index among the indices of elements of S which have the same position with respect to the elements of (12) as q^{n+1} has with respect to the elements of (13). Such an element s^{n+1} always exists. Associate q^{n+1} with s^{n+1}.

Consequently, whether n is odd or even, the above-mentioned similarity between (12) and (13) can be extended to a similarity between the sequences

$$\{s^1, s^2, s^3, \ldots, s^n, s^{n+1}\}$$

and:

$$\{q^1, q^2, q^3, \ldots, q^n, q^{n+1}\}$$

By the axiom of Choice and finite induction this similarity can be extended between the two infinite sequences

$$\{s^1, s^2, s^3, \ldots\}$$

and:
$$\{q^1, q^2, q^3, \ldots\}$$

Indeed, in view of our method of associating the elements of (10) with those of (11), we see that every element of S (or of Q) has a unique mate. For instance, for every natural number n, the elements s_n (or q_n) will be used. Clearly, at some stage of our association procedure n will be one of the lowest indices mentioned above, thus ensuring the use of s_n (or q_n). Hence, indeed S and Q are similar.

The above theorem gives a characterization of Q (the set of all rational numbers) in terms of order.

Remark 2.   Let us observe that in contrast with the properties of equipollence, two simply ordered sets each of which is similar to a subset of the other need not be similar. For instance, the set A of all rational numbers x such that $1 < x < 2$ is similar to a subset of the set B of all rational numbers x such that $1 \leq x \leq 2$ and vice versa. However, as one can easily see, A is not similar to B.

Corollary 6.   *Every two simply ordered sets each of which is denumerable, has no first and no last element and is dense, are similar.*

Theorems 10 and 12 provide an example of two denumerable simply ordered sets that are not similar. Obviously, ω and Q cannot be similar, since, for instance, ω is not dense.

There are many examples of denumerable simply ordered sets that are not similar to each other.

For instance, consider the following two denumerable simply ordered sets represented according to our notational convention, by
$$M = \{(1; 3; 5; \ldots ; 2; 4; 6; \ldots)\}$$
and:
$$N = \{(1; 4; 7; \ldots ; 2; 5; 8; \ldots ; 3; 6; 9; \ldots)\}$$

Clearly, both M and N are denumerable and simply ordered. However, M is not similar to N. Indeed if the element 3 of the set N has a mate in the set M, then the element 2 of the set N cannot have a mate in the set M.

Again, the set
$$\omega = \{(0; 1; 2; 3; \ldots)\}$$
is not similar to the set
$$\omega^* = \{(\ldots ; -3; 2; -1; 0)\}$$

because ω has a first element, whereas ω^* does not have a first element.

It is obvious that ω^* can be made similar to ω if the order chosen in ω is that of the converse of its natural order.

Remark 3.   In general, if S represents a simply ordered set, then it is customary to denote, by S^*, the set S ordered by the converse order.

Theorem 16.   *The set of all pairwise nonsimilar simple orders in the subsets of a denumerable set is of the power of the continuum.*

PROOF.   Clearly, it is enough to prove the theorem for the set S of all pairwise nonsimilar denumerable simply ordered subsets of a denumerable set D. However, every such simply ordered set is a subset of $D \times D$. Therefore, in view of (10) of Chapter VI (page 257), and the fact that $D \times D \cong D$, we have:

$$S \preceq 2^D$$

On the other hand, by Theorem 39 of Chapter VI (page 280), 2^D is of the power of the continuum. Consequently, S is equipollent to a subset of a set of the power of the continuum.

To prove the theorem, in view of (14) of Chapter VI (page 257), it is sufficient to show that S has a subset of the power of the continuum.

To this end, let

$$\{(k_1; k_2; k_3; k_4; \ldots)\}$$

be the denumerable simply ordered set D. Between every consecutive pair of the elements of the above set, and prior to k_1, insert the following configuration:

(14) $\ldots; -3; -2; -1; 0; 1; 2; 3; \ldots$

Let the resulting set be represented by

(15) $\{(\ldots; k_1; \ldots; k_2; \ldots; k_3; \ldots; k_4; \ldots)\}$

where the dots preceding any k_i represent the configuration given by (14).

Clearly, (15) is a denumerable simply ordered set.

Next, consider the infinite sequence

(16) $a_1, a_2, a_3, \ldots$

whose terms are 0 or 1.

With the sequence (16), associate the denumerable simply ordered set

(17) $\{(\ldots; k_1; a_1; \ldots; k_2; a_2; \ldots; k_3; a_3; \ldots; k_4; a_4; \ldots)\}$

with the condition that a_n be inserted immediately next to k_n provided $a_n = 1$; otherwise a_n is not inserted at all.

Thus, if

(18) $0, 1, 1, 0, 1, \ldots$

is the sequence under consideration, then (17) becomes:

(19) $\{(\ldots; k_1; \ldots; k_2; 1; \ldots; k_3; 1; \ldots; k_4; \ldots)\}$

We claim that every two distinct sequences of type (16) give rise to two nonsimilar denumerable simply ordered sets of type (17).

For instance, let

(20) $1, 1, 0, 1, 0, \ldots$

be a sequence of type (16) which is obviously distinct from (18). According to our rule, with (20), we associate:

(21) $\{(\ldots; k_1; 1; \ldots; k_2; 1; \ldots; k_3; \ldots; k_4; 1; \ldots)\}$

Obviously, (19) is not similar to (21). Indeed, if there were a similarity between (19) and (21), for obvious reasons each k_n would be mapped into k_n. This would imply that (18) and (20) are identical, contradicting the fact that they are distinct sequences.

Thus, corresponding to distinct sequences of type (16), we obtain nonsimilar denumerable simply ordered sets of type (19). However, in view of Theorem 38 of Chapter VI (page 279), the set of all distinct sequences of type (16) is of the power of the continuum. Thus, S has a subset of the power of the continuum. Consequently, since (as shown above) S is equipollent to a subset of a set of the power of the continuum, S is of the power of the continuum.

Definition 4. *Let A be a partially ordered set. A subset B of A is called dense in A if between every two distinct comparable elements of A there exists an element belonging to B.*

Lemma 4. *Let A be a partially ordered set and B be a subset of A that is dense in A. Then B is dense. Moreover, if a subset C of B is dense in B, then C is dense in A.*

PROOF. Since B is dense in A and is a subset of A, by Definition 4 between every two distinct comparable elements b_1 and b_2 of B, say, with $b_1 < b_2$, there exists an element b_3 of B, i.e., $b_1 < b_3 < b_2$. Therefore, B is dense. Similar reasoning proves the second part of the theorem.

Theorem 17. *Let C be a continuous set having no first and no last element, and let D be a subset of C that is dense in C. Then C is similar to the set of all lower cuts of D ordered by $\subset$.*

For the definitions of a lower cut and a continuous partially ordered set, the reader is referred to Definitions 8 and 13 of Chapter IV (pages 181 and 188).

PROOF. The case where C is empty is trivial. Hence, let C be nonempty and let c be an element of C. The set L of all elements of D less than c is a lower cut of D. Indeed, L is not empty since C has no first element and since D is dense in C; also, L is a proper subset of D since $c \notin L$, C has no last element and D is dense in C. Next, L has no last element since if p were the last element of L, then $p < c$, and since D is dense in C, there would exist an element q of D such that $p < q < c$, contradicting the assumption that p is the last element of L. Finally, if $x \in L$ and $y \in D$ and $y < x$, then $y < x < c$ and hence $y \in L$. Thus, indeed L is a lower cut of D.

Assign to c the lower cut L of D. Since c is an arbitrary element of C, and since D is dense in C, it is obvious that this assignment is a one-to-one order preserving mapping from C into the set V of all lower cuts of D where V is ordered by $\subset$.

To prove that the above-mentioned assignment is a similarity between C and V, we have to show (in view of Lemma 2) that every lower cut H of D has a mate in C.

Let H be a lower cut of D. Since D is simply ordered, H is bounded above. Consider the set E of all elements e of C such that there exists an element h of

H with $e \leq h$. Clearly, E is nonempty and bounded above. Since $E \subset C$ and C is continuous lub E exists. Let $k = \text{lub } E$. We claim that the mate of k, according to our rule of assignment, is the lower cut H of D. This is obvious since every element of D that is less than k must be an element of H. (Otherwise, k would not be the least upper bound of E.)

Theorem 18. *For a simply ordered set C to be similar to the set R of all real numbers (in their natural order) it is necessary and sufficient that C have no first and no last element, that C have a denumerable subset dense in C and that C be continuous.*

PROOF. The necessity is easily established. Indeed, the set R of all real numbers (in their natural order) is a simply ordered continuous set having no first and no last element and containing a denumerable subset (namely, the rational numbers) dense in R. Moreover, all these properties are preserved under similarity.

To prove the sufficiency, let C be a simply ordered set satisfying the conditions in Theorem 17. Let D be the denumerable subset of C dense in C. Since C has no first and no last element and since D is dense in C, we see that D has neither a first nor a last element. Moreover, D is denumerable, and in view of Lemma 4, D is dense. Therefore, by Theorem 15, D is similar to the set of all rational numbers Q (in their natural order); i.e., $D \simeq Q$.

On the other hand, by Theorem 17, C is similar to the set V of all lower cuts of D. Also, by the same theorem, R is similar to the set U of all lower cuts of Q. Thus, $V \simeq C$ and $U \simeq R$.

However, since $D \simeq Q$ clearly $V \simeq U$, and therefore $C \simeq R$, as desired.

The above theorem gives a characterization of R (the set of all real numbers) in terms of order.

Corollary 7. *Every two simply ordered sets each of which has no first and no last element, has a denumerable subset dense in it and is continuous, are similar.*

Obviously, there are many simply ordered sets each of the power of the continuum and not similar to each other. For instance, the set A of all real numbers x such that $1 < x < 2$ and the set B of all real numbers x such that $1 \leq x \leq 2$ are both simply ordered sets of the power of the continuum. However, it is easily seen that A is not similar to B.

We only mention here that the set of all nonsimilar simply ordered sets each of which is of the power of the continuum, is of the power of the power-set of a set of the power of the continuum.

Remark 4. The examples below show that in contrast to the Trichotomy Law of the comparison of sets with respect to equipollence, any one of the four mutually exclusive possibilities between two simply ordered sets A and B may hold.

(i) *A is not similar to any subset of B and B is not similar to any subset of A.*

Example: Let $A = \{(0; 1; 2; 3; \ldots)\}$ and $B = \{(\ldots; -3; -2; -1; 0)\}$. Clearly, since every subset S of A has a first element, S cannot be similar to B. Also, since every subset P of B has a last element, P cannot be similar to A.

(ii) *A is not similar to any subset of B and B is similar to a subset of A.*

Example: $A = \{(\ldots; -2; -1; 0; 1; 2; \ldots)\}$ and $B = \{(0; 1; 2; \ldots)\}$

(iii) *A is similar to a subset of B and B is not similar to any subset of A.*

Example: $A = \{(0; 1; 2; \ldots)\}$ and $B = \{(\ldots; -2; -1; 0; 1; 2; \ldots)\}$

(iv) *A is similar to a subset of B and B is similar to a subset of A.*

Example: *A* is the set of all real numbers *x* (in their natural order) such that $1 \leq x \leq 2$, and *B* is the set of all real numbers *x* such that $1 < x < 2$.

In view of the mutual exclusiveness of the above-mentioned four cases, we have:

Lemma 5. *For every two simply ordered sets A and B, one and only one of the four cases above must hold.*

EXERCISES

1. Prove that for a simply ordered set *S* to be similar to the set *ω* of all natural numbers (in their natural order) it is necessary and sufficient that *S* be infinite and that every initial segment of *S* be finite.

2. Prove that for a simply ordered set *S* to be similar to *ω* it is necessary and sufficient that *S* contain a first and no last element and that *S* contain no lower cut.

3. Prove that for a simply ordered set *S* to be similar to the set *I* of all integers (in their natural order) it is necessary and sufficient that *S* have neither a first nor a last element, nor a lower cut.

4. Can you give a decomposition of the set *Q* of all rational numbers (in their natural order) into an infinite set of pairwise disjoint sets each dense in *Q*?

5. Prove that if a simply ordered set *S* is similar to the set *Q* of all rational numbers (in their natural order) and if *A* is an initial segment of *S*, then *A* or $S \frown A$ is similar to *Q*.

6. Prove that if a simply ordered set *S* is similar to the set *Q* of all rational numbers (in their natural order) and if *A* is any subset of *S*, then *A* or $S \frown A$ contains a subset similar to *Q*.

7. Prove that every dense simply ordered set is similar to a subset of a continuous simply ordered set *C* dense in *C*.

8. Prove that every two continuous simply ordered sets each of which has no first and no last element and contains similar dense simply ordered subsets, are similar.

9. Let *R* be the set of all real numbers (in their natural order) and *A* the subset of all real numbers *x* such that $1 \leq x < 2$. Is $R \frown A$ similar to *R*?

10. Prove that the complement of a finite or of a denumerable subset of the set *E* of all irrational numbers (in their natural order) is similar to *E*.

11. Prove that every continuous simply ordered set contains a subset similar to the set R of all real numbers (in their natural order).

12. Let Q be the set of all rational numbers (in their natural order). Can you give an example of a subset A of Q such that neither A nor $Q \smile A$ is similar to Q?

13. Can you give an example of a simply ordered set S not similar to ω and such that S has a first and no last element, and such that every element of S other than its first element has an immediate predecessor?

3. SIMILARITY BETWEEN WELL ORDERED SETS

In this section we shall study questions related to the similarity between well ordered sets. According to Theorem 24 of Chapter IV (page 198), every set can be well ordered; therefore, the study of well ordered sets has special significance.

Before proceeding further, let us prove:

Theorem 19.   *A necessary and sufficient condition that a simply ordered set S be well ordered is that S contain no subset similar to ω^*.*

PROOF.   We recall that

$$\omega^* = \{(\ldots ; 3; 2; 1; 0)\}$$

i.e., ω^* is the set of all natural numbers ordered conversely to their natural order.

Now, since every simply ordered set similar to ω^* has no first element, no subset of a well ordered set S can be similar to ω^*. This proves the necessity.

To prove the sufficiency, let S be a simply ordered set containing no subset similar to ω^*. Let A be any nonempty subset of S. We shall show that A has a first element. Assume on the contrary that A has no first element. Then, corresponding to every element x of A, the set P_x of all elements in A which precede x is not empty. By the axiom of Choice, there exists a function f defined on A such that $f(x) \in P_x$ for every $x \in A$. Let a be any element of A. Consider the subset $\{a, f(a), f(f(a)), f(f(f(a))), \ldots\}$ of S, which is similar to ω^* since $a > f(a) > f(f(a)) > \ldots$. However, this contradicts the fact that S contains no subset similar to ω^*. Hence, our assumption is false and therefore A has a first element. Consequently, S is a well ordered set and Theorem 19 is proved.

The set ω of all natural numbers (in their natural order) is a well ordered set. In connection with ω, we have repeatedly encountered the following two facts:

(i) In proving theorems concerning the elements or subsets of ω, we often employ the method of proof by induction given by the theorem of Finite Induction (Chapter II, page 105) or by Corollary 3 of Chapter II (page 105).

(ii) In proving the existence of functions defined on ω (and naturally satisfying certain conditions), we often employ the Finite Recursion Theorem

(Chapter V, page 206) or its special case given by Theorem 2 of Chapter V (page 208).

Clearly, if a well ordered set is similar to ω, then these two general methods can be used in answering questions relative to that set. However, as we know, not every well ordered set is similar to ω. For one thing, not every element (other than the first of a well ordered set) has an immediate predecessor, as is the case with ω.

The counterpart of (i), for the case of an arbitrary well ordered set, stems from the theorem of *Transfinite Induction* (Chapter IV, page 192).

The counterpart of (ii), for the case of an arbitrary well ordered set, stems from the *Transfinite Recursion Theorem* which is introduced after the following motivation.

Since every nonzero element m of ω has an immediate predecessor m^-, the Finite Recursion Theorem (Chapter V, page 206), with s replaced by $p(0)$ can be stated as:

Theorem 20 (Finite Recursion Theorem). *Let $p(x,y)$ be a binary predicate functional in x such that for every x there exists a (and therefore unique) y, denoted by $p(x)$, such that $p(x, p(x))$ is true. Then there exists a unique function g defined on the set of all natural numbers ω such that:*

$$\text{(22)} \qquad\qquad g(0) = p(0)$$

$$\text{(23)} \qquad\quad g(m) = p(g(m^-)) \qquad \text{for every nonzero} \quad m \in \omega$$

Theorem 20 is not applicable in general to well ordered sets because condition (23) is meaningless when referred to an arbitrary well ordered set. Indeed, not every element, other than the first element of a well ordered set W, need have an immediate predecessor.

Although an element w, other than the first element of a well ordered set W, does not always have an immediate predecessor w^-, *every element w of a well ordered set W has an initial segment $I(w)$ which is the set of all elements x of W such that $x < w$.*

Motivated by the above, it is clear how the Finite Recursion Theorem must be modified in reference to the arbitrary well ordered sets. The notion of the immediate predecessor of w is replaced by the notion of the initial segment $I(w)$, determined by w.

Theorem 21 (Transfinite Recursion Theorem). *Let W be a well ordered set and $p(x,y)$ a binary predicate, functional in x, such that for every x there exists a (and therefore unique) y, denoted by $p(x)$, such that $p(x, p(x))$ is true. Then there exists a unique function g defined on W such that:*

$$g(w) = p(g^1(I(w))) \qquad \text{for every} \quad w \in W$$

In the above, $g^1(I(w))$ is the image under g of the set $I(w)$, i.e., $g^1(I(w)) = \{g(u) \mid u < w\}$. Therefore, the conclusion of the theorem guarantees the existence of $g(w)$ such that:

$$\text{(24)} \qquad g(w) = p(g^1(I(w))) = p(\{g(u) \mid u < w\}) \qquad \text{for every} \quad w \in W$$

PROOF. First, we show that there cannot exist two different functions g_1 and g_2 satisfying the conclusion of the theorem. Assume on the contrary that $g_1 \neq g_2$ and let w be the smallest element of W on which g_1 and g_2 differ, i.e.,

$$(25) \qquad g_1(w) \neq g_2(w) \qquad \text{and} \qquad g_1^1(I(w)) = g_2^1(I(w))$$

In view of (24) and (25), we have

$$g_1(w) = p(g_1^1(I(w))) = p(g_2^1(I(w))) = g_2(w)$$

contradicting (25). Thus, our assumption is false and $g_1 = g_2$ on W. Hence, if there exists a function g satisfying (24), then g is *unique*.

Next, we prove that there exists a function g satisfying (24).

According to Lemma 8 of Chapter IV (page 191), the set S of all initial segments of a well ordered set is a well ordered set with respect to $\subset$. Clearly, if the set S is enlarged to include W as an element, then the resulting set V is again well ordered with respect to $\subset$.

We shall prove the existence of g by the theorem of Transfinite Induction in the set V, well ordered by $\subset$, and whose elements are all the initial segments of W and W itself.

There are elements h of V and functions g_h such that g_h is defined on h and satisfies:

$$(iii) \qquad g_h(w) = p(g_h^1(I(w))) \qquad \text{for every} \quad w \in h$$

The initial segment $I(a)$ of W, where a is the first element of W and the function $g_{I(a)} = \varnothing$ is an example. Moreover, corresponding to every $h \in V$, there is at most one function g_h satisfying (iii). This fact is proved as we showed the uniqueness of g above.

Now, let H be the set of all elements h of V such that corresponding to every $h \in H$ there exists a (and therefore unique) function g_h defined on h and satisfying (iii). In view of the uniqueness of g_h, it follows that:

$$(iv) \qquad g_h|_k = h_k \qquad \text{for every} \quad h, k \in H$$

Since $W \in V$, to prove the theorem it is enough to show that $H = V$, because in this case the function g_W will be the desired function g.

Now, to prove $H = V$ by virtue of the theorem of Transfinite Induction (page 192), it is enough to show that the presence in H of all the elements of V that precede a given element q of V implies the presence of q in H.

Thus, let q be an element of V and let us assume that every element of V that precedes q belongs to H. Two cases may occur:

(v) q *has a last element* w. This means that the initial segment $I(w)$ of W belongs to H, and consequently there is a function $g_{I(w)}$ satisfying (iii) on $I(w)$. We define the function g_q as follows:

$$g_q = g_{I(w)} \quad \text{on} \quad I(w) \qquad \text{and} \qquad g_q(w) = p(g_{I(w)}^1(I(w)))$$

We see from the axioms of Replacement and Sum-Set that g_q exists because $g_{I(w)}$ exists. Clearly, g_q satisfies (iii), for $w \in q$. Hence, $g_q \in H$, as desired.

(vi) *q has no last element.* This means that:

$$q = \cup\{h \mid h \subset q \text{ and } h \neq q\}$$

Now, consider the set

$$G = \{g_h \mid h \subset q \text{ and } h \neq q\}$$

of all functions g_h such that g_h is defined on h with $h \subset q$ and $h \neq q$, and such that g_h satisfies (iii) for every $w \in h$. The set G exists in view of the axiom of Replacement.

Since every function g_h is a set of ordered pairs, in view of (iv), we see that

$$g_q = \cup G$$

is a function whose domain is q and which satisfies (iii) for every $w \in q$. Hence, in this case also $g_q \in H$, as desired.

In view of the above and by virtue of the theorem of Transfinite Induction, we conclude that $H = V$, and Theorem 21 is proved.

An immediate consequence of the Transfinite Recursion Theorem is the following theorem, also called the Transfinite Recursion Theorem.

Theorem 22 (Transfinite Recursion Theorem). *Let e be an element of a set E and f a mapping from the power-set $\mathscr{P}(E)$ of E into E. Let W be a well ordered set. Then there exists a unique mapping g from W into E such that, if a is the first element of W,*

$$g(a) = e \qquad and \qquad g(w) = f(g^1(I(w)))$$

for every element w of W such that $w \neq a$.

PROOF. To prove the theorem, it is enough in the hypothesis of Theorem 21 to take $p(x,y)$ as

$$p(x,y) \equiv ((x = \varnothing) \wedge (y = e)) \vee ((x \notin \mathscr{P}(E)) \wedge (y = \varnothing)) \vee$$
$$((x \in (\mathscr{P}(E) \smallsetminus \{\varnothing\}) \wedge (y = f(x))$$

where f is the mapping from $\mathscr{P}(E)$ into E given in the hypothesis of Theorem 22. We see at once that with the above choice of the binary predicate $p(x,y)$, the proof of the theorem follows from that of Theorem 21.

Remark 5. Theorem 21 can also be proved by Zorn's lemma. Indeed, it is enough to consider the set P of all the subsets of W on each of which a function, satisfying the conclusion of our theorem, can be defined. Then show that X has a maximal element necessarily equal to W.

Remark 6. In Theorem 22 the condition $w \neq a$ may be dropped provided we require that $f(\varnothing) = e$.

In the sequel, we shall use the theorem of Transfinite Induction (see page 192) for proving theorems concerning well ordered sets, and the Transfinite Recursion Theorem (in either of its forms) for securing the existence of functions defined on well ordered sets.

Now, continuing with matters concerning similarity, let us prove:

Theorem 23. *Let f be a one-to-one order preserving mapping from a well ordered set W into itself. Then,*

(26) $w \le f(w)$ *for every* $w \in W$

PROOF.   Assume the contrary and let U be the nonempty subset of W such *that*:

$$f(u) < u \qquad \text{for every} \quad u \in U$$

Let a be the first element of U. Thus, in particular:

$$f(a) < a$$

Since f is a one-to-one order preserving mapping, the above inequality yields:

$$f(f(a)) < f(a) < a$$

Consequently, $f(a) \in U$. However, $f(a) < a$ which contradicts the choice of a. Thus, our assumption is false and the theorem is proved.

Let us observe that Theorem 23 can also be proved by means of the theorem of Transfinite Induction (page 192). To this end we consider the subset V of W such that $v \le f(v)$, for every $v \in V$. Then, we show that

$$\text{if} \quad I(w) \subset V \qquad \text{then} \quad w \in V$$

where in the above, $I(w)$ is the initial segment of W determined by w. Finally, in view of the theorem of Transfinite Induction, we conclude that $V = W$, as desired.

Theorem 24. *No well ordered set is similar to a subset of any of its initial segments.*

PROOF.   Let W be a well ordered set and $I(w)$ the initial segment of W determined by w. Assume on the contrary that there exists a similarity f between W and a subset of $I(w)$. Since similarity is a one-to-one order preserving mapping, by Theorem 23, $f(w) \ge w$. However, since $w \notin I(w)$, we conclude that f cannot be a similarity between W and a subset of $I(w)$. Hence, our assumption is false and the theorem is proved.

In particular, we have:

Corollary 8. *No well ordered set is similar to an initial segment of itself.*

Let us observe that although a well ordered set is not similar to any subset of any of its initial segments, it may be similar to a proper subset of itself. For instance, ω is similar to its proper subset $\{(1; 2; 3; 4; \ldots)\}$.

Theorem 25. *If a well ordered set W is similar to an initial segment of a well ordered set V, then V is not similar to any subset of W.*

PROOF.   Let f be a similarity between W and an initial segment $I(v)$ of V. Assume on the contrary that there exists a similarity g between V and a subset of W. But then $f \cdot g$ would be a similarity mapping between V and a subset of its initial segment $I(v)$, contradicting the conclusion of Theorem 24. Hence, our assumption is false and Theorem 25 is proved.

Theorem 26. *There is at most one similarity mapping between two well ordered sets.*

PROOF. Let W and V be two well ordered sets and let g and h be two similarity mappings between W and V. Clearly, $f = g_{-1}h$, as well as $f_{-1} = h_{-1}g$, is a similarity mapping between W and W. By Theorem 23, $w \leq f(w)$ for every $w \in W$. Similarly, $f(w) \leq f_{-1}(f(w))$, which implies $f(w) \leq w$ for every $w \in W$. Thus, on the one hand $w \leq f(w)$, and on the other hand $f(w) \leq w$. Consequently, $w = f(w)$ for every $w \in W$. Hence f is the identity mapping, and therefore $g = h$, as desired.

In particular, we have:

Corollary 9. *The identity mapping is the only similarity mapping between a well ordered set and itself.*

In Chapter IV we proved that the set S of all initial segments of a well ordered set is a well ordered set with respect to $\subset$ [see Lemma 8 (page 191)]. Now, let W be a well ordered set and S the set of all initial segments of W. Let us associate with every element w of W, the initial segment $I(w)$ of W determined by w. It is clear that this association gives rise to a similarity between W and S. Moreover, if a union of initial segments of W is not equal to an initial segment of W, then it must be equal to W. Thus, we have:

Lemma 6. *The set of all initial segments of a well ordered set W is similar to W. Moreover, any union of initial segments of W is either equal to W or is an initial segment of W.*

Next, we prove an important theorem.

Theorem 27. *Two well ordered sets are either similar or one and only one of them is similar to an initial segment of the other.*

PROOF. To prove the theorem, let us consider two nonempty well ordered sets W and E, and let us suppose that neither is similar to an initial segment of the other. We shall show that under these circumstances $W \simeq E$. We define a function g from W into E as follows. Let f be a mapping from the power-set $\mathscr{P}(E)$ into E such that for every proper subset S of E,

$$f(S) = \text{the first element of } E \text{ not belonging to } S$$

and

$$f(E) = e \qquad \text{where } e \text{ is the first element of } E$$

Let a be the first element of W. The mapping g from W into E, defined by

$$g(a) = e \qquad \text{and} \qquad g(w) = f(g^1(I(w)))$$

exists by virtue of the Transfinite Recursion Theorem (Theorem 22). We shall prove that g is a similarity mapping between W and E. First, we show that no element x of W except a is such that $g(x) = e$. Assume the contrary and (since W is a well ordered set) let c be the smallest such element, i.e.,

$$c \neq a, \qquad g(c) = e \qquad \text{and} \qquad g(x) \neq e \qquad \text{for} \quad a < x < c$$

Then in view of the definition of g, we see that g maps the initial segment $I(c)$ of W onto E. Moreover, again in view of the definition of g, for every two elements u and v of $I(c)$, if $u < v$, then $g(u) < g(v)$. Thus, g is a similarity mapping between $I(c)$ and E, contrary to our supposition that E is not similar to any initial segment of W. Hence our assumption is false, and indeed a is the only element of W whose image under g is e. But then in view of the definition of g, for every two elements x and y of W, if $x < y$, then $g(x) < g(y)$. Thus, g is a one-to-one order preserving mapping from W into E.

To prove that g is a similarity mapping between W and E it remains to show that g is onto. Assume the contrary and (since E is a well ordered set) let k be the smallest element of E that is not an image of any element of W under the mapping g. But then in view of the definition of g, no element of E not preceding k is an image of any element of W. Consequently, g is a similarity mapping between W and the initial segment $I(k)$ of E, contrary to our supposition that W is not similar to any initial segment of E. Hence our assumption is false, and indeed g is an onto mapping; therefore, g is a similarity mapping between W and E.

Thus, Theorem 27 is proved.

Let us observe that Theorem 27 can be proved by means of Zorn's lemma. To this end, in view of Lemma 6 it is enough to apply Zorn's lemma to the set (partially ordered by $\subset$) whose elements are W and the initial segments of W each of which is similar to an initial segment of E or to E itself.

Theorem 28 (Trichotomy Law). *For every two well ordered sets V and W, one and only one of the following three cases must hold:*

(i) *V is similar to W.*

(ii) *V is similar to an initial segment of W and W is not similar to any initial segment of V.*

(iii) *W is similar to an initial segment of V and V is not similar to any initial segment of W.*

PROOF.   The case where V is not similar to any initial segment of W and W is not similar to any initial segment of V, by Theorem 27, implies case (i). The case where V is similar to an initial segment of W and W is similar to an initial segment of V is excluded by Theorem 25. Hence, there remain the three above-mentioned cases which by Corollary 8 are mutually exclusive.

Theorem 29.   *Two well ordered sets each of which is similar to a subset of the other are similar.*

PROOF.   Let V and W be two well ordered sets. Let f be a similarity between V and a subset of W, and g a similarity between W and a subset of V. We shall prove that $V \simeq W$. Assume on the contrary that V is not similar to W. Hence, by Theorem 28 either V is similar to an initial segment of W, or else W is similar to an initial segment of V. If V is similar to an initial segment $I(w)$ of W, let h be that similarity. But then $h \cdot g$ is a similarity between W and a subset of its initial segment $I(w)$, which by Theorem 24 is impossible. On the other hand, if t is a similarity between W and an initial segment $I(v)$ of V, then $t \cdot f$ is a similarity between V and a subset of its initial segment $I(v)$, which again by Theorem 24 is impossible. Hence our assumption is false, and indeed $V \simeq W$, as desired.

Theorem 30 (Trichotomy Law). *For every two well ordered sets V and W, one and only one of the following three cases must hold*:

   (i) *V is similar to W.*
   (ii) *V is similar to a subset of W and W is not similar to any subset of V.*
   (iii) *W is similar to a subset of V and V is not similar to any subset of W.*

PROOF. The case where V is not similar to any subset of W and W is not similar to any subset of V, is excluded by Theorem 27. Moreover, the case where V is similar to a subset of W and W is similar to a subset of V, by Theorem 29, implies case (i). Hence, the only possibilities are the three cases above which are mutually exclusive.

Remark 7. Let us observe that since similarity between two well ordered sets implies equipollence between them, and since, by Theorem 24 of Chapter IV (page 198), every set can be well ordered, we see immediately that Theorem 30 implies the Trichotomy Law given by Corollary 15 of Chapter VI (page 259).

EXERCISES

1. Prove that each subset of a well ordered set W is similar either to W or to an initial segment of W.

2. Prove that a simply ordered set S is well ordered if and only if every initial segment of S is well ordered.

3. Prove that if S is an infinite simply ordered set, then one and only one of the following four cases must hold.

   (i) ω is similar to a subset of S and S is not similar to any subset of ω.
   (ii) S is similar to ω.
   (iii) ω^* is similar to a subset of S and S is not similar to any subset of ω^*.
   (iv) S is similar to ω^*.

In the above, ω^* is ω ordered by the converse order.

4. A subset G of a simply ordered set S is called a segment of S if $x \in G$, $y \in S$ and $y \leq x$, then $y \in G$. Prove the following theorem (Blumberg).
Let S be a simply ordered set and A a subset of it such that:

   (i) There exists a nonempty segment of S contained in A.
   (ii) For every nonempty segment G_1 of S such that $G_1 \subset A$ and $G_1 \neq S$, there exists a segment G_2 of the set S such that $G_1 \subset G_2 \subset A$ and $G_2 \neq G_1$.

Then $S = A$.

5. Prove the following induction theorem (Khintchine) for the set R of all real numbers.

Let P be a subset of R such that:

    (i) There is a real number r such that every real number less than r belongs to P.

    (ii) If every real number less than a real number b belongs to P, then there exists a real number $c > b$ such that every real number less than c belongs to P.

Then $P = R$.

4. COMPARABILITY OF WELL ORDERED SETS

According to Definition 3, two well ordered sets V and W are called similar (in symbols, $V \simeq W$) if there exists a one-to-one order preserving correspondence between V and W. In this connection and in view of the theorems of Section 3, it is natural to introduce:

Definition 5. *If a well ordered set V is similar to a subset of a well ordered set W, then V is said to be smaller than or similar to W. In symbols this is represented as:*

$$V \preccurlyeq W$$

Moreover, if V is similar to a subset of W and W is not similar to V, then V is said to be smaller than W. In symbols,

$$V \prec W$$

Clearly,

(27) $W \preccurlyeq W$ for every well ordered set W.

(28)   If $V \preccurlyeq W$ and $W \preccurlyeq V$, then $V \simeq W$ for every two well ordered sets V and W.

(29)   If $U \preccurlyeq V$ and $V \preccurlyeq W$, then $U \preccurlyeq W$ for every three well ordered sets U, V and W.

The truth of (27) follows from (1) and that of (28) from Theorem 29. Finally, (29) follows immediately from Definition 5.

In view of Definition 5 and Theorem 30, we have the following:

Corollary 10. *For every two well ordered sets V and W:*

$$V \preccurlyeq W \qquad or \qquad W \preccurlyeq V$$

Corollary 11. *For every two well ordered sets V and W one and only one of the following three cases must hold.*

$$V \prec W \qquad or \qquad W \prec V \qquad or \qquad V \simeq W$$

Next, we prove:

Theorem 31. *Let the elements of a set S be well ordered sets. Then there is no infinite decreasing sequence*

$$\cdots \lhd W_3 \lhd W_2 \lhd W_1$$

of elements of S.

PROOF. Assume on the contrary that there is an infinite decreasing sequence $\cdots \lhd W_3 \lhd W_2 \lhd W_1$ where, for $i = 1, 2, 3, \ldots$, W_i is an element of S and is a well ordered set. Then, in view of Theorem 28, W_2 is similar to an initial segment $I(w_1)$ of W_1. Likewise, W_3 is similar to an initial segment $I(w_2)$ of $I(w_1)$ or of W_1. Continuing in this manner, we find an infinite decreasing sequence

$$\cdots \lhd I(w_3) \lhd I(w_2) \lhd I(w_1)$$

of initial segments of W_1. Consequently, the well ordered set W_1 contains the subset $\{(\ldots; w_3; w_2; w_1)\}$ similar to ω^*. However, this contradicts Theorem 19. Hence, our assumption is false and Theorem 31 is proved.

Let W be a set whose elements are well ordered sets. Let us call an element w of W a *minimal* (in the sense of Definition 5) element of W if $w \unlhd u$, for every $u \in W$.

Theorem 32. *Every nonempty set whose elements are well ordered sets has a minimal element.*

PROOF. Let W be a nonempty set whose elements are well ordered sets and let w_1 be an element of W. If w_1 is not a minimal element of W, then by Corollary 11 there must be an element w_2 of W such that $w_2 \lhd w_1$. Hence, if W has no minimal element, then by reasoning analogous to the above, there must be an infinite decreasing sequence $\cdots \lhd w_2 \lhd w_1$ of elements of W contradicting Theorem 31. Thus, W must have a minimal element, as desired.

Remark 8. Let us observe again that since similarity between two well ordered sets implies equipollence between them, and since by Theorem 24 of Chapter IV (page 198), every set can be well ordered, we see immediately that Theorem 32 implies Theorem 14 of Chapter VI (page 264).

EXERCISES

1. Prove that for any well ordered set V there exists a well ordered set W such that $V \lhd W$ (in the sense of Definition 5).

2. Prove that there is no set of all well ordered sets.

3. Give an example of a family of well ordered sets having two minimal (in the sense of Definition 5) elements.

4. Give an example of two equipollent well ordered sets that are not similar.

5. Prove that a minimal (in the sense of Definition 5) denumerable well ordered set is similar to ω.

6. Give three examples of denumerable well ordered sets such that ω is smaller (in the sense of Definition 5) than each of them.

7. Prove that a well ordered set v is smaller than a well ordered set w (in the sense of Definition 5) if and only if v is similar to an initial segment of w.

5. ORDERED SUMS

For reasons that will become obvious, we shall consider in this section partially ordered sets that are simply ordered or well ordered.

First, we shall introduce the definition of an ordered sum (or ordered union) of two simply ordered sets U and V. Our aim is to unite U and V into a third simply ordered set in a manner appropriate to our purpose. For this purpose, let us consider the two disjoint simply ordered sets:

$$U = \{(a;b;c)\} \qquad \text{and} \qquad V = \{(m;n;p;q)\}$$

It is natural to define the ordered sum of U and V (in this order) as the simply ordered set

(30) $\{(a;b;c;m;n;p;q)\}$

where every element of V succeeds every element of U and where in each of the simply ordered sets U and V the original order is preserved.

We shall denote the simply ordered set given in (30) by $U + V$. Thus,

$$U + V = \{(a;b;c)\} + \{(m;n;p;q)\} = \{(a;b;c;m;n;p;q)\}$$

Let us observe that in the above the disjointness of U and V is essential.

Motivated by the above, we introduce:

Definition 6. *The ordered sum of two disjoint simply ordered sets U and V (in this order) is denoted by $U + V$ and is defined to be the set $U \cup V$ simply ordered as follows*:

(i) *If x and y belong to the same set U or V, then $x \leq y$ in $U + V$ whenever $x \leq y$ in U or in V.*

(ii) *If $x \in U$ and $y \in V$, then $x \leq y$ in $U + V$.*

Clearly, the above ordering yields a simple order in $U \cup V$ since U and V are simply ordered sets and since every two elements of $U + V$ are comparable.

Definition 6 introduces the operation of *ordered addition* among pairwise disjoint simply ordered sets. Ordered addition can also be defined so that it applies to the case of simply ordered sets that are not pairwise disjoint. However, this is of no particular interest.

Lemma 7. *Let V and W be two disjoint well ordered sets. Then $V + W$ is a well ordered set.*

PROOF.   Obviously, every nonempty subset of $V \cup W$ has a first element in $V + W$.

Accordingly, the ordered sum of the well ordered sets ω and $\{\omega\}$ is:

$$\omega + \{\omega\} = \{(0; 1; 2; \ldots ; \omega)\}$$

The main feature of an ordered sum is embodied in the following.

Lemma 8. *Let U and V as well as P and Q be disjoint simply ordered sets such that $U \simeq P$ and $V \simeq Q$. Then:*

$$U + V \simeq P + Q$$

The proof of this lemma is straightforward and is left to the reader.
In view of Lemma 8, ordered sums are invariant under similarity.

Lemma 9. *Let U, V and W be three pairwise disjoint simply ordered sets. Then:*

$$(U + V) + W = U + (V + W)$$

The proof of this lemma is straightforward and is left to the reader.
In view of Lemma 9 ordered addition is associative, and hence either of $(U + V) + W$ and $U + (V + W)$ can be denoted by $U + V + W$.

However, let us observe that if U and V are two disjoint simply ordered sets, then in general $U + V \neq V + U$ and even $U + V \not\simeq V + U$.

For instance

$$\omega + \{\omega\} \not\simeq \{\omega\} + \omega$$

since $\omega + \{\omega\}$ has a last element, whereas $\{\omega\} + \omega$ has no last element.

The concept of an ordered sum of a finite number of pairwise disjoint simply ordered summands can be generalized to an infinite number of pairwise disjoint summands as follows:

Definition 7. *Let $(U_i)_{i \in V}$ be a family of pairwise disjoint simply ordered sets U_i indexed by a simply ordered set V. The ordered sum of $(U_i)_{i \in V}$, denoted by*

$$(31) \qquad\qquad\qquad \sum_{i \in V} U_i$$

is defined to be the set $\underset{i \in V}{\cup}\, U_i$ simply ordered as follows:

(i) *If a and b belong to the same summand U_i, then $a \le b$ in (31) whenever $a \le b$ in U_i.*

(ii) *If $a \in U_i$ and $b \in U_j$, with $i \neq j$, then $a \le b$ in (31) whenever $i \le j$ in V.*

It is easily seen that this ordering yields a simple order in $\underset{i \in V}{\cup}\, U_i$.

Lemma 10. *Let $(W_i)_{i \in V}$ be a family of pairwise disjoint well ordered sets W_i indexed by a well ordered set V. Then $\sum_{i \in V} W_i$ is a well ordered set.*

The proof of this lemma is straightforward and is left to the reader.
A generalization of Lemma 8 is given by:

Lemma 11. *Let $(U_i)_{i \in V}$ as well as $(U_i')_{i \in V}$ be a family of pairwise disjoint simply ordered sets, indexed by a simply ordered set V. If $U_i \simeq U_i'$ for every $i \in V$, then:*

$$\sum_{i \in V} U_i \simeq \sum_{i \in V} U_i'$$

The above lemma can be proved easily by using the axiom of Choice, and its proof is left to the reader.

EXERCISES

1. Corresponding to a simply ordered set S, let S^* denote S ordered by the converse order.

Prove that $(U + V)^* = V^* + U^*$, for every two disjoint simply ordered sets U and V.

2. Let K represent the simply ordered set of all irrational numbers (in their natural order). Let J be a simply ordered set disjoint from K. Prove that if $J \simeq K$, then $(K + J) \simeq K$ and $(K + \{K\} + J) \simeq K$.

3. Let A be disjoint from ω. Prove that if $A \simeq \omega$, then:

$$(\omega + \{\omega\} + A) \simeq (\omega + A)$$

4. Let Q represent the set of all rational numbers in their natural order. Prove that

$$Q, \quad \{Q\} + Q, \quad Q + \{Q\}, \quad \{Q\} + Q + \{\{Q\}\}$$

are pairwise nonsimilar simply ordered sets.

5. Prove Lemmas 8, 9, 10 and 11.

6. Let $(W_i)_{i \in \omega}$ be a family of pairwise disjoint well ordered sets W_i indexed by ω such that $W_i \simeq 1$ for every $i \in \omega$. Prove that:

$$\omega \simeq \sum_{i \in \omega} W_i$$

7. Let R denote the set of all real numbers in their natural order. Let $(K_i)_{i \in \omega}$ be a family of pairwise disjoint simply ordered sets K_i indexed by ω and such that $K_i \simeq R$ for every $i \in \omega$. Prove that:

$$R \simeq \sum_{i \in \omega} (K_i + \{\omega\})$$

8. Let Q denote the set of all rational numbers in their natural order. Let $(H_i)_{i \in \omega}$ be a family of pairwise disjoint simply ordered sets H_i indexed by ω and such that $H_i \simeq Q$ for every $i \in \omega$. Prove that:

$$Q \simeq \sum_{i \in \omega} H_i$$

6. ORDERED PRODUCTS

In this section we shall again consider simply and well ordered sets.

First, we shall introduce the definition of an ordered product of two simply ordered sets U and V. Our aim is to simply order the Cartesian product $U \times V$ in a manner appropriate to our purpose.

Now, consider the two simply ordered sets:

$$U = \{(a;b;c)\} \qquad \text{and} \qquad V = \{(m;n)\}$$

Their Cartesian product $U \times V$, i.e.,

$$\{(b,n), (c,m), (a,m), (a,n), (c,n), (b,m)\}$$

can be simply ordered in different ways. One of them is:

(32) $$\{((a,m); (b,m); (c,m); (a,n); (b,n); (c,n))\}$$

The above ordering of $U \times V$ is called *ordering according to the principle of last differences*, or *antilexicographic*. It is characterized by the fact that in (32)

$$(x,u) \le (y,v)$$

if $u < v$ and if $u = v$ then $x \le y$.

Clearly, $u < v$ refers to the order in V and $x \le y$ to that in U.

Motivated by the above, we introduce:

Definition 8. *The ordered product of two simply ordered sets U and V (in this order) is denoted by $U \cdot V$ and is defined to be the set $U \times V$ simply ordered according to the principle of last differences, i.e., antilexicographically.*

The fact that the ordering according to the principle of last differences yields a simple order in $U \times V$ is easily verified. *Moreover, $U \cdot V$ will often be denoted simply by UV.*

Let us observe that Definition 8 introduces the operation of *ordered multiplication* among simply ordered sets. Also, let us note that Definition 8 does not require that U and V be disjoint.

Lemma 12. *Let V and W be two well ordered sets. Then VW is a well ordered set.*

PROOF. Clearly, every nonempty subset of $V \times W$ has a first element in VW.

Accordingly, the ordered product of the well ordered sets ω and 1 is:

$$\omega 1 = \{((0,0); (1,0); (2,0); (3,0); \ldots)\} \simeq \omega$$

Similarly, the ordered product of the well ordered sets ω and 2, where $2 = \{0,1\}$, is given by

$$\omega 2 = \{((0,0); (1,0); (2,0); (3,0); \ldots (0,1); (1,1); (2,1); (3,1); \ldots)\}$$

and thus we see that:

(33) $$\omega 2 \simeq \omega + H \qquad \text{where} \quad H \simeq \omega$$

Likewise, the ordered product of ω with itself is given by

$$\omega\omega = \{((0,0); (1,0); \ldots (0,1); (1,1); \ldots (0,2); (1,2); \ldots)\}$$

and thus we see that:

$$\omega\omega \simeq \sum_{i\in\omega} H_i \qquad \text{where } H_i \simeq \omega \quad \text{for every} \quad i \in \omega$$

The main feature of an ordered product is embodied in the following:

Lemma 13. *Let U, V, P and Q be simply ordered sets such that $U \cong P$ and $V \simeq Q$. Then:*

$$UV \simeq PQ$$

The proof of the above lemma is straightforward and is left to the reader. According to Lemma 13, ordered products are invariant under similarity.

Lemma 14. *Let U, V and W be three simply ordered sets. Then:*

$$(UV)W \simeq U(VW)$$

The proof of Lemma 14 is straightforward and is left to the reader.

According to Lemma 14, ordered multiplication is *associative under similarity,* and hence either of $(UV)W$ and $U(VW)$ can be denoted *up to similarity* by UVW.

However, let us observe that if U and V are two simply ordered sets, then UV need not equal VU nor be similar to it.

For instance

$$2\omega = \{((0,0); (1,0); (0,1); (1,1); (0,2); (1,2) \ldots)\} \simeq \omega$$

whereas in view of (33), we have $\omega 2 \simeq (\omega + H)$, where $H \simeq \omega$. Since $(\omega + H) \not\simeq \omega$, we see at once that $2\omega \not\simeq \omega 2$.

It is easy to verify that for every simply ordered set U we have

$$0U = U0 = 0 \qquad \text{and} \qquad 1U \simeq U1 \simeq U$$

where, in the above, $0 = \varnothing$ and $1 = \{\varnothing\}$.

Lemma 15. *Let U and V be two simply ordered sets. Then*

$$UV \simeq \sum_{i\in V} U_i$$

where $U_i \simeq U$ for every $i \in V$, and $U_i \cap U_j = \varnothing$, for $i \neq j$.

The proof of the above lemma is straightforward and is left to the reader.

According to Lemma 15, the ordered product UV is similar to the ordered sum of a family of pairwise disjoint sets each similar to U and where the family is indexed by the set V. Thus, UV can be interpreted as: *U taken V times.*

Lemma 16. *Let U, V and W be three simply ordered sets such that V and W are disjoint. Then:*

$$U(V + W) = UV + UW$$

PROOF. In view of the fact that $V \cap W = \varnothing$, we have (see Problem 7 in Section 9 of Chapter II, page 119)

$$U \times (V \cup W) = (U \times V) \cup (U \times W)$$

from which, in view of Definitions 6 and 8, the truth of Lemma 6 follows.

The above lemma shows that ordered multiplication is *left distributive* with respect to ordered addition.

Accordingly, we have

$$\omega(\{\omega\} + \{\{\omega\}\}) = \omega\{\omega\} + \omega\{\{\omega\}\} \simeq \omega + H$$

where $H \simeq \omega$, and $H \cap \omega = \varnothing$.

Let us observe, however, that ordered multiplication is not right distributive with respect to ordered addition; i.e., not only may we have $(V + W)U \neq VU + WU$ but even:

$$(V + W)U \not\simeq VU + WU$$

Thus, for instance

$$(\{\omega\} + \{\{\omega\}\})\omega \simeq 2\omega \simeq \omega$$

whereas

$$\{\omega\}\omega + \{\{\omega\}\}\omega \simeq \omega 2$$

and as we know, $\omega 2 \not\simeq \omega$.

In contrast to the possibility of defining infinite ordered sums by extension of the definition for finite ordered sums, infinite ordered products cannot be defined by extension of the notion of finite ordered products. For instance, the product set $\prod_{i \in \omega} V_i$ where V_i is equal to the simply ordered set $\{(0;1)\}$ for every $i \in \omega$, cannot be ordered antilexicographically. For example, corresponding to the two sequences $0, 1, 0, 1, 0, 1, \ldots$ and $1, 0, 1, 0, 1, \ldots$ there are no last different terms with the same index.

EXERCISES

1. For a simply ordered set S, let, as usual, S^* denote S ordered by the converse order.

Prove that $(UV)^* = U^*V^*$ for every two simply ordered sets U and V.

2. Prove that $\omega\omega^* \not\simeq \omega^*\omega$.

3. Let Q be the set of all rational numbers in their natural order. Prove that $Q\omega \simeq Q$ and $QQ \simeq Q$.

Also, prove that:

$$(Q + \{Q\})\,\omega \simeq Q \qquad \text{and} \qquad (\{Q\} + Q)\omega \simeq Q$$

4. Let A be a finite simply ordered set disjoint from ω. Prove that

$$(\omega + A)\omega \simeq \omega\omega$$

5. Let A and B be two finite simply ordered sets such that A, B and ω are pairwise disjoint. Prove that:

$$(\omega + A)(\omega + B) \simeq \omega\omega + \omega B + AB$$

6. Let K be a simply ordered set similar to the set of all rational numbers in their natural order. Moreover, let A be a finite simply ordered set. If A and ω are disjoint, prove that:

$$(\omega + \omega K + A)(\omega + \omega K + A) \simeq \omega + \omega K + A$$

7. Let G be a simply ordered set similar to the set of all real numbers in their natural order. Moreover, let A and B be two nonsimilar finite ordered sets. Prove that:

$$GA \not\simeq GB \qquad \text{and} \qquad AG \not\simeq BG$$

Also, prove that $GG \not\simeq G$.

8. Let Q be the set of all rational numbers in their natural order. Prove that:

$$(\{Q\} + Q)(Q + \{Q\}) \simeq (Q + \{Q\})(\{Q\} + Q) \simeq Q$$

Also, prove that:

$$(\{Q\} + Q)(\{Q\} + Q)(\{Q\} + Q) \simeq \{Q\} + Q$$

and

$$(Q + \{Q\})(Q + \{Q\})(Q + \{Q\}) \simeq Q + \{Q\}$$

9. Prove Lemmas 13, 14 and 15.

10. Let Q be the set of all rational numbers in their natural order. Prove that:

$$(\omega(\{Q\} + Q))(\omega(\{Q\} + Q)) \simeq \omega(\{Q\} + Q)$$

Also, prove that:

$$(\omega + \{\omega\})(Q + \{Q\})(\omega + \{\omega\})(Q + \{Q\}) \simeq (\omega + \{\omega\})(Q + \{Q\})$$

7. SUMMARY

In this chapter various ordered sets were studied in connection with similarity. Two partially ordered sets are called similar if there exists a one-to-one order-preserving correspondence between them. Two similar partially ordered sets are indistinguishable with respect to properties involving order. Thus, various notions such as precedence, succession, partial order, simple order, well order, denseness, continuity, and so forth, are preserved (invariant) under similarity.

Also in this chapter various special simply ordered sets were completely characterized up to similarity. For instance, the set ω of all natural numbers (in their natural order) is characterized as a nonempty simply ordered set having no last element and such that every initial segment of it is finite. Moreover, the set Q of all rational numbers (in their natural order) is characterized as a dense denumerable simply ordered set having no first and no last element. Furthermore, the set R of all real numbers (in their natural order) is characterized as a continuous (simply ordered) set having no first and no last element and having a denumerable subset that is dense in it.

A simply ordered set was shown to be well ordered if and only if it contains no subset similar to ω^*.

It was also pointed out that in handling questions related to well ordered sets, the following two general methods are usually employed. Transfinite Induction, for proving theorems; and Transfinite Recursion, for ensuring the existence of various mappings defined on well ordered sets.

The following theorems are important in connection with similarity mappings involving well ordered sets. If f is a one-to-one order preserving mapping from a well ordered set $(W, \leq)$ into itself, then $w \leq f(w)$ for every $w \in W$. No well ordered set is similar to a subset of any of its initial segments. There is at most one similarity mapping between two well ordered sets. For every two well ordered sets, either they are similar or one and only one of them is similar to an initial segment of the other.

In Section 4, the notion of *a well ordered set smaller than another well ordered set* was introduced, and it was proved that every nonempty set whose elements are well ordered sets has a minimal element.

In the concluding sections of this chapter, the notions of ordered sums and ordered products of simply ordered sets were introduced. As we shall see shortly, these notions are used in developing the arithmetic of ordinal numbers.

Chapter VIII

ORDINAL NUMBERS
AND THEIR ARITHMETIC

1. ORDINAL NUMBERS

In this section we shall consider special kinds of sets each of which admits a particular well ordering. Each of these sets will be called an *ordinal number*. The reader should observe once more that, like every other mathematical object in this book, an ordinal number is first of all a set.

The definition of an ordinal number is motivated by a particular property (mentioned below) that every natural number possesses.

First, we recall that evey natural number is well ordered by the natural order defined by (3) of Chapter IV (page 172). Accordingly, for every two elements x and y of a natural number,

(1) $\qquad\qquad x \leq y \quad$ *if and only if* $\quad (x \in y) \vee (x = y)$

Equivalently,

(2) $\qquad\qquad x \leq y \quad$ *if and only if* $\quad x \subset y$

Similarly, the set ω of all natural numbers with respect to their natural order [which is again defined by (1) or by (2)] is a well ordered set.

Thus, according to our notational convention, the natural number 5 is represented (with respect to the natural order) as the well ordered set:

$$5 = \{(0; 1; 2; 3; 4)\}$$

Now, let us take an element of 5, say, 3, and let us consider the initial segment $I(3)$ of 5. Clearly,

$$I(3) = \{0, 1, 2\}$$

However, the set $\{0, 1, 2\}$ is equal to the natural number 3. Thus,

$$I(3) = 3$$

The same phenomenon occurs in connection with every element of 5. Thus, for example,

$$I(0) = 0 = \varnothing, \qquad I(1) = \{0\} = 1, \qquad I(2) = 2, \qquad I(4) = 4$$

Consequently, we may conclude that the initial segment $I(v)$, determined by any element v of 5 [where 5 is well ordered by the natural order given by (1) or (2)], is equal to v. This property prevails with respect to every natural number. Explicitly, we have:

Lemma 1. *For every natural number n well ordered by the natural order [given by (1) or (2)], the initial segment I(v) determined by an element v of n is equal to v.*

PROOF.   We show that for every natural number n:

$$(v \in n) \to (v = I(v))$$

Let N be the set of all natural numbers n each of which satisfies (3). Clearly, $0 \in N$ since $(v \in 0) \to (v = I(v))$ is always true. Now, assume that a natural number m is an element of N, and let us prove that the immediate successor m^+ of m is also an element of N. However, $m^+ = m \cup \{m\}$, and since by our assumption (3) is true for the elements of m, all we need do is verify the validity of (3) for the element m of m^+. But in view of (1) and the fact that $m^+ = m \cup \{m\}$, we see at once that $I(m) = m$. Thus, by the theorem of Finite Induction (page 105) we conclude that $N = \omega$. Hence, (3) is valid for every natural number n, as desired.

Motivated by Lemma 1, we introduce:

Definition 1. *A set w is called an ordinal number (or simply an ordinal) if w can be well ordered so that for every element v of w the initial segment I(v) of w is equal to v, i.e.,*

(4) $I(v) = v$ *for every* $v \in w$

According to the above definition and Lemma 1, every natural number is an ordinal number. Also, the set ω of all natural numbers (in their natural order) is an ordinal number.

Likewise, each of the sets

$$\omega \cup \{\omega\} \quad \text{and} \quad \omega \cup \{\omega\} \cup \{\omega \cup \{\omega\}\}$$

is an ordinal number since each is well ordered by (1) or (2) in accordance with the condition mentioned in Definition 1.

An ordinal number that is a finite set is called a *finite ordinal*. An ordinal number that is an infinite set is called an *infinite ordinal* or a *transfinite ordinal*.

For instance, every natural number is a finite ordinal. On the other hand, ω, $\omega \cup \{\omega\}$, and so forth, are examples of transfinite ordinals.

Next, we prove the following fundamental theorem.

Theorem 1. *A set w is an ordinal number if and only if:*

(i) *Every element of w is a subset of w.*
(ii) *w is well ordered by $\subset$.*
(iii) *No element of w is an element of itself.*

PROOF.   Let w be an ordinal number well ordered by $\leq$ in accordance with Definition 1. In view of (4), for every element x of w we have $x = I(x)$, and since $I(x) \subset w$ we have $x \subset w$. Thus, w satisfies (i). Now, in view of the definition of an initial segment and (4), for every two elements x and y of w we have:

$$(x \leq y) \leftrightarrow (I(x) \subset I(y)) \leftrightarrow (x \subset y)$$

But then since w is well ordered by $\leq$ we see that w is also well ordered by $\subset$. Thus, w satisfies (ii). Again, in view of (4), for every element x of w we have $x = I(x)$, and therefore $x \notin x$. Thus, w satisfies (iii).

Next, suppose (i), (ii) and (iii) are valid. We shall prove that w is an ordinal number. To this end, we shall show that $x = I(x)$, for every element x of w [where naturally, $I(x)$ is the initial segment of x in w and w is well ordered by $\subset$].

First, we prove that for every element x of w we have:

(iv) $$x \subset I(x)$$

Indeed, let $y \in x$. Then by (i) we have $x \subset w$ and therefore $y \in w$. But then by (ii) we have $x \subset y$ or $y \subset x$. However, $x \subset y$ is impossible, since in view of $y \in x$ it would imply $y \in y$, contradicting (iii). Hence, if $y \in x$ then $y \subset x$, $y \neq x$ and therefore $y \in I(x)$. Thus, indeed (iv) is valid.

Now, we prove that $I(x) \subset x$, for every element x of w. Assume the contrary, and in view of (ii) let a be the first element of w for which $I(a) \nsubseteq a$. Hence, in view of (iv) we have $a \subsetneq I(a)$. Thus, there exists an element b of w such that:

$$b \in I(a) \qquad \text{and} \qquad b \notin a$$

But then, in view of (ii) and the choice of a we have:

$$b \subsetneq a \qquad \text{and} \qquad b = I(b)$$

Thus, in view of (i) there exists an element h of w such that:

$$h \in a \qquad \text{and} \qquad h \notin b$$

However, since $b \notin a$ and $h \in a$ we have $b \neq h$. Also, since $b = I(b)$ and $h \notin b$, in view of (ii) and the fact that $b \neq h$, we have $b \subsetneq h$. Moreover, since $h \in a$, in view of (iv) we see that $h \subsetneq a$. In short, we have:

$$b \subsetneq h \subsetneq a$$

Finally, in view of the choice of a we have $h = I(h)$, and by the above $b \in I(h)$ and hence $b \in a$, contradicting $b \notin a$. Thus, our assumption is false, and indeed $I(x) \subset x$, for every element x of w. But this in view of (iv) implies that $x = I(x)$, for every element x of w.

Hence, Theorem 1 is proved.

Corollary 1. *A set w is an ordinal number if and only if:*

  (v) *Every element of an element of w is an element of w.*
  (vi) *w is well ordered by $(\in$ or $=)$.*
(vii) *No element of w is an element of itself.*

PROOF. Let us observe that conditions (i) and (iii) are respectively equivalent to (v) and (vii). Thus, to prove the corollary, we have to show that (i), (ii) and (iii) imply

(viii) $$(x \subset y) \rightarrow ((x \in y) \vee (x = y))$$

for every two elements x and y of w, and that (v), (vi) and (vii) imply

(ix) $((x \in y) \lor (x = y)) \to (x \subset y)$

for every two elements x and y of w.

However, in view of Theorem 1 if $x \subset y$ and $x \neq y$, then $x \in I(y)$, and since $I(y) = y$ we have $x \in y$. Thus, (viii) is proved.

On the other hand, let $x \in y$ and $x \neq y$. Now, if $z \in x$, then by (v), $z \in w$. Since $z \in x$ and $x \in y$, in view of (vi) we have $z \in y$. Consequently, $x \subset y$ and (ix) is proved.

Thus, Corollary 1 is proved.

It is customary to call ($\in$ or $=$) or $\subset$ the *natural order* of an ordinal number. In view of Theorem 1 and Corollary 1 we have: *every ordinal number w is well ordered by the natural order whereby the initial segment determined by an element v of w is equal to v.*

Remark 1.   *Unless otherwise specified, in all matters pertaining to order in an ordinal number, the order under consideration will be the natural order ($\in$ or $=$) or $\subset$ with respect to which (by abuse of terminology) an ordinal number will be referred to as a well ordered set.*

Lemma 2.   *No ordinal number is an element of itself. Moreover, if w is an ordinal number, then $w \cup \{w\}$ is an ordinal number distinct from w.*

PROOF.   Let w be an ordinal number. Then by Theorem 1, $w \in w$ is impossible. Thus, in particular $w \neq w \cup \{w\}$. On the other hand, clearly $w \cup \{w\}$ satisfies conditions (i), (ii) and (iii) of Theorem 1. Consequently, $w \cup \{w\}$ is an ordinal number distinct from w.

Lemma 3.   *The empty set 0 is an ordinal number that is the first element of every nonempty (nonzero) ordinal number. Moreover, every initial segment of an ordinal number is an ordinal number, and every ordinal number is an initial segment of some ordinal number. Furthermore, every element of an ordinal number is an ordinal number, and every ordinal number is an element of some ordinal number.*

PROOF.   Let us observe that the empty set $\varnothing$ is an ordinal number since it satisfies the conditions set forth in Definition 1. Now, let w be an ordinal number distinct from $\varnothing$ and let a be its first element (see Remark 1). In view of (v) of Corollary 1, for no set x is it the case that $x \in a$. Consequently, $a = \varnothing = 0$. Thus, indeed 0 is the first element of every nonempty (nonzero) ordinal number. Next, let $I(v)$ be an initial segment of an ordinal w. Inasmuch as w is a well ordered set in which $x = I(x)$, for every element x of w, we see at once that $I(v)$ satisfies the conditions set forth in Definition 1. Thus, $I(v)$ is an ordinal. On the other hand, every ordinal w is equal to the initial segment $I(w)$ of the ordinal $w \cup \{w\}$. Finally, since every element v of an ordinal w is equal to the initial segment $I(v)$ of w, and since as shown above $I(v)$ is an ordinal, v is also an ordinal number. On the other hand, clearly every ordinal w is an element of the ordinal number $w \cup \{w\}$.

Thus, Lemma 3 is proved.

Theorem 2.   *Two ordinal numbers are equal if and only if they are similar, i.e.,*

$$(v = w) \leftrightarrow (v \simeq w)$$

for every two ordinals v and w.

PROOF.   Clearly, if two ordinals are equal, then they are similar. Thus, the necessity is established trivially.

To prove the sufficiency, let f be a similarity between two ordinal numbers v and w. We show that $v = w$.

Let U be the subset of v such that:

$$u = f(u) \qquad \text{for every } u \in U$$

To prove the theorem, in view of the theorem of Transfinite Induction (page 192), it is enough to show that

$$\text{if} \quad I(x) \subset U \qquad \text{then} \quad x \in U$$

where in the above, $I(x)$ is the initial segment of v determined by x. Now, assume $I(x) \subset U$. Since f is a similarity between v and w

$$I(f(x)) = f^1(I(x))$$

where $f^1(I(x))$ is the image of $I(x)$ under f. Moreover, since $I(x) \subset U$,

$$f^1(I(x)) = I(x)$$

However, since v and w are both ordinal numbers

$$I(f(x)) = f(x) \qquad \text{and} \qquad I(x) = x$$

which, in view of the two preceding equalities, implies $f(x) = x$, as desired. Thus, Theorem 2 is proved.

Theorem 3   (Trichotomy Law).   *For every two ordinal numbers v and w, one and only one of the following three cases holds;*

  (i) $v = w$.
 (ii) *v is equal to an initial segment of w.*
(iii) *w is equal to an initial segment of v.*

PROOF.   Since ordinal numbers v and w are well ordered sets, by Theorem 28 of Chapter VII (page 304), one and only one of the following three cases holds:

  (i) $v \simeq w$, in which case by Theorem 2, $v = w$.

 (ii) v is similar to an initial segment of w, in which case, by Lemma 3 and Theorem 2, v is equal to an initial segment of w.

(iii) w is similar to an initial segment of v, in which case, by Lemma 3 and Theorem 2, w is equal to an initial segment of v.

In view of Theorem 3, we have:

Corollary 2.   *For every two ordinal numbers v and w,*

$$v \subset w \qquad or \qquad w \subset v$$

Also, in view of Theorem 3, Lemma 3 and (4), we have:

Corollary 3 (Trichotomy Law).   *For every two ordinal numbers v and w, one and only one of the following three cases holds:*

$$v = w \quad or \quad v \in w \quad or \quad w \in v$$

Theorem 4.   *If an ordinal number w is equipollent to a natural number n, then w = n.*

PROOF.   Clearly, every natural number is an ordinal number. However, since w and n are two finite equipollent sets, (ii) and (iii) of Theorem 3 are excluded. Thus, $w = n$, as desired.

Corollary 4.   *An ordinal number is finite if and only if it is a natural number.*

Next, we introduce the natural order among ordinals.

Definition 2.   *Let v and w be two ordinal numbers. We define $v \le w$ if v is equal to w or v is equal to an initial segment of w.*

Thus, in view of Corollary 2, for every two ordinals v and w, we have,

(5) $v \le w$ if and only if $v \subset w$

If $v \le w$, then as usual we say that the ordinal v is *less than or equal to* the ordinal w or w is *greater than or equal to v.* If $v \le w$ and $v \ne w$, then we say that v is *less* than w or w is *greater* than v and as usual we denote this by $v < w$.

In view of the above and Corollary 3, for every two ordinals v and w, we have:

(6) $v < w$ if and only if $v \in w$

In view of Definition 2 and Corollary 3, we have:

Corollary 5 (Trichotomy Law).   *For every two ordinal numbers v and w, one and only one of the following three cases holds:*

$$v = w \quad or \quad v < w \quad or \quad w < v$$

Theorem 5.   *Every ordinal w is equal to the set of all ordinals less than w.*

PROOF.   If an ordinal number x is such that $x < w$, then by (6), $x \in w$. Conversely, if $y \in w$, then by Lemma 3, y is an ordinal number and $y < w$, in view of (6).

Theorem 6.   *Every set of ordinal numbers is well ordered with respect to the order given by Definition 2 (natural order).*

PROOF.   For an empty set of ordinals, the theorem is trivially true. Now, let W be a nonempty set of ordinals. Thus, W is a nonempty set of well ordered sets. By Theorem 32 of Chapter VII (page 307), every nonempty subset V of W has a minimal element. This means that there exists an element u of V such that u is similar to v or u is similar to an initial segment of v, for every $v \in V$. However, since the elements of V are ordinal numbers, by Theorem 2, u is equal to v or u is equal to an initial segment of v, for every $v \in V$. But this means that $u \leq v$ (in the sense of Definition 2), for every $v \in V$. Thus, Theorem 6 is proved.

Corollary 6. *Every set of ordinal numbers is well ordered by $\leq$.*

Let us call an ordinal w (the) *immediate successor* of an ordinal v if $v < w$; and if an ordinal u is such that $v < u$, then $w \leq u$.

Theorem 7. *The immediate successor of every ordinal number v is the ordinal number $v \cup \{v\}$.*

Proof. By Lemma 2, $v \cup \{v\}$ is an ordinal number. Moreover, since $v \in (v \cup \{v\})$, by (6) we have $v < (v \cup \{v\})$. Now, if u is an ordinal such that $v < u$, then in view of (6) every element of v as well as v itself is an element of u. But this, in view of (5), means that $(v \cup \{v\}) \leq u$. Hence, $v \cup \{v\}$ is an immediate successor of v. On the other hand, in view of Corollary 5 it is obvious that v has only one immediate successor. Thus, indeed $v \cup \{v\}$ is *the immediate successor* of v.

As usual, the immediate successor of an ordinal v is denoted by v^+. Thus, for every ordinal v,

(7) $$v^+ = v \cup \{v\}$$

Let us call an ordinal u (the) *immediate predecessor* of an ordinal v if v is the immediate successor of u. By Corollary 5 if the ordinal v has an immediate predecessor, then the latter is unique and is called *the immediate predecessor* of v.

The immediate predecessor (when it exists) of an ordinal number v is denoted by v^-.

Let us observe that by Theorem 7 every ordinal number has an immediate successor. However, not every ordinal number has an immediate predecessor. For instance, the immediate successor of ω is $\omega \cup \{\omega\} = \omega^+$. However, ω has no immediate predecessor. On the other hand, the immediate predecessor of ω^+ is ω.

In view of Corollary 4, every finite ordinal has an immediate predecessor.

Definition 3. *A nonzero ordinal number having no immediate predecessor is called a limit ordinal or a limit number.*

Clearly, no finite ordinal is a limit number. Also, not every transfinite ordinal is a limit number. The transfinite ordinal ω is a limit number. However, the transfinite ordinal $\omega \cup \{\omega\} = \omega^+$ is not a limit number.

For a set W of ordinals, an ordinal w is called the *least upper bound* of W if w is greater than or equal to every element of W; and if v is an ordinal greater than or equal to every element of W, then $w \leq v$. Similarly, an ordinal u is called the *greatest lower bound* of W if u is less than or equal to every element of W; and if v is an ordinal less than or equal to every element of W, then $v \leq u$.

In view of the general theory of partially ordered sets, the uniqueness of least upper bounds and that of greatest lower bounds is assured.

Theorem 8. *For every set W of ordinal numbers the sum-set $\cup W$ of W is an ordinal number. Moreover, $\cup W$ is the least upper bound of W, i.e.,*

$$\cup W = \text{lub } W = \sup W$$

PROOF. First, we show that $\cup W$ is an ordinal number. Inasmuch as every element of an ordinal number is an ordinal number (see Lemma 3) and inasmuch as every set of ordinal numbers is well ordered (see Theorem 6), $\cup W$ is a well ordered set. Now, if $v \in \cup W$, then $v \in w$ for some ordinal $w \in W$. On the other hand, by Theorem 5, w is equal to the set of all ordinals less than w, and since $v \in w$, i.e., $v < w$, we see that every ordinal less than v is an element of $\cup W$. Now, if $I(v)$ is the initial segment determined by v of $\cup W$, then by Theorem 5, $v = I(v)$. Therefore, in view of Definition 1, $\cup W$ is an ordinal number.

Next, we show that $\cup W$ is an upper bound of W. Clearly, $w \subset \cup W$, for every $w \in W$. Thus, by (5), $w \leq \cup W$, for every $w \in W$. Hence, $\cup W$ is an upper bound of W.

Finally, we show that $\cup W$ is the least upper bound of W. For let an ordinal u be an upper bound of W. This means that $w \leq u$, for every $w \in W$. Thus, in view of (5), $w \subset u$, for every $w \in W$. Consequently, $\cup W \subset u$, which again in view of (5) implies that $\cup W \leq u$. Therefore, indeed the ordinal $\cup W$ is the least upper bound of W, as desired.

In the special case where W is the empty set, $\cup W = \cup \varnothing = \varnothing = 0$, which implies that 0 is the least upper bound of an empty set of ordinals. This is to be expected, since in the case where $W = \varnothing$ every ordinal is an upper bound of W, and 0, being the least ordinal, is the least upper bound of W.

Theorem 9. *For every ordinal number w we have*:

$$\cup w = w \text{ if } w \text{ is a limit ordinal or if } w = 0$$

and

$$\cup w = w^- \text{ if } w \text{ is not a limit ordinal and } w \neq 0$$

PROOF. Inasmuch as every ordinal w is the set of all ordinals less than w (see Theorem 5), by Theorem 8, $\cup w = \text{lub } w$. Now, if w is a limit ordinal or $w = 0$, then w has no immediate predecessor and hence $\cup w = \text{lub } w = w$. On the other hand, if w is not a limit ordinal and $w \neq 0$, then w has an immediate predecessor w^- equal to lub $w = \cup w$. Thus, $w^- = \cup w$, as desired.

Theorem 10. *For every set W of ordinal numbers there exists an ordinal number greater than every element of W.*

PROOF. If W has no greatest element, then by Theorem 8, $\cup W$ is an ordinal greater than every element of W. If, however, W has a greatest element (which by Theorem 8 is necessarily equal to $\cup W$), then $\cup W \cup \{\cup W\} = (\cup W)^+$ is an ordinal number greater than every element of W.

Theorem 11. *There is no set of all ordinal numbers.*

PROOF. Assume on the contrary that W is the set of all ordinals. Then $\cup W \cup \{\cup W\} = (\cup W)^+$ is an ordinal greater than every ordinal belonging to

W. However, this contradicts the fact that $(\cup W)^+$, as an ordinal, must belong to W. Hence, our assumption is false and indeed there is no set of all ordinals.

Next, we prove a fundamental theorem.

Theorem 12. *For every well ordered set W there exists a unique ordinal number similar to W.*

PROOF. Let us observe that W cannot be similar to two distinct ordinals p and q. Indeed, if $W \simeq p$ and $W \simeq q$, then from (3) of Chapter VII (page 284), it follows that $p \simeq q$, which in view of Theorem 2 implies $p = q$, contradicting the fact that p and q are two distinct ordinals. Consequently, W can be similar to at most one ordinal number.

Clearly, W has a subset X such that:

(i) if $x \in X$ and $y < x$ then $y \in X$, for every two elements x and y of W.

(ii) X is similar to an (and hence unique) ordinal number.

For instance, the empty set (which is a subset of W), being similar to the ordinal 0, satisfies conditions (i) and (ii).

Thus, the set

$$(8) \qquad\qquad S = \{X \mid \cdots\}$$

of all subsets X of W each of which satisfies conditions (i) and (ii) is not empty. Moreover, in view of the axiom of Replacement (page 81), the set

$$(9) \qquad\qquad w = \{u \mid \cdots\}$$

of all ordinals u, each of which is similar to an element of S, exists.

Partial order S [given by (8)] by inclusion ($\subset$). Let P be any simply ordered subset of $(S, \subset)$. Consider $\cup P$. Clearly, $\cup P$ is a subset of W. Moreover, $\cup P$ satisfies (i). Now, let v be the set of all the elements of w [given by (9)] each of which is similar to an element of P. By Theorem 8, $\cup v$ is an ordinal. We claim that $\cup v \simeq \cup P$. For let $x \in \cup P$ and let $X \in P$ such that $x \in X$. Let u be the ordinal that is similar to X, and let $k \in u$ be the corresponding mate of x. Now, let us associate x with k. In view of Theorem 26 of Chapter VII (page 303), it is easy to verify that this association gives rise to a similarity between $\cup P$ and the ordinal $\cup v$. Thus, $\cup P$ satisfies condition (ii), and $\cup P$ is an element of S [given by (8)]. Consequently, in view of Zorn's lemma, S has a maximal element M satisfying (i) and (ii). Let m be the ordinal similar to M. We claim that $M = W$. Assume on the contrary that $M \neq W$ and let h be the first element of $W \sim M$. Consider the set $M \cup \{h\}$ and the ordinal $m^+ = m \cup \{m\}$. Clearly, $M \cup \{h\}$ is a subset of W, which satisfies (i). Moreover, since M is similar to m, $M \cup \{h\}$ is similar to m^+. Hence, $M \cup \{h\}$ satisfies (ii). Consequently, $M \cup \{h\}$ is an element of S [given by (8)] which contradicts the maximality of M. Hence our assumption is false, and indeed $M = W$. However, since M is similar to the ordinal number m, we see that W is also similar to the ordinal number m, as desired.

Theorem 12 asserts the existence of a similarity mapping between a well ordered set W and an ordinal number. Therefore, as expected, its proof can be given by means of the Transfinite Recursion Theorem (Theorem 21 of Chapter VII, page 299).

Below we sketch the proof of Theorem 12 using the Transfinite Recursion Theorem.

Consider the binary predicate $p(x,y)$ given by:

(i) $p(x) = (\cup x)^+$ if x is a set of ordinal numbers that has a greatest element.
(ii) $p(x) = \cup x$ if x is a set of ordinal numbers that has no greatest element.
(iii) $p(x) = 0$ if x is not as given in (i) or (ii).

It can be easily verified that $p(x,y)$, defined by (i), (ii) and (iii), is a binary predicate, functional in x.

Now, let W be a well ordered set. By the Transfinite Recursion Theorem there exists a unique function g defined on W and such that

$$g(w) = p(g^1(I(w))) \qquad \text{for every} \quad w \in W$$

where $g^1(I(w))$ is the image under g of the initial segment $I(w)$.

By the axiom of Replacement the range of the function g exists. It can be easily proved that the range of g is an ordinal number which is similar to the well ordered set W.

Corollary 7. *For every set S there exists an ordinal number equipollent to S.*

PROOF. By Theorem 24 of Chapter IV (page 198), S can be well ordered. Thus, S is equipollent to a well ordered set. Consequently, in view of Theorem 12, S is equipollent to an ordinal number. Thus, indeed every set is equipollent to an ordinal number (which may not be unique).

Remark 2. Let u be a well ordered set. It is customary to denote by $\bar{u}$ the unique ordinal number similar to the well ordered set u.

Obviously, if w is an ordinal number, then $\bar{w} = w$. Consequently, for every well ordered set u, we have $\overline{(\bar{u})} = \bar{u}$.

Clearly, $\overline{\{(a;b)\}} = 2$, $\overline{\{(a;b;c)\}} = 3$, and so on.

EXERCISES

1. Prove that no finite ordinal is a limit number.

2. Prove (5), (6) and (7).

3. Prove that the union of two ordinal numbers is equal to the one that is not smaller than the other.

4. Prove that the intersection of two ordinal numbers is equal to the one that is not greater than the other.

5. Prove Theorem 12 by using transfinite induction and without using Zorn's lemma.

6. Prove that for every ordinal number W, it is the case that $\cap W = 0$.

7. Prove that if w is a limit number or zero, then:

$$w = \bigcup_{x \in w} x = \bigcup_{x < w} x$$

8. Prove that if w is neither zero nor a limit number, then:

$$w = \left(\bigcup_{x \in w} x \right)^+ = \left(\bigcup_{x < w} x \right)^+$$

9. Prove that every finite set is equipollent to a unique ordinal number.

10. Give an example of a set equipollent to two distinct ordinal numbers.

2. ORDINAL ARITHMETIC

In this section we shall study addition of ordinals. Addition is an operation. In general, we define an operation in a set S as a mapping from $S \times S$ into S. As such, an operation in a set S is a certain subset of the Cartesian product $(S \times S) \times S$. For instance, addition in the set ω of all natural numbers can be defined as a certain subset of $(\omega \times \omega) \times \omega$ (see page 205).

Since there is no set of all ordinals (Theorem 11), the addition of ordinals cannot be introduced along the lines mentioned above. As we shall see shortly, addition of ordinals is introduced via the notion of ordered sums of well ordered sets (see Chapter VII, Section 5) and the fundamental Theorem 12. Note that the proof of the latter was based on the axiom of Replacement.

The sum of two natural numbers n and m was defined [see Definition 3 of Chapter V (page 208)] via the Recursion Theorem [see Theorem 2 of Chapter V (page 208)]. As mentioned at the end of this section, the sum of two ordinals v and w can also be defined recursively. However, for the reasons mentioned above, the recursive definition of the sum of two ordinals (in contrast to the case of the sum of two natural numbers) is justified by virtue of the axiom of Replacement.

Now, let us consider two ordinal numbers u and v. By Corollary 2, $u \subset v$ or $v \subset u$. Thus, if u and v are not both equal to 0, then they are not disjoint. Consequently, the ordered sum of two nonzero ordinal numbers cannot be defined by Definition 6 of Chapter VII (page 308). However, motivated by the latter, we may proceed as follows.

For every two ordinals u and v, we form the sets $u \times \{1\}$ and $v \times \{2\}$ and order them as follows. For every two elements a and b of u

$$(a,1) \leq (b,1) \quad \text{if} \quad a \leq b \quad \text{in} \quad u$$

and for every two elements m and n of v,

$$(m,2) \leq (n,2) \quad \text{if} \quad m \leq n \quad \text{in} \quad v$$

Obviously, since u and v are ordinals, $u \times \{1\}$ and $v \times \{2\}$, when ordered as indicated in the above, become two disjoint well ordered sets. Consequently, we may form the ordered sum $(u \times \{1\}) + (v \times \{2\})$ of $u \times \{1\}$ and $v \times \{2\}$

according to Definition 6 of Chapter VII (page 308). Now, by Theorem 12 the resulting well ordered set is similar to a unique ordinal. Thus we may define the latter as the ordered sum of the two ordinals u and v (in this order).

Furthermore, if $u \neq v$, then instead of $u \times \{1\}$ and $v \times \{2\}$, we may use $u \times \{u\}$ and $v \times \{v\}$ respectively.

For example, let $u = 3$ and $v = 2$; then we form $3 \times \{3\}$ and $2 \times \{2\}$ and order them by

$$(a,3) \leq (b,3) \quad \text{if} \quad a \leq b \text{ in } 3$$

and:

$$(m,2) \leq (n,2) \quad \text{if} \quad m \leq n \text{ in } 2$$

Obviously, with the above order, $3 \times \{3\}$ and $2 \times \{2\}$ become two disjoint well ordered sets and we define

$$3 + 2 = \overline{(3 \times \{3\}) + (2 \times \{2\})} = \overline{\{(0_3;1_3;2_3;0_2;1_2)\}}$$

which as we know is equal to the ordinal 5.

Motivated by the above, let us introduce:

Definition 4. *The (ordered) sum of two ordinal numbers u and v (in this order) is denoted by u + v and is defined by*

$$u + v = \overline{(u \times \{1\}) + (v \times \{2\})}$$

and if $u \neq v$, then also by:

$$u + v = \overline{(u \times \{u\}) + (v \times \{v\})}$$

In the above, $(u \times \{1\}) + (v \times \{2\})$ stands for the ordered sum of two mutually disjoint well ordered sets $u \times \{1\}$ and $v \times \{2\}$, as defined by Definition 6 of Chapter VII (page 308). The configuration $\overline{(u \times \{1\}) + (v \times \{2\})}$, as introduced in Remark 1, stands for the unique ordinal number that is similar to the well ordered set $(u \times \{1\}) + (v \times \{2\})$.

Here are some examples. According to Definition 4, we have:

$$\omega + 1 = \overline{(\omega \times \{1\}) + (1 \times \{2\})}$$
$$= \overline{\{(0_1; 1_1; 2_1; 3_1; \ldots ; 0_2)\}} = \omega \cup \{\omega\} = \omega^+$$

Thus,

(10) $$\omega + 1 = \omega \cup \{\omega\} = \omega^+$$

On the other hand,

$$1 + \omega = \overline{(1 \times \{1\}) + (\omega \times \{2\})}$$
$$= \overline{\{(0_1; 0_2; 1_2; 2_2; 3_2; \ldots)\}} = \omega$$

Hence,

(11) $$1 + \omega = \omega$$

Comparing (10) with (11), we observe that:

$$(\omega + 1) \neq (1 + \omega)$$

Thus, we see immediately that ordinal addition is *not commutative*.

Lemma 4. *For every ordinal number u,*

$$0 + u = u + 0 = u$$

PROOF. By Definition 4,

$$0 + u = \overline{(0 \times \{1\}) + (u \times \{2\})}$$
$$= \overline{0 + (u \times \{2\})} = \overline{\varnothing \cup (u \times \{2\})} = u$$

Similarly, one can show that $u + 0 = u$.

Lemma 5. *For every ordinal number u,*

$$u + 1 = u^+$$

PROOF. Using Definition 4, we derive:

$$u + 1 = \overline{(u \times \{1\}) + (1 \times \{2\})} = u \cup \{u\}$$

However, by Theorem 7, $u \cup \{u\}$ is the immediate successor u^+ of u. Hence, $u + 1 = u^+$, as desired.

Note that for every finite ordinal n, we have:

(12) $$n + \omega = \omega$$

However, if n and m are two distinct finite ordinals, then:

(13) $$\omega + n \neq \omega + m$$

Next, we prove:

Theorem 13. *For every three ordinals u, v and w:*

$$(u + v) + w = u + (v + w)$$

PROOF. Obviously, in view of Lemma 9 of Chapter VII (page 309)

$$\overline{(u \times \{1\} + v \times \{2\}) + w \times \{3\}} = \overline{u \times \{1\} + (v \times \{2\} + w \times \{3\})}$$

and therefore:

$$(u + v) + w = u + (v + w)$$

Theorem 13 shows that ordinal addition is *associative*, and therefore there is no ambiguity in writing $u + v + w$ for either $(u + v) + w$ or $u + (v + w)$.

Thus,

$$3 + (\omega + 4) = (3 + \omega) + 4$$

and since, in view of (12), $3 + \omega = \omega$, we have:

$$3 + \omega + 4 = \omega + 4$$

Corollary 8. *For every two ordinals u and v:*

$$u + v^+ = (u + v)^+$$

PROOF. By Lemma 5, $u + v^+ = u + v + 1$, and similarly $(u + v)^+ = u + v + 1$. Hence, indeed $u + v^+ = (u + v)^+$.

Next, let us consider $\omega + \omega$. By Definition 4, we have:

$$\omega + \omega = \overline{(\omega \times \{1\}) + (\omega \times \{2\})}$$
$$= \overline{\{(0_1; 1_1; 2_1; \ldots ; 0_2; 1_2; 2_2; \ldots)\}}$$

Clearly, $\omega + \omega \neq \omega$ and $\omega + \omega \neq \omega + n$ and $\omega + \omega \neq n + \omega = \omega$ for every finite ordinal n.

The sum of finitely many ordinals presents no problem. For instance, we have:

$$2 + \omega + 5 + \omega = \omega + \omega$$

Similarly:

$$\omega + 5 + \omega + 3 + \omega + 1 = \omega + \omega + \omega + 1$$

Theorem 14.   *For every two ordinal numbers u and v if $v > 0$, then $u < u + v$.*

PROOF.   By Definition 4,

$$u + v = \overline{(u \times \{1\}) + (v \times \{2\})}$$

However, u is similar to the initial segment of $(u \times \{1\}) + (v \times \{2\})$, determined by $(b,2)$, where $(b,2)$ is the first element of the well ordered set $v \times \{2\}$. Thus, u is equal to the initial segment u of $u + v$. Consequently, by Definition 2, $u < u + v$, as desired.

Theorem 15.   *For every two ordinal numbers u and v if $u > v$, then there exists a unique ordinal number $w > 0$ such that:*

$$u = v + w$$

PROOF.   Since $u > v$, we see that v is equal to an initial segment of u. Therefore, $u \frown v$ is a nonempty well ordered set. In view of Theorem 12, $u \frown v$ is similar to an ordinal w obviously greater than zero. However

$$(v \times \{1\}) + (w \times \{2\}) \simeq u$$

hence

$$\overline{(v \times \{1\}) + (w \times \{2\})} = u$$

or

$$u = v + w$$

as desired.

To prove the uniqueness of w, assume on the contrary that there exist two distinct ordinals w and w_1, say with $w > w_1$, such that:

$$u = v + w \qquad \text{and} \qquad u = v + w_1$$

But then by (14) there exists an ordinal $h > 0$ such that $w = w_1 + h$. Consequently,

$$u = v + w = v + w_1 + h = u + h$$

However, in view of Theorem 14, $u < u + h$, which contradicts $u = u + h$ obtained above. Hence our assumption is false, and indeed $w = w_1$.

If v and w are two ordinal numbers and $v < w$, then it is customary to denote the unique ordinal $\overline{w \frown v}$ by $w - v$. Thus,

$$(15) \qquad\qquad w = v + (w - v)$$

In (15) the ordinal $w - v$ is called a *remainder* of the ordinal w.

Let us observe that in view of (15), if v and w are two ordinals such that $v < w$, then the equation $v + x = w$ has a unique solution, namely, $w - v$. On the other hand, the equation $x + v = w$, with $v < w$, is not solvable in general.

Below, we mention some consequences of Theorem 15.

Corollary 9. *For every three ordinal numbers u, v and w we have*:

$$u + v = u + w \qquad \textit{if and only if} \qquad v = w$$

Corollary 10. *For every three ordinal numbers u, v and w we have*:

$$u + v < u + w \qquad \textit{if and only if} \qquad v < w$$

Moreover

$$v + u < w + u \qquad \textit{implies} \qquad v < w$$

and:

$$v < w \qquad \textit{implies} \qquad v + u \leq w + u$$

Corollary 11. *Let u and v be two ordinal numbers such that $v \neq 0$. Then v is a limit ordinal if and only if $u + v$ is a limit ordinal.*

Theorem 16. *For every ordinal number v and every nonempty set W of ordinal numbers we have*

$$v + \cup W = \cup \{v + w \mid \ldots\}$$

where $\{v + w \mid \ldots\}$ is the set of all ordinal numbers $v + w$, with $w \in W$.

PROOF. The case where $W = \{0\}$ presents no difficulty. Thus, in what follows we may suppose that W has elements greater than zero.

By Theorem 8, $\cup W$ and $\cup \{v + w \mid \ldots\}$ are ordinals that are respectively the least upper bounds of the sets W and $\{v + w \mid \ldots\}$. Now, since $w \leq \cup W$, for every $w \in W$, in view of Corollaries 9 and 10 we have $v + w \leq v + \cup W$, for every $w \in W$. Consequently, $v + \cup W$ is an upper bound of $\{v + w \mid \ldots\}$. Next, we show that $v + \cup W$ is the least upper bound of $\{v + w \mid \ldots\}$. Assume the contrary, and let there exist an ordinal u such that:

$$(16) \qquad\qquad v + w \leq u \qquad \text{for every} \quad w \in W$$

and:

$$(17) \qquad\qquad u < v + \cup W$$

Since W has elements greater than zero, in view of (16) and Theorem 14, $v < u$. Consequently, by Theorem 15 there exists an ordinal h such that:

$$(18) \qquad\qquad v + h = u \qquad \text{with} \quad h > 0$$

Comparing (16) and (18), in view of Corollary 10 we derive that $w \leq h$, for every $w \in W$, i.e., h is an upper bound of W. On the other hand, comparing (17) and (18), in view of Corollary 10 we derive $h < \cup W$, contradicting the fact that h is an upper bound of W. Hence our assumption is false, and indeed $v + \cup W$ is the least upper bound of $\{v + w \mid \ldots\}$, i.e., $v + \cup W = \cup \{v + w \mid \ldots\}$, as desired.

Theorem 17. *For every ordinal number v and every limit ordinal w we have:*

$$v + w = \bigcup_{u < w} (v + u)$$

PROOF. Since w is a limit ordinal, by Theorem 9, $\cup w = w$. Also, by Theorem 5, $w = \{u \mid \ldots\}$, where $u < w$. Consequently, the proof of Theorem 17 follows from that of Theorem 16.

Remark 3. At the beginning of this section, we mentioned that the addition of ordinals can be defined recursively. The recursive definition is justified by virtue of the axiom of Replacement, the Transfinite Recursion Theorem [see Theorem 21 of Chapter VII (page 299)] and Theorems 7 and 8.

The recursive definition of ordinal addition is given as follows: *for every two ordinal numbers v and w,*

(19) $v + 0 = v$

(20) $v + w = (v + w^-)^+$ *if w is not a limit ordinal and $w \neq 0$*

(21) $v + w = \bigcup_{u < w} (v + u),$ *if w is a limit ordinal*

Naturally, (19), (20) and (21) are proved using Definition 4. As a matter of fact, Lemma 4, Corollary 8 and Theorem 17 imply (19), (20) and (21) respectively.

EXERCISES

1. Find how many different ordinal numbers result when the ordinals 1, 2 and ω are summed in all possible ways.

2. Prove (12), (13) and (15).

3. Let w be an ordinal number that has an immediate predecessor. Prove that $u + w^- = (u + w)^-$, for every ordinal u.

4. Prove Corollaries 9, 10 and 11.

5. Prove that if u is an ordinal number, then $1 + u = u$ if and only if $u \geq \omega$.

6. Prove that $u + 1 + u = 1 + u + u$ holds for every ordinal number u.

7. Prove that every ordinal number has a finite number of distinct remainders.

8. Prove that if u, v and w are ordinal numbers such that $u \leq v \leq w$, then $(w - u) - (v - u) = w - v$.

9. Prove that if u, v and w are ordinal numbers such that $u < v < w$, then $v - u < w - u$.

10. Prove that if u, v and w are ordinal numbers such that $u < v < w$, then $w - v \leq w - u$.

11. Prove that if the ordinal numbers u and v, with $u < v$, are two remainders of the same ordinal number, then u is a remainder of v.

3. INFINITE SUMS OF ORDINAL NUMBERS

In this section we define *the ordered sum of a family of ordinal numbers indexed by an ordinal number*. The definition is based on Definition 7 of Chapter VII (page 309). According to the latter, and as Lemma 10 of Chapter VII (page 309) indicates, the ordered sum $\sum_{i \in V} W_i$ of a family $(W_i)_{i \in V}$ of pairwise disjoint well ordered sets W_i, indexed by a well ordered set V, is again a well ordered set. Now, if every element of the family as well as the index set is an ordinal number, then the ordered sum $\sum_{i \in V} W_i \times \{i\}$ is a well ordered set which by Theorem 12 is similar to a unique ordinal number. The latter is defined to be the sum of the family of ordinal numbers under consideration. Thus, we introduce:

Definition 5. *The (ordered) sum of a family* $(w_i)_{i \in u}$ *of ordinal numbers* w_i, *indexed by an ordinal* u, *is denoted by*

$$\overline{\sum_{i \in u} w_i} \qquad or \qquad \overline{\sum_{i < u} w_i}$$

and is defined as the ordinal:

$$\overline{\sum_{i \in u} w_i \times \{i\}} \qquad or \qquad \overline{\sum_{i < u} w_i \times \{i\}}$$

(The reader is reminded that $i \in u$ if and only if $i < u$, for every two ordinals i and u.)

According to Definition 5

(22)
$$\overline{\sum_{i < u} w_i} = \overline{\sum_{i < u} w_i \times \{i\}}$$

where w_i for every $i \in u$, as well as u, is an ordinal number.

We give some examples of infinite sums of ordinal numbers.

For instance, if $w_i = 1$, for every $i \in \omega$, then by (22) we have:

$$\overline{\sum_{i < \omega} w_i} = \overline{\{(0_0; 0_1; 0_2; 0_3; 0_4; \ldots)\}} = \omega$$

When the index ordinal u is the ordinal ω, then the family $(w_i)_{i \in \omega}$ is called an *infinite sequence* and the left side of the equality sign in (22) is usually written as

(23)
$$w_0 + w_1 + w_2 + \ldots$$

and is called an *infinite series*.

From Theorem 12, it follows in particular that the sum of an infinite sequence of ordinals always exists and is an ordinal number.

Note that whereas the sum of an infinite sequence of natural numbers is not defined, the sum of an infinite sequence of ordinal numbers always exists and is an ordinal number.

The following are some examples of infinite series of ordinals written in the form of (23).

First, let us consider

$$1 + 1 + 1 + 1 + \cdots$$

which, according to (23) and Definition 5 (as shown above), is equal to:

$$\overline{\bigcup_{i \in \omega} (1 \times \{i\})} = \overline{\{(0_0; 0_1; 0_2; 0_3; \ldots)\}} = \omega$$

Thus,

$$1 + 1 + 1 + 1 + \cdots = \omega$$

Next, let us consider

$$2 + 2 + 2 + 2 + \cdots$$

which is equal to:

$$\overline{\bigcup_{i \in \omega} (2 \times \{i\})} = \overline{\{(0_0; 1_0; 0_1; 1_1; 0_2; 1_2; \ldots)\}} = \omega$$

In general, if n is a finite positive ordinal, we have:

$$n + n + n + \cdots = \overline{\bigcup_{i \in \omega} (n \times \{i\})}$$

$$= \overline{\{(0_0; 1_0; \ldots; n_0^-; 0_1; 1_1; \ldots; n_1^-; 0_2; 1_2; \ldots; n_2^-; \ldots)\}} = \omega$$

Thus, for every finite positive ordinal n,

(24) $$n + n + n + \cdots = \omega$$

Similarly,

$$1 + 2 + 3 + 4 + \cdots = \overline{\{(0_0; 0_1; 1_1; 0_2; 1_2; 2_2; 0_3; 1_3; 2_3; \ldots)\}} = \omega$$

Thus,

(25) $$1 + 2 + 3 + 4 + \cdots = \omega$$

Note that (24) and (25) are meaningless in the context of the arithmetic of the natural numbers.

As we know, it is customary to call a family $(w_i)_{i \in u}$ of ordinals w_i a *sequence* of ordinals. Moreover, if $u = \omega$, then $(w_i)_{i \in \omega}$ is called an *infinite sequence*. Motivated by this, we call a family

(26) $$(w_i)_{i \in u}$$

of ordinals indexed by an ordinal u, a *sequence of type u*. According to this terminology, an infinite sequence of ordinals is also called a sequence of type ω.

If the ordinal u is an infinite ordinal, then (26) is called a *transfinite sequence of type u*.

A sequence $(w_i)_{i \in u}$ is called *nondecreasing* if, for every two elements i and j of u,

$$i \leq j \quad \text{implies} \quad w_i \leq w_j$$

It is customary to call the union-set, i.e., the sum-set [see (31) of Chapter II (page 92)] of a nondecreasing sequence of ordinals, the *limit* of that sequence. More formally, we introduce:

Definition 6. *The union-set of a nondecreasing sequence* $(w_i)_{i \in u}$ *of ordinals* w_i *is called the limit of that sequence and is denoted by:*

$$\lim_{i<u} w_i \qquad or \qquad \lim_{i \in u} w_i$$

The existence of the limit of a nondecreasing sequence of ordinals is secured by Theorem 8.

Thus, for every nondecreasing sequence $(w_i)_{i \in u}$ of type u of ordinals w_i:

(27)
$$\lim_{i<u} w_i = \bigcup_{i<u} w_i$$

According to (27),
$$\lim \{(1;2;3;4;5)\} = 5$$

Also,
$$\lim \{(1;2;3;4;\ldots)\} = \omega$$

In view of Theorem 8, we have

(28)
$$\lim_{i<u} w_i = \sup_{i<u} w_i = \operatorname{lub}_{i<u} w_i = \bigcup_{i \in u} w_i$$

where in the above $(w_i)_{i \in u}$ is a nondecreasing sequence of type u of ordinals w_i.

In view of Theorem 5, every ordinal u is equal to the set of all ordinals less than u. Thus, every ordinal u can be considered as a nondecreasing sequence of type u of ordinals i, i.e.,

$$u = (i)_{i \in u}$$

Moreover, in view of Theorem 9, we have

(29)
$$u = \lim_{i<u} i$$

if u is a limit ordinal or if $u = 0$. Furthermore

(30)
$$u = (\lim_{i<u} i)^+$$

if u is not a limit ordinal and $u \neq 0$.

For every two sequences $(u_i)_{i \in w}$ and $(v_i)_{i \in w}$ of ordinal numbers, we may form their ordered sum:

$$(u_i + v_i)_{i \in w}$$

It is easy to observe that the limit of the sum of two nondecreasing sequences of ordinals is not necessarily equal to the sum of their limits. For instance

$$\lim \{(0;2;4;6;\ldots)\} = \omega$$
$$\lim \{(1;3;5;7;\ldots)\} = \omega$$
$$\lim \{(0+1;2+3;4+5;\ldots)\} = \omega$$

whereas $\omega + \omega \neq \omega$.

However, we have the following.

Theorem 18. *Let $(w_i)_{i\in u}$ be a nondecreasing sequence of ordinals such that $u > 0$ and:*

$$\lim_{i<u} w_i = a$$

Then, for every ordinal v:

$$\lim_{i<u} (v + w_i) = v + a$$

PROOF. Clearly, $(v + w_i)_{i\in u}$ is a nondecreasing sequence of ordinals. Now, in view of (28) we have $a = \bigcup_{i<u} w_i$. Also, in view of Theorem 16, we have:

$$v + \bigcup_{i<u} w_i = \bigcup_{i<u} (v + w_i) = v + a$$

However, again, in view of (28) we have:

$$\lim_{i<u} (v + w_i) = \bigcup_{i<u} (v + w_i)$$

Thus, the last two equalities assert the theorem.

Let us observe that if $\lim_{i<u} w_i = a$, then it is not necessarily true that $\lim_{i<u} (w_i + v) = a + v$. For instance, in view of (29) and (30) we have $\lim_{i<u} (i + 1) \neq \lim_{i<u} i + 1$.

The proofs of the following two lemmas are left to the reader.

Lemma 6. *Let $(a_i)_{i\in u}$ and $(c_i)_{i\in u}$ be two nondecreasing sequences of ordinals such that $a_i \leq c_i$ for every $i \in u$. Then:*

$$\lim_{i<u} a_i \leq \lim_{i<u} c_i$$

Lemma 7. *Let $(a_i)_{i\in u}$, $(c_i)_{i\in u}$ and $(e_i)_{i\in u}$ be three nondecreasing sequences of ordinals such that:*

$$a_i \leq c_i \leq e_i \quad \text{for every} \quad i < u$$

and

$$\lim_{i<u} a_i = \lim_{i<u} e_i = v$$

Then:

$$\lim_{i<u} c_i = v$$

Just as for an infinite sequence $(w_i)_{i\in\omega}$, the sum $\sum_{i\in\omega} w_i$ is called an infinite series, we may call

$$(31) \qquad \sum_{i<u} w_i$$

a series of type u of ordinals w_i.

If the ordinal u is an infinite ordinal, then (31) is called a *transfinite series* of type u. We may even use notation similar to (23) for the case of a transfinite series. Thus, if in (31) the ordinal u is equal to $\omega + \omega + 1$, then (31) may be written as:

$$w_0 + w_1 + w_2 + \cdots + w_\omega + w_{\omega+1} + \cdots + w_{\omega+\omega}$$

Next, we introduce the notion of a partial sum of a series of ordinals.

Definition 7. *Let* $s = \sum\limits_{i<u} w_i$ *be a series of type* $u > 0$ *of ordinals* w_i. *Then the ordinal* s_v, *given by*

$$s_v = \sum_{i<v^+} w_i \qquad \text{with} \quad v < u$$

is called the v-*th partial sum of* s.

For instance, if

$$s = w_0 + w_1 + w_2 + w_3 + \cdots$$

then

$$s_3 = w_0 + w_1 + w_2 + w_3$$

and

$$s_5 = w_0 + w_1 + w_2 + w_3 + w_4 + w_5$$

are examples of the two partial sums s_3 and s_5 of s.

Let us observe that the set of all partial sums of a series of type u forms a sequence of type u (in an obvious way).

For instance, let us consider the series

$$s = w_0 + w_1 + w_2$$

which is of type 3. Then

$$s_0 = w_0, \qquad s_1 = w_0 + w_1, \qquad s_2 = w_0 + w_1 + w_2$$

are all the partial sums of s and they form a nondecreasing sequence of type 3.

The following theorem establishes the relation between a series and the limit of the sequence of its partial sums. As shown below, the latter is nondecreasing.

Theorem 19. *Every series of ordinal numbers is equal to the limit of the sequence of its partial sums.*

PROOF. Let $s = \sum\limits_{i<u} w_i$ be a series of ordinals where we assume $u > 0$. Let $(s_v)_{v<u}$ be the sequence of the partial sums of s, where, according to Definition 7,

(32) $$s_v = \sum_{i<v^+} w_i \qquad \text{for} \quad v < u$$

First, we show that $(s_v)_{v<u}$ is nondecreasing, i.e.,

$$m \leq n \quad \text{implies} \quad s_m \leq s_n \qquad \text{for} \quad n < u$$

Now, in view of (32) and Definition 5, s_m is similar to the set $\bigcup\limits_{i<m^+} (w_i \times \{i\})$, well ordered according to Definition 7 of Chapter VII (page 309). Similarly, s_n is similar to the set $\bigcup\limits_{i<n^+} (w_i \times \{i\})$, well ordered according to Definition 7 of Chapter VII. However, since $m \leq n$, we see that $m + 1 \leq n + 1$ and thus, $\bigcup\limits_{i<m^+} (w_i \times \{i\}) \subset \bigcup\limits_{i<n^+} (w_i \times \{i\})$. Therefore, s_m is similar to s_n or to an initial segment of s_n. Consequently, $s_m \leq s_n$, as required.

Also, since $v < u$ implies $v^+ \leq u$, it follows from the above that:

(33) $$\sum_{i<v^+} w_i \leq \sum_{i<u} w_i \qquad \text{for} \quad v < u$$

Consequently, $s_v \leq s$ for every $v < u$. But this means that s is an upper bound of the set $(s_v)_{v<u}$ of all partial sums of s.

If u is not a limit ordinal, then $v^+ = u$, for some $v < u$. Therefore, in this case (33) shows that s is the least upper bound of $(s_v)_{v<u}$. Thus, the theorem is proved when u is not a limit ordinal.

Next, consider the case where u is a limit ordinal. Assume on the contrary that $s = \sum_{i<u} w_i$ is not the least upper bound of $(s_v)_{v<u}$. However, since s is an upper bound of $(s_v)_{v<u}$, there must exist an ordinal p such that $p < s$ and $s_v \leq p$, for every $v < u$. Thus, p is similar to an initial segment of s. Consequently, p is similar to an initial segment $I(a)$ of the set $\cup_{i<u} (w_i \times \{i\})$, well ordered according to Definition 7 of Chapter VII (page 309). Therefore, it follows that there exists $j < u$ such that $a \in (w_j \times \{j\})$. However, since u is a limit ordinal, $j^+ < u$, and hence $I(a)$ is an initial segment of $\cup_{i<j^+} (w_i \times \{i\})$, well ordered according to Definition 7 of Chapter VII. But this, in view of (32), means that p is equal to an initial segment of the partial sum s_j of s. Consequently, $p < s_j$, which contradicts the fact that $s_v \leq p$, for every $v < u$. Thus, our assumption is false, and indeed s is the least upper bound of $(s_v)_{v<u}$. Therefore, s is equal to the limit of the sequence of its partial sums, as desired.

The following examples illustrate some applications of Theorem 19.

$$1 + 1 + 1 + 1 + \cdots = \lim \{(1; 2; 3; 4; \ldots)\} = \omega$$
$$1 + 3 + 5 + 7 + \cdots = \lim \{(1; 4; 9; \ldots)\} = \omega$$
$$2 + 4 + 6 + 8 + \cdots = \lim \{(2; 6; 12; \ldots)\} = \omega$$

EXERCISES

1. Prove that $1 + 2 + 3 + 4 + \cdots$ remains equal to itself no matter how its terms are permuted.

2. Prove that $1 + 2 + \omega + 3 + 4 + \cdots$ remains equal to itself no matter how its terms are permuted.

3. Change the order of terms in the series

$$s = 1 + 2 + 3 + \cdots + \omega$$

such that the resulting series is distinct from s.

4. Let s be the limit of a nondecreasing sequence $(w_i)_{i<u}$ of ordinals w_i, where u is a limit ordinal. Prove that for every ordinal $v < s$ there exists an ordinal n such that:

$$v < w_i \leq s \qquad \text{for} \quad n \leq i < u$$

5. Prove Lemmas 6 and 7.

4. PRODUCT OF ORDINAL NUMBERS

The product of two ordinal numbers is introduced via the notion of the ordered product of two well ordered sets (see Chapter VII, Section 6) and the fundamental Theorem 12. However, as will be mentioned at the end of this section, the product of two ordinals can also be defined recursively by virtue of the axiom of Replacement.

Now, consider the two ordinals $2 = \{0,1\}$ and $3 = \{0,1,2\}$. The ordered product 2·3 is defined [see Definition 8, of Chapter VII (page 311)] as the set 2×3 ordered antilexicographically, i.e.,

$$2 \cdot 3 = \{((0,0); (1,0); (0,1); (1,1); (0,2); (1,2))\}$$

The above is a well ordered set and, in view of Theorem 12, is similar to a unique ordinal number equal to 6.

Motivated by the above, we introduce:

Definition 8.   *The (ordered) product of two ordinal numbers u and v (in this order) is denoted by uv and is defined by:*

$$uv = \overline{u \cdot v}$$

In the above, $\overline{u \cdot v}$ indicates the unique ordinal number similar to the well ordered set $u \cdot v$ (i.e., $u \times v$ ordered antilexicographically. See Definition 8 of Chapter VII.). The fact that $u \cdot v$ is well ordered follows from Lemma 12 of Chapter VII (page 311).

Accordingly, in view of considerations on page 312 and Theorem 12,

(34) $2\omega = \omega$ and $\omega 2 = \omega + \omega$

Hence, ordinal multiplication is *not commutative*.

Since by Theorem 12 a well ordered set is similar to a unique ordinal number, in view of Lemma 14 of Chapter VII (page 312), we have:

Lemma 8.   *For every three ordinal numbers u, v and w,*

$$u(vw) = (uv)w$$

Thus, ordinal multiplication is *associative*, and therefore there is no ambiguity in writing uvw for either $u(vw)$ or $(uv)w$.

Accordingly, in view of (34), we have:

$$\omega 2\omega = \omega(2\omega) = \omega\omega = (\omega 2)\omega = (\omega + \omega)\omega$$

Hence,

(35) $(\omega + \omega)\omega = \omega\omega$

Again, in view of Lemma 15 of Chapter VII (page 312), and in view of Theorem 12, we have:

Lemma 9.   *For every two ordinal numbers u and v,*

$$uv = \sum_{i<v} u_i$$

where $u_i = u$ for every $i < v$.

According to Lemma 9, the product uv of two ordinals u and v can be interpreted as a repeated addition, i.e., as *u taken v times*.

Thus, $\omega 2$ is $\omega + \omega$, whereas 2ω is 2 taken ω times, and hence is equal to ω.

Again, in view of Lemma 16 of Chapter VII (page 312), and in view of Theorem 12, we have:

Lemma 10. *For every three ordinal numbers u, v and w,*

$$u(v + w) = uv + uw$$

Thus, according to Lemma 10, ordinal multiplication is *left distributive* with respect to ordinal addition. However, ordinal multiplication is not right distributive with respect to ordinal addition, since as (35) shows:

$$(\omega + \omega)\omega = \omega\omega \neq \omega\omega + \omega\omega$$

A generalization of Lemma 10 is given by:

Lemma 11 (the left distributive law). *For every ordinal number v and every series $\sum_{i<u} w_i$ of ordinal numbers w_i we have:*

$$v \sum_{i<u} w_i = \sum_{i<u} vw_i$$

The proof of the above lemma is straightforward and is left to the reader.

Lemma 12. *For every ordinal*

$$u0 = 0u = 0 \qquad and \qquad u1 = 1u = u$$

The proof of the above lemma is straightforward and is left to the reader.

Lemma 13. *For every two ordinal numbers u and v,*

$$uv^+ = uv + u$$

PROOF. By Lemma 5, $v^+ = v + 1$; hence, in view of Lemmas 10 and 12, we have:

$$uv^+ = u(v + 1) = uv + u$$

In view of the above lemma, if v is not a limit ordinal and $v \neq 0$, then:

(36) $$uv = uv^- + u$$

Lemma 14. *For every two ordinal numbers u and v,*

$$uv = 0 \qquad if \ and \ only \ if \qquad u = 0 \qquad or \qquad v = 0$$

PROOF. The proof of Lemma 14 follows from the fact that the Cartesian product of two sets is empty if and only if one of the sets is empty.

Theorem 20. *For every three ordinal numbers u, v and w, if*

$$u > 0 \qquad and \qquad v > w$$

then,

$$uv > uw$$

PROOF. Since $v > w$, by Theorem 15 there exists an ordinal $a > 0$ such that $v = w + a$. But then by Lemma 10,

(37) $$uv = u(w + a) = uw + ua$$

However, by Lemma 14, $ua > 0$, and therefore by Theorem 14, $uw + ua > uw$. Hence, in view of (37) we derive

$$uv > uw$$

as desired.

Let us observe that if $v > w$, we have, in general,

$$vu \geq wu$$

For instance, $2 > 1$; however, $2\omega = \omega$.

Theorem 21. *For every four ordinal numbers e, c, u and v, if*

$$e \leq c \quad and \quad u \leq v$$

then,

$$eu \leq cv$$

PROOF. Clearly, the set $e \times u$, well ordered antilexicographically, is a subset of the set $c \times v$, well ordered antilexicographically. Thus, $e \times u$ is either similar to an initial segment of $c \times v$ or is similar to $c \times v$. Hence, $eu \leq cv$, as desired.

Corollary 12. *For every two ordinal numbers u and v, if*

$$u > 0 \quad and \quad v > 0$$

then,

$$uv \geq u \quad and \quad uv \geq v$$

PROOF. Since $u \leq u$ and $1 \leq v$, by Theorem 21, $u \leq uv$. Similarly, since $v \leq v$ and $1 \leq u$, by Theorem 21, $v \leq uv$.

Corollary 13. *For every two ordinal numbers u and v, if*

$$u > 0 \quad and \quad v > 1$$

then,

$$uv > u$$

PROOF. Since $u > 0$ and $v > 1$, by Theorem 20, $uv > u1$. However, by Lemma 12, $u1 = u$. Hence, indeed $uv > u$.

Corollary 14. *For every three ordinal numbers a, e and v,*

$$ae < av \quad implies \quad e < v$$

PROOF. Assume $e \geq v$. Then by Theorem 21, $ae \geq av$, contradicting the hypothesis. Thus, $ae < av$, as desired.

Corollary 15. *For every three ordinal numbers a, e and v,*

$$ae < ve \quad implies \quad a < v$$

PROOF. Assume $a \geq v$. Then by Theorem 21, $ae \geq ve$, contradicting the hypothesis. Thus, $ae < ve$, as desired.

Corollary 16. *For every three ordinal numbers u, v and w; if*

$$u > 0 \quad\text{and}\quad uv = uw$$

then:

$$v = w$$

PROOF.   If $v > w$, then by Theorem 20, $uv > uw$, contradicting the hypothesis. If $v < w$, then again by Theorem 20, $uv < uw$, contradicting the hypothesis. Thus, indeed $v = w$.

Let us observe that $uv = wv$, with $v > 0$, does not necessarily imply $u = w$. For instance, $2\omega = 3\omega = \omega$, although $2 \neq 3$.

Theorem 22. *For every two ordinal numbers w and b, if $b > 0$, then there exists a unique pair of ordinals q and r such that:*

$$w = bq + r \quad\text{and}\quad r < b$$

PROOF.   Let us observe that, in view of Corollary 12,

$$b(w + 1) \geq w + 1 > w$$

On the other hand, $b(w + 1)$ is similar to the set $b \times (w + 1)$, well ordered antilexicographically, i.e.,

$$b(w + 1) = \overline{\{((b_0,w_0); (b_1, w_0); (b_2,w_0); \ldots)\}}$$

where:

$$b = \{(b_0; b_1; b_2; \ldots)\} \quad\text{and}\quad w = \{(w_0; w_1; w_2; \ldots)\}$$

Now, since $w < b(w + 1)$, there exists an initial segment $I(b_u, w_v)$ of $\{((b_0, w_0); (b_0,w_1); (b_0,w_2); \ldots)\}$ similar to w. Obviously, $I(b_u,w_v)$ contains all the pairs (b_i,w_j) for which $w_j < w_v$ or $w_j = w_v$ and $b_i < b_u$. Moreover, b_u determines the initial segment $I(b_u)$ of b, and w_v determines the initial segment $I(w_v)$ of $w + 1$. Clearly

$$I(b_u,w_v) = b \cdot I(w_v) + I(b_u) \cdot \{w_v\}$$

where $I(b_u) \cdot \{w_v\}$ is similar to an initial segment of b.

From the above equality, we obtain

$$\overline{I(b_u,w_v)} = \overline{b \cdot I(w_v)} + \overline{I(b_u) \cdot \{w_v\}}$$

where:

$$\overline{I(b_u) \cdot \{w_v\}} < b$$

Let $\overline{I(w_v)} = q$ and $\overline{I(b_u) \cdot \{w_v\}} = r$. Consequently,

$$w = bq + r \quad\text{with}\quad r < b$$

To prove that q and r are unique, let us assume the contrary. Clearly, in view of Theorem 15, it is enough to assume that $q \neq m$ and

$$w = bq + r = bm + c \quad\text{with}\quad r < b \quad\text{and}\quad c < b$$

Since $q \neq m$, without loss of generality we may suppose that $q + 1 \leq m$, and therefore in view of our assumption and Theorems 15 and 21,

$$bq + b + c \leq bq + r$$

However, the above inequality contradicts the fact that $r < b$. Hence our assumption is false, and indeed $q = m$. But then $bq + r = bq + c$, which in view of Theorem 15 implies that $r = c$. Thus, indeed in $w = bq + r$ with $r < b$, the ordinals q and r are uniquely determined by w and b.

From Theorem 22, it follows that every ordinal w is uniquely represented as:

$$w = \omega q + r \qquad \text{where} \quad r \text{ is a finite ordinal}$$

In particular, if w is a limit ordinal, then:

$$w = \omega q \qquad \text{for some ordinal } q$$

From Theorem 22, it also follows that every ordinal number w is such that either $w = 2q$ or $w = 2q + 1$, for some ordinal q. In the former case, w is called *even*, in the latter, *odd*.

Theorem 23. *For every ordinal number v and every set W of ordinal numbers, we have:*

$$v(\cup W) = \cup \{vw \mid \cdots\}$$

where $\{vw \mid \cdots\}$ is the set of all ordinals vw with $w \in W$.

PROOF. If $v = 0$, then the proof of the theorem is trivial. Therefore, in what follows we suppose $v > 0$.

By Theorem 8, $\cup W$ and $\cup \{vw \mid \cdots\}$ are ordinals, respectively equal to the least upper bounds of the sets W and $\{vw \mid \cdots\}$.

First, consider the case where W has a greatest element g. Thus, $\cup W = g$ and $v(\cup W) = vg$. Moreover, since $g \geq w$, for every $w \in W$, we see that $vg \geq vw$, for every $w \in W$. However, $vg \in \{vw \mid \cdots\}$, and therefore $vg = \cup \{vw \mid \cdots\}$. But since, as shown above, $v(\cup W) = vg$, we see that $v(\cup W) = \cup \{vw \mid \cdots\}$, as desired.

Next, consider the case where W has no greatest element. Thus, $\cup W > w$, for every $w \in W$, and since $v > 0$, by Lemma 14, $v(\cup W) > vw$ for every $w \in W$. Consequently, $v(\cup W)$ is an upper bound of $\{vw \mid \cdots\}$. Let u be any other upper bound of $\{vw \mid \cdots\}$. Since W has no greatest element, $\{vw \mid \cdots\}$ has no greatest element either. Thus, $u > vw$ for every $w \in W$. Now, since $v > 0$, by Theorem 22,

$$u = vq + r \qquad \text{with} \qquad r < v$$

Consequently, $v(q + 1) = vq + v > u$, and therefore

$$v(q + 1) > vw \qquad \text{for every} \quad w \in W$$

which, in view of Corollary 14, implies $q + 1 > w$, for every $w \in W$. Thus, $q + 1 \geq \cup W$. However, $\cup W$ cannot have an immediate predecessor. Otherwise, W would have a greatest element. Consequently, $q \geq \cup W$. Then $u = vq + r \geq v(\cup W) + r \geq v(\cup W)$, which implies that $v(\cup W)$ is the least upper bound of $\{uv \mid \cdots\}$, as desired.

Corollary 17. *For every ordinal number v and every nondecreasing sequence $(w_i)_{i<u}$ of ordinal numbers w_i, we have:*

$$\lim_{i<u} (vw_i) = v \lim_{i<u} w_i$$

Note that $\lim_{i<u} (w_i v)$ is not necessarily equal to $(\lim_{i<u} w_i)v$. For instance,

$$\lim_{i<\omega} (i\omega) = \omega < (\lim_{i<\omega} i)\omega = \omega\omega$$

Theorem 24. *For every ordinal number v and every limit ordinal w, we have:*

$$vw = \bigcup_{u<w} vu$$

PROOF. Since w is a limit ordinal, by Theorem 9, $\cup w = w$. Also by Theorem 5, $w = \{u \mid \cdots\}$ where $u < w$. Consequently, Theorem 24 follows from Theorem 23.

Remark 4. At the beginning of this section, we mentioned that the multiplication of ordinals can be defined recursively. This definition is justified by virtue of the axiom of Replacement, the Transfinite Recursion Theorem and Theorem 8.

The recursive definition of ordinal multiplication is given as follows: *for every two ordinal numbers v and w,*

(38) $$v0 = 0$$

(39) $$vw = vw^- + v \qquad \textit{if } w \textit{ is not a limit ordinal and } w \neq 0$$

(40) $$vw = \bigcup_{u<w} vu \qquad \textit{if } w \textit{ is a limit ordinal}$$

Naturally, (38), (39) and (40) are consequences of Definition 8. As a matter of fact, Lemma 12, (36) and Theorem 24 imply (38), (39) and (40), respectively. Accordingly, we have:

$$\omega 2 = \omega + \omega$$
$$\omega 3 = \omega 2 + \omega$$
$$\omega\omega = \lim \{(\omega; \omega 2; \omega 3; \ldots)\}$$

EXERCISES

1. Let u and v be ordinals. Prove that if $u > 0$ and v is a limit ordinal, then uv, as well as vu, is a limit ordinal.

2. Let u, v and w be ordinals. Prove that if $u > v$ and if w is neither zero nor a limit ordinal, then $uw > vw$.

3. Prove that if u, v and w are ordinals such that $uw = vw$, and if w is neither zero nor a limit ordinal, then $u = v$.

4. Let u, v and w be ordinals. Prove that if $uw = vw$ and $u \neq v$, then w is zero or a limit ordinal.

5. Let u and v be ordinals. Prove that $uv = vu$ if and only if $uuvv = vvuu$.

6. Let u, v and w be ordinals. Prove that if $u < vw$, then $u = va + c$ for some $a < w$ and some $c < v$.

7. Prove that u is a limit ordinal or zero if and only if $nu = u$ for every finite ordinal number n.

8. Let u be an ordinal that is neither zero nor a limit ordinal and let v be, zero or a limit ordinal. Prove that for every $w > 0$, $(w + 1)u > wu$ and $(w + 1)v = wv$.

9. Let $u > 0$ be a limit ordinal and v be neither zero nor a limit ordinal. Prove that $(u + 1)v = uv + 1$.

10. Let u and v be two nonzero ordinals. Prove that uv is not a limit ordinal if and only if u and v are not limit ordinals.

11. Prove Lemmas 11 and 12.

12. Prove (36) and Corollary 17.

5. INFINITE PRODUCTS OF ORDINAL NUMBERS

Let us again observe (see Chapter VII, Section 6) that in contrast with the possibility of defining infinite (well ordered) sums of ordinals by extension of the definition of finite (well ordered) sums of ordinals, infinite (well ordered) products of ordinals cannot be defined by extension of the definition of finite (well ordered) products of ordinals. For instance, the product set $\prod_{i \in \omega} V_i$, where V_i is the ordinal 2 (for every $i \in \omega$), cannot be ordered antilexicographically. Indeed, corresponding to the two sequences 0, 1, 0, 1, 0, 1, . . . and 1, 0, 1, 0, 1, 0, . . . there are no last different terms with the same index.

Motivated by Theorem 19, which asserts that every series of ordinal numbers is equal to the limit of the sequence of its partial sums, it is possible to give a satisfactory definition of a (well ordered) product of infinitely many positive ordinals. This is done by defining the partial products of the terms of a sequence of positive ordinals. When the partial product of a sequence $(w_i)_{i \in u}$ of positive ordinals is defined, then the product of $(w_i)_{i \in u}$ is defined as the limit of the sequence of partial products of $(w_i)_{i \in u}$. The definition of the partial products of a sequence of positive ordinals employs the notion of the (well ordered) finite products of ordinals, and it is in this sense that (well ordered) products of infinitely many ordinals are related to those of finitely many ordinals.

However, it can easily be seen that the definition of an arbitrary partial product of a sequence $(w_i)_{i < u}$ of positive ordinals and the definition of the product of the sequence $(w_i)_{i < u}$ are equivalent problems. Thus, we give below the definition of the product of a sequence $(w_i)_{i < u}$ of positive ordinals and prove later that the product of $(w_i)_{i < u}$ is the limit of the sequence of the partial products of $(w_i)_{i < u}$.

The definition of the product of a sequence $(w_i)_{i < u}$ of positive ordinals w_i is given recursively, and its existence is secured by the theorem below (whose proof is based on the Transfinite Recursion Theorem).

Theorem 25.   *For every sequence* $(w_i)_{i<u}$ *of type* $u > 0$ *of ordinal numbers* w_i *there exists a unique function* h *defined on the ordinal* u *such that its values are ordinal numbers and:*

$$h(0) = w_0$$
$$h(i) = h(i^-)w_i \qquad \textit{if} \ \ i < u \ \ \textit{is not a limit ordinal and} \ i \neq 0$$
$$h(i) = \bigcup_{j<i} h(j) \qquad \textit{if} \ \ i < u \ \ \textit{is a limit ordinal}$$

PROOF.   Consider the binary predicate $p(x,y)$ defined by

(i) $p(0) = (0,w_0)$

(ii) $p(x) = (i, x(i^-) \cdot w_i)$ if x is an ordinal valued function whose domain is the ordinal i, where $i < u$ and i is not a limit ordinal and $i \neq 0$.

(iii) $p(x) = (i, \bigcup_{j<i} x(j))$ if x is an ordinal valued function defined on the ordinal i, where $i < u$ and i is a limit ordinal.

(iv) $p(x) = (x,0)$ if $x \neq 0$ and x is not as given in (ii) or (iii).

In the above, w_0 and w_i are elements of $(w_i)_{i<u}$ as given in the hypothesis of the theorem.

It can be easily verified that $p(x,y)$, defined by (i), (ii), (iii) and (iv), is a binary predicate, functional in x.

Now, since the ordinal u is a well ordered set, in view of the Transfinite Recursion Theorem (Theorem 21, Chapter VII, page 299), there exists a unique function g defined on u and such that:

$$g(w) = p(g^1(I(w))) \qquad \text{for every} \ \ w \in u$$

Clearly,

$$g(0) = p(0) = (0,w_0), \qquad g(1) = p(\{(0,w_0)\}) = (1,w_0 w_1),$$
$$g(2) = p(\{(0,w_0), (1,w_0 w_1)\}) = (2, w_0 w_1 w_2), \qquad \text{and so forth.}$$

To prove the existence and the uniqueness of a function h satisfying the properties mentioned in Theorem 25, it is enough to take:

$$h(i) = \text{the second coordinate of } g(i)$$

The existence and the uniqueness of h are secured by the existence and the uniqueness of g.

Obviously, the values of the function h are ordinal numbers. This is because the product of two ordinal numbers, as well as the union of a set of ordinal numbers (see Theorem 8), is an ordinal number.

Next, referring to Theorem 25, we introduce:

Definition 9.   *The product (ordered product) of a sequence* $(w_i)_{i<u}$ *of type* $u > 0$ *of positive ordinals* w_i *is denoted by*

$$\prod_{i<u} w_i$$

and is defined as the ordinal

$$h(u^-) \qquad \text{if} \quad u > 0 \text{ is not a limit ordinal}$$

and

$$\bigcup_{i < u} h(i) \qquad \text{if} \quad u \text{ is a limit ordinal}$$

where h is the function defined in Theorem 25.

In the above definition, for obvious reasons we have confined ourselves to a sequence $(w_i)_{i < u}$ of positive ordinals w_i. Naturally, if $w_i = 0$, for some $i < u$, then as expected we set

$$(41) \qquad \prod_{i < u} w_i = 0 \qquad \text{for} \qquad u > 0$$

in order to extend Definition 9 to include sequences of ordinal numbers containing the zero ordinal as a term.

Now, if according to (83) of Chapter III (page 162), we set

$$(42) \qquad \prod_{i < 0} w_i = 1$$

then in view of Definition 9, for a sequence $(w_i)_{i < u}$ of type u of positive ordinals w_i, we have:

$$(43) \qquad \prod_{i < u} w_i = \left(\prod_{i < u^-} w_i \right) w_{u^-} \qquad \text{if} \quad u > 0 \text{ is not a limit ordinal}$$

and

$$(44) \qquad \prod_{i < u} w_i = \bigcup_{i < u} \left(\prod_{j < i} w_j \right) \qquad \text{if} \quad u \text{ is a limit ordinal.}$$

Definition 10. *Let $(w_i)_{i < u}$ be a sequence of type $u > 0$ of positive ordinals w_i. Then the ordinal P_v given by*

$$p_v = \prod_{i < v^+} w_i \qquad \text{with} \quad v < u$$

is called the v-th partial product of $(w_i)_{i < u}$.

Thus, the first four partial products of $(w_i)_{i < 6}$ are:

$$p_0 = w_0, \qquad p_1 = w_0 w_1, \qquad p_2 = w_0 w_1 w_2, \qquad p_3 = w_0 w_1 w_2 w_3$$

The set of all partial products of a sequence $(w_i)_{i < u}$ of type $u > 0$ of positive ordinals w_i is (in an obvious way) again a sequence of the same type. Also, since $w_i > 0$, for every $i < u$, the sequence of partial products is nondecreasing.

Theorem 26. *For every sequence $(w_i)_{i < u}$ of type $u > 0$ of positive ordinal numbers w_i the product of $(w_i)_{i < u}$ is equal to the limit of the partial products of $(w_i)_{i < u}$, i.e.,*

$$\prod_{i < u} w_i = \lim_{v < u} \prod_{i < v^+} w_i$$

PROOF. If $u > 0$ is not a limit ordinal, then u has a last element, and therefore there is an ordinal v such that $v^+ = u$. Consequently, in view of (43), (44) and Definition 10, the nondecreasing sequence of the partial products of $(w_i)_{i < u}$ has a largest element, namely $\prod_{i<v^+} w_i$, which is equal to the limit of the sequence of the partial products. But clearly (since $v^+ = u$), this limit is equal to $\prod_{i<u} w_i$, as desired.

If u is a limit ordinal, then for every $v < u$ we have $v^+ < u$. Consequently, the theorem follows from (43), (44) and Definition 10.

In view of Theorem 26, we have:

$$2 \cdot 3 \cdot 5 \cdot 4 = \lim \{(2;6;30;120)\} = 120$$
$$2 \cdot 2 \cdot 2 \cdot 2 \cdot 2 \cdots = \lim \{(2; 4; 8; 16; 32; \ldots)\} = \omega$$
$$1 \cdot 2 \cdot 3 \cdot 4 \cdot 5 \cdots = \lim \{(1; 2; 6; 24; 30; \ldots)\} = \omega$$

However, let us observe that:

$$2 \cdot 3 \cdot 0 \cdot 5 = 0 \neq \cup \{2,6,0,0\} = 6$$

The above explains why it is assumed in Definition 9 that $(w_i)_{i<u}$ is a sequence of positive ordinal numbers w_i.

Again, in view of Theorem 26, we have:

$$2 \cdot \omega \cdot 3 \cdot 4 \cdot 5 \ldots = \lim \{(2; 2\omega; \omega3; \omega12; \omega60; \ldots)\} = \omega\omega$$

EXERCISES

1. Let $(w_i)_{i<u}$ and $(v_i)_{i<u}$ be two sequences of type u of ordinals w_i and v_i. Prove that if $w_i \leq v_i$ for every $i < u$, then $\prod_{i<u} w_i \leq \prod_{i<u} v_i$

2. Let $(w_i)_{i<u}$ be a sequence of type $u > 0$ of ordinals w_i. Let v be an ordinal. Prove that:

$$v \prod_{i<u} w_i = \prod_{i<u} v w_i$$

Give an example to show that, in general,

$$\left(\prod_{i<u} w_i\right) v \neq \prod_{i<u} w_i v$$

3. Prove that:

$$(2 \cdot \omega \cdot 3 \cdot \omega \cdot 4 \cdot \omega \ldots) = (\omega \cdot \omega \cdot \omega \cdot \omega \ldots)$$

4. Let $(w_i)_{i>\omega}$ be a sequence of ordinals such that $w_i = n$ for every $i < \omega$, where $n > 1$ is a finite ordinal. Prove that:

$$\sum_{i<\omega} w_i = \prod_{i<\omega} w_i = \omega$$

5. Using the definition of finite products of ordinals justify

$$\prod_{i<0} w_i = 1$$

and prove (43).

6. Prove that:

$$(\omega + 1)(\omega + 1)(\omega + 1) \cdots = \omega \cdot \omega \cdot \omega \cdots$$

7. Give an example of a sequence $(w_i)_{i<\omega}$ of ordinals w_i such that $\prod\limits_{i<\omega} w_i$ assumes at least 3 different values as some of the factors are interchanged.

6. EXPONENTIATION OF ORDINAL NUMBERS

Just as in ordinary arithmetic, in the arithmetic of ordinals also, exponentiation is defined as a repeated multiplication; i.e., the exponentiation of an ordinal w by an ordinal u (denoted by w^u) is defined as the product of the sequence $(w_i)_{i<u}$ where $w_i = w$ for every $i < u$. In other words,

$$w^u = \prod_{i<u} w_i \quad \text{with} \quad w_i = w \quad \text{for every} \quad i < u$$

In view of the above, we introduce:

Definition 11. *Let w and u be two ordinals. Then the u-th power of w, denoted by w^u is defined as:*

(45) $$w^u = \prod_{i<u} w_i \quad \text{with} \quad w_i = w \quad \text{for every} \quad i < u$$

Clearly, in view of (41), (42) and Definition 11, we have:

(46) $$0^u = 0 \quad \text{for every ordinal number} \quad u > 0$$

(47) $$w^0 = 1 \quad \text{for every ordinal number} \quad w$$

Accordingly, we have:

$$2^3 = 2 \cdot 2 \cdot 2 = \lim \{(2; 4; 6)\} = 6$$
$$2^\omega = 2 \cdot 2 \cdot 2 \cdot 2 \cdots = \lim \{(2; 4; 8; 16; \ldots)\} = \omega$$
$$\omega^2 = \omega \cdot \omega$$
$$\omega^3 = \omega \cdot \omega \cdot \omega$$
$$\omega^\omega = \omega \cdot \omega \cdot \omega \cdot \omega \cdots = \lim \{(\omega; \omega^2; \omega^3; \ldots)\}$$

Note that each of the ordinals $\omega, \omega^2, \omega^3, \ldots$ is a denumerable ordinal, and hence ω^ω is also a denumerable ordinal.

Theorem 27. *For every two ordinal numbers w and u,*

(48) $$w^u = (w^{u^-})w \quad \text{if } u > 0 \text{ is not a limit ordinal.}$$

(49) $$w^u = \bigcup_{i<u} w^i \quad \text{if } u \text{ is a limit ordinal and } w > 0.$$

PROOF. If $w = 0$ and $u > 0$ is not a limit ordinal, then by (46) and Lemma 12,

$$w^u = 0^u = 0 = (0^{u^-})0 = 0 = (w^{u^-})w.$$

Thus, the theorem is true for $w = 0$. Hence, in what follows we suppose $w > 0$.

If $u > 0$ is not a limit ordinal, then by (45) and (43), with $w_i = w$, for $i < u$, we have:

$$w^u = \prod_{i<u} w_i = \left(\prod_{i<u^-} w_i \right) w_{u^-} = (w^{u^-})w$$

If u is a limit ordinal, then by (45) and (44), with $w_i = w$, for $i < u$, we have:

$$w^u = \prod_{i<u} w_i = \bigcup_{i<u} \left(\prod_{j<i} w_j \right) = \bigcup_{i<u} w^i$$

Lemma 15.   *For every ordinal u,*

$$u^1 = u \qquad and \qquad 1^u = 1$$

PROOF.   By (48), (47) and Lemma 12, we have:

$$u^1 = (u^0)u = u$$

To prove $1^u = 1$, we use transfinite induction on u.

If $u = 0$, then in view of (47) we have $1^u = 1$.

Now, assume that $u > 0$ is not a limit ordinal and that $1^{u^-} = 1$. But then by (48),

$$1^u = (1^{u^-})1 = 1 \cdot 1 = 1$$

Next, assume that u is a limit ordinal and that $1^i = 1$ for every $i < u$. But then by (49),

$$1^u = \bigcup_{i<u} 1^i = \bigcup_{i<u} 1 = 1$$

Lemma 16.   *For every two ordinals u and w,*

$$w > 0 \qquad implies \qquad w^u > 0$$

PROOF.   We use transfinite induction on u.

If $u = 0$, then the proof follows from (47).

Now, assume that $u > 0$ is not a limit ordinal and that $w^{u^-} > 0$. But then in view of Lemma 14 and (48),

$$w^u = w^{u^-}w > 0$$

Next, assume that u is a limit ordinal and that $w^i > 0$ for every $i < u$. But then in view of (49)

$$w^u = \bigcup_{i<u} w^i > 0$$

Theorem 28.   *For every three ordinals u, v and w,*

$$w > 1 \qquad and \qquad v < u \qquad implies \qquad w^v < w^u$$

PROOF.   We use transfinite induction on u.

If $u = 0$, then the proof is trivial.

Now, assume that $u > 0$ is not a limit ordinal and that $v < u^-$ implies $w^v < w^{u^-}$. But then since $v < u$ implies $v \leq u^-$, we see that $v < u$ implies $w^v \leq w^{u^-}$. However, $w > 1$, and consequently in view of Lemma 16, Theorem 20 and (48),

$$w^v < w^{u^-}w = w^u$$

Next, assume u is a limit ordinal and that $w^v < w^i$, for every i such that $v < i < u$. But then by (49),

$$w^v < \bigcup_{v<i<u} w^i \leq \bigcup_{i<u} w^i = w^u$$

Corollary 18. *For every three ordinals u, v and w*

$$w > 0 \qquad and \qquad v \leq u \qquad implies \qquad w^v \leq w^u$$

The proof of the above corollary follows from Lemma 15 and Theorem 28.

Corollary 19. *For every three ordinal numbers u, v and w, if w > 1 then*

$$w^u = w^v \qquad implies \qquad u = v$$

and

$$w^u < w^v \qquad implies \qquad u < v$$

The proof of the above corollary follows from Theorem 28.

Theorem 29. *Let $(v_i)_{i<u}$ be a nonempty family of ordinal numbers and let $v = \bigcup_{i<u} v_i$. Then, for every positive ordinal w,*

$$(50) \qquad \bigcup_{i<u} w^{v_i} = w^v$$

PROOF. If v is not a limit ordinal, then since $v = \bigcup_{i<u} v_i$, we have $v = v_j$ for some $j < u$ and thus:

$$(51) \qquad w^{v_j} = w^v \qquad \text{for some} \quad j < u$$

Again, since $v = \bigcup_{i<u} v_i$ we have $v_i \leq v$ for every $i < u$, and therefore by Corollary 18, $w^{v_i} \leq w^v$ for every $i < u$. Hence, $w^{v_j} \leq \bigcup_{i<u} w^{v_i} \leq w^v$, which in view of (51) yields (50), as desired.

Now, let v be a limit ordinal. Then again, since $v = \bigcup_{i<u} v_i$, we have $v_i \leq v$, for every $i < u$. Therefore, by Corollary 18, $w^{v_i} \leq w^v$ for every $i < u$. Hence,

$$(52) \qquad \bigcup_{i<u} w^{v_i} \leq w^v$$

However, by (49), $w^v = \bigcup_{k<v} w^k$. Thus, from (52) it follows that:

$$(53) \qquad \bigcup_{i<u} w^{v_i} \leq \bigcup_{k<v} w^k = w^v$$

Now, since $v = \bigcup_{i<u} v_i$, for every $k < v$, there exists an $i < u$ such that $k < v_i \leq v$, which, in view of Corollary 18, yields:

$$\bigcup_{k<v} w^k \leq \bigcup_{i<u} w^{v_i}$$

Comparing the above relations with (53), in view of (49), we obtain (50), as desired.

Corollary 20. *For every limit ordinal u and every ordinal number s and every positive ordinal number w we have:*

(54)
$$\bigcup_{i<u} w^{s+i} = w^{s+u}$$

Moreover,

(55)
$$\bigcup_{i<u} w^{si} = w^{si}$$

PROOF. To prove (54), it is enough to take in Theorem 29, $v_i = s + i$, and to observe that by Theorem 17, $s + u = \bigcup_{i<u} s + i$.

To prove (55), it is enough to take in Theorem 29, $v_i = si$, and to observe that by Theorem 24, $su = \bigcup_{i<u} si$.

Corollary 21. *For every nondecreasing sequence $(v_i)_{i<u}$ of type $u > 0$ of ordinal numbers v_i and every positive ordinal number w, we have:*

$$\lim_{i<u} w^{v_i} = w^{\lim_{i<u} v_i}$$

PROOF. The proof follows from Theorem 29 and the fact that $\lim_{i<u} v_i = \bigcup_{i<u} v_i$.

Theorem 30. *For every three ordinal numbers u, v and w, we have:*

$$w^v \cdot w^u = w^{v+u}$$

PROOF. We use transfinite induction on u.

If $u = 0$, then in view of (47) and Lemmas 12 and 4,

$$w^v \cdot w^u = w^v \cdot w^0 = w^v = w^{v+0}$$

Now, assume that $u > 0$ is not a limit ordinal and that $w^v \cdot w^{u^-} = w^{v+u^-}$. But then in view of the fact that $v + u$ is not a limit ordinal, (48), the associativity of multiplication and the fact that $(v + u^-) = (v + u)^-$, we have:

$$w^v w^u = w^v(w^{u^-})w = w^{v+u^-}w = w^{(v+u)^-}w = w^{v+u}$$

Next, assume that u is a limit ordinal [we suppose $w > 0$, since, if $w = 0$, the proof follows from (46)], and that $w^v w^i = w^{v+i}$, for every $i < u$. But then by (49), Theorem 24 and (54),

$$w^v w^u = w^v \bigcup_{i<u} w^i = \bigcup_{i<u} w^v w^i = w^{v+u}$$

Thus Theorem 30 is proved.

Accordingly, we have:

$$\omega \cdot \omega^\omega = \omega^{1+\omega} = \omega^\omega = \lim \{(\omega; \omega^2; \omega^3; \ldots)\}$$
$$\omega^\omega \cdot \omega = \omega^{\omega+1} \neq \omega \cdot \omega^\omega$$
$$\omega^\omega \cdot \omega^\omega = \omega^{\omega 2} = \lim \{(\omega; \omega^{\omega+1}; \omega^{\omega+2}; \omega^{\omega+3}; \ldots)\}$$

Note that each of the above ordinal numbers is denumerable.

Theorem 31. *For every three ordinal numbers u, v and w:*

$$(w^v)^u = w^{vu}$$

PROOF. We use transfinite induction on u.

If $u = 0$, then in view of (47) and Lemma 12,

$$(w^v)^u = (w^v)^0 = 1 = w^0 = w^{vu}$$

Now, assume $u > 0$ is not a limit ordinal and that $(w^v)^{u^-} = w^{vu^-}$. But then in view of Theorem 30 and the fact that $(vu^- + v) = vu$, we have:

$$(w^v)^u = (w^v)^{u^-}(w^v) = w^{vu^-} \cdot w^v = w^{vu^-+v} = w^{vu}$$

Next, assume u is a limit ordinal [we suppose $w > 0$ and $v > 0$, since if $w = 0$ or $v = 0$ the proof follows from (47) and (46)], and that $(w^v)^i = w^{vi}$ for every $i < u$. But then by (49) and (55),

$$(w^v)^u = \bigcup_{i<u} (w^v)^i = \bigcup_{i<u} w^{vi} = w^{vu}$$

Thus, Theorem 31 is proved.

Accordingly, we have:

$$(\omega^\omega)^\omega = \omega^{\omega^2} = \lim \{(\omega; \omega^{\omega 2}; \omega^{\omega 3}; \omega^{\omega 4}; \ldots)$$
$$(2^\omega)^2 = 2^{\omega 2} = \lim \{(2^\omega; 2^{\omega+1}; 2^{\omega+2}; \ldots)\}$$
$$= \lim \{(\omega; \omega 2; \omega 4; \ldots)\} = \omega^2$$
$$(2^\omega)^\omega = 2^{\omega^2} = \lim \{(2^\omega; 2^{\omega 2}; 2^{\omega 3}; \ldots)\}$$
$$= \lim \{(\omega; \omega^2; \omega^3; \ldots)\} = \omega^\omega$$
$$(n^\omega)^\omega = \omega^\omega \quad \text{for} \quad 1 < n < \omega$$

Note that each of the ordinals in the above is denumerable.

Theorem 32. *For every two ordinal numbers u and w:*

$$w > 1 \qquad implies \qquad w^u \geq u$$

PROOF. We use transfinite induction on u.

If $u = 0$, then the proof follows from (47).

Now, assume that $u > 0$ is not a limit ordinal and that $w^{u^-} \geq u^-$. Then by Theorem 21 and (48),

$$w^{u^-} w \geq u^- w \qquad \text{or} \qquad w^u \geq (u-1)w$$

However, since $w > 1$ we have $w \geq 2$, and from the above, again in view of Theorem 21, we derive:

$$w^u \geq (u-1)2 \qquad \text{or} \qquad w^u \geq (u-1) + (u-1)$$

Since by Lemma 15, the theorem holds for $u = 1$, in the last inequality we may suppose $u \geq 2$ and obtain:

$$w^u \geq (u-1) + 1 \qquad \text{or} \qquad w^u \geq u$$

Next, assume that u is a limit ordinal and that $w^i \geq i$ for every $i < u$. Since $w > 1$, in view of (49) and Theorems 8 and 9, we derive:

$$\bigcup_{i<u} w^i \geq \bigcup_{i<u} i \quad \text{or} \quad w^u \geq u$$

Theorem 33. *For every three ordinal numbers u, v and w:*

$$v \leq w \quad implies \quad v^u \leq w^u$$

PROOF. We use transfinite induction on u.

If $u = 0$, then the proof follows from (47).

Now, assume $u > 0$ is not a limit ordinal and that $v^{u^-} \leq w^{u^-}$. But then in view of Theorem 21 and (48) we have $v^{u^-}v \leq w^{u^-}w$ or $v^u \leq w^u$.

Next, assume u is a limit ordinal [we suppose $v > 0$, since, if $v = 0$, the proof follows from (47) and (46)] and that $v^i \leq w^i$, for every $i < u$. But then in view of Theorem 8 and (49) we derive:

$$\bigcup_{i<u} v^i \leq \bigcup_{i<u} w^i \quad \text{or} \quad v^u \leq w^u$$

Theorem 34. *For every ordinal $w > 1$ and every ordinal $u > 0$, there exists a unique ordinal v such that:*

$$w^v \leq u < w^{v+1}$$

PROOF. By Theorems 28 and 32, for every two ordinals u and w, with $w > 1$,

$$u \leq w^u < w^{u+1}$$

Therefore there exists an ordinal, say, r, such that $u < w^r$. Let s denote the smallest such ordinal r. Hence,

(56) $$u < w^s$$

We shall show that s is not a limit ordinal. Assume on the contrary that s is a limit ordinal. Consequently,

$$c + 1 < s \quad \text{for every } c < s$$

However, in view of the definition of s, we have $u \geq w^{c+1}$ or:

$$u > w^c \quad \text{for every } c < s$$

Thus, $u \geq w^s$, which contradicts (56). Hence our assumption is false, and indeed s is not a limit ordinal.

Consequently, $s = v + 1$, for some ordinal v, and therefore

(57) $$w^v \leq u < w^{v+1}$$

as desired.

Now, let us show that v is unique. Assume that the ordinal e is such that:

$$w^e \leq u < w^{e+1}$$

Comparing the above with (57), we derive

$$w^e < w^{v+1} \quad \text{and} \quad w^v < w^{e+1}$$

which, in view of Corollary 19, implies:

$$e < v + 1 \quad \text{and} \quad v < e + 1$$

or

$$e \leq v \quad \text{and} \quad v \leq e$$

Hence, $e = v$, as desired.

Theorem 35. *For every ordinal number $b > 1$, every ordinal number $u > 0$ can be uniquely represented as*

$$(58) \qquad u = b^{e_1}c_1 + b^{e_2}c_2 + \cdots + b^{e_n}c_n$$

where $n \geq 1$ is a finite ordinal number and the ordinal numbers c_i and e_i satisfy the inequalities:

$$e_1 > e_2 > \cdots > e_n \geq 0$$

and

$$0 < c_i < b \qquad \text{for} \quad i = 1, 2, \ldots, n$$

PROOF.   By Theorem 34, there exists a unique ordinal number $e_1 \geq 0$ such that:

$$(59) \qquad b^{e_1} \leq u < b^{e_1+1}$$

Also, in view of Lemma 16 and Theorem 22, there exist ordinals c_1 and r_1 such that:

$$(60) \qquad u = b^{e_1}c_1 + r_1' \quad \text{with} \quad r_1 < b^{e_1}$$

From (59), (60) and Lemma 16, we derive

$$0 < b^{e_1}c_1 < b^{e_1+1} \quad \text{or} \quad 0 < b^{e_1}c_1 < b^{e_1}b$$

which in view of Corollary 19 implies $0 < c_1 < b$.

If $r_1 = 0$, then (60) gives a representation of u of the form (58), since $e_1 \geq 0$ and $0 < c_1 < b$.

If $r_1 > 0$, then in view of the above (replacing u by r_1), we obtain:

$$(61) \qquad r_1 = b^{e_2}c_2 + r_2 \quad \text{with} \quad r_2 < b^{e_2}$$

and

$$0 < c_2 < b$$

If $r_2 = 0$, then in view of (60) and (61) we have

$$(62) \qquad w = b^{e_1}c_1 + b^{e_2}c_2$$

where:

$$b^{e_1} > r_1 \geq b^{e_2}, \quad \text{which implies} \quad e_1 > e_2 \geq 0$$

Consequently, if $r_2 = 0$, then (62) is a representation of u of the form (58), since $e_1 > e_2 \geq 0$ and $0 < c_i < b$, for $i = 1, 2$.

If $r_2 > 0$, then in view of the above we obtain

$$r_2 = b^{e_3}c_3 + r_3 \quad \text{with} \quad r_3 < b^{e_3}$$

where

$$e_1 > e_2 > e_3 \geq 0 \qquad \text{and} \qquad 0 < c_3 < b$$

and we may continue the process.

However, in view of Corollary 6 the decreasing sequence of ordinals $e_1 > e_2 > e_3 \ldots$ must have finitely many terms. Therefore, there must exist a finite ordinal $n \geq 1$ such that $r_n = 0$ and corresponding to which

$$w = b^{e_1}c_1 + b^{e_2}c_2 + \cdots + b^{e_n}c_n$$

with

$$e_1 > e_2 > \cdots > e_n \geq 0$$

and:

$$0 < c_i < b \qquad \text{for} \quad i = 1, 2, \ldots, n$$

Thus, a representation of u of the form (58) is obtained.

To prove the uniqueness of (58), let us assume that u has another representation of the form (58). Hence,

$$u = b^{e_1}c_1 + b^{e_2}c_2 + \cdots + b^{e_n}c_n = b^{a_1}v_1 + b^{a_2}v_2 + \cdots + b^{a_m}v_m$$

Without loss of generality, we may suppose that $e_1 < a_1$ and therefore $e_1 + 1 \leq a_1$. But then in view of (59)

$$u < b^{e_1+1} \leq b^{a_1}$$

which implies that $u < b^{a_1}$, which is impossible since $b^{a_1} \leq u$. Hence, we must have $e_1 = a_1$. Now, if $c_1 \neq v_1$, without loss of generality we may suppose that $c_1 < v_1$, and therefore $v_1 = c_1 + h$ with $h > 0$. But then

$$u = b^{e_1}c_1 + b^{e_2}c_2 + \cdots + b^{e_n}c_n = b^{e_1}(c_1 + h) + b^{a_2}v_2 + \cdots + b^{a_m}v_m$$

which implies that

$$b^{e_2}c_2 + \cdots + b^{e_n}c_n = b^{e_1}h + \cdots + b^{a_m}v_m$$

which (as in the case of e_1 and a_1) is impossible since $e_2 < e_1$. Therefore $c_1 = v_1$. In the same manner we may show that $e_2 = a_2$, $c_2 = v_2, \ldots, e_n = a_m$ and $c_n = v_m$, which implies the uniqueness of the representation of u in the form of (58).

Theorem 35 states that every ordinal $u > 0$ is represented as a polynomial in $b > 1$ whose coefficients are positive ordinals smaller than the base b.

In particular (with $b = \omega$) every ordinal $u > 0$ is represented uniquely as a polynomial in ω with finite positive coefficients. The representation of an ordinal $u > 0$ as a sum of a finite number of powers of ω with finite positive coefficients is called *the normal expansion* of u.

For instance, the normal expansion of

$$u = (\omega + 1)2(\omega + 1)3(\omega + 1)4$$

is given by:

$$\omega^3 4 + \omega^2 3 + \omega 2 + 1$$

The normal expansion of ordinals may be used to define the so called *natural sum* of two ordinals.

In connection with ordinal exponentiation, let us observe that for some ordinals u, v and w it may happen that

$$(uv)^w \neq u^w v^w$$

contrary to the familiar rule of exponentiation of natural numbers.

For instance,

$$(\omega 2)^2 = \omega 2 \omega 2 = \omega^2 \cdot 2$$

However,

$$\omega^2 \cdot 2^2 = \omega^2 \cdot 4 \neq \omega^2 \cdot 2$$

Thus,

$$(\omega 2)^2 \neq \omega^2 \cdot 2^2$$

In connection with ordinal exponentiation, let us observe that:

$$1 + \omega = \omega$$
$$1 + \omega + \omega^2 = \omega + \omega^2 = \omega(1 + \omega) = \omega^2$$
$$1 + \omega + \omega^2 + \omega^3 = \omega^2(1 + \omega) = \omega^3$$

Consequently,

$$1 + \omega + \omega^2 + \omega^3 + \cdots = \lim (1, \omega, \omega^2, \omega^3, \ldots) = \omega^\omega$$

Also, in view of Theorem 28, we have:

$$\omega < \omega^2 < \omega^\omega < \omega^{\omega^\omega} < \omega^{\omega^{\omega^\omega}} < \cdots$$

Now, let

$$\varepsilon_0 = \lim \{\omega, \omega^\omega, \omega^{\omega^\omega}, \ldots\}$$

and let us consider ω^{ε_0}. According to (49):

$$\omega^{\varepsilon_0} = \lim \{\omega^\omega, \omega^\omega, \omega^{\omega^\omega}, \omega^{\omega^{\omega^\omega}}, \ldots\} = \varepsilon_0$$

It is customary to call an ordinal u, an *epsilon number* if $\omega^u = u$. It is easy to prove that ε_0 is the smallest epsilon number.

EXERCISES

1. Prove that if w is a limit ordinal, then $(wn)^m = w^m n$, for every two finite positive ordinals m and n.

2. Prove that if w is a limit ordinal, then:

$$1^w + 2^w = 3^w$$

3. Let n be a finite positive ordinal. Prove that for every two ordinals u and v,

$$uv = vu \quad \text{if and only if} \quad u^n v^n = v^n u^n$$

4. Let u, v and w be three ordinals such that $w = u2 = v3$. Prove that $w = s6$, for some ordinal s.

5. Let u, v and w be three ordinals such that $w = (\omega + 2)u = (\omega + 3)v$. Is $w = \omega^2 s$, for some ordinal s?

6. Let u be an ordinal. Prove that $\omega u = u$ if and only if $u = \omega^\omega s$, for some ordinal s.

7. Let u, v and w be ordinals such that $uv = vu$ and $uw = wu$. Prove that:

$$u(vw) = (vw)u$$

8. Let u, v and w be ordinals such that $u > 1$, $uv = vu$ and $uw = wu$. Prove that $vw = wu$.

9. Let $u > 0$ be an ordinal. Knowing the natural expansion of u, determine the natural expansion of u^ω.

10. Let u be an epsilon number. Prove that $w + u = u$, for every ordinal $w < u$; also, that $wu = u$, for every ordinal w such that $1 \leq w < u$; finally, that $w^u = u$, for every ordinal w such that $2 \leq w < u$.

11. Let u and v be ordinals such that $\omega \leq u$ and $u^v = v$. Prove that v is an epsilon number.

12. Let u be an epsilon number. Prove that for every ordinal w,

$$w^{\omega^u} = (w^\omega)^u$$

7. SUMMARY

In this chapter we studied ordinal numbers and their arithmetic. Motivated by the properties of a natural number, we defined an ordinal number (or an ordinal) as a set w which can be well ordered so that for every element v of w, the initial segment $I(v)$ of w is equal to v. Accordingly, every natural number, as well as the set ω of all natural numbers, is an ordinal number.

Among the important theorems concerning ordinal numbers, let us mention the following ones. Two ordinal numbers are equal if and only if they are similar. Every element (and hence every initial segment) of an ordinal number is an ordinal number. Every well ordered set is similar to a unique ordinal number. There is no set of all ordinal numbers.

The natural order among ordinals is introduced by defining $v \leq w$, if the ordinal v is equal to the ordinal w or is equal to an initial segment of w. It is also proved that every set of ordinals is a well ordered set (with respect to $\leq$). Moreover, every ordinal w is equal to the set of all ordinals less than w. Furthermore, $w \cup \{w\}$ is the immediate successor of w, and $\cup W$, where W is any set of ordinals, is the least upper bound of W.

The sum $v + v$ (in this order) of ordinals u and v is defined as the ordinal similar to the well ordered set $u \times \{1\} + v \times \{2\}$. The product uv (in this order) of ordinals u and v is defined as the ordinal similar to the set $u \times v$ well ordered antilexicographically. Addition as well as multiplication of ordinals, is associative but not commutative; moreover, multiplication is only left distributive with respect to addition.

The notion of the limit of a nondecreasing sequence of ordinals is constantly used in performing operations involving infinitely many ordinals. This is revealed particularly in the fact that the sum and the product of an infinite sequence of ordinals are most conveniently evaluated as the limit of the partial sums and the partial products of that sequence. In turn, the limit of a non-decreasing sequence $(w_i)_{i<u}$, of type u of ordinals w_i, is defined simply as $\bigcup_{i<u} w_i$.

In connection with the arithmetic of natural numbers, constant use was made of the Finite Induction (Chapter II, page 105) and Finite Recursion (Chapter V, page 208) Theorems. The former was used in proving theorems concerning natural numbers, and the latter in proving the existence of functions defined on a set of natural numbers.

Similarly, in connection with the arithmetic of ordinal numbers, constant use was made of the Transfinite Induction (Chapter IV, page 192) and Transfinite Recursion (Chapter VII, page 299) Theorems. The former was used in proving theorems concerning ordinals, and the latter in proving the existence of functions defined on a set of ordinals.

Although in the arithmetic of natural numbers, infinite sums and infinite products such as:

$$1 + 2 + 3 + 4 + 5 + \cdots$$
$$1 \cdot 2 \cdot 3 \cdot 4 \cdot 5 \cdots \cdot$$

are meaningless, in the arithmetic of ordinals both of these are meaningful expressions, and both are equal to the ordinal ω.

Chapter IX

CARDINAL NUMBERS AND THEIR ARITHMETIC

1. CARDINAL NUMBERS

In this section we shall consider a special kind of ordinal numbers called *cardinal numbers*. The reader should observe once more that, like every other mathematical object in this book, every cardinal number is first of all a set. Moreover, since every cardinal number is an ordinal number, a cardinal number is a well ordered set every initial segment of which is equal to the element determining that initial segment. As will be pointed out later, in order that the sum as well as the product of two cardinal numbers be again a cardinal number, the arithmetical operations among cardinal numbers are defined in a manner quite different from that used for ordinal numbers.

The definition of a cardinal number is based on the following considerations.

Lemma 1. *If an ordinal number u is of smaller power than an ordinal number v, then u is less than v.*

PROOF. The hypothesis of the lemma [in view of Definition 3 of Chapter VI (page 257)] implies that u is equipollent to a subset of v, but v is not equipollent to any subset of u. To prove the lemma, let us assume on the contrary that $u \geq v$. This [in view of Definition 2 of Chapter VIII (page 321)] means that v is equal to u or to an initial segment of u, contradicting the fact that v is not equipollent to any subset of u. Hence, our assumption is false and indeed $u < v$.

Theorem 1. *The set of all ordinal numbers that are equipollent to a given ordinal number exists.*

PROOF. Let u be a given ordinal. Consider the power-set $\mathscr{P}(u)$ of u. By Corollary 7 of Chapter VIII (page 325), there exists an ordinal v equipollent to $\mathscr{P}(u)$. By Theorems 7 and 9 of Chapter VI (pages 256 and 259), the ordinal u, as well as every ordinal equipollent to u, is of power less than that of v. Consequently, if an ordinal w is such that $w \cong u$, then $w < v$, i.e., $w \in v$. Therefore, the set of all ordinals equipollent to u is a subset of v, and hence by the theorem of Separation (see Chapter II, page 83), the set of all ordinals equipollent to u exists.

Based on Theorem 1, we introduce:

Definition 1. *For every ordinal number u, the set of all ordinal numbers equipollent to u is called the number class determined by u and is denoted by $\mathbf{Z}(u)$.*

According to Theorem 4 of Chapter VIII (page 321), the number class determined by a finite ordinal n consists of the singleton $\{n\}$.

Thus

$$\mathbf{Z}(0) = \{0\}, \qquad \mathbf{Z}(1) = \{1\}, \ldots, \qquad \mathbf{Z}(n) = \{n\}$$

for every finite ordinal n.

Now, let us consider $\mathbf{Z}(\omega)$. This set consists of all ordinal numbers equipollent to ω. In other words, $\mathbf{Z}(\omega)$ consists of all denumerable ordinals. We have encountered many of the elements of $\mathbf{Z}(\omega)$. For instance,

$$\omega, \qquad \omega + 1, \qquad \omega + 2, \qquad \ldots, \qquad \omega 2, \qquad \ldots, \qquad \omega^2,$$
$$\omega^\omega, \qquad \omega^{\omega^\omega}, \qquad \omega^\omega + \omega^2 + \omega 2 + 2, \qquad \ldots$$

are all elements of $\mathbf{Z}(\omega)$. Therefore, in view of the above, we have:

$$\mathbf{Z}(\omega) = \mathbf{Z}(\omega + 1) = \mathbf{Z}(\omega 2) = \mathbf{Z}(\omega^2) = \mathbf{Z}(\omega^\omega) = \cdots$$

Lemma 2. *If $\mathbf{Z}(u)$ and $\mathbf{Z}(v)$ are two distinct number classes, then they are disjoint, i.e.,*

$$\mathbf{Z}(u) \neq \mathbf{Z}(v) \qquad implies \qquad \mathbf{Z}(u) \cap \mathbf{Z}(v) = \varnothing$$

PROOF. Assume on the contrary that $\mathbf{Z}(u) \cap \mathbf{Z}(v) \neq \varnothing$ and let

$$w \in (\mathbf{Z}(u) \cap \mathbf{Z}(v))$$

Hence, $w \cong u \cong v$. Now, if $x \in \mathbf{Z}(u)$, then $x \cong u$ and consequently $x \cong v$, and therefore $x \in \mathbf{Z}(v)$. Thus, $\mathbf{Z}(u) \subset \mathbf{Z}(v)$. Similarly, we can show that $\mathbf{Z}(v) \subset \mathbf{Z}(u)$. Therefore, $\mathbf{Z}(u) = \mathbf{Z}(v)$, contradicting the fact that $\mathbf{Z}(u) \neq \mathbf{Z}(v)$. Hence our assumption is false, and indeed $\mathbf{Z}(u) \cap \mathbf{Z}(v) = \varnothing$, for every two non-equipollent ordinals u and v.

Corollary 1. *For every two ordinal numbers u and v,*

$$u \not\cong v \qquad implies \qquad \mathbf{Z}(u) \cap \mathbf{Z}(v) = \varnothing$$

In Chapter VIII, Section 1, we introduced the natural order among ordinals by writing $u < v$ if the ordinal u is equal to an initial segment of the ordinal v. Also, according to Theorem 6 of Chapter VIII (page 321), every set of ordinals is well ordered with respect to their natural order $\leq$. Consequently, for every ordinal u, the set $\mathbf{Z}(u)$ is a well ordered set. As such, $\mathbf{Z}(u)$ has a first element. It is customary to refer to the first element of any number class as an *initial ordinal*.

Next, we introduce:

Definition 2. *A cardinal number is defined as an initial ordinal.*

Equivalently, we have:

An ordinal number u is a cardinal number (or simply a cardinal) if, for every ordinal number w,

(1) $$u \cong w \quad implies \quad u \le w$$

Obviously, every finite ordinal is a cardinal since $\{n\} = \mathbf{Z}(n)$ for every finite ordinal n. Similarly, ω is a cardinal since ω is the initial ordinal of $\mathbf{Z}(\omega)$.

However, $\omega + 1$, $\omega 2$, ω^2, ..., ω^ω are not cardinals.

Let us observe that the only denumerable cardinal number is the ordinal ω, also denoted by $\aleph_0$(read: *aleph null*). Thus,

(2) $$\aleph_0 = \omega$$

Theorem 2. *Two cardinal numbers are equal if and only if they are equipollent.*

PROOF. Clearly, if two cardinal numbers are equal, then they are equipollent. Now, let us assume that a cardinal u is equipollent to a cardinal v, i.e., $u \cong v$. But then by (1) we obtain $u \le v$ and $v \le u$. Consequently, $u = v$, as desired.

Theorem 3. *Every ordinal number is equipollent to a unique cardinal number.*

PROOF. Let u be an ordinal number. By Theorem 1, $\mathbf{Z}(u)$ exists. Clearly, u is equipollent to every element of $\mathbf{Z}(u)$ and, in particular, to the initial ordinal w (which is a cardinal number) of $\mathbf{Z}(u)$. The uniqueness of w follows from Theorem 2.

Theorem 4. *Every set is equipollent to a unique cardinal number.*

PROOF. Let s be a set. By Corollary 7 of Chapter VIII (page 325), s is equipollent to an ordinal number u. However, by Theorem 3 the ordinal u is equipollent to a unique cardinal w. Thus, $s \cong w$ and w is unique.

Remark 1. Let s be a set. It is customary to denote by $\bar{\bar{s}}$ the unique cardinal number equipollent to the set s.

Thus, for every two sets s and c:

(3) $$s \cong c \quad implies \quad \bar{\bar{s}} = \bar{\bar{c}}$$

Consequently, in view of (2) and (3) we have:

$$\bar{\bar{\omega}} = \overline{\overline{(\omega + 1)}} = \overline{\overline{(\omega^\omega)}} = \omega = \aleph_0$$

Also, since the set I of all integers and the set Q of all rationals are denumerable sets, we have:

$$\bar{\bar{I}} = \bar{\bar{Q}} = \omega = \aleph_0$$

Moreover, if S is an infinite set and A a set of power not greater than that of S [i.e., $A \preceq S$ in the sense of Definition 3 of Chapter VI (page 257)], then in view of Corollaries 16 and 24 of Chapter VI (pages 261 and 276), we have:

(4) $$\overline{\overline{S \cup A}} = \overline{\overline{S \times A}} = \bar{\bar{S}}$$

Furthermore, in view of Lemma 21 of Chapter VI (page 280),

(5) $$\overline{\overline{\mathscr{P}(S)}} = \overline{\overline{2^S}} \qquad \text{for every set} \quad S$$

where $\mathscr{P}(S)$ is the power-set of S, and 2^S [according to (54) of Chapter III (page 146)], is the set of all functions from S into $2 = \{0, 1\}$.

According to Theorem 4, every set is equipollent to a unique cardinal. It is customary to denote by $\aleph$ (read: *aleph*) the unique cardinal equipollent to the set R of all real numbers. Thus,

(6) $$\aleph = \overline{\overline{R}} \qquad \textit{where R is the set of all real numbers}$$

Since R is nondenumerable, we see that $\aleph$ is also nondenumerable, and in view of Definition 6 of Chapter VI (page 278), the cardinal $\aleph$ is of the power of the continuum.

Note that by Theorem 39 of Chapter VI (page 280), $R \cong 2^D$, where R is the set of all real numbers (or any set of the power of the continuum) and D is any denumerable set. Hence in view of (6) we have

(7) $$\overline{\overline{2^{\aleph_0}}} = \aleph$$

where $2^{\aleph_0}$ is in the sense of Definition 6 of Chapter VI (page 278).

By Theorem 7 of Chapter VI (page 256), no set is equipollent to its power-set. Hence:

(8) $$\aleph \neq \aleph_0$$

Let us observe that although $\aleph_0 = \omega$, in (7) we have deliberately written $2^{\aleph_0}$ instead of 2^ω. This is done to prevent any confusion between $2^{\aleph_0}$ and the ω-th power of the ordinal 2, in the sense of the ordinal exponentiation (see Chapter VIII, Section 6). As we know, according to the ordinal exponentiation, $2^\omega = \omega$; however, as (8) shows, $\overline{\overline{2^{\aleph_0}}} \neq \aleph_0$.

Theorem 5. *No cardinal number is equipollent to any of its initial segments.*

PROOF. Let c be a cardinal. Assume on the contrary that c is equipollent to one of its initial segments $I(v)$, determined by v. Since c is an ordinal, by Lemma 3 of Chapter VIII (page 319), $I(v)$ is an ordinal. However, by our assumption, $c \cong I(v)$, which in view of (1) implies $c \leq I(v)$. Thus, by (2) of Chapter VIII (page 316), we have $c \subset I(v)$, contradicting the fact that no set is a subset of any of its proper subsets. Hence, our assumption is false and the theorem is proved.

Corollary 2. *No cardinal number is equipollent to any of its elements.*

PROOF. Since every element v of a cardinal c is equal to the initial segment $I(v)$ of c, the corollary follows from Theorem 5.

EXERCISES

1. Prove that the relation: *belonging to the same number class*, is an equivalence relation in every set of ordinals.

2. Prove that $\overline{\overline{s}} \subset \overline{s}$ *for every set s.*

3. Prove that every infinite cardinal is a limit ordinal.

4. Prove that the union, as well as the intersection, of every two cardinals is again a cardinal.

5. Prove that the union-set $\cup S$ of any set S of cardinals is again a cardinal.

6. Let S^n represent the set of all functions from a nonempty finite set n into an infinite set S. Prove that $\overline{\overline{S^n}} = \overline{\overline{S}}$.

7. Prove that for every two cardinals r and s, if r is equipollent to a subset of s, then r is equal to an initial segment of s or to s.

8. Prove that $\mathbf{Z}(\aleph_0) \cap \mathbf{Z}(\aleph) = \varnothing$.

9. Prove that a cardinal c is either equal to or is an element of every element of the number class to which c belongs.

10. Prove that no cardinal number is equal to any of its elements.

11. Prove that for every cardinal c and every ordinal u if $u < c$, then u is not equipollent to c.

2. THE NATURAL ORDER AMONG CARDINAL NUMBERS

The natural orders among cardinals is defined in the same way as among ordinals. Thus:

Definition 3.   *For every two cardinal numbers a and b, we define: $a \le b$ if a is equal to b or a is equal to an initial segment of b.*

In view of Theorem 6 of Chapter VIII (page 321), we have:

Theorem 6.   *Every set of cardinal numbers is well ordered with respect to the order given by Definition 3.*

As usual, if a and b are two cardinals such that $a \ne b$ and $a \le b$, then we write $a < b$.

Moreover, in view of (5) and (6) of Chapter VIII (page 321), we have:

Theorem 7.   *For every two cardinal numbers a and b, we have:*

$$a \le b \qquad \textit{if and only if} \qquad a \subset b$$
$$a < b \qquad \textit{if and only if} \qquad a \in b$$

Let us observe that in contrast to the fact that every element of an ordinal number is an ordinal number, *not every element of a cardinal number is a cardinal number.*

In view of Theorems 6 and 7 we have the following corollaries which are similar to Corollaries 2, 3 and 5 of Chapter VIII (pages 320 and 321).

Corollary 3. *For every two cardinal numbers a and b,*

$$a \subset b \quad or \quad b \subset a$$

Corollary 4. *For every two cardinal numbers a and b,*

$$a \leq b \quad or \quad b \leq a$$

Corollary 5 (Trichotomy Law). *For every two cardinal numbers a and b, one and only one of the following three cases must hold:*

$$a = b \quad or \quad a < b \quad or \quad b < a$$

Corollary 6. *For every two cardinal numbers a and b, one and only one of the following three cases must hold:*

$$a = b \quad or \quad a \in b \quad or \quad b \in a$$

Note that $w = w$, for every ordinal w. Hence, according to Corollary 3 of Chapter VIII (page 321), $w \in w$ is excluded for every ordinal w. In other words, no ordinal is an element of itself. Similarly, we have:

Corollary 7. *No cardinal number is an element of itself.*

PROOF. Let c be a cardinal number. Since $c = c$, we see that $c \in c$ is impossible in view of Corollary 6.

The main feature of cardinal numbers not shared by some ordinal numbers is described in:

Theorem 8. *Every cardinal number is of power greater than that of any of its elements.*

PROOF. Let c be a cardinal number and u an element of c. Clearly, u is equal to an initial segment of c, and therefore u is of power less than or equal to that of c. On the other hand, in view of Corollary 2, we see that c is not equipollent to u. Thus, indeed in view of Definition 3 of Chapter VI (page 257), c is of power greater than that of any element u of c.

Theorem 9. *For every two cardinal numbers a and b,*
$a < b$ if and only if a is of power less than that of b.

PROOF. If $a < b$, then by Theorem 7, $a \in b$, and hence by Theorem 8, a is of power less than that of b. Now, let a be of power less than that of b. Then by Corollary 6 one and only one of the two remaining cases $a \in b$ or $b \in a$ must hold. However, $b \in a$ cannot hold since in that case, by Theorem 8, a is of power greater than that of b. Hence indeed $a \in b$, which in view of Theorem 7 implies $a < b$, as desired.

Remark 2. In view of Theorem 9, we see that the natural order among cardinals is compatible with the order among sets, which is based on the equipollence of sets as given in Chapter VI, Section 3. Moreover, we have:

Corollary 8. *For every two sets s and h,*
s is of power less than that of h if and only if $\bar{\bar{s}} < \bar{\bar{h}}$.

PROOF. If s is of power less than that of h, then $\bar{\bar{s}}$ (being equipollent to s) is of power less than that of $\bar{\bar{h}}$ (being equipollent to h), and hence in view of Theorem 9, $\bar{\bar{s}} < \bar{\bar{h}}$. Conversely, if $\bar{\bar{s}} < \bar{\bar{h}}$, then in view of Theorem 9, $\bar{\bar{s}}$ is of power less than that of $\bar{\bar{h}}$, and hence s is of power less than that of h.

Corollary 9. *For every two sets s and h,*

$$s \simeq h \qquad \text{if and only if} \qquad \bar{\bar{s}} = \bar{\bar{h}}$$

PROOF. If $s \simeq h$, then $\bar{\bar{s}} \simeq \bar{\bar{h}}$ and by Theorem 2, $\bar{\bar{s}} = \bar{\bar{h}}$. Conversely, if $\bar{\bar{s}} = \bar{\bar{h}}$, then by Theorem 2, $\bar{\bar{s}} \simeq \bar{\bar{h}}$, and hence $s \simeq h$.

Remark 3. In view of Corollaries 8 and 9, we see that the order between two sets s and h that is based on the equipollence of sets, as given in Chapter VI, Section 3, is compatible with the order among the unique cardinals $\bar{\bar{s}}$ and $\bar{\bar{h}}$, as given by Definition 3.

Combining Corollaries 8 and 9, we have:

Corollary 10. *For every two sets s and h, s is of power less than or equal to that of h if and only if $\bar{\bar{s}} \leq \bar{\bar{h}}$.*

Theorem 10. *For every two ordinal numbers u and v,*

$$\bar{\bar{u}} < \bar{\bar{v}} \qquad \text{implies} \qquad u < v$$

PROOF. Assume the contrary, that $u \geq v$. This means that $v \subset u$. Hence, v is equipollent to a subset of u. Therefore, by Corollary 10, $\bar{\bar{v}} \leq \bar{\bar{u}}$, contradicting $\bar{\bar{u}} < \bar{\bar{v}}$. Hence our assumption is false, and indeed $u < v$.

Lemma 3. *For every two ordinal numbers u and v,*

$$u < v \qquad \text{implies} \qquad \bar{\bar{u}} \leq \bar{\bar{v}}$$

PROOF. Clearly, if $u < v$, then $u \subset v$, and hence by Corollary 10, $\bar{\bar{u}} \leq \bar{\bar{v}}$.

Theorem 11. *For every ordinal number u and every cardinal number c,*

$$\bar{\bar{u}} < c \qquad \text{if and only if} \qquad u < c$$

PROOF. Since $\bar{\bar{c}} = c$, we see that if $\bar{\bar{u}} < c$, then by Theorem 10, $u < c$. On the other hand, if $u < c$, then $u \in c$, and hence by Theorem 8, $\bar{\bar{u}} < c$, as desired.

Let us recall that if u is an ordinal, then according to Definition 1, $\mathbf{Z}(u)$ is the set of all ordinals equipollent to u. Bearing this in mind, we have:

Lemma 4. *For every ordinal number w, $w \cup \mathbf{Z}(w)$ is the set of all ordinal numbers of power less than or equal to that of w.*

PROOF. Let $u \in (w \cup \mathbf{Z}(w))$; then $u \in w$ or $u \in \mathbf{Z}(w)$. If $u \in w$, then $u < w$, and hence by Lemma 3, $\bar{\bar{u}} \leq \bar{\bar{w}}$. If $u \in \mathbf{Z}(w)$, then by Definition 1, $\bar{\bar{u}} = \bar{\bar{w}}$. Thus, every element of $w \cup \mathbf{Z}(w)$ is an ordinal of power less than or equal to that of w.

Next, let v be an ordinal such that $\bar{\bar{v}} \leq \bar{\bar{w}}$. If $\bar{\bar{v}} = \bar{\bar{w}}$, then by Definition 1, $v \in \mathbf{Z}(w)$. If $\bar{\bar{v}} < \bar{\bar{w}}$, then by Theorem 10, $v < w$, and hence $v \in w$. Thus, in either case $v \in (w \cup \mathbf{Z}(w))$.

In view of Lemma 4, we have

(9) $$w \cup \mathbf{Z}(w) = \{u \mid \bar{\bar{u}} \leq \bar{\bar{w}}\}$$

where u and w are ordinals.

Theorem 12. *For every ordinal number w, the set $w \cup \mathbf{Z}(w)$ is an ordinal number.*

PROOF. Since $w \cup \mathbf{Z}(w)$ is a set of ordinals, by Theorem 6 of Chapter VIII (page 321), $e \cup \mathbf{Z}(w)$ is a well ordered set with respect to $\leq$. To prove that $w \cup \mathbf{Z}(w)$ is an ordinal, we have to show that every element v of $w \cup \mathbf{Z}(w)$ is equal to the initial segment $I(v)$ of $w \cup \mathbf{Z}(w)$. However, if u is an ordinal such that $u < v$, then by Lemma 3, $\bar{\bar{u}} \leq \bar{\bar{v}}$, and since by (9), $\bar{\bar{v}} \leq \bar{\bar{w}}$, we see that $\bar{\bar{u}} \leq \bar{\bar{w}}$. Consequently, in view of (9), $u \in (w \cup \mathbf{Z}(w))$. Thus, every ordinal u less than v is an element of $w \cup \mathbf{Z}(w)$. Therefore, in view of Theorem 5 of Chapter VIII (page 321), the initial segment $I(v)$ of $w \cup \mathbf{Z}(w)$ is equal to v. Thus, indeed $w \cup \mathbf{Z}(w)$ is an ordinal number.

Theorem 13. *For every ordinal number w, the ordinal number $w \cup \mathbf{Z}(w)$ is of power greater than that of w, i.e.,*

$$\bar{\bar{w}} < \overline{\overline{w \cup \mathbf{Z}(w)}}$$

PROOF. Assume on the contrary that $\overline{\overline{w \cup \mathbf{Z}(w)}} \leq \bar{\bar{w}}$. Then by Theorem 12 and (9) we conclude that $(w \cup \mathbf{Z}(w)) \in (w \cup \mathbf{Z}(w))$, contradicting the fact that no ordinal is an element of itself [see Corollary 3 of Chapter VIII (page 321)]. Hence our assumption is false, and indeed $\bar{\bar{w}} < \overline{\overline{w \cup \mathbf{Z}(w)}}$.

Corollary 11. *For every infinite ordinal number w,*

$$\overline{\overline{\mathbf{Z}(w)}} = \overline{\overline{w \cup \mathbf{Z}(w)}}$$

PROOF. Clearly, $\mathbf{Z}(w)$ is an infinite set since $w, w+1, w+2, w+3, \ldots$ are elements of $\mathbf{Z}(w)$. Also, in view of the fact that $\mathbf{Z}(w) = (w \cup \mathbf{Z}(w)) \smile w$, and $\bar{\bar{w}} < \overline{\overline{w \cup \mathbf{Z}(w)}}$, we conclude by Theorem 11 of Chapter VI (page 261), that $\overline{\overline{\mathbf{Z}(w)}} = \overline{\overline{w \cup \mathbf{Z}(w)}}$, as desired.

Theorem 14. *For every ordinal number w, the ordinal number $w \cup \mathbf{Z}(w)$ is a cardinal number.*

PROOF. To prove the theorem, in view of (1) we have to show that if u is an ordinal such that $u \cong (w \cup \mathbf{Z}(w))$, then $w \cup \mathbf{Z}(w) \leq u$. Assume on the contrary that $u < (w \cup \mathbf{Z}(w))$. Hence, $u \in (w \cup \mathbf{Z}(w))$. Therefore, by (9), $\bar{\bar{u}} \leq \bar{\bar{w}}$, which in view of Theorem 13 yields $\bar{\bar{u}} < \overline{\overline{w \cup \mathbf{Z}(w)}}$, contradicting the fact that $u \cong (w \cup \mathbf{Z}(w))$. Hence our assumption is false, and indeed $w \cup \mathbf{Z}(w) \leq u$. Thus, $w \cup \mathbf{Z}(w)$ is a cardinal number.

As usual, we say that a cardinal b is the *immediate successor* of a cardinal a if $a < b$ and, if for no cardinal c is it the case that $a < c < b$. Clearly, a cardinal can have at most one immediate successor.

Theorem 15. *For every cardinal number c the cardinal number $c \cup \mathbf{Z}(c)$ is the immediate successor of c.*

PROOF. By Theorem 13, $c < c \cup \mathbf{Z}(c)$. Assume on the contrary that there exists a cardinal b such that:

$$c < b < c \cup \mathbf{Z}(c)$$

Consequently, $b \in (c \cup \mathbf{Z}(c))$, and hence by Lemma 4, $b \leq c$, contradicting the fact that $c < b$. Hence our assumption is false, and indeed the cardinal $c \cup \mathbf{Z}(c)$ is the immediate successor of the cardinal c.

Let us observe that:

$$0 \cup \mathbf{Z}(0) = 0 \cup \{0\} = 1 \qquad \text{and} \qquad 2 \cup \mathbf{Z}(2) = 2 \cup \{2\} = 3$$

According to Theorem 15, the immediate successor of the denumerable cardinal $\aleph_0$ is given by:

$$\aleph_0 \cup \mathbf{Z}(\aleph_0) = \omega \cup \mathbf{Z}(\omega)$$

It is customary to denote the immediate successor of $\aleph_0$ by $\aleph_1$ (read: *aleph one*) or by Ω or ω_1. Thus,

(10) $$\aleph_1 = \Omega = \omega_1 = \omega \cup \mathbf{Z}(\omega) = \aleph_0 \cup \mathbf{Z}(\aleph_0)$$

Clearly, $\aleph_1$ or Ω or ω_1 is the smallest nondenumerable ordinal.

Likewise, the immediate successor of $\aleph_1$ is denoted by $\aleph_2$ (read: *aleph two*) or by ω_2. Thus,

$$\aleph_2 = \omega_2 = \Omega \cup \mathbf{Z}(\Omega) = \aleph_1 \cup \mathbf{Z}(\aleph_1)$$

In general we have:

(11) $$\aleph_0 = \omega$$
$$\aleph_n = \aleph_{n-1} \cup \mathbf{Z}(\aleph_{n-1}) \qquad \text{for every} \quad n = 1, 2, \ldots$$

or

(12) $$\omega_0 = \omega$$
$$\omega_n = \omega_{n-1} \cup \mathbf{Z}(\omega_{n-1}) \qquad \text{for every} \quad n = 1, 2, \ldots$$

Accordingly

$$\aleph_0 < \aleph_1 < \aleph_2 < \aleph_3 < \cdots$$

or

$$\omega_0 < \omega_1 < \omega_2 < \omega_3 < \cdots$$

where, in each of the sequences of inequalities, each cardinal is the immediate successor of the cardinal immediately to its left.

As expected, a cardinal that is a finite set (or a finite ordinal) is called a *finite cardinal*. As we know, the natural numbers are the only finite ordinals, and hence they are also the only finite cardinals.

A cardinal number that is an infinite set (or an infinite ordinal) is called an *infinite* or *transfinite cardinal*. $\aleph_0, \aleph_1, \aleph_2, \ldots$ (i.e., $\omega, \omega_1, \omega_2, \ldots$) are examples of transfinite cardinal numbers.

Remark 4. Although $\omega_n = \aleph_n$ for $n = 0, 1, 2, \ldots$, in view of the discrepancies (cf. below) between ordinal and cardinal arithmetic, the aleph notation for cardinals will be used in connection with cardinal arithmetic.

According to (6), $\aleph$ is the unique cardinal equipollent to the set of all real numbers. Clearly, since $\aleph_0$ is denumerable and $\aleph$ is of the power of the continuum, we have:

$$(13) \qquad \qquad \aleph_0 < \aleph$$

On the other hand, according to (10), $\aleph_0 < \aleph_1$, and since $\aleph_1$ is the immediate successor of $\aleph_0$, we see that $\aleph_1 \leq \aleph$. The hypothesis that $\aleph_1 = \aleph$ is called the *Continuum Hypothesis*.

It has been established that the Continuum Hypothesis is consistent with (K. Goedel) and independent of (P. J. Cohen) the axioms of the Theory of Sets (including the axiom of Regularity) introduced in Chapter II.

Let us observe also that according to the Continuum of Hypothesis, the cardinal $\aleph_1$ is of the power of the continuum.

Theorem 16. *For every set S of cardinal numbers, the sum-set $\cup S$ of S is a cardinal number. Moreover, $\cup S$ is the least upper bound of S, i.e.,*

$$\cup S = \text{lub } S = \text{sup } S$$

PROOF. Since every cardinal is an ordinal, in view of Theorem 8 of Chapter VIII (page 323), $\cup S$ is an ordinal that is the least upper bound of the set S of ordinals. To prove the theorem, it is enough to show that $\cup S$ is a cardinal. To this end, in view of (1) we have to prove that if w is an ordinal such that $\cup S \cong w$, then $\cup S \leq w$. Assume on the contrary that $\cup S > w$. Then $w \in \cup S$, and therefore there exists a cardinal c such that $c \in \cup S$ and $w \in c$. Then by Theorem 8, $\overline{\overline{w}} < c$. However, obviously $c \leq \overline{\overline{\cup S}}$, and thus $\overline{\overline{w}} < \overline{\overline{\cup S}}$, contradicting the fact that $\cup S \cong w$. Hence our assumption is false, and indeed $\cup S$ is a cardinal number that is the least upper bound of S.

Theorem 17. *Every infinite cardinal number is a limit ordinal.*

PROOF. Let c be an infinite cardinal. Assume on the contrary that c is not a limit ordinal. Then there exists an ordinal w such that $w + 1 = c$. But then $w \cong c$. However, $w < c$, which in view of (1) contradicts the fact that c is a cardinal number. Hence our assumption is false, and indeed c is a limit ordinal.

Theorem 18. *For every infinite cardinal number c,*

$$\cup c = c$$

PROOF. By Theorem 17, c is a limit ordinal, and hence by Theorem 9 of Chapter VIII (page 323), $\cup c = c$, as desired.

Theorem 19. *For every set S of cardinal numbers there exists a cardinal number greater than every element of S.*

PROOF. If S has no greatest element, then by Theorem 16, $\cup S$ is a cardinal greater than every element of S. If, however, S has a greatest element (which in view of Theorem 16 is necessarily equal to $\cup S$), then $\cup S \cup \mathbf{Z}(\cup S)$ is a cardinal number greater than every element of S.

Theorem 20. *There is no set of all cardinal numbers.*

PROOF. Assume on the contrary that C is the set of all cardinals. Then $\cup C \cup \mathbf{Z}(\cup C)$ is a cardinal greater than every cardinal belonging to C. However, this contradicts the fact that $\cup C \cup \mathbf{Z}(\cup C)$, as a cardinal, must belong to C. Hence our assumption is false, and indeed there is no set of all cardinals.

Although in Chapter II (page 90), we showed that there exists no set of all sets, here we prove once more:

Theorem 21. *There is no set of all sets.*

PROOF. Assume the contrary, that E is the set of all sets. In view of the fact that every cardinal is a set, by the theorem of Separation, we can derive from the existence of E that of the set C of all cardinals, contradicting Theorem 20. Hence our assumption is false, and indeed there is no set of all sets.

Theorem 22. *There is no set of all sets equipollent to a given nonempty set.*

PROOF. Assume on the contrary that the set P of all sets which are equipollent to a given nonempty set c exists. Clearly, for every set s, $c \times \{s\}$ is equipollent to c. The set H of all such sets $c \times \{s\}$ is a subset of P, and therefore the existence of H is secured from that of P by the theorem of Separation. But then in view of the axioms of Sum-Set and Replacement, the set E of all the second coordinates of the elements of the set $\cup H$ exists. Clearly, E would be the set of all sets, contradicting Theorem 21. Hence our assumption is false, and the theorem is proved.

EXERCISES

1. Let u and v be two ordinals. Prove that $\bar{\bar{u}} = \bar{\bar{v}}$ does not imply $u = v$. Give an example of an ordinal equipollent to one of its elements.

2. Prove that there is no infinite decreasing sequence of cardinals.

3. Prove that $\overline{\overline{(\mathbf{Z}\omega)}} = \aleph_1$.

4. Prove that if c is a finite cardinal, then $\cup c = c^-$, where c^- is the immediate predecessor of c.

5. Prove that an ordinal u is a cardinal if and only if $w < u$ implies $\bar{\bar{w}} < \bar{\bar{u}}$, for every ordinal w.

6. Prove that $\Omega - \omega \cong \Omega$ and $\Omega - \omega \sim \Omega$.

7. Is Ω an ε-number? Justify your answer.

8. Prove that $\omega_1 \cup \omega_2 = \omega_2$.

9. Prove that the limit of an infinite nondecreasing sequence (of type ω) of elements of $\mathbf{Z}(\omega)$ is again an element of $\mathbf{Z}(\omega)$.

10. Prove that there exists no greatest cardinal.

3. TRANSFINITE CARDINAL NUMBERS

In Section 2 we encountered many infinite (transfinite) cardinals such as $\aleph_0, \aleph_1, \aleph_2, \ldots$. In this section we shall derive some further properties of infinite cardinals. Let us recall that a cardinal that is an infinite ordinal or an infinite set is called a transfinite cardinal.

As shown below, Theorems 15 and 16 of the previous section are primarily used to ensure the existence of greater and greater transfinite cardinals.

For instance, according to (11) or (12) the existence of the cardinal $\aleph_1$ is secured from that of $\aleph_0$ via Theorem 15.

Motivated by (11), we prove:

Theorem 23. *For every ordinal number w, there exists a unique cardinal number denoted by $\aleph_w$ such that*:

(14) $\aleph_0 = \omega$

(15) $\aleph_w = \aleph_{w^-} \cup \mathbf{Z}(\aleph_{w^-})$ *if $w > 0$ is not a limit ordinal.*

(16) $\aleph_w = \underset{v<w}{\cup} \aleph_v$ *if w is a limit ordinal.*

PROOF.   Consider the binary predicate $p(x,y)$ given by $p(x,y) \equiv (y = p(x))$ such that $p(0) = \omega$; and $p(x) = (\cup x) \cup \mathbf{Z}(\cup x)$ if x is a set of cardinals and x has a greatest element; and $p(x) = \cup x$ if x is a set of cardinals and x has no greatest element; and $p(x) = 0$ otherwise. Clearly, $p(x,y)$ is functional in x, and if w is an ordinal, then, in view of the Transfinite Recursion Theorem [Theorem 21 of Chapter VII (page 299)], there exists a unique function g defined on w^+ (the immediate successor of w) such that:

$$g(0) = \omega$$
$$g(u) = g(u^-) \cup Z(g(u^-)) \qquad \text{if } u > 0 \text{ is not a limit ordinal.}$$
$$g(u) = \underset{v<u}{\cup} (g(v)) \qquad \text{if } u \text{ is a limit ordinal.}$$

In view of Theorems 15 and 16, the values of the function g are cardinal numbers. Denoting $g(u)$ by $\aleph_u$ for every $u \in w^+$, we see at once that $g(w) = \aleph_w$ is a cardinal number which satisfies (14), (15) and (16).

Accordingly, $\aleph_\omega = \aleph_0 \cup \aleph_1 \cup \aleph_2 \cup \aleph_3 \cup \cdots$

Similarly, $\aleph_\Omega = \underset{v<\Omega}{\cup} \aleph_v$

As in the case of a nondecreasing sequence of ordinals [see Definition 6 of Chapter VIII (page 334)], here also the sum-set (union-set) of a nondecreasing sequence $(c_i)_{i<w}$ of type w of cardinals c_i is called the limit of that sequence and is denoted by:

$$\underset{i<w}{\lim} c_i \qquad \text{or} \qquad \underset{i\in w}{\lim} c_i$$

Accordingly,

(17) $\underset{i<w}{\lim} c_i = \underset{i<w}{\cup} c_i$

Thus, in view of (17) we have:

$$\aleph_\omega = \lim_{n<\omega} \aleph_n \quad \text{and} \quad \aleph_\Omega = \lim_{u<\Omega} \aleph_u$$

In view of Theorem 16 it is obvious that the limit of a (nondecreasing) sequence of cardinals is a cardinal number.

Corollary 12. *If $w > 0$ is not a limit ordinal, then the cardinal number $\aleph_w$ is the immediate successor of the cardinal number $\aleph_{w^-}$. If w is a limit ordinal, then $\aleph_w$ is the least upper bound of the family $(\aleph_v)_{v<w}$ of cardinal numbers $\aleph_v$.*

PROOF. The first part of the corollary follows immediately from (15) and Theorem 15; the second, from (16) and Theorem 16.

Theorem 24. *For every two ordinal numbers u and w,*

$$u < w \quad implies \quad \aleph_u < \aleph_w$$

PROOF. We use transfinite induction on w.

If $w = 0$, then the proof of the implication is trivial.

Now, assume $w > 0$ is not a limit ordinal and that $u < w^-$ implies $\aleph_u < \aleph_{w^-}$. But then since $u < w$ implies $u \leq w^-$, we see that $u < w$ implies $\aleph_u \leq \aleph_{w^-}$. However, in view of Corollary 12, $\aleph_{w^-} < \aleph_w$. Hence, $\aleph_u < \aleph_w$.

Next, assume w is a limit ordinal and that $\aleph_u < \aleph_v$, for every v such that $u < v < w$. But then by Corollary 12 and (16) we see that $\aleph_v \leq \bigcup_{v<w} \aleph_v = \aleph_w$. Hence, $\aleph_u < \aleph_w$.

Corollary 13. *For every two ordinal numbers u and w,*

$$u < w \quad if\ and\ only\ if \quad \aleph_u < \aleph_w$$

Theorem 25. *For every nonempty set V of ordinal numbers,*

$$(18) \qquad \bigcup_{v\in V} \aleph_v = \aleph_{\cup V}$$

PROOF. If V has a greatest element w, then $\aleph_{\cup V} = \aleph_w$. Moreover, in view of Theorems 24 and 16 we have also $\bigcup_{v\in V} \aleph_v = \aleph_w$. Consequently, (18) is valid when V has a greatest element.

If V has no greatest element, then $v < \cup V$, for every $v \in V$, and therefore by Theorem 24, $\aleph_v < \aleph_{\cup V}$, for every $v \in V$, which in view of Theorem 16 implies:

$$(19) \qquad \bigcup_{v\in V} \aleph_v \leq \aleph_{\cup V}$$

On the other hand, since V has no greatest element, for every $w < \cup V$, there exists $v \in V$ such that $w < v < \cup V$, which in view of Theorems 24 and 7 implies $\bigcup_{w<\cup V} \aleph_w \leq \bigcup_{v\in V} \aleph_v$. However, in view of (16) the left side of the above inequality is equal to $\aleph_{\cup V}$. Consequently, $\aleph_{\cup V} \leq \bigcup_{v\in V} \aleph_v$. Comparing this inequality with (19) we derive (18), as desired.

Corollary 14. *For every nonempty nondecreasing sequence $(u_i)_{i<v}$ of ordinal numbers u_i, if*

$$\lim_{i<v} u_i = u$$

then:

$$\lim_{i<v} \aleph_{u_i} = \aleph_u$$

PROOF. Consider the set $V = (u_i)_{i<V}$. Then the proof of the corollary follows from Theorem 25.

Theorem 26. *For every infinite cardinal number c, there exists a unique ordinal number w such that:*

$$c = \aleph_w$$

PROOF. Let V be the set of all ordinals v such that $\aleph_v \le c$, for every $v \in V$. The set V exists since the set of all cardinals less than or equal to c exists. Moreover, since $\aleph_0 \le c$ we see that $0 \in V$. Hence, V is nonempty. Let $w = \cup V$. Since $\aleph_v \le c$, for every $v \in V$, we see that $\underset{v \in V}{\cup} \aleph_v \le c$. Consequently, in view of Theorem 25 we derive $\aleph_w \le c$. On the other hand, since the immediate successor w^+ of w is not an element of V, we have $c < \aleph_{w^+}$. Thus,

$$\aleph_w \le c < \aleph_{w^+}$$

However, in view of Corollary 12, $\aleph_{w^+}$ is the immediate successor of $\aleph_w$. Hence, $\aleph_w = c$, as desired. The uniqueness of w follows from Corollary 13.

Remark 5. In view of Theorem 26, for every infinite cardinal number c there exists a unique ordinal number w such that $c = \aleph_w$ (read: *aleph sub w*). Motivated by this, we say that *every infinite cardinal number is an aleph.*

Remark 6. It is customary to call $\aleph_0$ *the first number class*. Moreover, $\mathbf{Z}(\aleph_0)$ is called *the second number class*, $\mathbf{Z}(\aleph_1)$, *the third number class*, and so forth.

Let us restate some of the properties of the infinite cardinals in their "aleph" setting.

In view of (15) and Corollary 11, we have:

(20) $$\overline{\overline{\mathbf{Z}(\aleph_w)}} = \aleph_{w^+} = \aleph_{w+1}$$

Theorem 27. *The sum-set of every denumerable set of elements of the second number class [i.e., elements of $\mathbf{Z}(\aleph_0)$] is an element of the second number class.*

PROOF. The proof of the theorem follows from Theorem 25 of Chapter VI (page 271), according to which a denumerable union of denumerable sets is denumerable.

Theorem 28. *For every denumerable set S of elements of the second number class there exists an element of the second number class which is greater than every element of S.*

PROOF. In view of Theorem 27, $\cup S$ is an element of the second number class. Clearly, $\cup S + 1$ is also an element of the second number class, and, moreover, in view of Theorem 8 of Chapter VIII (page 323), $\cup S + 1$ is greater than every element of S.

EXERCISES

1. Prove that every element of $\mathbf{Z}(\omega)$ that is a limit number is the limit of a certain infinite increasing sequence of elements of $\omega \cup \mathbf{Z}(\omega)$.

2. Prove that every element w of the second number class which is a limit number is the sum of an infinite sequence of elements of the first or the second number class which are smaller than w.

3. Let the transfinite sequence $(u_i)_{i \in \Omega}$ of ordinals u_i be such that $u_i \in \Omega$, for every $i \in \Omega$. Prove that for every ordinal $v < \Omega$, there exists a limit ordinal w such that $v < w < \Omega$ and such that $u_i < w$, for every $i < w$.

4. Prove that if w is an ordinal such that $\Omega \leq w < \Omega^\omega$, then $w^\omega = \Omega^\omega$.

5. Prove that there exist no nonzero ordinals u and v such that $u\omega = v\Omega$.

6. Let S be the sum of a finite or transfinite sequence of type w (where w is an element of the second number class) of elements of the first or second number class. Prove that S is an element of the first or second number class.

4. CARDINAL ARITHMETIC

In this section we shall introduce addition and multiplication among cardinals. Clearly, we expect that the sum as well as the product of two cardinal numbers will again be a cardinal number. Although every cardinal number is an ordinal number, in general the sum and the product of two cardinals, when obtained according respectively to Definitions 4 and 8 of Chapter VIII (pages 327 and 338), need not be cardinal numbers. For instance ω and 2 are both cardinal numbers, whereas $\omega + 2$ (in the sense of ordinal addition) and $\omega 2$ (in the sense of ordinal multiplication) are not cardinal numbers since the only denumerable cardinal number is ω.

Therefore, as expected, we define cardinal addition and cardinal multiplication quite differently from the way we defined ordinal addition and ordinal multiplication.

Definition 4. *For every two cardinal numbers a and b, we define their sum $a + b$ as*

$$a + b = \overline{\overline{u \cup v}}$$

where $a \cong u$, $b \cong v$ and $u \cap v = \varnothing$.

In view of Lemma 2 of Chapter VI (page 249) and Theorem 2, we see that in the above $a + b$ is determined uniquely by a and b.

In view of the associativity and commutativity of the set-theoretical union operation, for every three cardinal numbers a, b and c, we have:

$$(21) \qquad (a + b) + c = a + (b + c)$$

$$(22) \qquad a + b = b + a$$

Thus, cardinal addition is *associative* and *commutative*.

According to Definition 4, we have:

$$\aleph_0 + 1 = \aleph_0 = 1 + \aleph_0 \qquad \text{and} \qquad 3 + \aleph_0 = \aleph_0 = \aleph_0 + 3$$

Moreover, for every cardinal number c,

$$(23) \qquad c + 0 = 0 + c = c$$

Obviously, the sum of two finite cardinals is the same whether it is obtained according to ordinal or cardinal addition.

Theorem 29.   *For every four cardinal numbers a, b, c and d,*

$$a \leq b \qquad and \qquad c \leq d$$

implies

$$a + c \leq b + d$$

PROOF.   Let s, u, v and w be four pairwise disjoint sets such that $a \simeq s$, $b \simeq u$, $c \simeq v$ and $d \simeq w$. Then clearly under the hypothesis of the theorem, there is an equipollence between $a \cup c$ and a subset of $b \cup d$.

Next, we prove the following important theorem.

Theorem 30.   *For every cardinal number a and every infinite cardinal number c,*

$$a \leq c \qquad implies \qquad a + c = c$$

PROOF.   Let u and v be two disjoint sets such that $a \simeq u$ and $c \simeq v$. In view of the hypothesis of the theorem, v is an infinite set. Moreover, $u \preceq v$, in the sense of Definition 3 of Chapter VI (page 257). Therefore, by Corollary 16 of Chapter VI (page 261), we have $u \cup v \simeq v$. Consequently, in view of Definition 4 and Corollary 9 we obtain $a + c = c$, as desired.

From Theorem 30, it follows that *if of two cardinals at least one is infinite, then their sum is equal to the larger one if they are unequal, and otherwise to each of them.*

Corollary 15.   *For every four cardinal numbers a, b, c and d,*

$$a < b \qquad and \qquad c < d$$

implies

$$a + c < b + d$$

PROOF.   If b and d are finite cardinals, then the proof is obvious. If b or d is an infinite cardinal, then the proof follows from the fact that in view of Theorem 30, $b + d$ is equal to that one of b and d which is not less than the other.

Corollary 16. *For every two cardinal numbers a and b,*

$$a \leq b \quad \text{if and only if} \quad b = a + c$$

or some cardinal number c.

PROOF. Clearly, if $b = a + c$, then $a \leq b$.

Next, if b is a finite cardinal, then obviously $a \leq b$ implies the existence of a finite cardinal c such that $b = a + c$. If b is an infinite cardinal, then in view of Theorem 30 it is enough to choose $c = b$.

According to Theorem 30, we have:

$$n + \aleph_0 = \aleph_0 \quad n = 0, 1, 2, \ldots$$
$$\aleph_0 + \aleph_0 = \aleph_0$$
$$\aleph_0 + \aleph_0 + \cdots + \aleph_0 = \aleph_0$$
$$n + \aleph = \aleph \quad n = 0, 1, 2, \ldots$$

Corollary 17. *For every two ordinal numbers u and v,*

$$u \leq v \quad \text{implies} \quad \aleph_u + \aleph_v = \aleph_v$$

PROOF. In view of Theorem 24, $u \leq v$ implies $\aleph_u \leq \aleph_v$, and therefore the proof of the corollary follows from Theorem 30.

Accordingly, we have:

$$\aleph_3 + \aleph_4 = \aleph_4, \quad \aleph_\omega + \aleph_3 = \aleph_\omega, \quad \aleph_\omega + \aleph_\Omega = \aleph_\Omega$$

Corollary 18. *Let $\aleph$ be the cardinal of the power of the continuum. Then:*

$$\aleph_0 + \aleph = \aleph_1 + \aleph = \aleph$$

PROOF. Since $\aleph$ is of the power of the continuum, we see that $\aleph_0 < \aleph$. However, since $\aleph_1$ is the immediate successor of $\aleph_0$, we see that $\aleph_1 \leq \aleph$. Consequently, the corollary follows from Theorem 30.

Definition 5. *For every two cardinal numbers a and b, we define their product ab as*

$$ab = \overline{\overline{u \times v}}$$

where $a \cong u$ and $b \cong v$.

In the above, $u \times v$ is the Cartesian product of u and v.

In view of Lemma 10 of Chapter VI (page 265) and Theorem 2, we see that in the above ab is determined uniquely by a and b.

Obviously, in Definition 5, we might have taken $a = u$ and $b = v$, and then we might have defined:

$$ab = \overline{\overline{a \times b}}$$

In view of Lemma 11 of Chapter VI (page 266) and Theorem 2, for every three cardinal numbers a, b and c, we have:

(24) $$(ab)c = a(bc)$$

(25) $$ab = ba$$

Thus, cardinal multiplication is *associative* and *commutative*.

According to the above definition and Theorem 27 of Chapter VI (page 272), we have:

$$2\aleph_0 = \aleph_0 2 = \aleph_0 \quad \text{and} \quad \aleph_0(2\aleph_0)3\aleph_0 = \aleph_0$$

Obviously, the product of two finite cardinals is the same whether it is obtained according to ordinal or cardinal multiplication.

Moreover, for every cardinal number c:

$$(26) \qquad c0 = 0c = 0 \quad \text{and} \quad 1c = c1 = c$$

Also, in view of the properties of the Cartesian product, we have

$$(27) \qquad ab = 0 \quad \text{if and only if} \quad a = 0 \quad \text{or} \quad b = 0$$

for every two cardinal numbers a and b; moreover,

$$(28) \qquad a(b + c) = ab + ac = (b + c)a$$

for every three cardinal numbers a, b and c.

Thus, in view of (28), multiplication of cardinals is *distributive* with respect to addition of cardinals.

Theorem 31. *For every four cardinal numbers a, b, c and d,*

$$a \leq b \quad \text{and} \quad c \leq d$$

implies

$$ac \leq bd$$

PROOF. Clearly, under the hypothesis of the theorem there is an equipollence between $a \times c$ and a subset of $b \times d$.

Next, we prove the following important theorem.

Theorem 32. *For every nonzero cardinal number a and every infinite cardinal number c,*

$$a \leq c \quad \text{implies} \quad ac = c$$

PROOF. In view of the hypothesis of the theorem, a is a nonempty set and c is an infinite set. Moreover, $a \prec c$, in the sense of Definition 3 of Chapter VI (page 257). Therefore, by Corollary 24 of Chapter VI (page 276), $a \times c \cong c$. Consequently, in view of Definition 5 and Corollary 9, we obtain $ac = c$, as desired.

From Theorem 32 it follows that *if of two positive (nonzero) cardinals at least one is infinite, then their product is equal to the larger one if they are unequal, and otherwise to each of them.*

Corollary 19. *For every four cardinal numbers a, b, c and d,*

$$a < b \quad \text{and} \quad c < d$$

implies

$$ac < bd$$

PROOF. If b and d are finite cardinals, then the result is obvious. If b or d is an infinite cardinal, then the proof follows from the fact that, in view of Theorem 32, bd is equal to that one of b and d which is not less than the other.

Corollary 20. *For every two ordinal numbers u and v,*

$$u \leq v \qquad implies \qquad \aleph_u \aleph_v = \aleph_v$$

PROOF. In view of Theorem 24, $u \leq v$ implies $\aleph_u \leq \aleph_v$, and therefore the proof of the corollary follows from Theorem 32.

Accordingly, we have:

$$\aleph_0 \aleph_1 = \aleph_1, \qquad \aleph_3 \aleph_2 = \aleph_3, \qquad \aleph \aleph_0 = \aleph$$

Also,

$$(\aleph_0 + \aleph_1)\aleph = \aleph, \qquad (\aleph_1 + \aleph)\aleph_0 = \aleph, \qquad (\aleph + \aleph_0)\aleph_1 = \aleph$$

Combining Theorem 30 and 32, we have:

Corollary 21. *For every nonzero cardinal number a and every infinite cardinal number c,*

$$a \leq c \qquad implies \qquad a + c = ac = c$$

Definition 6. *An aleph $\aleph_w$ such that*

$$\aleph_w = \bigcup_{u < v} \bar{\bar{c}}_u \qquad with \qquad \bar{\bar{c}}_u < \aleph_w \qquad and \qquad \omega \leq v < \omega_w$$

is called a singular aleph.

An aleph that is not a singular aleph is called a *regular aleph*. In particular, if $\aleph_w$ is the limit of a nondecreasing transfinite sequence of type less than ω_w of cardinals less than $\aleph_w$, then $\aleph_w$ is a singular aleph.

For instance, $\aleph_\omega$ is a singular aleph, since:

$$\aleph_\omega = \aleph_0 \cup \aleph_1 \cup \aleph_2 \cup \aleph_3 \cup \cdots$$

i.e., $\aleph_\omega$ is the limit of a nondecreasing transfinite sequence of type ω, which is less than ω_ω, of cardinals less than $\aleph_\omega$.

Similarly, $\aleph_{\omega\omega}$ is a singular aleph, since:

$$\aleph_{\omega\omega} = \aleph_\omega \cup \aleph_{\omega^2} \cup \aleph_{\omega^3} \cup \cdots$$

i.e., $\aleph_{\omega\omega}$ is the limit of a nondecreasing transfinite sequence of type ω, which is less than ω^ω, of cardinals less than $\aleph_{\omega\omega}$.

Also, $\aleph_{\omega_1} = \aleph_\Omega$ is a singular aleph, since:

$$\aleph_{\omega_1} = \bigcup_{v < \omega_1} \aleph_v$$

i.e., $\aleph_{\omega_1}$ is the limit of a nondecreasing transfinite sequence of type ω_1, which is less than ω_{ω_1}, of cardinals less than $\aleph_{\omega_1}$.

On the other hand, $\aleph_0$ is a regular aleph, since there is no ordinal v such that $\omega \leq v < \omega$. Also, $\aleph_1$ is a regular aleph, since $\aleph_1$ is not equal to the union of a denumerable set of cardinals each of which is less than $\aleph_1$.

Theorem 33. *For every ordinal w that is not a limit number, $\aleph_w$ is a regular aleph.*

PROOF. Since $\aleph_0$ is a regular aleph, it is enough to consider the case where w is a positive nonlimit ordinal number. But then for every ordinal u if $\bar{\bar{c}}_u < \aleph_w$, then $\bar{\bar{c}}_u \leq \aleph_{w^-}$. Consequently, $\aleph_w > \underset{u<v}{\cup} \bar{\bar{c}}_u$, and therefore $\aleph_w$ is a regular aleph, as desired.

Theorem 34. *If $\aleph_w$ is a regular aleph such that w is a limit number, then*

$$\aleph_w = w$$

PROOF. Since $\aleph_w$ contains the set $(\aleph_u)_{u \in w}$, we see that $w \subset \aleph_w$. Assume on the contrary that $\aleph_w \neq w$. Hence $w < \aleph_w$ and thus, $w < \omega_w$. Moreover, since w is a limit number, $\omega \leq w < \omega_w$. On the other hand, in view of (16)

$$\aleph_w = \underset{v<w}{\cup} \aleph_v$$

and since $\omega \leq w < \omega_w$ and $\aleph_v < \aleph_w$ for every $v \in w$, we see that $\aleph_w$ is a singular aleph, contradicting the hypothesis. Hence our assumption is false, and $\aleph_w = w$, as desired.

In connection with Theorem 34, let us observe that in general for every ordinal w,

(29) $\aleph_w = \bar{\bar{w}}$ implies $w = \bar{\bar{w}}$ (i.e., w is a cardinal number).

To prove (29) it is enough to note that, as mentioned above, $w \subset \aleph_w$ and hence $\bar{\bar{w}} \subset w \subset \aleph_w$. Therefore, in view of the hypothesis of (29), we derive $w = \bar{\bar{w}}$, as desired.

Let us remark that so far it is not known whether or not every aleph whose index is a limit number is a singular aleph. However, no example has been given of a regular aleph whose index is a limit number. (Such cardinal numbers are called *inaccessible cardinal numbers* by K. Kuratowski.)

EXERCISES

1. Let a, b, c and d be cardinal numbers such that $a + b = c + d$. Prove that there exist cardinal numbers m, n, p and q such that $a = m + p, b = n + q$, $c = m + n$ and $d = p + q$.

2. Let a and c be two cardinal numbers. Prove that:

$$a + c = \overline{\overline{a \cup c}} + \overline{\overline{a \cap c}}$$

3. Let a, c and e be three cardinal numbers. Prove that:

$$a + c + e = \overline{\overline{a - c}} + \overline{\overline{c - e}} + \overline{\overline{e - a}} + \overline{\overline{a \cap c \cap e}}$$

4. Let a, c and e be three cardinal numbers. Prove that:

$$a + c + e + \overline{\overline{a \cap c \cap e}} = \overline{\overline{a \cup c \cup e}} + \overline{\overline{a \cap c}} + \overline{\overline{a \cap e}} + \overline{\overline{c \cap e}}$$

5. Prove (23), (26) and (27).

6. Prove Corollary 21.

7. Let a and b be two cardinal numbers. Prove that $2a < a + b$ implies $a < b$, and also that $2a > a + b$ implies $a > b$.

8. Let a, b and c be three cardinals. Prove that $a + b = a + c$ implies $b = c$ or $b \leq a$ and $c \leq a$.

9. Let a, b and c be three cardinals. Prove that $ac < bc$ implies $a < b$.

10. Let u and v be two ordinals such that $u < v$. Prove that $\aleph_v - \aleph_u = \aleph_v$.

5. INFINITE SUMS OF CARDINAL NUMBERS

The sum of finitely many cardinals presents no problem and is obtained by adding two cardinals at a time. The sum of infinitely many cardinals is defined as follows:

Definition 7. *For every set C of cardinal numbers, the sum of all the cardinal numbers belonging to C is denoted by*

$$\overline{\overline{\sum_{c \in C} c}}$$

and is defined as:

$$\overline{\bigcup_{c \in C} (c \times \{c\})}$$

Note that the set $\bigcup_{c \in C} (c \times \{c\})$ exists since it is a subset of $(\bigcup C) \times C$. Consequently, in view of Theorem 2 the sum of all the cardinals belonging to a given set of cardinals is determined uniquely.

Accordingly,

$$\overline{\overline{\sum_{c \in C} c}} = \overline{\bigcup_{c \in C} (c \times \{c\})}$$

Now, let C be a set of cardinals and E be a disjointed set such that between C and E there exists a one-to-one correspondence assigning to every element c of C an element e of E with $c \cong e$. Then, in view of Theorem 15 of Chapter VI (page 265),

(30) $$\overline{\overline{\sum_{c \in C} c}} = \overline{\bigcup_{e \in E} e}$$

Definition 7 determines the sum of all the cardinals belonging to a given set C of cardinals. Naturally, all the cardinals belonging to C are distinct, a fact following directly from the definition of equality between sets. To cover the case where some of the summands may not be distinct, we introduce an indexed family of cardinals. Thus:

Definition 8. *For every indexed family $(c_i)_{i \in I}$ of cardinal numbers, the sum of all the cardinal numbers belonging to this family is denoted by*

$$\overline{\overline{\sum_{i \in I} c_i}}$$

and is defined as:

$$\overline{\bigcup_{i \in I} (c_i \times \{i\})}$$

Accordingly,

$$(31) \qquad \overline{\overline{\sum_{i \in I} c_i}} = \overline{\overline{\bigcup_{i \in I} (c_i \times \{i\})}}$$

Lemma 5.   *For every two families* $(a_i)_{i \in I}$ *and* $(c_i)_{i \in I}$ *of cardinal numbers* a_i *and* c_i

$$a_i \leq c_i \qquad \text{for every} \quad i \in I$$

implies:

$$\overline{\overline{\sum_{i \in I} a_i}} \leq \overline{\overline{\sum_{i \in I} c_i}}$$

The proof of the above lemma follows from Definition 8 and is similar to the proof of Theorem 29.

When the index set I is the set ω of all natural numbers (or the set of all positive natural numbers), then as we know the indexed family $(c_i)_{i \in I}$ is called an infinite sequence, and the left side of the equality sign in (31) is usually written as

$$(32) \qquad c_0 + c_1 + c_2 + c_3 + \cdots$$

and is called an *infinite series of cardinals*.

From Definition 8 it follows that *the sum of an infinite sequence of cardinal numbers always exists*.

Let us give some examples of sums of infinite sequences of cardinals.

First, let us consider the case where, in (32), $c_i = 1$, for every i, i.e.,

$$1 + 1 + 1 + \cdots$$

By Definition 8, we have:

$$1 + 1 + 1 + \cdots = \overline{\overline{\bigcup_{i \in \omega} (1 \times \{i\})}}$$

However, it is obvious that

$$\bigcup_{i \in \omega} (1 \times \{i\}) = \{(0,0), (0,1), (0,2), \ldots\}$$

since $1 = \{0\}$. Clearly, the right side of the above equality is a denumerable set, and hence its cardinal is equal to $\aleph_0$. Consequently, we have:

$$(33) \qquad 1 + 1 + 1 + \cdots = \aleph_0$$

Note that the left side of (33) has no meaning in the context of the arithmetic of natural numbers.

Similarly, in view of Definition 8 we have:

$$1 + 2 + 3 + 4 + \cdots = \aleph_0$$

Moreover, for every finite cardinal n,

$$n + n + n + \cdots = \aleph_0$$

It is worth noting that according to ordinal arithmetic (see page 333) each of the above infinite sums is equal to ω, which in turn is equal to $\aleph_0$.

Now, let us consider:

$$\aleph_0 + \aleph_0 + \aleph_0 + \cdots$$

By Definition 8, we have:

$$\aleph_0 + \aleph_0 + \aleph_0 + \cdots = \overline{\overline{\bigcup_{i\in\omega} (\aleph_0 \times \{i\})}}$$

However

$$\bigcup_{i\in\omega} (\aleph_0 + \{i\}) = (\aleph_0 \times \{0\}) \cup (\aleph_0 \times \{1\}) \cup (\aleph_0 \times \{2\}) \cup \cdots$$

which is a denumerable union of denumerable sets, and hence is itself a denumerable set. Thus,

$$\aleph_0 + \aleph_0 + \aleph_0 + \cdots = \aleph_0$$

Note that in contrast with the above, in the context of ordinal arithmetic we have:

$$\omega + \omega + \omega + \cdots = \omega\omega \neq \omega$$

In view of Theorem 17 of Chapter VI (page 266), and as mentioned in Remark 6 of Chapter VI (page 266), a Cartesian product is equipollent (in an obvious way) to a repeated union. Thus, in view of Theorem 32 we have:

$$\aleph + \aleph + \aleph + \cdots = \aleph_0\aleph = \aleph$$
$$\aleph_1 + \aleph_1 + \aleph_1 + \cdots = \aleph_0\aleph_1 = \aleph_1$$

Similarly, in view of the above remark and Theorem 32 we have:

$$\sum_{i\in\omega_2} c_i = \aleph_2 \quad \text{where} \quad c_i = \aleph_0 \quad \text{for every} \quad i \in \omega_2$$

Theorem 35. *For every ordinal number w,*

$$\aleph_w = \overline{\overline{\sum_{v\leq w}}} \aleph_v$$

PROOF. Since every $\aleph_w$ is an ordinal number, $\aleph_w$ is equal to the set of all ordinals less than $\aleph_w$. However, by Theorem 11 every ordinal less than $\aleph_w$ is also of power less than that of $\aleph_w$, and vice versa. Consequently, for every ordinal w:

$$\aleph_w = \aleph_0 \cup (\bigcup_{v<w} \mathbf{Z}(\aleph_v))$$

On the other hand, by Lemma 2, for $u \neq v$, the sets $\mathbf{Z}(\aleph_u)$ and $\mathbf{Z}(\aleph_v)$ are disjoint. Hence the above equality shows that $\aleph_w$ is a union of pairwise disjoint sets. Consequently, by (30):

$$\aleph_w = \aleph_0 + \overline{\overline{\bigcup_{v<w} \mathbf{Z}(\aleph_v)}}$$

In view of (20), the above equality can be written as:

$$\aleph_w = \aleph_0 + \overline{\overline{\sum_{v<w}}} \aleph_{v+1}$$

Now if w is a limit number, then $\overline{\overline{\sum}}_{v<w} \aleph_{v+1}$ is greater than every cardinal less than $\aleph_w$. Hence (34) can be written as:

$$\aleph_w = \overline{\overline{\sum}}_{v \leq w} \aleph_v$$

Corollary 22. *For every limit ordinal w,*

$$\aleph_w = \overline{\overline{\sum}}_{v<w} \aleph_v$$

In view of Corollary 22, we have:

(35)
$$\aleph_\omega = \aleph_0 + \aleph_1 + \aleph_2 + \cdots$$

EXERCISES

1. Prove that for every cardinal a and every sequence $(c_i)_{i<w}$ of type w of cardinals c_i:

$$a \overline{\overline{\sum}}_{i<w} c_i = \overline{\overline{\sum}}_{i<w} a c_i$$

2. Prove Lemma 5 and Corollary 22.

3. Prove Theorem 35 using the fact that $\aleph_w \aleph_w = \aleph_w$.

4. Let a, b and c_i $(i = 1, 2, 3, \ldots)$ be cardinal numbers. Prove that there exist cardinals $a_1, a_2, a_3, \ldots b_1, b_2, b_3, \ldots$ such that $a = a_1 + a_2 + a_3 + \cdots$, $b = b_1 + b_2 + b_3 + \cdots$ and $c_i = a_i + b_i$ $(i = 1, 2, \ldots)$.

5. Let $(c_i)_{i<w}$ be a sequence of type w of cardinal numbers c_i containing no greatest cardinal. Prove that:

$$\overline{\overline{\sum}}_{i<w} c_i > c_i, \quad \text{for every } i < w$$

6. Let $(c_i)_{i<w}$ be a sequence of type w of cardinals c_i. Can you introduce the notion of a partial sum of $(c_i)_{i<w}$ and prove that the sum of $(c_i)_{i<w}$ is equal to the limit of its partial sums?

7. Let (c_i) be an infinite sequence of cardinals c_i. Prove that:

$$c_0 + c_1 + c_2 + \cdots = c_0 + (c_0 + c_1) + (c_0 + c_1 + c_2) + \cdots$$

8. Let (c_i) be an infinite sequence of cardinals c_i and c a cardinal such that:

$$c \geq c_1 + c_2 + \cdots + c_n \quad \text{for } n = 1, 2, 3, \ldots$$

Prove that:

$$c \geq c_1 + c_2 + c_3 + \cdots$$

6. INFINITE PRODUCTS OF CARDINAL NUMBERS

The product of finitely many cardinals presents no problem and is obtained by multiplying two cardinals at a time. The product of infinitely many cardinals is defined as follows:

Definition 9. *For every set C of cardinal numbers, the product of all the cardinals belonging to C is denoted by*

$$\overline{\overline{\prod_{c \in C}}} c$$

and is defined as:

$$\overline{\overline{\prod_{c \in C} c}}$$

In the above, $\prod_{c \in C} c$ [according to Definition 9 of Chapter III (page 162)], denotes the Cartesian product of the set C. Moreover, the existence of the product of all the cardinals belonging to a set of cardinals C is ensured by the existence of the Cartesian product of a set, and the uniqueness of the product is secured by Theorem 4.

Accordingly:

$$\overline{\overline{\prod_{c \in C}}} c = \overline{\overline{\prod_{c \in C} c}}$$

Now, let C be a set of cardinals and E a set such that between C and E there exists a one-to-one correspondence assigning to every element c of C an element e of E with $c \cong e$. Then, in view of Theorem 18 of Chapter VI (page 266), and Theorem 2:

(36) $$\overline{\overline{\prod_{c \in C}}} c = \overline{\overline{\prod_{e \in E}}} e$$

As in the case of Definition 8, here also we introduce:

Definition 10. *For every indexed family $(c_i)_{i \in I}$ of cardinal numbers the product of all the cardinal numbers belonging to this family is denoted by*

$$\overline{\overline{\prod_{i \in I}}} c_i$$

and is defined as:

$$\overline{\overline{\prod_{i \in I} c_i}}$$

Accordingly,

(37) $$\overline{\overline{\prod_{i \in I}}} c_i = \overline{\overline{\prod_{i \in I} c_i}}$$

In the above, $\prod_{i \in I} c_i$ is given according to the definition on page 161.

Theorem 36. *For every family $(c_i)_{i \in I}$ of cardinal numbers*

$$\overline{\overline{\prod_{i \in I}}} c_i = 0 \quad \textit{if and only if} \quad c_i = 0 \quad \textit{for some} \quad i \in I$$

PROOF. The proof of the theorem follows immediately from Theorem 4 of Chapter III (page 161), and Theorem 2.

Lemma 6. *For every two families* $(a_i)_{i \in I}$ *and* $(c_i)_{i \in I}$ *of cardinal numbers* a_i *and* c_i,

$$a_i \leq c_i \quad \textit{for every} \quad i \in I$$

implies:

$$\overline{\overline{\prod_{i \in I}}} a_i \leq \overline{\overline{\prod_{i \in I}}} c_i$$

The proof of the above lemma follows from Definition 10 and is similar to the proof of Theorem 31.

When the index set I of $(c_i)_{i \in I}$ is the set ω of all natural numbers, then the left side of the equality sign in (37) is usually written as:

$$c_0 \cdot c_1 \cdot c_2 \cdot c_3 \cdots$$

Theorem 37. *For every two families* $(a_i)_{i \in I}$ *and* $(b_i)_{i \in I}$ *of cardinal numbers* a_i *and* b_i,

$$a_i < b_i \quad \textit{for every} \quad i \in I$$

implies:

$$\overline{\overline{\sum_{i \in I}}} a_i < \overline{\overline{\prod_{i \in I}}} b_i$$

PROOF.   Let $(B_i)_{i \in I}$ be a family of pairwise disjoint sets such that $\overline{\overline{B}}_i = b_i$ for every $i \in I$.

Since by the hypothesis $a_i < b_i$, there exists a proper subset A_i of B_i such that $\overline{\overline{A}}_i = a_i$, for every $i \in I$. Thus, in view of (30), (31), (36) and (37) we have:

$$(38) \qquad \overline{\overline{\sum_{i \in I}}} a_i = \overline{\overline{\cup_{i \in I} A_i}} \quad \text{and} \quad \overline{\overline{\prod_{i \in I}}} b_i = \overline{\overline{\prod_{i \in I} B_i}}$$

Since A_i is a proper subset of B_i, for every $i \in I$ we see that $B_i \smallsetminus A_i = C_i$ is not empty.

Let u_i, v_i and w_i denote arbitrary elements of A_i, B_i and C_i respectively.

Naturally, an element of $\prod_{i \in I} B_i$ is $(v_i)_{i \in I}$ (see page 161).   Using the axiom of Choice, associate with every element u_j of A_j element $(v_i)_{i \in I}$ such that $v_i = u_j$ for $i = j$, and $v_i = w_i$ for $i \neq j$. In view of the fact that $(B_i)_{i \in I}$ is a family of pairwise disjoint sets, the above association gives rise to a one-to-one correspondence between $\cup_{i \in I} A_i$ and a subset of $\prod_{i \in I} B_i$.   Consequently,

$$(39) \qquad \overline{\overline{\cup_{i \in I} A_i}} \leq \overline{\overline{\prod_{i \in I} B_i}}$$

To prove the theorem, we have to show that $\cup_{i \in I} A_i$ is not equipollent to $\prod_{i \in I} B_i$. Were this established, (39) would imply $\overline{\overline{\cup_{i \in I} A_i}} < \overline{\overline{\prod_{i \in I} B_i}}$, which in turn in view of (38) would imply $\overline{\overline{\sum_{i \in I}}} a_i < \overline{\overline{\prod_{i \in I}}} b_i$, as desired.

Let us assume on the contrary that there exists a one-to-one correspondence f between $\cup_{i \in I} A_i$ and $\prod_{i \in I} B_i$ whereby every element u_i of A_i is matched with a certain element $(v_i)_{i \in I}$ of $\prod_{i \in I} B_i$. Since, by the hypothesis $\overline{\overline{A}}_i < \overline{\overline{B}}_i$, there must exist a nonempty subset N_i of B_i whose elements do not occur as elements of any of the mates (under f) of any of the elements of A_i. Let an arbitrary element of N_i be denoted by n_i. By the axiom of Choice there exists a set $(n_i)_{i\in I}$ which is an element of $\prod_{i\in I} B_i$. Clearly, in view of the very definition of N_i, we see at once that $(n_i)_{i\in I}$ cannot be the mate of any of the elements of any A_i. Consequently, $\bigcup_{i\in I} A_i$ and $\prod_{i\in I} B_i$ are not equipollent. Thus our assumption is false, and indeed

$$\overline{\overline{\sum_{i\in I}}} a_i < \overline{\overline{\prod_{i\in I}}} b_i, \text{ as desired.}$$

Corollary 23. *The sum of every infinite increasing sequence of positive cardinals is less than their product.*

PROOF. Consider the two infinite increasing sequences of positive cardinals

$$a_1, a_2, a_3, \ldots \quad \text{and} \quad a_2, a_3, a_4, \ldots$$

where:

$$a_1 < a_2 < a_3 < \cdots$$

By Theorem 37, we have immediately

$$a_1 + a_2 + a_3 + \cdots < a_2 \cdot a_3 \cdot a_4 \cdots$$

and since $a_1 \neq 0$, we derive

$$a_1 + a_2 + a_3 + \cdots < a_1 \cdot a_2 \cdot a_3 \cdots$$

as desired.

Corollary 24. *For every two families $(a_i)_{i\in I}$ and $(b_i)_{i\in I}$ of cardinal numbers a_i and b_i*

$$a_i \leq b_i \quad \text{and} \quad b_i > 1 \quad \text{for every} \quad i \in I$$

implies:

$$\overline{\overline{\sum_{i\in I}}} a_i \leq \overline{\overline{\prod_{i\in I}}} b_i$$

The proof of this theorem is similar to that of the first part of Theorem 37 and is left to the reader.

According to Corollary 23, we have, for instance:

(40) $$1 + 2 + 3 + \cdots < 1 \cdot 2 \cdot 3 \cdots$$

Similarly, according to Corollary 24, we have:

$$2 + 2 + 2 + \cdots \leq 2 \cdot 2 \cdot 2 \cdots$$

However, we shall see shortly that the right side of the above inequality is greater than the left side.

Inequality (40) gives another instance of the discrepancy between ordinal and cardinal arithmetic. Whereas in the context of ordinal arithmetic

$$1 + 2 + 3 + \cdots = 1 \cdot 2 \cdot 3 \cdots = \omega$$

in the context of cardinal arithmetic:

$$1 + 2 + 3 + \cdots = \aleph_0 < 1 \cdot 2 \cdot 3 \cdots$$

EXERCISES

1. Prove that if A is an infinite set whose cardinal is a, then the set of all n-element subsets (where n is a positive natural number) of A is of power greater than or equal to a.

2. Let (c_i) be an infinite sequence of cardinals c_i. Prove that:

$$c_0 \cdot c_1 \cdot c_2 \cdots = c_0 \cdot (c_0 \cdot c_1) \cdot (c_0 \cdot c_1 \cdot c_2) \cdots$$

3. Prove (36).

4. Prove Lemma 6.

5. Prove Corollary 24.

6. Let $(c_i)_{i<w}$ be a sequence of type w of cardinals c_i. Introduce the notion of the partial product of $(c_i)_{i<w}$.

Would the product of $(c_i)_{i<w}$ be equal to the limit of the sequence of its partial products? Justify your answer.

7. EXPONENTIATION OF CARDINAL NUMBERS

As mentioned in Chapter VI (page 267), the Cartesian product of a family $(X_i)_{i \in I}$ where $X_i = S$ for every $i \in I$, is denoted by

$$S^I$$

and is equal to the set of all the functions from I into S.

Motivated by the above, we introduce:

Definition 11. *For every two cardinal numbers a and c the c-th power of a, denoted by a^c, is defined as:*

$$a^c = \overline{\overline{a^c}}$$

In the above, a^c on the right side of the equality sign is the set of all functions from the cardinal c into the cardinal a.

Although in the above there is notational ambiguity, the context will prevent any misunderstanding.

The existence of the c-th power of a (as defined by Definition 11) is ensured by the existence of the Cartesian product of a family of sets, and its uniqueness is secured by Theorem 4.

Now, let a and c be two cardinals and u and v two sets such that $a \cong u$ and $c \cong v$. Then in view of Theorem 20 of Chapter VI (page 268), and Theorem 2,

(41)
$$a^c = \overline{\overline{u^v}}$$

Theorem 38. *For every three cardinal numbers a, b and c,*

(42)
$$a^{(b+c)} = a^b \cdot a^c$$

(43)
$$(a \cdot b)^c = a^c \cdot b^c$$

(44)
$$(a^b)^c = a^{bc}$$

PROOF.   The proof of (42) follows from Theorem 21 of Chapter VI (page 268), and (41). The proof of (43) follows from Theorem 22 of Chapter VI (page 268), and (41). The proof of (44) follows from Theorem 23 of Chapter VI (page 269), and (41).

Also, in view of Definition 11,

(45) $$0^c = 0 \quad \text{for every cardinal} \quad c > 0$$

Moreover,

(46) $$c^1 = c \quad \text{for every cardinal} \quad c$$

Furthermore, in view of (83) of Chapter III (page 162),

(47) $$c^0 = 1 \quad \text{and} \quad 1^c = 1 \quad \text{for every cardinal} \quad c$$

From (5) it follows that

(48) $$2^c = \overline{\overline{\mathscr{P}(c)}} \quad \text{for every cardinal} \quad c$$

where $\mathscr{P}(c)$ is the power-set of c.

In view of Theorem 7 of Chapter VI (page 256), Corollary 5 and (48) we have

(49) $$c < 2^c \quad \text{for every cardinal} \quad c$$

Moreover, in view of Definition 11 and (7) we have

(50) $$2^{\aleph_0} = \aleph$$

where $\aleph$ is the cardinal (of the power) of the continuum.

Furthermore, since $\aleph_0\aleph_0 = \aleph_0$, in view of (50) and (44) we obtain:

$$\aleph^{\aleph_0} = (2^{\aleph_0})^{\aleph_0} = 2^{\aleph_0} = \aleph$$

In short,

(51) $$\aleph^{\aleph_0} = 2^{\aleph_0} = \aleph$$

Also, since $\aleph_1$ is the immediate successor of $\aleph_0$, according to (49) and (50) we have:

(52) $$\aleph_0 < \aleph_1 \leq \aleph$$

Theorem 39.   *For every four cardinal numbers a, b, c and d,*

$$a \leq b \quad \text{and} \quad c \leq d \quad \text{implies} \quad a^c \leq b^d$$

PROOF.   From Definition 11, in view of the hypothesis of the theorem, it follows at once that:

(53) $$a^c \leq b^c$$

Now, since $c \leq d$, by Corollary 16 there exists a cardinal m such that $d = c + m$, and therefore in view of (42),

(54) $$b^d = b^{c+m} = b^c \cdot b^m$$

In view of (45), the theorem is true for $a = b = 0$. Hence we may suppose $b > 0$, and thus $b^m \geq 1$, in which case from (53), (54) and Theorem 31 it follows that:

$$a^c \leq b^c \leq b^d$$

Theorem 40. *For every cardinal number a greater than* 1 *and every infinite cardinal number c, if* $a \leq c$ *then:*

$$a^c = 2^c$$

PROOF. In view of (49) we have $a < 2^a$, and hence by Theorem 39, $a^c \leq (2^a)^c$. From this, in view of (44) we derive $a^c \leq 2^{ac}$. However, since c is an infinite cardinal and $a \leq c$, by Theorem 32, $ac = c$. Consequently,

(55) $a^c \leq 2^c$

On the other hand, since $2 \leq a$, by Theorem 39

$$2^c \leq a^c$$

which in view of (55) yields $a^c = 2^c$, as desired.

From (50), (51) and Theorem 40, we derive:

(56) $2^{\aleph_0} = \aleph_0^{\aleph_0} = \aleph^{\aleph_0} = \aleph$

Similarly, from Theorem 40 and (52), it follows that:

(57) $2^{\aleph} = \aleph_0^{\aleph} = \aleph_1^{\aleph} = \aleph^{\aleph}$

Also, in view of Theorem 40 and (55), we have:

(58) $2^{\aleph_0} = 3^{\aleph_0} = 4^{\aleph_0} = \cdots = \aleph_0^{\aleph_0} = \aleph^{\aleph_0} = \aleph$

Similarly, in view of Theorem 40 and (56), we have:

(59) $2^{\aleph} = 3^{\aleph} = 4^{\aleph} = \cdots = \aleph_0^{\aleph} = \aleph_1^{\aleph} = \aleph^{\aleph}$

Moreover, in view of the fact that $\aleph_0 \aleph_0 = \aleph_0$ and $\aleph\aleph = \aleph_0\aleph = \aleph$, we have

(60) $\aleph_0 + \aleph_0^2 + \aleph_0^3 + \aleph_0^4 + \cdots = \aleph_0$

(61) $\aleph + \aleph^2 + \aleph^3 + \aleph^4 + \cdots = \aleph$

We see at once that (60) confirms the conclusion of Theorem 26 of Chapter VI (page 271), according to which *the set of all finite sequences of a denumerable set is again denumerable.*

Moreover, according to (61) we have:

Corollary 25. *The set of all finite sequences of a set of the power of the continuum is again of the power of the continuum.*

Since every finite set is equipollent to a finite sequence and since the set of all one-element subsets of a set of the power of the continuum is of the power of the continuum, in view of Corollary 25 we have:

Corollary 26. *The set of all finite subsets of a set of the power of the continuum is again of the power of the continuum.*

From (56) it follows that:

Corollary 27. *The set of all infinite sequences of a denumerable set is of the power of the continuum.*

Corollary 28. *The set of all infinite subsets of a denumerable set is of the power of the continuum.*

PROOF. Since, as we know, the set of all subsets of a denumerable set is of the power of the continuum, and since by Corollary 21 of Chapter VI (page 271), the set of all finite subsets of a denumerable set is denumerable, in view of Theorem 11 of Chapter VI (page 261), the set of all infinite subsets of a denumerable set is of the power of the continuum.

Next, we observe that (56) implies:

Corollary 29. *The set of all infinite sequences of a set of the power of the continuum is again of the power of the continuum.*

From Corollaries 28 and 29, and in view of the fact that every denumerable subset is equipollent to an infinite sequence, we obtain:

Corollary 30. *The set of all denumerable subsets of a set of the power of the continuum is again of the power of the continuum.*

Corollary 31. *The set of all nondenumerable subsets of a set of the power of the continuum is of the power $2^{\aleph}$.*

PROOF. Let C be a set of the power of the continuum. The set $\mathscr{P}(C)$ of all subsets of C, as we know, is of the power $2^{\aleph}$. However, $\mathscr{P}(C)$ is the union of the following three pairwise disjoint sets: (i) the set of all finite subsets of C; (ii) the set of all denumerable subsets of C; and (iii) the set of all nondenumerable subsets of C. By Corollary 26 the cardinal number of (i) is $\aleph$. By Corollary 30 the cardinal number of (ii) is also $\aleph$. Let x denote the cardinal number of (iii). Clearly,

$$\aleph + \aleph + x = 2^{\aleph}$$

However, since $\aleph < 2^{\aleph}$, it follows from Theorem 30 that $x = 2^{\aleph}$, as desired.

Remark 7. Let us observe that if a, b, c and d are cardinals, then $a < b$ does not imply $a^c < b^c$. For example, $2 < \aleph$; however, as (51) shows, $2^{\aleph_0} = \aleph^{\aleph_0}$. Similarly, $c < d$ does not imply $a^c < a^d$. For instance, $2 < 3$; however, as (61) shows, $\aleph^2 = \aleph^3$. Moreover, it has been proved that even $a < b$ and $c < d$ together do not imply $a^c < b^d$.

However, the following is an immediate consequence of Theorem 39.

Corollary 32. *For every four cardinal numbers a, b, c and d,*

$$a^c < b^c \quad implies \quad a < b$$
$$a^c < a^d \quad implies \quad c < d$$

Next, note that in view of (56):

(62) $$2 \cdot 2 \cdot 2 \cdot 2 \cdots = \aleph$$

Moreover, in view of (62) and (56) we have:

$$\aleph = 2 \cdot 2 \cdot 2 \cdot 2 \cdots \leq 1 \cdot 2 \cdot 3 \cdot 4 \cdot 5 \cdots \leq \aleph_0^{\aleph_0} = \aleph$$

Consequently,

(63) $$1 \cdot 2 \cdot 3 \cdot 4 \cdots = \aleph$$

Equalities (62) and (63) show two more instances of the discrepancy between ordinal and cardinal arithmetic. Whereas in the context of ordinal arithmetic

$$1 \cdot 2 \cdot 3 \cdot 4 \cdots = 2 \cdot 2 \cdot 2 \cdot 2 \cdots = 2^\omega = \omega = \aleph_0$$

in the context of cardinal arithmetic [as (62) and (63) show] each one of the above expressions is equal to $\aleph \neq \aleph_0$.

Theorem 41. *For every infinite sequence $(c_i)_{i \in \omega}$ of cardinal numbers c_i, if $c_i < \aleph$ for every $i \in \omega$, then*

$$c_0 + c_1 + c_2 + \cdots < \aleph$$

PROOF. By Theorem 37,

$$c_0 + c_1 + c_2 + \cdots < \aleph \cdot \aleph \cdot \aleph \cdots$$

However, the right side of the above inequality is equal to $\aleph^{\aleph_0}$, which in turn, in view of (56), is equal to $\aleph$.

Corollary 33. *If a set of the power of the continuum is a denumerable union of sets, then at least one of these sets must be of the power of the continuum.*

PROOF. If every one of the above sets is of power less than the power of the continuum, then by Theorem 41 their union would be of power less than the power of the continuum, contradicting the hypothesis of the theorem.

For another application of Theorem 37, note that the latter implies:

(64) $$\aleph_0 + \aleph_1 + \aleph_2 + \cdots < \aleph_0 \aleph_1 \aleph_2 \cdots$$

However, by Theorem 24, $\aleph_n < \aleph_\omega$, for $n = 0, 1, 2, \ldots$. Therefore, the right side of (64) is at most $\aleph^{\aleph_0}_\omega$. On the other hand, in view of (35) the left side of (64) is equal to $\aleph_\omega$. Hence:

(65) $$\aleph_\omega < \aleph_\omega^{\aleph_0}$$

Based on (65), we prove:

(66) $$\aleph_\omega \neq 2^{\aleph_0}$$

Assume on the contrary that $\aleph_\omega = 2^{\aleph_0}$. But then $\aleph_\omega^{\aleph_0} = (2^{\aleph_0})^{\aleph_0} = 2^{\aleph_0} = \aleph_\omega$, contradicting (65). Hence, indeed (66) is true.

Next, we prove:

(67) $$\aleph_0 \aleph_1 \aleph_2 \cdots = \aleph_\omega^{\aleph_0}$$

Clearly, since $\aleph_n < \aleph_\omega$ for $n = 0, 1, 2, \ldots$,

(68) $$\aleph_0 \aleph_1 \aleph_2 \cdots \leq \aleph_\omega^{\aleph_0}$$

On the other hand

$$\aleph_0 \aleph_1 \aleph_2 \cdots = (\aleph_0 \aleph_1 \aleph_3 \cdots)(\aleph_2 \aleph_6 \aleph_{10} \cdots)(\aleph_4 \aleph_{12} \aleph_{20} \cdots) \cdots$$

and hence by (64), (35) and Lemma 6, we have:

$$\aleph_0 \aleph_1 \aleph_2 \cdots \geq \aleph_\omega^{\aleph_0}$$

Comparing the above inequality with (68) we derive (67).

Among the important formulas concerning the exponentiation of cardinals, we mention the following ones.

It has been proved (F. Hausdorff) that:

(69) $$\aleph_{u+n}^{\aleph_v} = \aleph_u^{\aleph_v} \aleph_{u+n} \qquad \text{with} \quad n = 0, 1, 2, 3, \ldots$$

Moreover, it has been proved (F. Bernstein) that for $w \leq v + n$ where n is a finite ordinal,

(70) $$\aleph_w^{\aleph_v} = 2^{\aleph_v} \aleph_w$$

A special case of (70), in which w is a finite ordinal, can be obtained from (69), as follows.

For $u = 0$, (69) yields:

$$\aleph_n^{\aleph_v} = \aleph_0^{\aleph_v} \aleph_n \qquad \text{with} \quad n = 0, 1, 2, 3, \ldots$$

However, by Theorem 40, $\aleph_0^{\aleph_v} = 2^{\aleph_v}$. Hence, the above equality reduces to:

(71) $$\aleph_n^{\aleph_v} = 2^{\aleph_v} \aleph_n \qquad \text{with} \quad n = 0, 1, 2, 3, \ldots$$

Also, it has been proved (A. Tarski) (compare with Theorem 35 and Corollary 22) that:

$$\overline{\overline{\prod_{v \leq w}}} \aleph_v = \aleph_w^{\overline{\overline{w}}} \qquad \text{for every positive ordinal } w$$

and

$$\overline{\overline{\prod_{v < w}}} \aleph_v = \aleph_w^{\overline{\overline{w}}} \qquad \text{for every limit ordinal } w$$

EXERCISES

1. Prove (41), (45), (47) and Corollary 2.

2. Let a and c be two cardinals, and $(a_i)_{i \in \omega}$ and $(c_i)_{i \in \omega}$ two infinite sequences of cardinals a_i and c_i. Prove:

$$(a_1 \cdot a_2 \cdot a_3 \cdots)^c = a_1^c \cdot a_2^c \cdot a_3^c \cdots$$
$$a^{(c_1 + c_2 + c_3 + \cdots)} = a^{c_1} \cdot a^{c_2} \cdot a^{c_3} \cdots$$

3. Prove that if n is a finite cardinal, then:

$$1^n + 2^n + 3^n + \cdots = \aleph_0$$
$$1^n \cdot 2^n \cdot 3^n \cdots = \aleph \qquad \text{for} \quad n > 0$$
$$n^1 + n^2 + n^3 + \cdots = \aleph_0 \qquad \text{for} \quad n > 0$$
$$n^1 \cdot n^2 \cdot n^3 \cdots = \aleph \qquad \text{for} \quad n > 1$$

4. Using Theorem 40, prove that:

$$u \leq v \qquad \text{implies} \qquad \aleph_u^{\aleph_v} = 2^{\aleph_v}$$

5. Prove that the power of the set of all two-element subsets of a set of the power $2^{\aleph}$ is $2^{\aleph}$.

6. Prove that $c\aleph = 2^{\aleph}$ implies $c = 2^{\aleph}$ for every cardinal c.

7. Prove that $\aleph_3^{\aleph_2} = \aleph_2^{\aleph_2}\aleph_3$

8. Using (71), prove that $\aleph_2^{\aleph_0} = \aleph\aleph_2$

9. Using (70), prove that $\aleph_5^{\aleph_2} = 2^{\aleph_2}\aleph_5$ and that $\aleph_{\omega}^{\aleph_{\omega}} = 2^{\aleph_{\omega}}\aleph_{\omega}$.

8. THE CONTINUUM HYPOTHESIS

According to (50), the cardinal $\aleph$ is the cardinal (of the power) of the continuum, and hence, as indicated by (13), $\aleph_0 < \aleph$. Also, according to (10), the cardinal $\aleph_1$ is the immediate successor of $\aleph_0$. Consequently, as indicated by (52), we have:

$$\aleph_0 < \aleph_1 \leq \aleph$$

As mentioned in Section 2 of this chapter, the hypothesis according to which [in view of (50)]

(72) $$\aleph_1 = \aleph = 2^{\aleph_0}$$

is called the *Continuum Hypothesis*.

Next, let us observe that in view of (49),

$$c < 2^c \qquad \text{for every cardinal number } c$$

There is another hypothesis, according to which *if c is an infinite cardinal, then there exists no cardinal a such that*:

(73) $$c < a < 2^c$$

Since by Theorem 25 every infinite cardinal is an aleph and since, in view of Corollary 12, $\aleph_{u+1}$ is the immediate successor of $\aleph_u$, we see that (73) is equivalent to the hypothesis:

(74) $$\aleph_{u+1} = 2^{\aleph_u} \qquad \text{for every ordinal } u$$

Hypothesis (74) is called the *Generalized Continuum Hypothesis*.

Obviously, (74) implies (72), since the latter is the special case of (74) for $u = 0$. On the other hand, it has been established that (72) does not imply (74).

As in the case of the Continuum Hypothesis, it has been established that the Generalized Continuum Hypothesis is consistent with (K. Goedel) and independent of (P. J. Cohen) the axioms of the Theory of Sets (including the axiom of Regularity), which were introduced in Chapter II of this book. Consequently, if desired, (72) or (74) can be taken as an additional set-theoretical axiom.

In the mathematical literature there are many statements which are known to be equivalent to the Continuum or the Generalized Continuum Hypothesis. Naturally, each of these statements could be taken as an additional set-theoretical axiom.

In this section we give some theorems involving (72) and (74).

Obviously, (72) implies that the power of the set R of all real numbers is equal to $\aleph_1$, since, as we know:

$$\bar{\bar{R}} = \aleph = 2^{\aleph_0}$$

Also, in view of the fact that $\aleph_1$ is the immediate successor of $\aleph_0$ we see that (72) *implies that every nondenumerable infinite subset of the set R of all real numbers is equipollent to R.*

Theorem 42. *The Continuum Hypothesis is equivalent to:*

(75) $$\aleph_1^{\aleph_0} = \aleph_1$$

PROOF. Clearly, $2 < \aleph_1 \leq 2^{\aleph_0}$. Therefore, by Theorem 39,

$$2^{\aleph_0} \leq \aleph_1^{\aleph_0} \leq (2^{\aleph_0})^{\aleph_0} = 2^{\aleph_0}$$

Hence,

(76) $$\aleph_1^{\aleph_0} = 2^{\aleph_0}$$

Obviously, in view of (76), (72) implies (75) and (75) implies (72). Thus, indeed (72) is equivalent to (75), as desired.

Theorem 43. *The Continuum Hypothesis is equivalent to:*

(77) $$\aleph_1^{\aleph_0} < \aleph_2^{\aleph_0}$$

PROOF. Clearly, $\aleph_1 < \aleph_2^{\aleph_0}$.

Assume (72). Hence, in view of the above, $2^{\aleph_0} < \aleph_2^{\aleph_0}$, which in view of (76) implies (77).

Next, assume (77). Then from (76) it follows that:

(78) $$2^{\aleph_0} < \aleph_2^{\aleph_0}$$

We claim that $2^{\aleph_0} < \aleph_2$, since otherwise $2^{\aleph_0} \geq \aleph_2$, and as a result $2^{\aleph_0} \geq \aleph_2^{\aleph_0}$, contradicting (78). Therefore, $2^{\aleph_0} < \aleph_2$. Consequently, $\aleph_1 \leq 2^{\aleph_0} < \aleph_2$. But, since $\aleph_2$ is the immediate successor of $\aleph_1$, we see that $\aleph_1 = 2^{\aleph_0}$. Hence, indeed (77) implies (72), as desired.

Next, we prove:

Theorem 44. *The Generalized Continuum Hypothesis implies that for every two cardinal numbers c and a:*

$$if \quad c < a \quad then \quad 2^c < 2^a$$

PROOF. From Theorem 39, it follows that $c < a$ implies:

$$2^c \leq 2^a$$

Now, let us assume that $2^c = 2^a$. Since $a < 2^a$, we have

$$c < a < 2^c$$

contradicting the Generalized Continuum Hypothesis. Hence our assumption is false, and indeed $2^c < 2^a$, as desired.

Let us observe that the fact that $2^c < 2^a$ implies $c < a$ (as shown by Corollary 32) is proved without resorting to the Generalized Continuum Hypothesis.

From Theorem 44, we easily derive:

Corollary 34. *The Generalized Continuum Hypothesis implies that, for every two cardinal numbers c and a:*

$$c = a \qquad \text{if and only if} \qquad 2^c = 2^a$$

In closing this section, let us remark that it has been proved (W. Sierpinski) that the Generalized Continuum Hypothesis implies the axiom of Choice.

EXERCISES

1. Prove that the Continuum Hypothesis implies that the set of all real numbers is the union of an increasing (in the sense of set-theoretical inclusion) family of denumerable sets.

2. Prove that the Generalized Continuum Hypothesis implies that, except for cardinals of the form 2^a, there exists no infinite cardinal c such that $c = m^n$ with $m < c$ and where a and m are two cardinals.

9. SUMMARY

In this chapter we studied cardinal numbers and their arithmetic. A cardinal number is defined as an ordinal number u such that u is less than or equal to every ordinal number equipollent to u.

The natural order among cardinals (which are after all special kinds of ordinals) is defined in the same way as among ordinals. However, as Remark 3 indicates, the natural order among cardinals is compatible with the order among sets defined via the equipollence of sets (see Chapter VI, Section 3).

Just as in the case of ordinals, in the case of cardinals also the operation of forming the immediate successor of a cardinal and the operation of forming the least upper bound of a set of cardinals are the two fundamental operations for generating larger and larger cardinals.

Let us remind the reader that whereas in ordinal arithmetic the immediate successor of an ordinal w is given by $w \cup \{w\}$, in cardinal arithmetic the immediate successor of a cardinal c is given by $c \cup \mathbf{Z}(c)$, where $\mathbf{Z}(c)$ is the set of all ordinals which are equipollent to c. On the other hand, however, the least upper bound of a set S of ordinals or cardinals is given by $\cup S$.

Concerning cardinals, we have proved that two cardinals are equal if and only if they are equipollent, and also that every set is equipollent to a unique cardinal.

Moreover, we have shown that there is neither a greatest cardinal nor the set of all cardinals nor the set of all the sets equipollent to a given cardinal.

As mentioned in this chapter, a natural number is both a finite ordinal and a finite cardinal, and vice versa. Furthermore, ordinal or cardinal arithmetic, when referred to a finite set of finite ordinals or cardinals, coincides with the arithmetic of natural numbers. However, in general the definitions of the arithmetical operations of ordinal and cardinal arithmetics are quite different. In the former, the motivating factor is order, in the latter, equipollence. For instance, some of the discrepancies of these two arithmetics are revealed in the fact that, in contrast with the results of ordinal arithmetic, in cardinal arithmetic

$$a + c = c \quad \text{and} \quad ac = c$$

where a is any cardinal and c is any infinite cardinal such that $a \leq c$.

To avoid any confusion between ordinal and cardinal arithmetics, infinite cardinals ω, ω_1, ω_2, ... are denoted respectively by $\aleph_0$, $\aleph_1$, $\aleph_2$, ... They satisfy equalities (14), (15) and (16).

The exponentiation of cardinals reveals further discrepancies between ordinal and cardinal arithmetics. Whereas in ordinal arithmetic

$$2 \cdot 2 \cdot 2 \cdot 2 \cdots = 2^\omega = \omega$$

in cardinal arithmetic:

$$2 \cdot 2 \cdot 2 \cdot 2 \cdots = 2^{\aleph_0} > \aleph_0$$

Also, whereas in ordinal arithmetic

$$\omega_1 \cdot \omega_2 \cdot \omega_3 \cdots = \omega_\omega$$

in cardinal arithmetic:

$$\aleph_0 \cdot \aleph_1 \cdot \aleph_2 \cdot \aleph_3 \cdots = \aleph_\omega^{\aleph_0} > \aleph_\omega$$

Recall that $c < 2^c$ for every cardinal number c, and therefore $\aleph_0 < 2^{\aleph_0} = \aleph$. However, $\aleph_1$ is the immediate successor of $\aleph_0$, and thus $\aleph_1 \leq \aleph$. The hypothesis that $\aleph_1 = \aleph$ is known as the Continuum Hypothesis. Similarly, the hypothesis that *if c is an infinite cardinal, then there exists no cardinal a such that* $c < a < 2^c$ is known as the Generalized Continuum Hypothesis. As shown in the text, the latter hypothesis is equivalent to the assumption that $\aleph_{u+1} = 2^{\aleph_u}$, for every ordinal u.

Finally, let us mention that the consistency of the system of axioms of (1) Extensionality, (2) Replacement, (3) Power-Set, (4) Sum-Set, (5) Infinity and (6) Regularity is not known. In fact it has been established (K. Goedel) that the consistency of this system of axioms cannot be proved within the Theory of Sets. However, under the assumption that axioms (1) to (6) form a consistent system of axioms, the incompleteness and undecidability of this system have been established. Moreover, under the same assumption, it has been established that each of the axiom of Choice, the Generalized Continuum Hypothesis and the Continuum Hypothesis is consistent with (K. Goedel) and independent of (P. J. Cohen) the system of axioms (1) to (6). Furthermore, with axioms (1) to (6) at hand, it has been established that (i) the axiom of Choice does not imply (P. J. Cohen) either the Continuum Hypothesis or, naturally, the Generalized Continuum Hypothesis; (ii) the Generalized Continuum Hypothesis implies (W. Sierpinski) the axiom of Choice and, naturally, the Continuum Hypothesis; (iii) the Continuum Hypothesis does not imply (R. M. Solovay) the axiom of Choice and consequently the Generalized Continuum Hypothesis; and (iv) the axiom of Choice and the Continuum Hypothesis together do not imply (R. M. Solovay) the Generalized Continuum Hypothesis.

LIST OF SYMBOLS

INDEX

Absolute value, 228
Addition
  of cardinal numbers, 373
  of integers, 214
  of natural numbers, 205, 208
  of ordered sets, 308
  of ordinal numbers, 327
  of rational numbers, 222
  of real numbers, 234, 240
  ordered, 308, 326, 327, 332
Aleph, 362, 370, 372
  regular, 377
  singular, 377
Aleph null, 361
Algebraic number, 273
Antecedent, of an implication, 35
Antilexicographic order, 311, 338
Antisymmetric predicate, 75, 76
Antisymmetric relation, 283
Argument, of a function, 145
Arithmetic
  of cardinal numbers, 367, 373, 385, 390
  of integers, 212
  of natural numbers, 205, 333, 380
  of ordinal numbers, 326, 367, 380, 385, 390
  of rational numbers, 220
  of real numbers, 232
Associativity, 41, 94, 95, 99, 130, 159, 374
  generalized, 95, 99, 159
  of addition, 209, 215, 222, 309, 328, 374
  of multiplication, 210, 215, 338, 375
  under similarity, 312
Assumption, of an implication, 35
Asymmetric relation, 173
Attached variable, to a quantifier, 52, 56
Axiom(s)
  dependent and independent, 18, 27, 62
  of a model, 2, 26
  of a theory of sets, 60
  of Choice, 115, 162, 195, 198, 265, 298, 384, 385
  of Extensionality, 71, 72
  of Infinity, 102, 156
  of Power-Set, 85, 87, 104, 115
  of Regularity, 74, 120
  of Replacement, 81, 82, 104, 324, 326, 331, 343
  of Sum-Set, 92, 95, 104, 115

Axiom(s)—(*Continued*)
  of the Theory of Sets, 65, 71, 81, 85, 92, 102, 115, 120
  Peano, 108
  set-theoretical, 26, 60, 61
  systems of, 62
Axiom scheme, logical, 26, 30, 61
  of Replacement, 81

Basic set-theoretical predicate, 2, 4
Biimplication, 40
Binary predicate, 65, 75, 77, 140
  functional in x, 79, 143, 144, 206, 325, 345, 370
  in a model, 78
Boolean algebra, 134
Boolean ring, 134
Bounded above and below, definitions, 176
Bounded variable, 52, 56

Cancellation, law of, 211
Canonical map, 204
Cantor-Bernstein theorem, 253
Cantor's theorem, 256
Cardinal, denumerable, 361
  infinite, 367, 370, 372
  of the power of the continuum, 362
Cardinal addition, 373
Cardinal arithmetic, 367, 373, 385, 390
Cardinal exponentiation, 386
Cardinal multiplication, 375
Cardinal number(s), 360, 361
  addition of, 373
  arithmetic of, 367, 373, 385, 390
Cartesian diagram, 138, 143
Cartesian product
  of a family, 161
  of a set, 162, 266, 383
  of two sets, 118, 135, 170, 266, 272, 274, 311, 375
Chain, 193
Characteristic function, 148
Choice
  axiom of, 115, 162, 195, 198, 265, 298, 384, 385
  General Principle of, 117, 162
  Principle of, 117

399

Existence, in the Theory of Sets, 68
Existential quantifier, 50
Exponentiation
  of cardinals, 386
  of natural numbers, 211
  of ordinals, 348
  of sets, 268
Extension, of a function, 146
Extensionality, axiom of, 71, 72

Family
  Cartesian product of, 161
  intersection of, 158
  of cardinals, 379, 383
  of ordinals, 332
  of sets, 157, 161
  union of, 158
Field, 223, 236
  ordered, 228, 236
Finite cardinal, 367
Finite character, 199
Finite Induction, principle of, 105
  theorem of, 105, 192, 209
Finite ordinal, 317
Finite Recursion Theorem, 206, 208, 299
Finite sequence, 163
Finite set, 155, 244, 245
First element, 175, 189
First set, 89
Fixed point, 182, 183, 253
Formal symbols, 2, 4, 26, 50, 58, 60
  auxiliary, 60
Formation rules of formulas, 2, 15, 24, 26,
  28, 45, 50, 61, 65, 140
Formula(s), 2, 15, 24, 26, 28, 45, 50, 61, 140
  decidable, 27, 62
  derivable, 27, 60
  disprovable, 27, 60
  nonsatisfiable, 27, 29, 47, 60
  prime, 24, 60
  proof of, definition, 27
  provable, 27, 60
  satisfiable, 30, 47, 48
  set-theoretical, 2, 25, 26, 61
  universally valid, 29, 47
Formula scheme, 24, 28, 33, 34, 39, 50, 56
  nonsatisfiable, 48
  satisfiable, 30, 48
  undecidable, 30, 48
  universally valid, 48
Free variable, 52, 56
Function, 142, 145
  characteristic, 148
  choice, 117, 198
  composite, 146
  domain of, 143
  image under, 150
  into, 144
  inverse image under, 151
  many-to-one, 144

Function—(*Continued*)
  nondecreasing, 182, 252
  of one and two variables, 145
  one-to-one, 144, 145, 153
  onto, 144, 145, 152
  range of, 145

General Principle of Choice, 117, 162
Generalization, rule of, 58
Generalized associativity laws, 95, 99, 159
Generalized Continuum Hypothesis, 392
Greatest element, 175, 177, 286
Greatest lower bound, 176, 177, 286, 322

Hypothesis
  Continuum, 368, 392
  Generalized Continuum, 392
  of an implication, 35
Hypothetical syllogism, law of, 37

Idempotence, 41, 94, 99
Identity mapping, 148
Image, under a function, 150
  under a relation, 139
Immediate predecessor, 108, 190, 286, 322
Immediate successor, 102, 104, 190, 286, 322,
  366
Implication, 35
Inaccessible cardinal, 378
Inclusion, 74, 124, 150, 152
Incomplete model, 27
Incomplete theory, 62
Incompleteness, 68
Inconsistent context, 7
Inconsistent ε-truth table, 11
Inconsistent model, 7, 8, 27
Inconsistent system of axioms, 62
Inconsistent theory, 62
Independent axiom, of a model, 18, 27
  of a theory, 62
Index, 158, 332
Index set, 158, 380
Indirect proof, 36
Indistinguishable, definition, 20, 40, 70
  set-theoretically, 70, 72
Individual constant, 2, 3, 26, 60, 66
Individual variable, 3, 44, 60, 65, 67
Individual variable scheme, 50
Induction, theorem of Finite, 105, 192, 209
Inference, 2, 5, 26, 37, 61
  rules of, 2, 4, 15, 26, 31, 61
Infimum, 176
Infinite cardinal, 367, 370, 372
Infinite decimal, 237
Infinite ordinal, 317
Infinite products, of cardinals, 382, 383
  of ordinals, 344, 345